A HISTORY OF
THE ROCKEFELLER
INSTITUTE

JOHN D. ROCKEFELLER AND JOHN D. ROCKEFELLER, JR.

A HISTORY OF THE ROCKEFELLER INSTITUTE

INSTITUTE

1901–1953
ORIGINS AND GROWTH

George W. Corner

THE ROCKEFELLER INSTITUTE PRESS

NEW YORK CITY · 1964

Foreword

THE FIFTY YEARS encompassed by this History was a period of extraordinary scientific progress in the United States. The Rockefeller Institute played a unique and important role in that dramatic development.

During the latter half of the nineteenth century, education in the natural sciences was slowly evolving in colleges that were mostly devoted to instruction in the classics, philosophy, and theology. University professors had few experimental facilities and little time for scientific research. Medical schools and colleges of technology were especially destitute of research because their faculties were committed to private practice for their livelihood, with little leisure for instruction and investigation in poorly equipped laboratories. Not until 1876 was the first graduate school of significance founded as The Johns Hopkins University.

The beginning of the twentieth century was a favorable time for a bold venture in the development of science in this country. The useful values of science were being demonstrated by scores of colleges of agriculture and the mechanic arts that had been created and financed by the Federal Government under the Congressional authority of the Land Grant Act of 1862. Following the notable example of The Johns Hopkins, a half dozen universities had recently laid strong foundations for graduate education. Spectacular achievements of European scientists were extending the vision of their American students who returned to this country eager to continue their research. The appalling weakness of most medical colleges was soon to be revealed by Abraham Flexner. Our industrial economy had at last developed the capacity to support research as a means for creating new industries and improving human welfare.

The founding of The Rockefeller Institute in 1901 was a timely leap forward in that ready, but still barren period of American science. In well-equipped laboratories of the new and unique Institute, eager scientists found freedom from long hours of formal teaching; adequate salaries enabled physicians to devote their lives to research unimpeded by the distractions of private practice. Research in the physical and chemical aspects of biology was recognized as being essential for the advance of medical science.

Hundreds of young scientists came to the Institute to learn the methods of research from eminent scholars who had been recruited from many countries. From the Institute, scores of future professors returned to universities where they built schools of medicine and graduate study and there played major roles in the spectacular scientific progress of recent years.

The bold undertaking of 1901 had a profound effect on the development of science in America. But the final pages of this History describe the reasons why "the once distinctive character of the Institute was disappearing" as its first half century ended. The Rockefeller Institute for Medical Research had so successfully fostered research in the academic world that a career of teaching and research in a university had become more desirable than life in an intellectually limited research institute that lacked the vital stimulus of eager graduate students.

After fifty years the Institute had a rich heritage that is revealed in this History: traditions of exacting devotion to excellence, freedom for self-directed research as a means of teaching and learning, a truly international staff of eminent scientists, and courage to adventure. In 1952, when more graduate schools of the highest quality were an urgent national need, the trustees determined to use those spiritual legacies, large physical resources capable of great expansion in culturally rich New York, and an endowment of more than one hundred million dollars for the creation of a graduate university. It was an action that had been suggested in 1886 by Daniel Coit Gilman, first President of The Johns Hopkins University, and by William Henry Welch of the Hopkins while the Institute was being planned.

It is worthy of comment that there have been many remarkable relations between The Rockefeller Institute and The Johns Hopkins University. Both have pioneered in graduate education. Many of the most influential members of the Institute staff were Hopkins men: the first and last presidents of the Board of Scientific Directors, all the Directors of the Institute and of the Institute Hospital, scores of its most distinguished Members—Welch, Longcope, Simon Flexner, Gasser, Cole, Rivers, Rous, Opie are but a few of many who brought the ideals of Gilman and Hopkins traditions to the Rockefeller. It is less well known that the new character of the Institute as a graduate university owes much to another Hopkins man: Abraham, the brother of Simon Flexner. Personally, I am with affection deeply indebted to him; he was for thirty years my wise mentor in the ideals and traditions of Gilman whom he greatly revered as his teacher. At the age of 90, Abraham Flexner urged that the functions of the Institute first directed by his brother be changed and broadened to meet new needs. By happy chance, two brothers were able to influence the character of the Institute at the beginning of two eras.

For fifty years the Institute was widely known as a great institution about which little was known by other than biologists. Now good fortune has provided an historian who is uniquely qualified to tell the story of this remarkable institution. He is a distinguished teacher, investigator, and editor who has been associated with many of the scientific discoveries he describes. He has been a personal friend of most of the men and women who guided the course of the Institute. And George Corner has the ability and the will to write with clarity and grace.

DETLEV W. BRONK *President*

December 1964

Table of Contents

LIST OF ILLUSTRATIONS

Here is an institution whose value touches the life of every man that lives. . . . Who has not felt the throbbing of desire to be useful to the whole wide world? Here at least is a work for all humanity, which fully satisfies and fills that glorious aspiration. . . . Your vocation goes to the foundations of life itself. . . . Whatever you learn about nature and her forces and prove and incorporate into your science will be carried forward, though all else be forgotten.

FREDERICK T. GATES to the staff of
The Rockefeller Institute on the tenth
anniversary of the laboratories, 1914

CHAPTER ONE

The Background and the Need

Science and education in the United States at the beginning of the twentieth century. The advance of medical research in Europe. The need of medical research centers in America. John D. Rockefeller as philanthropist; Frederick T. Gates and the idea of a research institute. Medical research institutions in other countries.

IN THE DECADE from 1897 to 1906, when The Rockefeller Institute was planned and organized, America was growing and changing rapidly, and American medicine along with it. As we trace the story of John Davison Rockefeller's far-sighted benefaction, we can wonder why such a gift was made at all; why it came at that particular time, just at the turn of the century; what needs it filled, why it was successful, who made it succeed. The answers to these questions are not to be found in the history of medical affairs alone. They must be looked for in the whole pattern of political, economic, and cultural events in the latter part of the nineteenth century. Only by so wide a survey, moreover, can we comprehend the founders' breadth of vision that made the Institute from the start something more than a center for the study of disease, and kept the way open for its development, after half a century, into a graduate university.

During three and a half decades of peace after the Civil War, the United States had reached unprecedented levels of wealth and industrial power. The population had grown to seventy-six million, and the national wealth was approaching a hundred billion dollars. Cities were growing rapidly, out of proportion to the rural population; in 1900 almost 40 per cent of the people lived in cities, as contrasted with about 15 per cent in 1850. In factories and on farms, enterprising and inventive men were setting machines to work. Railroads and the telegraph had already spread from coast to coast; electric light and power, the telephone, and pipe lines for oil were following. The old frontier along which pioneers had wrested a living from nature was disappearing. The new frontiers were those of the inventor, engineer, and architect, scientist, industrialist, economist, and administrator. The Chicago World's Fair of 1892 had shown to astonished Europe an America conscious of its own enormous achievements in industry, agriculture, and commerce, and yet awake to the need for similar excellence in arts, science, and general culture.

Looking behind the material prosperity to scholarship and the learned professions, we find a similar advance and growth. The people, eager for education, had built a system of universal free public schools and had created hundreds of colleges, universities, and schools of engineering. Not all of these were worthy of their names, but some were excellent. Among the universities, a few were beginning to rival the older academic establishments of Europe, not only in the teaching of traditional subjects, but in original scholarship and research, and in postgraduate training. In 1888 there were already perhaps a dozen American universities of this class.[1] Their faculties, and certain centers of research such as the Smithsonian Institution and the Naval Observatory, contained many men of distinction and a few of genius in mathematics, physics, astronomy, chemistry, geology, and biology. It may have seemed to hopeful observers that the United States, founded upon the ideals of the eighteenth-century Enlightenment, and looking to a civic life based upon the exercise of reason, the benefits of science, and the self-government of an educated people, had gone far toward realizing its dream. Such indeed was the verdict of the keenest British observer of the American scene, James Bryce, who ended the first edition of *The American Commonwealth* (1888) with the statement that "America marks the highest level, not only of material well-being, but of intelligence and happiness, that the race has yet attained."

The highest hopes of the founding fathers remained, however, unfulfilled. The nation had grown faster than it could organize its corporate gains for the good of all. With increasing wealth went extremes of poverty at one end of the scale, of affluence and financial power at the other; with democratic government, boss rule; with big business, sweatshops; with mechanized factories, child labor; with free public schools, a population 8 per cent illiterate. A poet, looking at the future of the growing republic, could see "... beyond the years, Thine alabaster cities gleam, Undimmed by human tears"; but a historian's verdict upon the era was that

> in the land of plenty there was never enough of food, clothing and shelter for the underprivileged, and cyclical depressions, apparently unavoidable, plunged millions into actual want. In the great cities slums grew apace, and from the slums spread dirt and disease, crime and vice. Science told how to control many of the diseases that plagued mankind, but poverty interposed between science and health, and tuberculosis, hookworm, malaria and other diseases of poverty and ignorance took an annual toll that ran into the millions.[2]

These various ills required various cures. Some of the more obvious social, political, and economic abuses could be corrected by immediate action, or so it seemed to reformers. The years 1880 to 1900 called forth an array of forward-looking personalities and programs as diverse as Jane Addams and her Hull House settlement, Carrie Nation and the Anti-Saloon League, William Jennings Bryan and the Populist party, the Sherman Anti-Trust Act, direct primary elections. Reform required slow adjustment and education at every level of the community. Labor took its own great part in the fight for social justice, and big business had to look to its ethics as well as submit to governmental controls. Basic deficiencies in civic life and culture demanded more than social, legal, and economic reform, more than philanthropic relief; they called for growth of the corporate moral conscience and for national self-understanding of a kind that could come only from a higher level of competence in government and in the professions. This understanding must be won by education and research. Particularly, the nation's universities were beginning to realize their potentialities in the humanities, economics, and the basic natural sciences.

The specific problems of public health were also diverse and difficult. Some of them were to be solved by basic scientific information. Typhoid fever, for example, was destined to be reduced almost to the vanishing point as soon as public health officers, sanitary and waterworks engineers, and the dairy industry could organize the precautions by which the typhoid bacillus is kept out of drinking water, milk, and foods. The control of diseases such as tuberculosis depended upon less easily curable evils, for example crowding and malnutrition. Failure to control such infections as scarlet fever and poliomyelitis resulted from ignorance of matters then beyond the frontier of advancing knowledge. These must be attacked by the slow processes of scientific investigation, for which facilities were inadequate and research men too few.

The infectious diseases presented the most obvious problem. To see how great this was, we need only look at the death rates. In the ten states which in 1900 were included in the United States registration area, deaths from tuberculosis (all forms) were 194.4 per 100,000 of population (in 1957 in the continental United States the figure was 7.9); diphtheria 40.3 (0.0 in 1957); typhoid and paratyphoid fevers 31.3 (0.0 in 1957). Infant mortality figures for the same year (1900) show that in New York, Philadelphia, and Boston, of every thousand babies born, about 190 died before reaching the age of one year; in Baltimore the rate was 235, in Fall River 304, in Savannah 387, and in Charleston 419.[3]

European laboratories during this period were announcing dramatic developments in their investigation of infectious diseases. Alphonse Laveran discovered the parasite of malaria in 1880; in 1882 Robert Koch announced the discovery of the tubercle bacillus; in 1883 and 1884 Edwin Klebs and Friedrich Loeffler isolated the germ of diphtheria, and in 1884 George Gaffky that of typhoid fever. One kind of dysentery was explained by the discovery of the causative bacillus by Kiyoshi Shiga in 1897. The microorganisms causing surgical and puerperal infections were brought to light by Louis Pasteur, Robert Koch, and George Gaffky between 1878 and 1892. Most encouraging of all, in its demonstration that control of one of the most tragic plagues could result from understanding of its cause, was the preparation of the antitoxin against diphtheria, the achievement of Emil von Behring, announced in 1890–1893 and made available to the public of Europe in 1894. The United States fortunately had a public laboratory, that of the New York City Board of Health, competent to prepare diphtheria antitoxin for clinical use. When, however, the enterprising health officer of Rochester, New York, George W. Goler, needed antitoxin to combat a local epidemic, he had first to visit W. H. Park in New York City to learn how to make it. He then bought a horse from which to obtain blood, and rigged up a laboratory in the basement of the University of Rochester's biology building where he and the professor of biology, Charles Wright Dodge, worked up the immune horse serum with makeshift apparatus.[4] With such limited facilities even for applying discoveries already made abroad, how much less was the country equipped to make its own attacks against disease!

Thus the struggle against disease led thoughtful people within the medical profession and outside it to see the necessity for new facilities for research. The nation had, moreover, assumed obligations abroad that made further demands upon the scientific resources of American medicine. At the end of the nineteenth century the United States, emerging victorious from the brief war of 1898 with Spain, suddenly found itself a world power with colonial responsibilities in the Caribbean and the Pacific. New territorial possessions and ever-broadening trade contacts in the Americas and the Orient created new medical problems: typhoid fever and cerebrospinal meningitis in the army camps; hookworm in Puerto Rico; malaria and yellow fever in Cuba and Panama; dysentery in the Pacific; and bubonic plague, which had reached San Francisco from China. These great public health problems, and a host of lesser ones incidental to the welfare of native populations and of the soldiers, administrators, teachers, missionaries, and merchants who were moving overseas because of the war and its aftermath, weighed heavily upon a nation that was strong in arms and technological resources but weak in medical education and research. Yet one brilliant episode in this era of overseas expansion demonstrated that America possessed men of ardor and high ability for the study of disease. In 1900 the members of an army commission headed by Walter Reed risked their lives, and one of them — Jesse Lazear — sacrificed his, in proving by experimentation in the field, in Cuba, Carlos Finlay's hypothesis that yellow fever is transmitted by mosquitoes. Within a year the Medical Corps, under William C. Gorgas, freed Havana of that disease for the first time in 150 years. It is significant that Major Reed had been trained in research at the Johns Hopkins Hospital in Baltimore by William H. Welch, foremost among those who were beginning to transplant European medical science to America.

In Europe, as the nineteenth century advanced toward its close, medicine reached great heights. For a century medical research had been opening up a new understanding of disease, and the ten years ending in 1890 were, as William H. Welch has said, "perhaps the most wonderful decade in the history of medicine."[5] This resulted from several causes, one of which was the general advance of science during the past three centuries. The study of physics and chemistry had developed scientific habits of thinking which physicians now began to apply to medicine. Inspired by the mechanistic philosophy of René Descartes, the iatrophysical, or iatromathematical, school sought in the seventeenth century to explain the body as a machine and disease as a disturbance of mechanical functions, while the iatrochemists, attempting to deal with physiology in terms of chemistry, looked for excessive acidity or alkalinity and similar elementary chemical causes of disordered health. These crude new ideas destroyed the ancient physiology and pathology of the four humors — black bile and yellow bile, phlegm, and blood — without at first substituting an adequate body of new facts. The resulting confusion in medical thought lasted through the eighteenth century and into the nineteenth, while one theoretical "system of medicine" succeeded another with little or no basis of factual observation. The saving fact was that the explanations proposed by the iatromathematical and iatrochemical thinkers could be subjected to laboratory test. It was quite possible, for example, with methods then at hand, to consider the heart a pump, and to measure pulse and blood pressure in the light of that concept; or to look for acid in the digestive juices of the stomach. Galvani's discovery of electrical currents that could stimulate nerves and muscles emphasized the direct value of physics for physiological study. In the long run, the followers of Descartes, however crude their earliest concepts, started a rapid rebuilding of medical science on a sound experimental foundation.

During the nineteenth century the contributions of basic science to biology and medicine became more precise. The chemists put forward the great principle that life is maintained by chemical reactions of the same nature as those that occur in test tubes. Lavoisier had proved by 1784 that respiration is the same process as combustion; like coal or wood burning in a fireplace, carbon compounds in the body are oxidized to yield carbon dioxide and water. Helmholtz showed in 1827 that the law of the conservation of energy applies to processes in living tissues as well as in non-living things. Organic chemists, beginning to unravel the structure of the carbon compounds that form the major portion of the body's chemical constituents, could now follow the utilization of food substances and calculate energy transfers within the body. They identified the main chemical ingredients of the tissues — fats, carbohydrates, and proteins — and traced their transformations when tissues are built up or broken down. Chemical changes produced by disease, such as the appearance of albumen in the urine in nephritis, or uric acid in gouty deposits, acquired meaning.

Mathematics, too, made its contribution. Early in the nineteenth century physicians who found themselves skeptical of the empirical thinking of the profession called to their aid the statistical method, which emphasizes facts and logical analysis as against uncontrolled observation and mere speculation. Claims for specific medication or statements about the cause or spread of a disease must now meet tests for validity set up by the calculus of probability.

Physics proved especially fertile in supplying a host of new mechanical and electrical devices as research tools for the study of the organs and tissues at work. With the induction coil, developed between 1830 and 1850, with galvanometers of improved sensitivity, with the recording drum (kymograph), and with accurate manometers and other apparatus made possible by the recently developed precision lathe, the physiologist could record muscle contraction, exchanges of oxygen and carbon dioxide in the lungs, and even such obscure processes as the transmission of nerve impulses.

Among all the products of technological advance, none proved more valuable than the modern microscope. Dating from about 1830, when opticians began to produce good achromatic lenses of high magnifying power, this new instrument made possible fundamental new observations on the minute structure of animals and plants and opened to view intimate details of diseased tissues invisible to the unaided eye. Microscopists now discovered that all living organisms are made up of very small units or cells. They were able to distinguish and describe particular types of cells responsible for specific vital functions, among them nerve cells, muscle fibers, red and white blood cells, and the cells of the various glands. They found, moreover, that wound healing, inflammation, and the changes produced by degenerative diseases all depend upon the reactions of the cellular elements of the tissues. Hence by 1858

Rudolf Virchow in his great work *Die Zellularpathologie* was able to announce a general concept of disease based on the cell structure of the human body.

The modern microscope also revealed that the minute germs first seen with crude lenses by Leeuwenhoek and others in the seventeenth century are single cells, similar in general to those that make up the bodies of larger creatures. On these beginnings Pasteur, Koch, and many brilliant contemporaries developed the science of bacteriology. In a flood of discoveries beginning about 1875, they not only isolated the germs responsible for a number of common infectious diseases, but also explained how germs attack their hosts by poisoning or even invading their cells, and how the host reacts by the development of immunity. In short, the laboratory workers of the nineteenth century, speeding up a movement which had been going on for three hundred years, had by the 1890's cleared the way for a new attack on disease based on an understanding of the physical aspects of illness, the natural history of disease-producing germs, and the chemistry and physiology of bodily functions.

A few decades earlier, in the middle years of the century, advances in fundamental knowledge had relatively little effect on medical practice, but now their promise was becoming more apparent. The new sciences were revolutionizing the use of drugs. Doctors had been writing prescriptions for centuries on the strength of tradition and faith, checked to a certain extent by observation of their patients. Among the hundreds of medicaments in their books, scarcely half a dozen could pass the test of critical experiment: a few cathartics, quinine for malaria, morphine for pain, digitalis for the failing heart, iron for anemia; but even these were often misapplied in conditions beyond their scope. Now pharmacologists, armed with the controllable methods of chemistry and physiology, were throwing nine tenths of the old pharmacopeia into oblivion, showing physicians how to use the rest properly, and developing new drugs of genuine value.

At the time when The Rockefeller Institute was first proposed, the most conspicuous promise of the new medicine was in the field of infectious diseases. Bacteriologists led the attack; their achievements had made the years from 1880 to 1890 a memorable era in medical history. They had given good reason to hope that, as the germs that cause the great pestilences became known to science, further investigation might provide not only cures but measures for guarding against infection, and, best of all, for preventing the spread of epidemics. Such hope was widespread, even among the lay public. In France popular contributions built a research institute for Louis Pasteur. The German government supplied laboratories for Robert Koch and Paul Ehrlich. In England and Japan private philanthropists set up institutes, the one honoring Joseph Lister's introduction of antiseptic surgery, the other providing facilities for Shibasaburo Kitasato, co-discoverer with Emil von Behring of the diphtheria antitoxin. In all civilized countries public health laboratories were equipping themselves to put the new discoveries to practical use.

Greater imagination was needed to foresee how the medical sciences could attack the constitutional and degenerative diseases. Yet a physiologist such as Carl Ludwig, watching the heart of a frog record its pulsations on a smoked drum, might hope that when the structure and the action of the human heart became fully known, physicians would understand the causes of heart failure and learn how to regulate the disorderly action of weakening ventricles. Ehrlich, looking through his microscope at the malformed blood corpuscles of a patient with pernicious anemia, could ask himself what might be the nature of the bone-marrow disturbance by which the sufferer was doomed to a lingering death. The students of Claude Bernard, watching the master demonstrate the absorption of sugar from the alimentary canal of a laboratory rabbit and its storage in the liver in the form of glycogen, might foresee further research leading to the control of diabetes.

There can be no better illustration of the way in which medical science progressed in the nineteenth century than the succession of discoveries about the nature and site of diabetes. In 1869 a medical student, Paul Langerhans, discovered the special endocrine cell islands in the pancreas which are now known to produce the sugar-burning hormone, insulin. In 1889 Joseph von Mering and Oscar Minkowski, biochemists, produced diabetes experimentally by removing the whole pancreas. At once several medical scientists, the first of them a Frenchman, Paul Laguesse (1893), conjectured that the islands of Langerhans furnish something to the blood that enables the body to use sugar. Eugene L. Opie, who was later to be a member of the original Rockefeller Institute staff, in 1901 proved the connection of the islets with human diabetes by finding them degenerated or destroyed in the fatal cases of the disease which he examined. Thus was the evidence assembled upon which the discovery of insulin by chemical extraction from the islets was founded. Every step was taken in a research laboratory by men trained in anatomy, biochemistry, physiology, and pathology.

The experience of such men taught them how medical problems present themselves for investigation, some ripe for early solution, some needing an indefinitely long period of exploration, and others impossible even to formulate without the light of further discoveries. They had good reason to expect that patient search for knowledge in any field of science might ultimately contribute to the relief or prevention of disease. For such an effort Europe had well-equipped laboratories and a corps of trained investigators. America had yet to create them.

The history of medical science in the United States is closely bound to that of medical education. In 1900 the schools were beginning to recover from the low estate to which they had fallen during the past century. The first medical school, at the University of Pennsylvania, founded in 1765 by men trained abroad, took as its model the University of Edinburgh. Early in the nineteenth century, however, schools were founded which followed the precedent of the London hospital schools, which were conducted by their faculties without university control. Unfortunately they lacked the traditions by which the quality of the London schools was maintained, and too often became mere trade schools operated by local doctors ill equipped for intellectual leadership. Even the university-connected schools suffered from a relative lack of academic spirit. The universities — Pennsylvania, Yale, Harvard, and Columbia — left the control of teaching to busy physicians and surgeons for whom academic duties were a side issue. The schools did not develop laboratories, except the traditional dissecting rooms, nor did they possess hospitals in which clinical teaching could be conducted under proper direction. What intellectual strength there was in the medical profession was overshadowed by general mediocrity. Students of medicine were being largely trained by teachers without experience in scientific medicine and without standards for judging theories of disease and methods of treatment. A symptomatic result of this condition was the persistent strength of the homeopathic sect, which had never gained a great following in Europe but had more than twenty medical colleges in the United States. Under such conditions, scientific medicine could not get a footing. Research, now advancing at an astonishing rate in the European universities, was still sporadic in America.[6]

Before the turn of the century, however, the situation began to improve. William Osler, reminiscing about the opening of the Johns Hopkins Hospital in 1889, said that this event

> came at a most favourable period, when the profession had at last awakened to its responsibilities, the leading universities had begun to take medical education seriously, and to the public at large had come a glimmering sense of the importance of the scientific investigation of disease and of the advantages of having well-trained doctors in a community.[7]

Two circumstances contributed largely to this advance. One was the general improvement of the universities, including the development of graduate education and the introduction and growth of scientific laboratories. A university president who watched his professors of physics and chemistry conducting investigations and training advanced students in their laboratories could hardly fail to note by contrast the weaknesses of his medical faculty. The first sign of impending reform was given at Harvard by Charles W. Eliot, who began a vigorous reorganization of Harvard Medical School as soon as he became president of the University in 1869. The University of Pennsylvania and the University of Michigan soon followed his lead. A second great factor in the advance of American medical science was the influence of physicians returning from European study. In the late eighteenth century the chief foreign centers for American youths who went abroad to study medicine were Edinburgh and London. There they found excellent practical teaching in anatomy, surgery, and midwifery. Early in the nineteenth century American students were attracted to France, where medical training emphasized clinical medicine in the hospitals and the study of post-mortem pathology. After our Civil War, when it became apparent that great advances were being made in Germany, young physicians went to that country, where they worked in well-organized, well-rounded clinics of university caliber supported by research laboratories which were manned by distinguished scientists and filled with competent students — a startling contrast to conditions at home. Some of these Americans, having deliberately chosen the scientific career, went abroad to prepare themselves for it. Others were young physicians who went overseas to perfect their practical experience but caught the spirit of research from one or another of the great professors and came home determined to be laboratory investigators. Thus at Harvard in 1871 President Eliot was able to put William P. Bowditch, who had recently returned to Boston from the laboratory of Carl Ludwig in Leipzig, in charge of a laboratory of physiology.

At the University of Pennsylvania, oldest medical school in the United States, the process of improvement began about 1877 under William Pepper (second of the name, 1843–1898). His efforts culminated in the endowment of the Henry C. Lea Laboratory and Department of Hygiene in 1889 with John S. Billings as director.[8] In 1883, Victor Vaughan, dean of the University of Michigan Medical School, appointed to his chair of physiology young Henry Sewall, back from work with Sir Michael Foster at Cambridge and with Willy Kühne and Ludwig in Germany. The recollections of a Michigan graduate, F. P. Mall, himself destined to be a distinguished medical educator, who witnessed the reformation under Vaughan and Sewall, epitomize the changing times:

> The principle involved appeared to me to be the development of the student while presenting the subject matter, and now it is plain to me that no one but an investigator in his subject can do this. . . . The majority of the students were seeking a certain quantity of knowledge, and preferred to have it drilled into them. Little did the solving of problems and the development of reason appeal to them. . . . An educational institution of the highest order must carry on perpetual warfare against drilling trades into inferior students, in order to retain its high position. And above all the medical profession should be filled with learned men, and not tradesmen, in order to be of the greatest good to the community. It appears to me that the change beginning to take place in the medical department in 1880 was toward training thinking physicians with an underlying foundation composed of recent medical research.[9]

The most notable step in the reform was the opening by the Johns Hopkins University in 1893 of a medical school attached to its already famous hospital. Under the leadership of President Daniel C. Gilman and Dean William H. Welch, the school was fully organized with laboratories in all pre-clinical branches headed by trained investigators, and with clinical professors of university caliber in complete control of the hospital. This was for some years the only one of the country's hundred medical schools of which so much could be said, but the leaven was also working elsewhere. By 1900 there were a dozen or more medical schools equipped with research laboratories, in which a few score research men, mostly trained in Europe, were conducting original investigations in anatomy, physiology, biochemistry, pathology, and bacteriology, and applying current knowledge in a scientific way to the analysis of practical medical questions. Outstanding among these were William H. Welch, Franklin P. Mall, John J. Abel, Simon Flexner, and William H. Howell at Johns Hopkins; Charles Sedgwick Minot, Harry Pickering Bowditch, William J. Porter, William T. Councilman, and Theobald Smith at Harvard; Russell H. Chittenden, Graham Lusk, and Lafayette B. Mendel at Yale in the Sheffield Scientific School; Ludvig Hektoen and Edwin Klebs at the University of Chicago; A. R. Cushny, Frederick G. Novy, and Henry Sewall at the University of Michigan; and Alexander Abbott and Alonzo Taylor at the University of Pennsylvania. Surgeon General George M. Sternberg was leading good bacteriological work in the Army Medical Corps. Although the medical schools of New York City could scarcely as yet be considered centers of research and modern teaching, W. H. Park at the New York Public Health Laboratories was actively investigating the infectious diseases. T. Mitchell Prudden and Christian Herter were doing good work in pathology and biochemistry, Herter in a small research laboratory in his own house, Prudden in a small laboratory at the medical school where he taught. Samuel J. Meltzer was making a name for himself as a physiologist with no more research facilities than he could beg from time to time in a corner of some hospital's small diagnostic laboratory.

A few clinical teachers were also contributing to medical science through their laboratories. Among these were the surgeons William H. Halsted and Howard A. Kelly and the physicians William Osler and William S. Thayer in Baltimore; the pediatrician L. Emmett Holt in New York; and the surgeon Nicholas Senn in Chicago. Their departments, all of modest size, were operated on budgets that were small by present-day standards. The largest of them had three or four permanent full-time staff members, a fellow or two on annual stipends, and a half-dozen students and other volunteers on part time. The number of places available for men who wanted to make a full-time career as medical investigators was thus very small even in 1900. But a few years earlier there had been none at all. T. Mitchell Prudden, one of the original Board of Directors of The Rockefeller Institute, poignantly recalled his own experience after returning from Germany in 1878. Writing in the third person, he says:

> When Prudden came home from Europe, full of enthusiasm to introduce into the lore and training of medicine the laboratory and special research study and teaching of normal histology, pathology, and pathological physiology, as related to medicine, with all of which he had been especially engaged in various places during his two years abroad, he was chagrined to find none of the authorities at the several medical schools whom he consulted and the few leading practitioners of medicine with whom he talked, seemed to care about these things as special subjects of knowledge or training. There were chairs of pathology and the practice of medicine, but no chairs of pathology as a special practical theme, and no one saw any occasion to establish them. . . . Thus it was that after vain efforts to get a place to work at pathology at any of the medical schools, even as a volunteer, Prudden finally came back to New Haven, opened an office and started to practice.[10]

Prudden was by no means the only young man who met such obstacles. Who can tell how many promising minds were lost to science for lack of opportunities in research?

The scarcity of places for full-time investigators was only slightly ameliorated by the few laboratories that were opened in the 1880's and 1890's. As late as 1901, the professor of pathology at McGill University actually feared that a proposed scheme for granting a dozen scholarships and fellowships each year in laboratory work in the United States and Canada would draw into research more men than the medical schools could employ.[11]

Two problems lay before the men who accepted John D. Rockefeller's call to organize a great institute for research: they must first find men capable of original thought and work, and then provide them with laboratories worthy of their talents.

THE EXISTENCE of a private fortune large enough to create The Rockefeller Institute, as one in a series of great benefactions, was a phenomenon of the industrial expansion of 1865 to 1900. The great chieftains of the oil and steel industries, of railways, mines, machinery, meat packing, and finance, built their empires under the same conditions that gave the nation as a whole its enormous economic power. Vast natural resources were available; the domestic markets were rapidly expanding; labor was plentiful and cheap. Business enterprise was largely unrestrained by government, and indeed actively supported by protective tariffs, land grants, and injunctions against labor. "The new economic barons," say the historians Charles and Mary Beard,

> were organizers of men and materials — masters of the administrative art — who saw with penetrating eyes the wastes and crudities of the competitive system in industry and transportation. . . . In cooperation with tireless workers in science and invention, they wrought marvels in large-scale production, bringing material comforts to millions of people who could never have wrung them barehanded from the hills and forests. . . . The best example of all is offered by the oil business. . . . In the unfolding of this single industry, we see modern science, invention, business acumen, economic imagination, and capacity for world enterprise creating material goods and organizing human services to supply not only every nook and cranny of this country but the uttermost parts of the world with useful commodities of a high standard.[12]

John D. Rockefeller was by common consent the greatest of all the magnates of his period in business acumen and executive skill. As head of the Standard Oil Company, which he established in 1870, he had the imagination and audacity to unify the scattered elements of a new kind of industry, linking in a chain of business enterprise the producers at the oil wells, the refiners, and the carriers of petroleum products by land and sea. At its peak the Standard Oil Company dominated the oil markets of the world, and Rockefeller was the undisputed chief of its able directorate. Although he freely used his unusual talent for finding men of ability to help him in whatever he undertook, and for guiding their joint efforts, all these men acknowledged his pre-eminent judgment and foresight. Even those who had opposed him in some industrial contest of wits or strength came later to get his advice. As one of his associates said, a decade after he retired:

> If he were placed in a group of any twenty of the greatest men of affairs today, he would be the most modest, retiring, and deferential man of them all, but before these giants had been with him long, the most self-confident, self-assertive of them would be coming to him in private for his counsel.[13]

Rockefeller's personal wealth of course expanded with the growth of the industry, giving him not only a major share of the ownership of

Standard Oil, but also a constantly growing surplus to be invested in other enterprises. The income from his properties rolled in so fast that he could scarcely have stopped it even had he wished to do so. By 1897, when he chose to give up the management of the Standard Oil Company, Rockefeller's holdings were approaching $200,000,000. He was well on the way to possession of a fortune by far the largest in the United States. In the dry words of another multimillionaire, Andrew Carnegie, ". . . men possessed of this peculiar talent for affairs must, of necessity, soon be in receipt of more revenue than can judiciously be expended upon themselves."[14]

Carnegie discussed the problem of dealing with great wealth and offered his own answers in an essay entitled "Wealth," published in the *North American Review,* in 1889.[15] His views, notable because they came from one of the greatest industrialists, reflected the general feeling of the nineteenth century that the accumulation of wealth by a few is a good thing. The gaining of individual wealth had its justification in the puritan ideals of thrift and industry. To these sanctions the social Darwinism of the nineteenth century added the view that great success in business reflects the survival of the fittest men. To give one's wealth away, moreover, was to exemplify the Christian doctrine of stewardship of this world's goods on behalf of the poor.

In the burgeoning commercial life of America, it was taken for granted that certain successful men made more money than they could spend. The special concern of Carnegie and Rockefeller was that they had more even than they could effectively take care of during their lives, and far too much to dispose of safely by last will and testament. Such vast accumulations had already brought down upon their heads, especially Rockefeller's, a good deal of popular resentment. If left to their heirs the excessive burden would merely be passed along to those not fitted by experience to carry it. Large bequests to philanthropic institutions carried another kind of risk: the judgment and foresight of the testator might not be equaled in his trustees, and the influence of the dead hand could be all the more injurious because of the great sums involved. There were at least a dozen multimillionaires in the latter half of the nineteenth century for whom this problem existed; among them Carnegie and Rockefeller perceived the difficulties most intelligently. The

FREDERICK T. GATES

WILLIAM H. WELCH

former was too philosophic and democratic, the latter too religious and conscientious, to risk the demoralization of their heirs through idle luxury; and both were inclined to trust their own wisdom, in the direction of large affairs, beyond that of others. We need not stop to consider here Carnegie's proposals for preventing dangerous accumulations of wealth in the future, one of which was a graduated inheritance tax. His advice to the multimillionaire was to place his excess fortune, while he still lived, in the hands of trustees of his own choice, directing them to use the money for public benefit through philanthropic and educational foundations, in accord with the needs of changing times.

This program was not entirely novel; George Peabody, for example, gave away several million dollars for education and social amelioration during his lifetime. He was, however, a bachelor who no doubt wished to see for himself the benefits his gifts would confer upon the public. Carnegie's proposals reflected, on the other hand, a far-ranging social philosophy. His ideas about inherited wealth aroused a great deal of comment in America and England. Cardinal Manning and Prime Minister William E. Gladstone, among others who replied in print, accepted the thesis in the main, though Gladstone did not endorse Carnegie's objection to hereditary wealth, which seemed to him to ignore the community value of hereditary power. "Is it too much to affirm," Gladstone wrote, "that the hereditary transmission of wealth and position, in conjunction with the calls of occupation and responsibility, is a good and not an evil thing? I rejoice to see it among our merchants, bankers, publishers: I wish it were commoner among our great manufacturing capitalists."[16]

Reading these statements sixty years later, one is led to reflect that men like Carnegie and Rockefeller, however powerful and independent, were after all controlled, in regard to the disposal of their fortunes, by personal circumstances as well as theoretical considerations. Carnegie, who married late in life and had only one child — a daughter — could scarcely have hoped, whatever his principles, to create a dynasty of wealth; Rockefeller and his wife lived to see grown grandchildren about them and left an inheritance of character as well as of money to a family line that matched Gladstone's ideal for the hereditary transmission of wealth and position. Carnegie's thesis appealed to the individualistic spirit of Americans. He won general approval when he carried out his

ideas by a series of large gifts, beginning with a welfare fund for employees of his steel mills, and followed by the scientific, educational, and
humanitarian foundations that still bear his name.

Among those who fully approved was John D. Rockefeller, who in
1896 wrote to the steel king:

> I am pleased with the sentiments you give expression to. I would that
> more men of wealth were doing as you are doing with your money; but,
> be assured, your example will bear fruits, and the time will come when
> men of wealth will more generally be willing to use it for the good of
> others.[17]

An acquaintance later remarked that about this time Rockefeller's mind
was wholly absorbed in working out the problem of how great accumulations of wealth could be left without doing harm.[18] He had not needed
Carnegie's example to start his giving. From a strong sense of religious
obligation imparted by his mother's early training, he gave to his church
and various charitable undertakings $9.09 out of his first four months'
salary, totaling $95, as a bookkeeper and clerk in Cleveland in 1855.
Later he said that his first ambition to earn more money was aroused by
a campaign for the building fund of his church which he directed when
twenty years of age. As his income increased, so did his gifts. Many,
though by no means all, went to Baptist and other Christian organizations; in time he gave to most of the Baptist colleges and to some outside
that denomination.

Although Rockefeller's donations in early years were large in relation to his income, by the 1880's they were, though constantly increasing,
no longer keeping pace with his increasing wealth.[19] The task merely of
investing his surplus was too large for him, and the demands for support
of every sort of charity and philanthropy were so bewildering that he
could not begin to study them all. Because of his cautious policy of making gifts only to groups and causes which he judged by direct examination to be sound and efficient, he could no longer administer a philanthropic program personally as he had done on a smaller scale in earlier
years. In dealing with oil, Rockefeller had possessed a grand vision, a set
of practical plans, and a group of able associates. A similar combination
was required to deal with his fortune, and the need was soon filled by the
discovery of Frederick T. Gates. After that, Rockefeller never lacked

grand visions, nor plans, nor an able associate in putting his fortune to work for the general good.

Rockefeller and the Reverend Mr. Gates first came together when they became involved in the affairs of the University of Chicago. As early as 1885 Baptist leaders, interested in the creation of a great university under the auspices of their church, began appealing for support to Rockefeller, their wealthiest member and one of the most faithful. When he became interested, a tug of war ensued between those who preferred an eastern location and those who favored Chicago, and further complications arose later from the effort to build the new university upon the scholarly but financially weak Morgan Park Theological Seminary and the remnants of the old University of Chicago. Rockefeller might have washed his hands of the whole affair had it not been for the founding in 1888 of the American Baptist Education Society, with Gates at its head, to encourage and strengthen the Baptist colleges and divinity schools. Its first major task was to consolidate the church's effort to establish the projected university. Gates's brilliant and forceful report to this society on the weakness of the denominational colleges in the Midwest and the need for a university to provide them with intellectual leadership turned the tide of opinion toward Chicago. In that document and in subsequent letters Rockefeller found the kind of clear, positive analysis he needed after having listened to so many contending advocates, and he soon had full opportunity to appraise Gates's general intelligence and capacity. Thenceforward the campaign for Rockefeller's support proceeded smoothly. It was to Gates in person that Rockefeller chose to announce in May 1889 his decision to make a gift of $600,000 to the University of Chicago. This was the first in a series from himself, his son, and the Rockefeller boards that has amounted to eighty million dollars.

Frederick Taylor Gates was born, like Rockefeller, in rural New York State. Son of a minister in the Baptist Home Missionary service, the boy had to earn his own way by teaching and working in a bank. After preparing himself at the University of Rochester and the Rochester Theological Seminary, young Gates was for eight years minister of a struggling Baptist church in Minneapolis. Not until the end of this pastorate, when church leaders assigned him to travel about Minnesota soliciting funds for one of the Baptist schools, did his business abilities come to the fore.

When the American Baptist Education Society was organized, his success in this task marked him as fitted to become its executive secretary. As Professor Allan Nevins says,

> It has been customary to treat Gates as a minister who developed an interest in education and philanthropy. Actually Gates was essentially a business man with a talent for large affairs, a keen interest in the power of money, and a passion for seeing it expended with the greatest possible efficiency.[20]

It is no wonder that Rockefeller, watching this intense, outspoken man put his full energies to work for the University of Chicago project, made up his mind to channel his personal gifts for education through the Baptist Education Society, nor that a couple of years later he invited Gates to join his own staff as his principal aide in philanthropy. In September 1891 Gates opened an office in New York City and began the huge task of organizing Rockefeller's program of gifts. He had to review and reassess a long list of benefactions, both private and institutional, which Mr. Rockefeller's generosity had built up. Unreasonable and inefficient applicants were weeded out. Gifts to churches, missions, schools, and hospitals were directed to central church boards which Gates strengthened for their task. For such work as this he was ideally suited; his quick enthusiasm and boldly constructive imagination were readily fired by good causes, while his hard-headed business sense protected his employer from a thousand impractical and selfish demands. The business of doing good with money became a pleasure to Rockefeller instead of an endless harassment.

Shortly after he became Rockefeller's chief almoner, Gates also began to look after his employer's investments. With growing experience in investigating every sort of enterprise, added to a great natural talent, he became as successful in big business as in philanthropic administration. Here again, because Rockefeller's investments had gotten out of hand from mere size, Gates had to straighten out a host of complications. He showed himself more than a match for men who had long been imposing upon Rockefeller and even defrauding him; and when he had thinned out the bad investments, he reorganized many of the companies and made them pay. Extraordinary success in these tasks culminated in his brilliant handling of Rockefeller's interests in the Mesabi iron range (1893–1901) with an ultimate profit of fifty million dollars. A former associate, seeking words strong enough to characterize Gates's shrewd business sense, said that on occasion he could even outdeal Mr. Rockefeller himself. If this was true, it did not vex the latter, whose own considered opinion of his aide was that he "had a great store of common sense . . . a combination of rare business ability, very highly developed and very honourably exercised, overshadowed by a passion to accomplish some great and far-reaching benefits to mankind, the influence of which will last."[21]

Gates himself has told, in a characteristically vivid statement, how the idea first occurred to him that Rockefeller should found an institute for medical research.[22] For years, he said, medicine had been of more interest to him than to most laymen. As a young pastor he had, of course, much contact with doctors and patients. From conversations with physicians — and we may be sure that he did not let them off with perfunctory questions — he became very skeptical about current medical practice. The doctors he saw at work seemed to be using mere rule-of-thumb methods, without any basis in scientific knowledge. One of the city's most prominent physicians admitted, he said, that nine out of every ten professional calls, for all the good they did, might just as well not have been made. A depressing feature of the medical situation as Gates saw it was the schism, then still very wide, between the "regular" physicians and the homeopaths. The former seemed to have no more valid basis of scientific information than their rivals, and he was equally skeptical of both schools.

It must be said parenthetically that Gates was unduly pessimistic about American medical practice. His personal experience in a relatively poor city parish and the countryside had not brought him into contact with the best of the profession. We must not let Gates's fervor mislead us into thinking that all American doctors were ill-trained sectarians or ignoramuses. There were indeed many practicing physicians and clinical teachers — not hundreds of them, but at least scores — like the "Blair" described by a contemporary of his student days:

> We had adjoining desks in the chemical laboratory, and I remember him as painstaking, slow, and thorough. Then we drifted apart. He became a house-physician, I a house-surgeon. He immersed himself in internal medicine, especially diseases of the chest. He has the rare faculty of perceiving in what a subject is weak; and has the capacity and insight to hurl

himself at the problem and produce a remedy. He studied in Europe when modern work on the blood was new. He came home, was called by Superbus to Liverpool, when the great new university hospital was founded, and there he is today. He has been through all the teaching and clinical grades, from Resident up; and now, since the resignation of Superbus, Blair is a full professor and head of his department. He is known the world over for his contributions to our knowledge of certain fevers, and of diseases of the blood and of the heart. He is a tireless worker; a careful and informing teacher, a profound and convincing writer, and a brilliant speaker. To these pleasant qualities he adds a capacity for practice. Through a large section of our country he is in demand; he flourishes as a prosperous consultant; and with it all he is the same good friend and agreeable companion that we knew twenty-five years ago.[23]

At the time when Gates's concern about medicine in America came to a head, "Blair" (William Sidney Thayer) had been home and working at Johns Hopkins about seven years. His story illustrates the situation as it actually was. The medical profession did not totally lack competent physicians, able to keep up with the best current practice; but such men were far too few. They had to go to Europe for training in scientific medicine, and when they returned by no means all of them could hope for "Blair's" good fortune in finding a position and facilities for basing his practice on a university hospital where medical research had gained a footing. The picture was still dark, even if not wholly black. It is perhaps fortunate that Gates's medical acquaintances included mostly men of the less enlightened sort. If he had known young doctors like Thayer, or some of the best older physicians and surgeons of his time, men, for example, like Weir Mitchell in Philadelphia, William Osler in Baltimore, Maurice Richardson in Boston, Abraham Jacobi in New York, Nicholas Senn in Chicago, he might never have been shocked into action by such a revelation of the need of science in medicine as that which occurred to him in 1897.

About three years after Gates joined Rockefeller's staff in 1891, he began to see a good deal of a young student of medicine, Elon O. Huntington, whom he had known as a small boy in his Minneapolis congregation, and who had come to New York to study at the College of Physicians and Surgeons.[24] The two men took long walks together, and they frequently talked about medicine. One day in the spring of 1897, Gates asked Huntington to recommend a professional textbook which a layman could understand and from which he could learn what the best physicians were teaching. Huntington, now a senior student, suggested Osler's *Principles and Practice of Medicine,* first published in 1892. Gates promptly bought this book, doubtless the second edition of 1896, and took it with him, together with a pocket medical dictionary, on vacation in the Catskills. This was no ordinary textbook. Though written for physicians and students, its readable style and humane outlook fascinated many laymen, for whom it provided the best possible introduction to the medical knowledge of the time. It dealt with the whole field of internal disease in the light of the newest information and with a critical scientific outlook. Gates read the thousand-page volume from cover to cover. His skepticism about the contemporary state of medical knowledge was fully confirmed, but at the same time he began to see the hope that lay in scientific investigation of the unsolved mysteries of disease. He learned from Osler that the best medical practice did not pretend to have specific cures for more than four or five diseases. Osler's discussion of each particular disease, as Gates says, began with a learned account of its definition and history, its prevalence, symptoms, and probable outcome; but when he came to describe the treatment he almost always disclosed an attitude of doubt. "In fact," wrote Gates,

I saw clearly from the work of this able and honest man, that medicine had, with the few exceptions above mentioned, no cures, and that about all that medicine up to 1897 could do was to nurse the patients and alleviate in some degree the suffering. Beyond this, medicine as a science had not progressed. I found further that a large number of the most common diseases, especially of the young and middle aged, were simply infectious or contagious, were caused by infinitesimal germs. . . . I learned that of these germs, only a very few had been identified and isolated. . . .

When I laid down this book, I had begun to realize how woefully neglected in all civilized countries and perhaps most of all in this country, had been the scientific study of medicine. I saw very clearly also why this was true. In the first place, the instruments for investigation, the microscope, the science of chemistry, had not until recently been developed. Pasteur's germ theory of disease was very recent. Moreover, while other departments of science, astronomy, chemistry, physics, etc., had been endowed very generously in colleges and universities throughout the whole civilized world, medicine, owing to the peculiar commercial organization of medical colleges, had rarely, if ever, been any where endowed, and research and instruction alike had been left to shift for itself dependent altogether on such chance as the active practitioner might steal from his practice.[25]

Here Gates was again characteristically exaggerating. In Europe medical research was receiving good support in university laboratories and clinics, especially in Germany, and in a number of research institutes. Two of the latter he knew at least by name, the Koch Institute of Berlin and the Pasteur Institute of Paris. What he says, however, was true of the United States. As far as this country was concerned, he was quite right when he went on to say that medicine could hardly hope to become a science until medical research should be endowed and qualified men could give themselves to uninterrupted study and investigation, on ample salary, entirely independent of practice. Here was an opportunity, the greatest the world could afford, for Rockefeller to become a pioneer.

This idea took possession of Gates. The more he thought of it, the more enthusiastic he became. He knew nothing of the cost of research; he did not realize its enormous difficulty; the only thing he saw was "the overwhelming need and the infinite promise, worldwide, universal, eternal."

When Gates returned to his office late in July, he dictated for Rockefeller's eye a memorandum advocating the establishment of an institute for medical research. To illustrate the condition of medical science as Osler's book disclosed it, he emphasized the infectious diseases, pointing out how few of their causative agents and how few cures had yet been found, how appalling the unremedied suffering, and how great the opportunities. In this or a subsequent memorandum, Gates insisted that even if the proposed institute should fail to discover anything, the mere fact that Rockefeller had founded it would lead to the donation of other funds for similar purposes, until research in America should come into its own.

Rockefeller was out of town when the memorandum was placed on his desk, and Gates never saw it again.[26] He knew his chief well enough to expect that a proposal of such magnitude and importance would be thought over privately, discussed quietly with experts, and turned over and over in Rockefeller's mind before he would come to a decision. For a time he had only indirect evidence that Rockefeller had taken any notice of the matter at all. Soon, however, Gates had the satisfaction of

knowing that he had an important ally. At this time the elder Rockefeller was quietly withdrawing from active management of the Standard
Oil companies, to devote himself to caring for his personal fortune and
to giving away a great share of it. At the same time John D. Rockefeller,
Jr., joined the office at 26 Broadway to begin his own long career of devotion to his father's philanthropic interests. Gates's first memorandum
about a research institute, and others which shortly followed, were
passed on to this young man, who was then twenty-four years of age and
only one year out of college.

"Gates was the brilliant dreamer and creator," Rockefeller, Jr., told
Raymond B. Fosdick many years later:

> I was the salesman, the go-between with father at the opportune moment.
> Gates and I were father's lieutenants, each of us with a different task, but
> acting in perfect harmony. Gates did the heavy thinking, and my part was
> to sell his ideas to father. Of course, I was in a unique position. I could
> talk with father at the strategic moment. It might be in a relaxed mood
> after dinner, or while we were driving together. Consequently I could
> often get his approval of ideas which others couldn't have secured because
> the moment wasn't right.[27]

Actually, Rockefeller, Jr., was much more than a mere liaison officer. In
this matter as in many others in subsequent years, his father relied upon
him to study and discuss the project and to marshal the facts upon which
a decision would be made.

As the two lieutenants discussed the plan, they soon realized how
little they knew about the details of the problem. Gates saw that any active steps toward founding the institute would require conferences with
leading research men in America, a study of similar institutions in Europe, and an amount of thought, correspondence, and travel that might
engage most of the time of a competent man. For this task he chose Starr
J. Murphy, a lawyer who lived near him in Montclair. Murphy went to
work, as Gates tells us, with a quiet competence revealed in results rather
than in documents. There is, in fact, almost no surviving record of
Murphy's activities at this time. He must have conferred with research
leaders in the United States, and he certainly investigated foreign research laboratories, at least by correspondence. A letter from the distinguished American-born scientist George H. F. Nuttall, then lecturer
in bacteriology and preventive medicine at Cambridge University, indi-

cates that Murphy had requested Nuttall's opinion as to the advisability of establishing "an institute for the study of the prevention of diseases" and asked for information about research laboratories in Great Britain. To these inquiries Nuttall replied at length, adding his enthusiastic hope that Rockefeller would carry out some such plan as Murphy had mentioned. The institute, Nuttall said, should be located at Washington or New York, and unless it was to be set up on "the really magnificent scale of the Pasteur Institute in Paris with its own hospital, it should be affiliated with a university."[28]

Rockefeller's advisers were at about that period conferring tentatively with the heads of at least two universities. According to Gates, active negotiations were conducted for a time with Harvard.[29] In the spring of 1900, moreover, Rockefeller, Jr., talked with President Seth Low of Columbia University about the possibility of establishing an institute similar in character to the Pasteur in Paris. A few months later Low wrote to William H. Welch of Baltimore and to T. Mitchell Prudden of New York, cautiously requesting advice as to the need for such an institute and especially as to whether it should be associated with a university. Rockefeller, Jr., had evidently not intended Low to build up hopes of securing the institute for Columbia, but between the lines of the President's letters one can perceive what he was thinking about.[30] As an unnamed member of the Board acknowledged, when the founding of the Institute was finally announced, "strong pressure was brought to bear upon Mr. Rockefeller to hand the control of his benefaction over to some one of the existing universities. Columbia and Harvard were particularly active in this respect."[31]

WHEN STARR J. MURPHY undertook, as part of the duty assigned to him by Gates and Rockefeller, Jr., to study the medical research institutions of Europe, one can imagine the questions that presented themselves. Which were the great institutions worthy of emulation, where located, how staffed? Who paid for their upkeep — government, universities, private benefactors? Why had several notable research institutions been set up as independent of the universities, even in countries such as Germany, where the universities had competently conducted research at the highest levels? When Mr. Murphy examined these questions, he must have been puzzled by the complexity and diversity of the answers.

The European institutions were not all alike in their history and aims.[32] When scientific investigation in the modern sense began, at the time of the Renaissance, it was usually undertaken as a private activity by men both within and outside the universities who were curious about nature. Later such private workers came together in many places to found academies, of which the Royal Society of London, Leopold de' Medici's Accademia del Cimento in Florence, and the Paris Académie des Sciences were in their several ways typical. Some of them provided only for the communication of scientific findings through meetings and journals. Others actually set up laboratories for their members, usually with government support. Thus in the seventeenth and eighteenth centuries a chain of national and local academies, extending all over Europe, was supporting the growth of science, while the universities were largely failing to do so. The membership and financial resources of the academies were limited, however; and by the nineteenth century the support of scientific investigation was to come from the universities through their acceptance of research as an essential part of their duty. This integration of teaching and research began at Göttingen in the eighteenth century, and received a notable stimulus by the founding of the University of Berlin in 1810. The prototype of the modern university institute, however, was built up by Justus von Liebig at Giessen in the 1820's and 1830's. Such an institute is headed by a professor, who controls the laboratory facilities, directs the training of both elementary and advanced students, and leads the latter in research projects which generally stem from his own program of investigation. Ultimately all or nearly all the professional chairs of the sciences in German universities were provided with such facilities. They set the standard for academic research schools all over the world.

After the middle of the nineteenth century, research institutes of a new sort began to grow up independently of the universities as had the academies of preceding centuries, and partly for the same reason, that science was again outrunning the ability of the universities to provide for it. A few, like the Naples Zoological Station, were founded by scientists with private means. Some were created by governments for a great investigator who did not fit the standard professorial pattern or for whom a suitable chair was not open, as, for example, Robert Koch's laboratory at the Imperial Health Office in Berlin (1880), which is considered the first modern non-university institute of medical science. Eight years later the Pasteur Institute, the first to be set up as a private corporation, opened in Paris with an endowment obtained largely by voluntary international subscription in recognition of Pasteur's work on rabies. Devoting itself chiefly to bacteriology and immunology, this institute, which acquired its own hospital in 1900, because of its size, its success, and its fame became the prototype of similar institutes throughout the world.

Among the earliest imitators was the Russian Institute for Experimental Medicine, founded in St. Petersburg in 1890 with advice from Pasteur. Its laboratories were equipped for physiology, biochemistry, bacteriology, pathology, and veterinary medicine, and it had a small hospital. It was operated as an independent government institution and after the Revolution became a branch of the All-Union Institute of Experimental Medicine. England followed the example of France and Russia by creating, with private support, an institute for medical research, chartered in 1891 under the chairmanship of Sir Joseph (later Lord) Lister, and since 1903 called the Lister Institute. Although bacteriology was its chief field, divisions of experimental pathology, biochemistry, nutrition, and other medicobiological subjects have been set up.

In Germany, Koch in 1885 had accepted the new chair of hygiene created for him at the University of Berlin, but six years later, when he decided to give up teaching in order to devote full time to research, the government established the Koch Institute for Infectious Diseases outside the university. Similarly, for the celebrated histologist and chemist Paul Ehrlich, the imperial government together with the city of Frankfurt founded in 1899 the Institute for Experimental Therapy. A disciple of Koch, Shibasaburo Kitasato, codiscoverer with von Behring of diphtheria antitoxin, returning to Japan in 1892, established, with the aid of the philanthropist Fukusawa, a small private laboratory which after 1893 was supported by the government as the Kitasato Institute. Here Kitasato, Shiga, and others made notable discoveries in bacteriology. It should be added that the founder resigned his post in 1914 when the Institute was affiliated, for reasons he deemed political, with Tokyo University. The present Kitasato Institute is a subsequent and entirely separate private organization.

In various other countries there were a dozen similar though smaller institutes, carrying on experimental studies chiefly in bacteriology.

These may be classed as non-university research institutes. The laboratories of the German Imperial Health Office and the Pasteur, Russian, Lister, Koch, Kitasato, and Ehrlich institutes were, however, the outstanding institutions of this kind when The Rockefeller Institute was being considered. The Pasteur Institute, largest and best known to the general public, was undoubtedly in the mind of Frederick T. Gates when he drew up his first memorandum, though he probably had little detailed knowledge about it. Mention of Koch's institute also occurs in the early correspondence. William H. Welch, who was to aid in organizing The Rockefeller Institute, with his encyclopedic knowledge and world-wide acquaintance, knew a great deal about all the institutes, and the four in France, Germany, and Britain were visited by those members of the Rockefeller Institute Board of Directors who went abroad during 1901 and 1902.

In Britain and France these establishments (which for convenience have been called non-university medical research institutes) grew up outside the universities because the sudden advance in bacteriology and related disciplines had created a need for intensive work, largely in the interest of preventive medicine, and the universities were not prepared to assume it. In Germany the universities were better prepared to take on new research departments, but there the two great institutes were also extramural for reasons that were chiefly personal: Koch's, because he did not care for teaching, and Ehrlich's, because as a Jew he was ineligible for a professorial chair. These institutes could not carry the heavy burdens of ordinary university instruction together with research, but most of them conducted courses for advanced students and for technical assistants. Because of the independent status of their staffs, and the breadth of view of the experimental scientists who led them, they tended to widen their scope by adding laboratories for biochemistry, physiology, and other medical sciences.

The Rockefeller Institute naturally followed in a general way the pattern of its predecessors, especially the Pasteur Institute, but because it was intended from the start to attack problems on a broad front, rather than to foster the work of any one eminent man, it was to exceed them all in the readiness of its leaders to include any branch of science that might aid medical research.

CHAPTER TWO

The Rockefeller Institute
Is Founded

First plans; organization of the Board of Directors. The Institute not to be affiliated with a university. Program of grants-in-aid; investigations of New York City's milk supply. Flexner appointed Director of the Institute. Planning for laboratory buildings.

THE ROCKEFELLERS in their careful fashion continued to think about Mr. Gates's proposal throughout the years 1898, 1899, and 1900. Rockefeller, Jr., for example, taking every opportunity to inform himself about medical research, sounded out the well-informed pediatrician L. Emmett Holt, his fellow parishioner of the Fifth Avenue Baptist Church, when the two chanced to spend a few hours together on a train in November 1900. Holt, who had been deeply impressed by the recent success of diphtheria antitoxin, made the point that this was not a chance discovery but the result of deliberate laboratory work in which fundamental biological principles had been applied. Men and resources, he told Rockefeller, Jr., were needed for similar attacks on other infectious diseases. The conversation led the young man to think highly of Holt, and he sought further opportunities to talk with him, finally drawing him into a leading role in discussions about the proposed institute.[1]

Within a few weeks of their first casual meeting, a grievous event in the Rockefeller family vividly demonstrated that the medical profession, though newly armed against diphtheria, was still impotent against other common and frequently fatal diseases of childhood. John D. Rockefeller's daughter Edith in 1895 had married Harold F. McCormick of Chicago, a member of the well-known family of manufacturers of agricultural machinery. Their first child was named, after his grandfather,

John Rockefeller McCormick. In December 1900, the boy, then three years old, fell ill with scarlet fever, and on January 2, 1901, he died. Sadly recalling little Jack's death more than a half century later, Rockefeller, Jr., remembered that his father had loved the little boy, his first grandchild, and when the doctors told him that they knew nothing about the cause of scarlet fever and had no effective treatment for it, he had determined to go ahead with the plan for an institute of medical research, which he had so long been considering.[2] The first sign that a decision had been reached came early in March 1901 when Rockefeller, Jr., joined Emmett Holt and his friend Christian A. Herter for dinner at Holt's house, with the express purpose of discussing ways and means of getting the institute under way.

The two doctors were well prepared for the momentous responsibility thus assigned to them. Holt had already won prominence in the field of pediatrics, which under the leadership of Abraham Jacobi was just then becoming recognized in the United States as a major specialty. After serving for seven years as consultant to the New York Infant Asylum, he became director of the Babies' Hospital, which he reorganized in 1889 along modern lines. At the bedsides of children stricken with diphtheria and summer diarrhea, or wasted by malnutrition, he learned how desperately needed were the methods of diagnosis and treatment promised by bacteriology and biochemistry. A quietly persistent organizer and teacher, Holt built up the laboratories in his hospital, helped to found the *Archives of Pediatrics,* and wrote the standard textbook in the field. His popular manual, *The Care and Feeding of Infants,* became the mainstay of thousands of young mothers. In 1901 he was about to be appointed professor of pediatrics in the College of Physicians and Surgeons.[3]

In contrast to Holt, a physician who founded his practical art upon science, Christian Herter was at heart far more of a scientific investigator than a practitioner. While still a medical student he had become convinced that the practice of medicine was destined to be based on exact science. After an apprenticeship in pathology and bacteriology at Johns Hopkins with William H. Welch, he returned to New York and became professor of pathological chemistry at Bellevue Hospital Medical School and, later, of pharmacology at the College of Physicians and Surgeons. These posts could then afford only an opportunity to lecture, not to conduct experimental research. Using his private means, Herter established a laboratory in his New York residence, and, giving but little time to medical consultations, plunged into research in biochemistry, pharmacology, and bacteriology. The quality of this private establishment may be judged by the number of brilliant men who worked there as assistants, including A. N. Richards, Carl TenBroeck, and Henry D. Dakin. The call to Herter to join Holt and Rockefeller, Jr., in their first practical steps toward organizing the Institute no doubt resulted chiefly from Holt's personal friendship and knowledge of his talents; but Herter was already acquainted with Rockefeller, Sr., as his summertime neighbor on Mount Desert Island. More deeply sensitive, perhaps, to the fundamental aspects of science than any of the other founders of the new Institute, he brought it, during the few years he was spared to serve, the fruits of a broadly inquiring philosophical spirit.[4]

When, over their after-dinner coffee, Rockefeller, Jr., asked Holt and Herter to suggest the names of a group of physicians who might best direct the far-reaching enterprise they had in mind, inevitably they first mentioned William H. Welch of Baltimore, their friend and former teacher. They named also Hermann M. Biggs and T. Mitchell Prudden of New York, and Theobald Smith of Harvard University. Mr. Rockefeller then asked his two friends to serve on the board of the projected institute, remarking, as Holt recalled, "We don't know these other gentlemen, but we do know you, and you can serve as a medium of connection between our family and the medical men you have suggested as advisers."[5]

When Herter wrote to Welch on March 15, 1901, to enlist him in the undertaking, he named nine additional men thought suitable for the board.[6] Most of them were earning or had earned international reputations, and their records show that, despite Frederick Gates's low opinion of the profession, the United States was by no means devoid of competent physicians and medical biologists. They were John J. Abel, professor of pharmacology at Johns Hopkins; Russell H. Chittenden, professor of physiological chemistry and dean of the Sheffield Scientific School at Yale; William T. Councilman, professor of pathology at Harvard; Edward K. Dunham, professor of pathology at University and Bellevue Hospital Medical College in New York City; Simon Flexner, professor of pathology at the University of Pennsylvania; Walter B.

JOHN D. ROCKEFELLER, JR.

The original Board of Scientific Directors of The Rockefeller Institute
Left to right: Theobald Smith, Hernan M. Biggs, Simon Flexner, William H. Welch,
T. Mitchell Prudden, L. Emmett Holt, Christian A. Herter

James, instructor in medicine in the College of Physicians and Surgeons at Columbia University; Edward G. Janeway, professor of medicine and dean at Bellevue; William H. Park, professor of pathology at Bellevue and director of the Bureau of Laboratories of the New York City Department of Health; and John S. Thacher, pathologist and physician in the Columbia University College of Physicians and Surgeons.

From this impressive list, Welch favored the five originally named, and E. K. Dunham (who, however, was not chosen, presumably to avoid overweighting the New York contingent). Flexner's name was added in time for the first formal meeting. Park would certainly have been appointed to the board if his senior colleague Biggs had not been chosen. Thus the remarkably able and effective first board of directors — Holt, Herter, Welch, Biggs, Prudden, Smith, and Flexner — was assembled.

The way in which Holt and Herter simultaneously turned to Welch shows that he was already reaching his destined place as chief counselor in American medical science. Both men knew him well. As an intern at Bellevue Hospital, Holt had attended Welch's pioneer laboratory course in pathology, given after Welch's return from study with Cohnheim, in Germany; and Herter had followed Welch to Baltimore to work with him in the young department of pathology at Johns Hopkins. Welch, at fifty-one, was the dean of that school. A genial bachelor, wise, urbane, a lover of good food and good company, he was at ease with people of all ranks. Gifted with an outgoing personality and a prodigious memory, he spoke in public, often extemporaneously, with exceptional clarity and grace. Welch had played a great part in bringing the achievements of German medical science to America and was acquainted with every movement and almost every man of consequence in the medical world. If, as a recent biographer claims,[7] he had private regrets that these gifts took him more and more out of his laboratory and into council rooms up and down the land, he never let such feelings appear on the surface. He devoted a long life to the service of medical education; and he who had been known as "Popsy" to his earliest students at Johns Hopkins was to hear at eighty the President of the United States declare him "our greatest statesman in the field of public health."

Hermann M. Biggs, at this time head of the Division of Bacteriology and Inspection of the New York City Department of Health, was conducting the pioneer health department laboratory in the United States, which he had set up during the cholera epidemic of 1892. In the fall of 1901 the reform mayor Seth Low wished to appoint him Commissioner of Health, but when Biggs, impatient of administrative routine, declined the invitation, the post of chief medical officer was created to hold him and utilize his great talents for public health generalship. He had built up and operated a city-wide system of collecting throat cultures for detection of diphtherial infections. As soon as the newly discovered antitoxin was tested in Europe and found effective, he put his able associate W. H. Park to work making the first American supplies of the serum. Against vigorous opposition, he introduced compulsory reporting of cases of tuberculosis and organized the administrative control of that disease — all this while actively practicing medicine and teaching at Bellevue. Welch and Holt wanted him on their board not only for his knowledge and experience, but also because of the opportunity he had to enlist the good will and support of the city government.[8]

T. Mitchell Prudden, teacher and investigator, had held a chair of pathology at the College of Physicians and Surgeons since 1892. A self-effacing bachelor of broad cultural interests, he had begun laboratory instruction at his school almost as early as Welch had at Bellevue, and had quietly stood at Biggs's side as consultant to the health department during the fight against cholera and diphtheria. As a young man he had studied with Julius Arnold at Heidelberg and for a few months, on a later visit, with Robert Koch. He and Francis Delafield wrote the first American textbook of pathology. Prudden had proved himself a faithful, painstaking laboratory administrator, good at planning budgets and construction, careful to the last degree. Like his associates, he was thoroughly conversant with current medical research and its applications at the bedside and for the public health. One of his students, Alfred E. Cohn, who graduated in 1904, said that Prudden was the only teacher in the College of Physicians and Surgeons whose lectures gave any idea that medical science was on the march and that knowledge could be advanced by research.[9] Prudden's little book for laymen, *Story of the Bacteria* (1889), interested the young Simon Flexner, with important consequences for the Institute, as will shortly appear.

The brilliant investigator Theobald Smith came from outside the circle of these five who were linked together by old associations. As a student he had been exposed to the influence of four great non-medical biologists, Simon H. Gage and Burt G. Wilder at Cornell, and Newell Martin and William Keith Brooks at Johns Hopkins. After graduating from Albany Medical College, he joined the United States Bureau of Animal Industry, where he taught himself modern bacteriological methods and applied them in a series of fundamental researches. His demonstration that Texas cattle fever is transmitted by an insect vector, a species of tick, is a classic achievement of American microbiology, antedating the discoveries that malaria and yellow fever are transmitted by mosquitoes. No less important was his introduction of the use of killed bacteria as immunizing agents, and of balanced mixtures of toxin and antitoxin for immunization against specific organisms. He was the first to detect the difference between the germs of human and bovine tuberculosis, evidenced by the distinctive types of disease they cause. In 1895 Theobald Smith was appointed to head a laboratory of the Massachusetts State Board of Health, with a chair of comparative pathology at Harvard. Welch and Herter hoped that this austere, critical master of the techniques of research would undertake the directorship of the projected institute.[10]

Simon Flexner was one of several remarkable sons of a German immigrant who had settled in Louisville, Kentucky. While studying medicine at the University of Louisville, the future Director read Prudden's *Story of the Bacteria* and, as a result, determined to go into research. In 1889 he arrived at Welch's laboratory in Baltimore, an M.D. with only a little self-training in science. Welch taught him to do research, saw to it that he got a wide-ranging experience, and left him to run the department while he himself was traveling about on his endless outside duties. On official assignments, first as investigator of an epidemic of cerebrospinal meningitis in a Maryland mountain town, then as leader of a commission from the Johns Hopkins Medical School to study the diseases of the Philippine Islands just after the Spanish-American War, Flexner continued to learn and think about the attack on epidemic infectious disease. In 1899 he went to the University of Pennsylvania as professor of pathology. Shortly thereafter he was sent to investigate an epidemic of bubonic plague in San Francisco's Chinatown and to advise on the campaign to eradicate it. Throughout these years of preparation, Flexner worked on all sorts of novel problems—snake venoms and other cell-dissolving poisons, experimental pancreatitis, intestinal infections of the Orient.

Reserved, seemingly impersonal, he was the embodiment of scientific efficiency; but behind the cool exterior there was an unsuspected breadth of mind and a sympathetic heart. When Flexner left Baltimore for Philadelphia, Welch, always undemonstrative, came nearer to expressing affection for him than for any other of his long line of able juniors. Flexner, on his side, was to repay his debt to Welch by lifelong admiration and regard. Now they were to work together on a new and larger task.[11]

The group was relatively homogeneous in age, background, and experience. Herter at thirty-six and Flexner at thirty-eight years of age were the youngest; Prudden at fifty-two was the oldest. All but Flexner were natives of one or the other of the two adjacent states, New York and Connecticut. All but Theobald Smith had studied in Germany. Their medical interests were likewise similar. Each of them, whether primarily pathologist or biochemist, health official or medical practitioner, was especially trained in pathology and predominantly interested in bacterial disease. This was neither a coincidence nor the result of personal bias in choosing them for the Board; nor would it in the long run limit the scope of the enterprise. The progress of research depends upon the timely application of known principles and methods to new problems. Like an army in action, science brings its weapons to bear upon points where a breakthrough can be achieved with the means at hand. In 1901 the infectious diseases presented the most conspicuous point of attack in the war against disease, and bacteriology offered the most powerful resources. Its general principles, revealed by a half century and more of research, were now being applied with revolutionary effectiveness in medical practice and public health. The members of the Board of Directors were not unaware that physiology and chemistry were coming up behind the front, so to speak, with new and different weapons. As the Institute went into action, however, it must begin its fight with the best available weapons, those provided by bacteriology.

When in 1901 Herter first wrote to Welch about Rockefeller's intention to found a research laboratory for the study of disease, he added that Rockefeller, Jr., Holt, and he himself had come to the preliminary conclusions that it would be wise to establish a small laboratory at first, without official connection with any hospital; that there was no need to organize it formally under a board of trustees, at least until an endowment was forthcoming. It had been suggested, Herter continued, that the New York City Health Department might shelter the laboratory until it could build its own quarters.

A director would have to be found. He should receive a salary comparable to those paid by well-endowed universities, say $5,000, and should begin with two or three assistants. Though Rockefeller, Sr., had suggested this gradual start, he expressed a willingness to increase the financial support as profitable lines of inquiry opened; and Herter thought he could be expected ultimately to endow the laboratory liberally. In conclusion, Herter said significantly that "while Mr. Rockefeller's interest in the establishment of a research laboratory is primarily humanitarian rather than scientific, . . . he would never allow his desire for practical results to hamper the laboratory in its direct or indirect efforts to obtain such results."[12]

Welch thought the proposal over for a fortnight and then wrote cordially approving all the suggestions and accepting membership on the advisory board, although he said he was too busy to be chairman and thought a New York man should take that responsibility.[13] Herter promptly sent copies of his own letter and Welch's to Rockefeller, Jr., by way of Holt, and on April 29 Mr. Rockefeller wrote to Holt as follows:

> I desire to put into concrete form the result of our various conversations regarding medical research. My father is prepared to give for the purpose of medical research, whatever amount may be required up to an average of twenty thousand ($20,000) dollars a year for ten years. This money he will give to a committee which shall be appointed and which shall be empowered to formulate the policy and direct the organization of the work.[14]

Thus at last authorized to begin their task, the five doctors who had been consulting by mail and in person — Holt, Herter, Biggs, Prudden, and Welch — took advantage of the annual meeting of the Association of American Physicians in Washington, April 30 to May 2, 1901, to hold a brief conference at the Arlington Hotel. Welch was president that year of the Association's sessions. The little Rockefeller group also chose him, over his protests, to preside at its own meeting, so much more important for the long run, and he took that day a chair he was to occupy for the rest of his life. There was no time for a full exchange of views, but the group was sure of two points: the new institute was to be in New York

City, and Theobald Smith, if he would accept the post, was to direct its first laboratories.

Things now moved rapidly. Welch informed Smith of what was in the air, urging him to attend a meeting in New York on May 10. On that day the conferees adopted simple bylaws and began to call themselves Directors. Simon Flexner's name was included, as he was to be invited at once to join the Board. Mr. Rockefeller consented to have the institute called by his name. On June 14, 1901, The Rockefeller Institute for Medical Research was incorporated, and the new corporation held its first regular meeting at Dr. Holt's office on Fifty-fifth Street.

The benefaction had already been announced through the daily papers. A present-day public relations director would say that the publicity work was perfect. The newspapers were deeply impressed. The New York *Tribune, Times,* and *Evening Post* printed full accounts of the proposed institute in their news columns on June 2 and discussed it intelligently on the editorial pages. They had been carefully briefed by someone — probably Prudden — in an authoritative position to explain the program. The journalists knew, or were now told, that America was backward in medical science. "The American medical profession," said the *Evening Post,* "have been criticized for lack of original work. The new institute will provide for the release from cares of men of trained scientific intelligence, who will be enabled to devote themselves to the solution of definite problems." The editors emphasized the high standing of the medical men with whom Mr. Rockefeller had taken counsel and who would now start the project, men who understood the difficulties and uncertainties of research well enough to avoid exaggerated hopes for quick practical results. The *Times* wrote:

> The new institution is to be wisely and conservatively managed. It begins its operations without flourish of trumpets and in an unpretentious way. It spends its funds in directions that seem to offer the best prospects of immediate results. Nobody can promise sensational discoveries of momentous value at any particular time. The directors of the Rockefeller foundation [sic] may hope for them, but they intend now to attack certain definite problems pressing for solution, and to let fame come to their new establishment when it has won it. They may at some future time see their work grow to be a great landmark in medical science, like that of the Pasteur Institute in Paris. But they are scientific men, working in the scientific spirit, and that spirit is not concerned with impressing the multitude.

Some years after the founding of The Rockefeller Institute, Frederick T. Gates recalled that "our earliest conceptions associated the proposed medical institution with some great institution of learning and with some great medical school."[15] The University of Chicago, he added, was first thought of in this connection, and in 1900 approaches were made to Harvard. When President Seth Low of Columbia University, alerted by the younger Rockefeller's inquiries in the spring of 1900, wrote to Welch and Prudden requesting general advice about the organization of a research institute, he asked them, among other questions, whether they favored a university connection for such an institution. Both replied in the affirmative.[16] Yet when Welch was first called into active consultation with Herter and Holt, he met with a strong inclination to set up the Institute independently. Writing to Theobald Smith, he ascribed this preference directly to one of the Rockefellers, presumably the senior:

> In my letter to President Low I favored a university connection, but it seems that Mr. Rockefeller is more favorable to the proposition of making use of the new laboratory [of] the New York City Board of Health . . . with the understanding that we shall be entirely independent of any control by the Health Board.[17]

As it turned out, however, the Health Department's laboratory building was never utilized. The new institution stood by itself.

The reasons for this shift were never put on paper, perhaps not even formally canvassed. Mr. Rockefeller, Jr., was the only person living when the writing of this history was begun who had taken part in whatever deliberations there had been concerning this matter. According to his recollection, the reason for independent organization was simply that his father and he wanted the investigators to work in utter freedom. Rockefeller, Sr., was accustomed to getting things done by supporting competent men and letting them work in their own way. He wished to avoid all extraneous pressure, academic or otherwise, upon the scientific staff of the Institute.[18] This is a general statement of a high ideal. We may properly look behind it to see what sort of pressure Rockefeller and his advisers may have feared.

One obvious kind of pressure to be avoided, some of the Board thought, was that of burdensome academic routine. The preparation of lectures, conduct of examinations, and all other tasks that go with teaching undergraduate medical students would seriously distract investigators from their research. Even if they were freed from professorial duties, association with a medical school could be a handicap unless the faculty were of the highest quality, able to provide an intellectual atmosphere in which basic research could thrive. For these reasons, affiliation with any medical institution then operating in New York City was not desirable. A broad program of research would have been beyond the intellectual and administrative resources of either of the two major New York medical schools, struggling at the time toward university status. Not all the members of the Board had been conditioned by personal experience to favor academic medical research. They understood, of course, the strength of the great German university laboratories in which some of them had worked; but only Flexner's scientific career had been totally fostered by universities. Herter in his private laboratory, Biggs in the Health Department, Holt in the hospitals, Theobald Smith in the Department of Agriculture and the Massachusetts State Board of Health had had non-academic support for their investigations. Welch and Prudden, moreover, had won command of university departments only after hard early struggles for space and equipment in the New York medical schools. "I remember," writes Alfred E. Cohn,

> . . . a report, current at the time of the founding of the Institute, that President Butler [sic] could not understand why . . . a separate institution needed to be created. Why could it not become part of his university? Why could he not, thought I at the time, have thought of this himself and have made the University great and forestalled the development of such institutions as the Rockefeller Institute?[19]

Another kind of pressure upon the scientist arises from preconceived theories which seek to block the free ranging of the investigator's mind. This danger is at its very worst in medical sectarianism. Gates and no doubt Rockefeller, Jr., were greatly concerned about the schism which then still divided American medical practitioners into the regulars (or "allopaths," as their opponents called them) and the homeopaths. Gates, whose acquaintance in the medical profession up to this time seems to have been with practitioners who were in the thick of this fight, rather than with academic and scientific leaders who were above it, had acquired healthy scorn for the sectarianism of the allopaths as well as of the homeopaths, and, speaking for the suffering public, might have cried like Mercutio, "A plague o' both your houses. They have made worms' meat of me." He saw that the new spirit of medical investigation must be above all "schools"; a research institute could do its work only in a clear atmosphere of disinterested inquiry. Rockefeller, Sr., tended to favor one side of the controversy—the homeopathic—because his trusted family physician and personal friend Dr. H. F. Biggar, with whom he played golf and who had accompanied the family more than once in their travels, was a homeopath. As Raymond B. Fosdick has written: "There was a quaint streak in the elder Rockefeller. He could support modern scientific medicine with millions of dollars but for himself he preferred the old methods that had the authority of tradition."[20] No doubt his friendly relationship with his doctor was a factor in Rockefeller's reluctance in 1898 to support an alliance between the University of Chicago and the "regular" (and therefore antihomeopathic) Rush Medical College. Gates also opposed the merger, because he was against all sectarianism and was diplomatically aligning Rockefeller's views with his own when he told Chicago's President William Rainey Harper: "I have no doubt that Mr. Rockefeller would favor an institution that was neither allopath nor homeopath, but simply scientific in its investigations into medical science. That is the ideal."[21]

That was the ideal, too, for The Rockefeller Institute. The influence of homeopathy, though already waning, was still potent in 1901, and an alliance of the new institute with the "allopathic" medical faculty of either Harvard or Columbia would have presented the same difficulties that arose at Chicago. Making the Institute independent avoided both a public issue and a private dilemma for Mr. Rockefeller, who doubtless accepted Gates's position intellectually. That the dilemma was real, and that it persisted for some years after the foundation of The Rockefeller Institute, is shown by Mr. Fosdick's account of two subsequent episodes in which first Gates and then Rockefeller, Jr., found it necessary to persuade the older man to avoid the appearance of sectarianism with respect to his medical benefactions.[20]

Finally, it is also possible that Mr. Rockefeller wished to create a distinctive institution in New York, the city of his residence and headquarters of his business empire. He had founded the University of Chicago against heavy pressure to build a Baptist university in New York. A great independent institute of university grade in Manhattan would adjust the balance of his philanthropies.

The decision to make The Rockefeller Institute independent thus seems to have rested upon several considerations of academic and medical policy, rather than on any single compelling principle except the basic need of complete freedom from extraneous pressures. The decision must have been reinforced by the reflection that the Pasteur Institute, prime exemplar in the founders' minds, was obviously successful in its independent status.

Did the founders contemplate a teaching as well as a research institute? It went without saying that there would be instruction of the informal sort that results from juniors working at an investigator's side. Life in a research laboratory is a continuous postgraduate course in which preliminary schooling is taken for granted. The Board was preoccupied with the program for research, and there is little in the records to show whether or not formal teaching was discussed. A long memorandum on over-all plans for the Institute, submitted by Theobald Smith when he was offered the directorship, suggests that the question had at least been raised. "All plans for advanced teaching," he wrote, "should be postponed for at least five or six years until the laboratory work shall have been thoroughly established and material useful in teaching shall have been accumulated."[22] A similar memorandum prepared a little later by Flexner does not mention teaching at all.[23] Only once in the first half century was anything like formal teaching tried. Late in 1906 Dr. G. W. Ross of Toronto gave a five-weeks' course of lectures on opsonins and vaccines, with demonstrations of Professor Almroth Wright's methods. Ross had been in London for a year with Wright, whose studies of opsonins (substances in the blood which facilitate the attack of white blood cells against invading bacteria) were thought to offer leads for treatment of infectious diseases with bacterial vaccines. Evidently Flexner wanted the staff brought up to date on this novel approach. Those who attended the course did not find it inspiring, and the experiment was not repeated.[24]

Flexner, looking back on the first twenty years of the Institute's history, thought it most fortunate that no formal, regular teaching had been required, because the Institute, thus enabled to disregard national boundaries and differences of language, could acquire men like Noguchi, Carrel, Meltzer, and Levene, who might not have made outstanding careers as professors under ordinary conditions of academic life.[25] No doubt he was right, as regards the early years of a small institution at a time when many of its leading investigators were necessarily Europeans. As the Institute grew in size and its staff was made up more and more of Americans familiar with our own educational problems and traditions, the advantage Flexner saw in abstention from teaching became less significant. By 1953, when Detlev W. Bronk became President, the staff was amply able to provide for graduate training without distracting those investigators who were not disposed to teach. In 1955, therefore, assuming the character of a university faculty, the Institute began to admit and train graduate students in the medical, biological, and basic physical sciences, and in relevant fields of the humanities.

THE FIRST duty of the newly organized Board of Directors of The Rockefeller Institute was to begin using the money which had been put at its disposal. Although all the doctors, as well as Rockefeller and Gates, hoped eventually to establish a special center for research with its own laboratories, they were not ready to go ahead immediately with any such plan. Looking back many years later, Gates accused the Board of overcaution and even futility at this time.[26] Between the staid lines of Secretary Holt's minutes, one gets a picture of the seven doctors sobered by the implications of the philanthropist's dream that they were to make come true. Gates, the impatient enthusiast, confessedly knew nothing of the way research is done nor what it costs. The doctors knew from personal experience. They perceived that the first requirement of an institution was people to work in it and a man to lead it; but before they could organize a staff, it would be necessary to discover who and where were the young people who wanted to undertake research and what were their qualifications. As for a director, the two men Welch had his eye on had both recently accepted attractive posts — Theobald Smith at Harvard and Flexner at Pennsylvania — and certainly neither would listen to an invitation until the new institute's potentialities became overwhelmingly clear. Meanwhile, he had them both safely bound to the institution as members of the Board of Directors.

Accordingly, the Board decided not to centralize work at once in a single place, but to create a number of scholarships and fellowships to be used in existing laboratories throughout the country. This plan was calculated to enlist the cooperation of research leaders already at work and to discover and finance promising young investigators who were being held back by lack of funds. Welch took personal charge of getting the program of grants-in-aid under way. He knew the leaders and, moreover, as editor of the *Journal of Experimental Medicine* for the past five years, had been publishing most of the good American research. He began writing to senior men in selected institutions asking whether they could use the proposed grants for their advanced students and assistants or, indeed, for themselves. Prudden and Biggs scouted for him in New York, Flexner in Philadelphia. The response, Prudden records, was pathetic in its eagerness and inspiring in its revelation of the devotion with which many young men who had caught the meaning and promise of the hour were struggling on with inadequate facilities and support.

W. T. Councilman of Harvard wrote to Welch scorning the smallness of the proffered aid. On the other hand, J. G. Adami of McGill University (for Canada was included) feared that too many men would be drawn into research, glutting the market for university appointments.[27] Nevertheless, laboratory heads at Harvard, Pennsylvania, Yale, Western Reserve, Chicago, Michigan, Stanford, and several other schools applied for grants, as did candidates recruited by members of the Board.

In the first fiscal period of a little more than a year, ending June 30, 1902, $13,200 was allotted in twenty-three grants of $250 to $1,500 each, putting men to work in nine American cities and sending two to Germany. The researches were nearly all in bacteriology, immunology, and biochemistry. Recipients of the grants were classified according to age and experience, as "Research Students," "Research Scholars," and "Fellows of the Institute," and were encouraged to use these titles in their publications. For the second fiscal year, 1902–1903, there were twenty-five similar grants, mostly to the same laboratories, but in many cases for other young investigators. The total voted for that year was $14,450.

While formal action on the grants was of course recorded in the minute books of the Board, Welch took care of practically all the correspondence and secretarial work, and the somewhat scanty memoranda are found in his papers. Writing in longhand, he approved the expense accounts and sent them to Herter, treasurer of the Board, for payment. At times the figures became somewhat confused. Considering Welch's well-known unwillingness to use secretarial help and his practice of "filing" his correspondence in his bachelor quarters in stacks on the seats of chairs, this is hardly surprising. It appears from the surviving memoranda that at times he even passed payments through his own bank account. In line with this informality the grantees had a free hand with their money. Some were expected to devote full time to the work, others to combine it with teaching. Apparatus purchased was to become the property of the Institute upon completion of the investigation. The investigators might publish their results in such form and place as they desired, but they had to submit their papers in advance of publication to the Board of Directors for approval. The Board purchased reprints of each paper and bound them up in volumes of *Studies from The Rockefeller Institute*.

This program diminished in significance after 1903 when the Institute's own laboratories were opened, but was continued with gradually decreasing allotments. At the dedication of the new buildings in May 1906, Holt referred to grants recently made and said it was not intended that the program be discontinued altogether. The next year twenty-two grants were made, totaling more than $11,000. After 1907 the number fell to an average of four or five each year. In 1914 the Board voted to curtail miscellaneous grants[28] and made only two or three more in the next three years, discontinuing them entirely after 1917.

This program of grants-in-aid deserves more attention than it has received from writers on the history of research support. Various accounts of the Institute have treated it as hardly more than a stopgap policy, but in fact it was a pioneering experiment with a way of promoting research which a few decades later was to become a major factor in American scientific effort. There had been a few sources of grants for research in the physical sciences and agriculture, but practically none for medical work.[29] Subsequent experience with similar programs in the National Research Council and elsewhere shows that the Rockefeller Institute Board adopted precisely those policies by which a committee can do most to build up research in new fields.[30] The committee was made up of experienced workers whose interests were sufficiently unified on the one hand, and just sufficiently diversified on the other, to make their work effective. Operating through research leaders who were well known to them, they personally appraised applicants and themselves sought out promising young people. The money was given without hampering restrictions, but the workers were held to responsibility by the requirement of systematic reports. Publication was facilitated, and the young men who did the research were made to feel that their distinguished sponsors actually studied their work and appreciated it as a contribution to the enterprise in which they were all equally interested.

It is difficult to weigh the product of such an effort. The most obvious result was a flood of research papers. The first few volumes of the *Studies* are made up entirely of contributions resulting from these grants. There are no obvious masterpieces; one does not expect young men working on problems largely parceled out from the programs of their elders to produce at once scientific classics. The papers do exhibit technical competence and up-to-date alertness rivaling that of European journals of the period. During the first two years (1901–1903), when the Directors gave undivided attention to the program, they chose for their grants thirty-eight young people. Of these at least twenty-two later held responsible posts in medical research, education, or public health; fifteen went on to full professorships on university faculties; five were elected to the National Academy of Sciences.[31] To have given early help in their scientific careers to these Research Scholars and Fellows, and during the next few years to many others who were destined to carry the research spirit into all parts of the nation, was the first distinguished achievement of The Rockefeller Institute. Another inestimable benefit of these grants was that in many institutions they revealed serious limitations, both of laboratory equipment and of free time for investigation. The heads of a score of medical schools were thus confronted with the needs of their own institutions and with their responsibility to their research-minded young men.

The Directors also allotted part of the first year's budget to a more immediately practical project, a study of New York City's milk supply and its relation to health, particularly of young children. Infant sickness and mortality due to contaminated milk were widespread in American cities, especially during the summer. To combat this situation, the philanthropist Nathan Straus and others established milk stations to supply pasteurized milk at low cost to New York's poor. Interested in having a scientific evaluation of this effort, Hermann Biggs proposed a study, in cooperation with the city health department, beginning in the summer of 1901. Up to October 1902 the Directors of The Rockefeller Institute appropriated about $7,000 to pay the salaries of a bacteriologist, a bio-chemist, and inspectors of dairies, tenement houses, and the children's hospitals, and to provide laboratory supplies and animals for the tests. At the end of the second summer, W. H. Park, representing the health department, and Holt presented their report.[32] The investigation showed that the milk sold to tenement dwellers from open cans in small stores, especially in hot weather, had a bacterial content so shockingly high in the summer of 1901 that even while the study was in progress the Board of Health issued new and improved regulations for the care and sale of milk. Even the better grades of milk sold in bottles were infe-rior, judged by bacterial count, to that distributed by the charitable milk dispensaries. Babies fed upon the latter were, on the average, healthier than those who received commercial bottled milk, although the investiga-tors attributed this difference as much to the helpful advice the mothers received from trained supervisors at the milk stations as to the greater purity of the milk itself.

This report aroused a good deal of excitement. On January 19, 1902, the New York *Sun, Journal,* and *Herald* all carried sensational accounts of the findings. The *Herald,* for example, printed its article under triple headlines: "Find Germs Swarming in City's Purest Milk . . . Rocke-feller Institute experts report that appalling uncleanliness prevails in most of the dairies which supply New York . . . trace 330 epidemics to this cause . . . Much more rigorous inspection is urged."

With the public thus aroused, the Board of Health was able to strengthen both the sanitary control of the milk supply and its pro-gram of instructing mothers in the care and feeding of babies. While public funds might properly have supported this study, the Board of Health's resources were inadequate at the time. From the Institute's viewpoint, the report helped to establish good public relations, and it demonstrated to Rockefeller, who had hoped for direct benefits to the public health from his gift, that medical science could indeed be put to practical use in an urgent cause.

Rockefeller and his immediate advisers presumably expected that the Institute would continue to promote work of this sort in its laboratories and in the field. Such problems he and Gates as laymen could see and understand. The distinction between so-called "pure" and "applied" science was not as clear to them as modern industrial and military needs have since made it. The establishment of practical measures necessarily rests upon prior "pure" research. Industrial laboratories or a wartime organization, such as the Office of Scientific Research and Development, can operate successfully by putting a team of trained men on a specific practical project, provided that the basic principles have already been worked out. The necessary theoretical information is usually the result of exploratory original research by individuals who were under no compulsion to produce immediately useful results and could therefore follow any leads they chose. There are, of course, intermediate stages between strictly basic and applied science, and there are men who can work at either; but on the whole the talents and the type of organization required to care for the two aspects of scientific progress are different.

The staff that was recruited for The Rockefeller Institute was made up almost entirely of men of the pathfinder type, who by inclination and training saw the need for basic knowledge and preferred to seek it rather than to aim directly at practical results. They may have hoped that their discoveries might in the long run be applied to the public welfare — when men of other talents and interests would apply the results of research to practical use — while they themselves went on with fundamental investigation.

As the Institute has grown larger, it has tended increasingly to concentrate upon basic research. Even though many discoveries of its investigators are highly useful in human pathology and in the practice of medicine, the new fields upon which it has entered have often been still farther removed from immediately practical applicability than were the bacteriology and physiology that formed the greater part of the original program. It is very much to the credit of the founding group, and particularly the two Rockefellers and Gates, who were not scientists, that they saw the need for fundamental principles as gradually revealed to them by the work of the laboratory staff, and that they gave their unquestioning support to basic scientific research.

ALTHOUGH the Board of Directors, feeling their way slowly, had devoted Rockefeller's gift during its first years to a grants-in-aid program, they never lost sight of the final goal, the development of an independent research laboratory. The essence of the grant scheme was its effective diffusion of encouragement and aid throughout the country, thus creating a favorable atmosphere for medical research and helping to build a corps of workers in many universities. It could, however, never achieve the concentration of effort that is possible for a group of men working together, with enthusiasm and efficiency daily compounded by mutual stimulation. The very success of the grants-in-aid program incidentally revealed its inherent limitations and convinced the Directors that they ought not long postpone the organization of a central laboratory under a competent head, with adequate support and permanent endowment.

Gates was getting more and more impatient for the realization of his original dream of a research institute. It can hardly have been a coincidence that Rockefeller, Jr., entertained Welch, the president of the Board, at dinner just before the Board was to meet on January 11, 1902, to review its plans and policies, and used this occasion to discuss the establishment of a laboratory and to re-emphasize the Rockefeller family's sympathetic interest in the Institute. Encouraged, no doubt, by Welch's report of this conversation, the Board that evening decided to go ahead at once. Their discussions became quite specific, for they asked Theobald Smith whether he would consider becoming head of a bacteriological department which would become the core of the Institute; and requested him to formulate in writing his ideas about the program and organization of the whole undertaking.

Toward the Rockefellers, however, the Directors displayed their usual very cautious manner. Welch wrote to Rockefeller, Jr., a couple of days later:

> I do not think the time has come to start out with a large plant with the permanent location and connections fixed, or to abandon our present plan of aiding investigations elsewhere, provided these are important, in the right field, and really need our help. It seems best, when we are ready, to start a laboratory in a comparatively modest way, and let time and experience indicate the best lines of organization and development. The most important matter is to secure a man of first-rate scientific and administrative ability to direct the work of a laboratory.[33]

After a month's reflection, Smith submitted a long and thoughtful outline of a program for the Institute, but simultaneously declined the post the Board had offered him.[34] He felt he could not abandon the chair of comparative pathology Harvard had created for him; he did not wish to lose the time a move would cost him; he feared that his own strong concern with animal pathology might give an impress to the work of the new laboratory and thus arouse adverse criticism. His suggestions for the organization of the Institute were rather too specific and narrow, partly, perhaps, because the post offered him was not explicitly the headship of the Institute as a whole, such as it became once Flexner was installed in it. The work, Smith wrote, should crystallize about the study of infectious diseases, with three laboratories devoted respectively to morphological study (*i.e.,* tissue pathology and the biology of animal parasites), pathological physiology, including bacteriology and immunology, and physiological chemistry.

Welch, informing the other Directors of Smith's declination by a letter to Prudden, put Flexner's name before them with a hint that he had already sounded him out and thought he might accept. The prospect evidently met Prudden's approval, for he wrote Holt, "I think that if we could get Flexner and all the potential energy which he represents, we would be very fortunate and our course in establishing a laboratory fully justified."[35] The others agreed, and at the next meeting, March 8, Welch read Theobald Smith's letter of declination and, turning to Flexner, said, "We hope that you will accept the directorship."[36]

Now it was Flexner's turn to draft a plan, and this he did at once, sending it to Welch in time for discussion by the Board on April 12. Theobald Smith's draft had been that of a working scientist anxious to get on with his work, and concerned with setting up laboratories in which the kind of research he himself knew how to do could best be carried on. Flexner's prospectus, broader and more statesmanlike, represented the thought of a scientific executive rather than that of a specialized investigator. It gave much more attention than Smith's to details of organization and operation, discussing even at this early stage such matters as janitorial and technical services and retirement pensions for the staff. On the other hand, because his scientific outlook was wider ("The scope of the Institute should be broad enough . . . to cover the whole field of medical research in respect both to men and animals"), he did not closely specify subjects for which laboratories should be provided, as Smith had done. He boldly proclaimed the necessity for eventual large endowments in order to secure and hold the best men. He called for a site large enough for a laboratory building, animal quarters, and a research hospital. The last paragraph of his long draft constituted a tentative acceptance of the directorship, "if it is the intention of the Founder and the Board of Directors to organize the Institute upon a liberal scale and with the most advantageous opportunities for research in medical science."

The Board then appointed Prudden, Holt, and Flexner to draw up a statement of plans for presentation to Rockefeller. With some help from Welch and the others, Prudden pieced this together chiefly from the letters of Smith and Flexner, adding a very tentative proposal of his own for a division of the Institute "for education of the people in the ways of healthful living, by popular lectures, by hygienic museums, by the diffusion of suitable literature, etc."[37] The report re-emphasized, however, the need for cautious step-by-step development, with limited objectives at first. Although Prudden, who now, as later, did much of the preliminary drafting of budgets and plans, was thinking of an initial annual expenditure of about $57,000 — a large sum for that time — the tentative budget appended to the committee's report, looking forward to an Institute of three laboratory departments and a hospital, amounted to $137,640 per annum. After approval by the Board on May 10, 1902, the committee's "Report and Recommendations of the Directors of The Rockefeller Institute for the year 1901–1902" was submitted to Rockefeller, Jr.

Both the Board and the Rockefeller family group now had a special reason for prompt action: a potential rival had appeared. On January 4, 1902, Andrew Carnegie incorporated the Carnegie Institution of Washington, and on January 28 he gave its trustees ten million dollars. Its chartered purpose was "to encourage, in the broadest and most liberal manner, investigation, research, and discovery, and the application of knowledge to the improvement of mankind." Although The Rockefeller Institute's concept of the scope of medical research was rapidly broadening, the Carnegie charter covered all its potential field and infinitely more. Neither philanthropists nor scientists are immune to considerations of prestige, or enjoy having other people steal their thunder. The Rockefeller Board gave frank evidence of its concern by saying in the "Report and Recommendations" that "the Directors are especially desirous, in view of another recently established organization for the promotion of public welfare through research, that this institute shall be able fully to occupy the field upon which we have entered and which so directly touches the national life and happiness." The Directors must also have known that Henry Phipps was about to launch an institute for the study of tuberculosis, in Philadelphia, and that the elder Rockefeller's son-in-law, Harold F. McCormick, was planning the John Rockefeller McCormick Memorial Institute for Infectious Diseases, in Chicago. Rockefeller, Jr., took at least the Carnegie challenge seriously enough to have a talk with the great ironmaster, who assured him that his institution would not enter the field of medical research.[38]

During these weeks Rockefeller, Jr., frequently talked with individual members of the Board, discussing provisionally such matters as the site of the laboratories and the cost of buildings and of operation. At last, on June 13, he informed his father that the Directors were ready to proceed with a program that would eventually require about five million dollars of capital funds. On the basis of immediate needs for land and a single building amounting in value to three or four hundred thousand dollars, and of annual expenses running at first from forty to sixty thousand, he recommended a pledge of one million dollars to be drawn at the option of the Board during the next ten years.

The elder Rockefeller's reply was characteristic both of his confidence in his son's judgment and of his shrewd business caution:

> As you so earnestly recommend, you may pledge one million dollars to be distributed through the next ten years. If it were left as you suggest, to be drawn at the option of the Board, they might take a large portion in the early part of the ten years. We cannot say anything about five millions now.

Prudden took the second sentence of this message to be a humorous tribute to the zeal of the Directors, but it was more likely a wry reference to Rockefeller's experience of a few years before with the University of Chicago, whose president, William Rainey Harper, did not hesitate to overdraw his resources, and practically forced Rockefeller to rescue him from several financial crises by extra gifts. Ten days later Rockefeller, Jr., formally confirmed the pledge in a letter to Welch.

With Rockefeller's support thus assured, Flexner accepted the directorship of the Institute. The decision must have been difficult for him, for the University of Pennsylvania had supported him well in his re-organization of its department of pathology and had given him a fine new laboratory building of his own design. As he privately explained to Welch, however, the reformation of the University's medical school as a whole was going slowly and its financial support was uncertain. He felt, moreover, that some members of the faculty were opposed to his activities in the reorganization. Thus he faced the prospect, for some years to come, of leading a strong department in a weak and not fully unified school.[39]

Flexner informally gave his acceptance to the Board on June 14, 1902, but his decision, so vitally important in the history of the Institute, was not mentioned in the minutes of that meeting,[40] and a public announcement was withheld for the sake of the University of Pennsylvania. The Board members talked and corresponded briefly about his salary. Some of them thought of a figure only slightly larger than he was receiving in Philadelphia, the cautious Prudden, for example, writing to Welch, "He is still young and in many fields still has his mark to make."[41] The matter was, however, soon adjusted to Flexner's satisfaction. He was elected Director of The Rockefeller Institute on October 25, 1902, at a salary of $10,000, and his formal employment began July 1, 1903. The salary was relatively large for the period and evidently fulfilled the expressed desire of the Board that the compensation should remove the incumbent from competition with university professorships.

The Board did not delay in looking for a building site. Prudden indeed had already made sketches for a building, and at the June 14 meeting, after Flexner's acceptance, the Directors took time out only to vote a message of thanks to Rockefeller, Sr., before proceeding to discuss building plans. During the next few weeks the four Board members resident in New York City and Rockefeller, Jr., looked over possible building sites. The search led to the Schermerhorn tract, about thirteen acres of farm land on the East River between Sixty-fourth and Sixty-eighth Streets, the eastern half of which forms a rocky bluff about forty feet high overlooking the river and a wide stretch of Long Island. It was the last of the open tracts in a district once noted for its great suburban estates.[42] Owned by one family since 1818, the land had come on the market after the death of William C. Schermerhorn. When Rockefeller, Jr., and the doctors inspected the old farm in June 1902 it presented almost the same appearance as it had a century before. A few cows grazed on the gentle slope toward the western boundary, at Avenue A (now York Avenue); on the river side, Exterior Street (now Franklin D. Roosevelt Drive) had not yet been opened. The old Schermerhorn house, dating from the eighteenth century, stood perched on the very edge of the cliff created by the cutting through of Sixty-fourth Street toward the river.

After the Board had approved this site, Rockefeller, Jr., bought it in May 1903 from the Schermerhorn estate, paying $650,000. The Board chose to take over at first only the northeastern portion, approximately the area now occupied by Founder's Hall, Flexner and Theobald Smith Halls, the President's residence, Welch Hall, and the animal house. Wishing, as Prudden records, to preserve "the strict business relationship which as custodians of its property the Directors of the Institute maintained," they chose not to accept the land as a gift, but went through the formality of having it appraised for both parties to the arrangement. Having thus reached a compromise figure, the Board bought the selected area, about one third of the entire tract, from Rockefeller, Jr., for $173,425 of the money his father had recently pledged to them.

By act of legislature in the session of 1903–1904, Sixty-sixth Street was permanently closed riverward from the Institute's front line. Later the city gave quitclaims to the beds of Sixty-fourth, Sixty-fifth, and Sixty-seventh Streets within the property. Gradually in subsequent years the Institute acquired the entire tract, together with the block south of Sixty-fourth Street, by purchase or gift from the younger Rockefeller.

During 1903 and 1904, the Board and Flexner were busy with plans for building and organizing the laboratories. In September 1903 the Director was authorized to rent an office and to employ an office helper. The latter's designation as "Assistant Secretary," implying that Holt was still Secretary to the enterprise in action, and not merely to the Board in its higher functions, illustrates how simply the administrative operations of the Institute were as yet conducted. Similarly, Herter administered the finances, drawing upon Mr. Rockefeller's office against the funds that had been pledged. The Institute did not even have a bookkeeper of its own until November 1905. This simplicity and the general caution of the Board seem to have deeply impressed the elder Rockefeller, who appreciated careful administration of his gifts, however bold his own business ventures. Gates, too, was happy now that a brick-and-mortar laboratory was almost in sight. Welch had the satisfaction of learning, through a friend at the University of Chicago to whom Gates had been talking, that Rockefeller thought the Institute was being handled better than any other benefaction he had ever made. "He [Gates] says that there is practically a blank check for you to be filled in as desired. He praised the very, very wise gradual method of development."[43]

A permanent building was now the first consideration. At a meeting in February 1903 the Building Committee — Flexner, Prudden, Biggs, and Holt — chose a firm of Boston architects recommended by Rockefeller, Jr., namely, Shepley, Rutan, and Coolidge. They showed Charles A. Coolidge, the firm's chief representative in working out the design, Prudden's tentative floor plans and told him of the Board's desire that "the style of the building be as simple as is consistent with its present purpose, future additions, and general utility." The Board's efforts to keep the cost within a limit of $250,000 ran the usual course. By September the architects had completed a set of plans and called for bids, but the lowest was over $350,000. New plans with less costly specifications and a smaller main building brought the bid down to $276,630 for the laboratory building, animal house, and powerhouse, exclusive of the heating system, which added about $40,000. Ground was broken in July 1904 for the first building, now called Founder's Hall. A faded photograph survives to commemorate the occasion on December 3 when without public ceremony Prudden, Holt, Biggs, and Flexner stood beside the masons to see the cornerstone well and truly laid.

CHAPTER THREE

The Laboratories Are Organized

Temporary quarters; first researches. Journal of Experimental Medicine. Permanent buildings. Fiscal and executive organization. Investigations in physiology, surgery, pathology. Transmission of poliomyelitis. Opposition to experiments on animals.

IN THE FALL OF 1903 Flexner went abroad for a year to observe the work and organization of European research laboratories, and to ground himself in biochemistry. Foreseeing that this subject was destined to become more and more important to the Institute's work, he needed to qualify himself to choose men in that field and to comprehend their work. He spent most of his time, therefore, at Berlin, working during part of the winter at Ernst Salkowski's laboratory and during the whole spring semester with Emil Fischer, leader of basic research in the chemistry of animal tissues. Herter also went abroad that year. The two men, entrusted with $5,000 to start purchasing books for the library, spent the entire sum on sets of scientific journals.

By the time Flexner returned, in the fall of 1904, the Institute's Board of Directors had rented as temporary quarters two brownstone houses on the corner of Lexington Avenue and Fiftieth Street. They were equipped as laboratories at small cost, and here Flexner and his first staff began work about November 1, 1904. Despite a serious obstacle to recruitment created by the uncertainty of the enterprise, which had as yet received no capital endowment and no real guarantee of permanence, the young director, with Welch's advice, got together a remarkable little group. The first junior appointed in pathology was Eugene L. Opie, who came from Welch's department at Johns Hopkins, where he had already received a grant-in-aid from the Board. Opie had done pioneer work on diseases of the pancreas, having been the first to demonstrate the association of diabetes with damage to the islands of Langerhans. Welch stated years later that Flexner had made it a condition of his acceptance of the directorship that Opie be released from Johns Hopkins in order to join the Institute.[1]

Samuel J. Meltzer became the Institute's first physiologist. Admirably trained in Germany, he had left that country because as a Jew he could not hope for a university chair, and had practiced medicine in New York, doing such research as circumstances permitted. Now at the age of fifty-three he happily agreed to cut down his practice in order to work half-time for a thousand-dollar stipend at his beloved physiological research. "Heretofore I have always paid laboratories to be permitted to work in them," he said.[2] Before long he was given a full-time appointment. From the University of Pennsylvania came the gifted Japanese youth Hideyo Noguchi, who had made his way to Philadelphia to work with Flexner and, under the latter's tutelage, had shown himself to be a brilliant investigator. Like Opie and Meltzer he was later to reach the highest rank in the Institute's staff. In a few months a first-class biochemist, Phoebus Aaron Theodor Levene, Russian-born and once a pupil of Emil Fischer in Berlin, came over from the Pathological Institute of the New York State Hospital on Welfare Island. Flexner showed courage in taking him on; Levene had recently spent more than two years at Saranac and Davos healing a tubercular lung. He was, moreover, thought to be esoteric in his scientific interests and impractical in administrative affairs; according to a story Flexner told later, Levene had been in trouble at the Pathological Institute because he had seriously overrun his budget by purchasing large quantities of alcohol for extracting tissues.

Several able young people filled out the group. The first Resident Fellow of the Institute was J. E. Sweet, soon to leave for a post in experimental surgery at the University of Pennsylvania. Henry Houghton, who was Flexner's personal assistant for a couple of years, was Research Scholar, destined for great service in China as dean of Peking Union Medical School, established by The Rockefeller Foundation. He later became dean at the University of Iowa. Alfred Newton Richards, John Howland, William Salant, John Auer, and his wife Clara (Meltzer's daughter), the voluntary workers, all in time made names for themselves in medical research.

Flexner did not attempt to make the laboratory merely an expression of his own particular interests, as he might well have done in view of European precedents. The Pasteur and the Koch institutes, for example, were each dedicated to the special program of one distinguished investigator, and at the Russian institute Pavlov's assistants had hardly more freedom than did mere technicians.[3] During his European travels of 1903–04, Flexner had been impressed by a conversation with Anton Dohrn, the benign founder of the famous Naples Zoological Station. "The advice that he urged most strongly," Flexner wrote to Herter, "was freedom."

> "Men work here," he said, "in a dozen different branches of biological science; can I be an authority on them all? No, no, give them perfect freedom; let them search where and how they will; help them in every way you can, but do not pretend to be master over them." It was a remarkable pronouncement, and coming from such an authority and one of the most successful research leaders of the world, worthy of the most thoughtful consideration. And the more I have thought over the subject the more I have come to his point of view. I wonder how it impresses you?[4]

Herter, alas, died before he had an opportunity to show how he would have conducted a department of his own, but Flexner followed Dohrn's principle of freedom and left his senior colleagues (except, occasionally, Noguchi, who at times needed special guidance) to direct their own experimental programs.

Judging from the written reminiscences of men who were in the group or watching it closely — Flexner himself, Opie, and Prudden — life in the temporary laboratories was not outwardly vivid. Prudden remembered, long afterward, that the place was dingy, and Opie that the chemical hoods let choking fumes into the rooms;[5] but what matter when the intellectual atmosphere was bright with hope and sparkling with such enthusiasm as comes only to men set free to work as their hearts desire?

Steady and competent work began at once. Opie studied the tissue-destroying substances by which white blood cells clean up damaged tissues, or form abscesses if the bacteria are too much for them. Noguchi continued his investigation of snake venoms, important in chemical pathology because of their remarkable power to cause disintegration of the red blood cells (hemolysis) of the snake's victim. While Noguchi was still in Philadelphia, the novelist-physician Weir Mitchell had suggested this investigation to him, and arranged financial support for it until Noguchi left for New York. Noguchi's live rattlesnakes, kept in dry-goods boxes, were regarded by his colleagues as something of a hazard in the laboratory.

Meltzer worked, according to his wont, on a half-dozen physiological investigations concurrently. He studied the formation of bile salts, the mechanism of swallowing, and the pattern of intestinal peristalsis. With his son-in-law John Auer he investigated the inhibitory and anesthetic properties of magnesium salts, looking toward the use of magnesium in treating tetanus; and with his daughter Clara Auer he had the distinction of publishing the first report credited to the new laboratories, a brief article on the action of adrenalin. Phoebus Levene was identifying and analyzing nucleic acids, doing pioneer work on substances that now, a half century later, are known to be involved in some of the subtlest chemical reactions of the body, even in the genes that transmit hereditary traits. Two young workers, John Howland and Newton Richards, embarked on a study of the thymus gland. Because equipment was needed that the Institute did not yet possess, Richards ingeniously assembled from ordinary laboratory wares a Kjeldahl apparatus for measuring nitrogen in the tissues, using a plain glass tube as a condenser.

Flexner collaborated with Holt in writing a report on bacillary dysentery, based largely on findings incidental to the investigation of the city's milk supply described in the previous chapter. He kept an eye on Noguchi's experiments with snake venom, and joined him in a prompt and successful effort, suggested by W. H. Welch, to confirm Fritz Schaudinn's sensational discovery of the parasite of syphilis, *Spirochaeta pallida*. They published their findings June 17, 1905, only sixty-six days after Schaudinn and Hoffman's original announcement. Flexner and James W. Jobling discovered an epithelial tumor of the rat, most likely of prostatic origin, which they were able to transplant to other rats, a considerable feat at that time. This tumor has served ever since as a unique test material in cancer research; transplanted from rat to rat for fifty years, the Flexner-Jobling carcinoma still flourishes in many laboratories.

Something more dramatic, however, was in store for Flexner. About a year after the Institute's temporary laboratory was opened, New York

City was struck by an outbreak of cerebrospinal meningitis, part of a great epidemic that had spread over Western Europe, the United States and Canada, and parts of Asia and Africa. In the winter of 1904–1905 New York City had four thousand cases, with more than three thousand deaths. In the spring of 1905, the city's Board of Health asked Flexner to serve on a commission formed to investigate the epidemic. Flexner knew the disease, for in 1893 he and Lewellys F. Barker had been given a similar assignment by the Governor of Maryland during an epidemic in that state. A small bacterium, the *Micrococcus* (or *Diplococcus*) *meningitidis,* first isolated by Anton Weichselbaum in 1887, was correctly suspected of being the causative agent, and the two young men, Flexner and Barker, had been able to find this germ in the inflamed membranes of the brain and spinal cord of persons who had died in the Maryland epidemic.

By 1905, when Flexner was again confronted with this disease, he had the advantage of knowing that the micrococcus had meanwhile been fully proved responsible and that it could now be cultivated without much difficulty. With cultures obtained from New York victims of the fever he quickly succeeded in infecting monkeys and in passing the disease by inoculation from monkey to monkey. The inoculated animals succumbed to a sickness closely resembling the human malady. European workers as well as the New York City Board of Health Laboratories had made a serum from the blood of inoculated horses. This was administered subcutaneously like diphtheria antitoxin; but it had little effect, and the death rate remained frightfully high. Flexner had the brilliant idea of placing the serum directly at the seat of the disease — the inflamed meningeal membranes — by injecting it into the spinal canal. Thus administered to monkeys soon after they had been inoculated with the germs, the serum made in Flexner's laboratory was strikingly effective. The first opportunity to test it in human cases occurred during an epidemic in Castalia and Akron, Ohio, in April 1907. Among the patients treated, only one in four died instead of three in four as in previous epidemics. Later statistics were somewhat less striking, the average mortality being reduced by half. News of the success in Akron reached New York through Cleveland newspapers. The modest Mr. Rockefeller may have winced when the New York *World* on August 6, 1907, told the story under the caption "Cure is Found for Meningitis with John D.'s

Aid"; but this was a scientific achievement which he could readily appreciate. When in May 1908 Rockefeller, Jr., wrote to Holt that his father would give the money needed for a hospital at the Institute, he had been directed to say,

> My father thus enlarges the scope and possibilities of the Institute in grateful recognition of the services of Dr. Simon Flexner, as Director, rendered in those orderly and progressive scientific investigations, which sanctioned and encouraged by your Board, and aided by his learned associates and assistants, led him at length to the discovery of a cure for epidemic cerebro-spinal meningitis.[6]

The episode had another sequel which illustrates the vexations that may arise when a scientist gets into the news. Because a potent anti-meningitis serum was difficult to make, Flexner kept its preparation under his own supervision for several years. In the twelve months ending with March 1908 the Institute distributed free about 7,000 bottles.[7] Naturally people called it "the Flexner serum" even though he had not originated it, and The Rockefeller Institute was popularly considered to be the source of all knowledge about epidemic cerebrospinal meningitis. William H. Park, director of the Board of Health Laboratories, was irritated by this situation, inasmuch as he had been supplying a similar serum for years before Flexner introduced the method of spinal administration. Park's biographer hints that there was at least one stormy interview between the two men about 1910. Finally, in 1912, when the newspapers, incorrectly, gave The Rockefeller Institute, but not the health department, credit for emergency help given by both to a Texas community, Park became alarmed. He feared for the reputation of his staff and felt that his budget might suffer if his laboratories failed to receive all possible credit for their work. Letting his wrath boil over in an interview with an *Evening Post* reporter, he complained of the Rockefeller "campaign of publicity," and denied Flexner credit for originality in demonstrating the efficacy of the spinal route of serum administration. Jochmann, a German bacteriologist, had indeed hit upon the same idea and tried it upon a few human patients before Flexner's first publication, but his report of favorable results was not in print until after Flexner had made his first trials with monkeys.[8] Technically Jochmann had priority, but it was Flexner's thorough investigation, carried out with great acumen and on a large scale, that proved the worth of intraspinal medication. Flexner replied to Park's onslaught only by a dignified personal letter, not given to the press, in which he declined to engage in controversy about the matter.[9]

For several decades the intraspinal administration of antimeningitis serum was the only known means of reducing deaths from this fulminant disease and of cutting down bad aftereffects in those who recovered. This treatment fell into disuse only when the sulfa drugs and later the natural antibiotics (penicillin, etc.) proved highly effectual against infectious cerebrospinal meningitis.

THE WORK ACCOMPLISHED in the temporary laboratories resulted in numerous papers, thus intensifying a difficulty already created by the grants-in-aid program. At the time there were only three American journals devoted to experimental research in the medical sciences, namely, the *Journal of Experimental Medicine,* founded in 1896 in Baltimore and edited by W. H. Welch, the *Journal of Medical Research,* begun in Boston under another name in 1896 and edited by Harold C. Ernst, and the *American Journal of Physiology,* started in 1898. As Welch had said in the introduction to Volume I of his *Journal,* before these periodicals were available American contributors to medical research had been obliged to publish their papers, often in condensed form and imperfectly illustrated, in journals devoted mainly to practical medicine, or else to send them to Europe. The new American journals only partially met the need, however, and when papers began to come from the recipients of The Rockefeller Institute's grants-in-aid, there was again a shortage of space. Obviously the Institute needed a journal of its own.

At the Board meeting of October 1902 somebody—doubtless Welch —suggested that the Institute might acquire the *Journal of Experimental Medicine.* Discussion was favorable, and Welch was requested to investigate the matter, about which he already knew too much for his own peace of mind. He had taken the lead in getting the journal started at the Johns Hopkins Medical School in 1896 with the moral support of colleagues in other institutions, and had managed it with great success but at heavy cost in time and energy, for he could never delegate the details of such a task to anyone else. Flexner, who in his biography of Welch narrates the whole seriocomic story of the *Journal* and its transfer to the Institute,[10] tells how the editorial work had distracted Welch from his teaching, ruined his holidays, and spoiled his Saturday recreation of watching a professional baseball game, for he was even seen reading galley proofs between innings. In 1901 he had tried unsuccessfully to give the *Journal* away to Harold Ernst of Boston, who was talking of developing a journal of medical research out of a local medical society's bulletin. At last Welch's sense of duty gave way under the burden of editorship. Suddenly, after the March number of 1902, he quit sending material to the printers and began stacking the incoming manuscripts on closet shelves and chairs in his office, intermingled with unanswered correspondence. Some stayed there until new work published elsewhere made them obsolete; not even President Gilman of the Johns Hopkins University could induce Welch to complete the half-published sixth volume. At this juncture The Rockefeller Institute took over the journal, to the mingled chagrin and relief of the University; but Flexner and Opie, who were to be the new editors, were unable to recover the unpublished manuscripts from their former teacher, and Flexner finally had to go to Welch's quarters in Baltimore and bring them away in a suitcase.

The second half of the interrupted volume was completed at the Institute and published in February 1905. Since that time the *Journal* has appeared regularly and has continued to be one of the world's most respected medical research journals. For fifteen years Flexner was active as chief editor, assisted by Opie, 1904–1910, and Benjamin T. Terry, 1911–1912. In 1921 Peyton Rous was appointed co-editor. Assuming practically the whole task, he was the effective editor for thirty-six years, although Flexner's name continued to be carried on the title page even after the Director's retirement, and until the latter's death in 1946. That Rous, during his long editorship, has set a high standard of verbal precision and clear exposition, many contributors, whose manuscripts have come back to them covered with wise and helpful suggestions, will testify. His editorial precepts moreover are reinforced by the example of his own excellent style.[11] Herbert S. Gasser became joint editor in 1935, René J. Dubos in 1946, and Vincent P. Dole, Jr., in 1953. Although the *Journal of Experimental Medicine* was originally taken over as an outlet for Institute papers, it has always welcomed articles from outside and applied the same criteria for judging their acceptability as for those from inside the Institute. The proportion of outside contributions was for a long time more than half the total, and in recent years has risen to five sixths.

THE TEMPORARY laboratories were used for only eighteen months, because the main building on the York Avenue site, together with an animal
house and the powerhouse, was ready for use in April 1906. On May 11
came the formal dedication with addresses by Holt, Welch, President
Nicholas Murray Butler of Columbia University, and President Charles
W. Eliot of Harvard.[12] In all these speeches not a word was said about
the buildings themselves, either in praise by the visitors, or vaunting by
their hosts. In fact, the main laboratory building reflected the caution
rather than the ambitions of the Board. Though commodious and well
equipped, it was by no means sumptuous in comparison with such contemporary buildings of similar purpose as those of Harvard Medical
School.

On the first floor were a library and an assembly room as well as administrative offices. The second floor was fitted for chemical research,
the third for experimental pathology, and the fourth for bacteriology and
parasitology.[13] Excellent operating rooms and animal quarters were located on the roof. The mechanical equipment was rather elaborate for
the time, including forced ventilation with filtered air and a central refrigeration system supplying cold storage rooms and individual refrig-
erators on each floor.

Flexner took with him to the new laboratories a staff of eight investigators organized in three departments: Pathology and Bacteriology (Flexner, Opie, Noguchi, Sweet, Houghton); Physiology and Pharmacology
(Meltzer, Auer); Chemistry (Levene, W. A. Beatty). There were also five
Resident Fellows and Scholars, three of them assigned to Flexner's group,
two to Levene's. In June 1907 the Board of Directors, after searching discussion, decided to designate the senior investigators as "Members of The
Rockefeller Institute," with indefinite tenure, and to create also a class
of "Associate Members" with tenure of five years, subject to renewal.
Flexner headed the list as Director of the Laboratories and Member;
Meltzer, Opie, and Levene followed as Members, and Noguchi as Associate Member. The Board adopted these titles, suggestive of membership
in a learned society rather than an academic faculty, preferring them to
those of "professor" and "associate professor." Staff members of lower
rank were designated as Associate, Assistant, Fellow, and Scholar, terms
already in use in the Institute.[14]

The chief practical effect of this classification was to ratify Flexner's position as executive head of the whole institution. Thus a clear pattern of organization, with proper delegation of responsibility from the Board through the Director to the several Members, had evolved from the ill-defined original scheme under which the Board would have been a sort of operating committee directing several equally ranking departmental heads. Flexner's force of character and wisdom had placed him unmistakably at the head of the whole enterprise, where he was to remain even when large new departments were added, namely, the hospital and the Princeton laboratories of animal and plant pathology.

WHILE FLEXNER and his staff were getting their work under way, the Board of Directors was grappling with long-term plans for financing the Institute and conducting its business affairs. Their concept of the size of the undertaking was growing from year to year. Early in 1907 they sent Rockefeller an estimate on which Prudden had been working for six months. His report, entitled "An estimate for the endowment of The Rockefeller Institute," proposed an expenditure of about $290,000 annually. To produce so large an income, a capital sum of six million dollars or more would be required.[15] Such an endowment would be far too large to be administered in the informal fashion that had served well enough when the doctors were in effect simply drawing upon Rockefeller's private funds for running expenses and the costs of building construction. Some sort of legal trusteeship would be necessary as soon as Rockefeller provided the endowment that was confidently expected by the Board.

About November 1906 Holt had written a plan for creating a Board of Trustees and designating its members. This started correspondence and discussions, lasting four years, about the proper division of authority between the scientists and the men of affairs. The problem was a novel one, and when the Board finally arrived at a solution, the members felt that they had made a significant advance in the theory of institutional administration. The Rockefeller Institute, being different from other American scientific organizations, could not in their opinion be effectively managed in the traditional manner of the private universities, most of which had grown out of small, paternally conducted colleges. In that system a legally omnipotent board of trustees, owning all the property and hiring a president and faculty, has potential control of all academic activities. As educational institutions grew more complex and more sophisticated, the concept of trusteeship matured. Wise trustees, not resting upon the strict letter of the law, learned to share authority. Nowadays they consider themselves responsible only for management of capital resources, for choosing the chief executive of the institution, and for deciding broad questions of policy and of public relations. The direction of educational and scientific programs is left to the faculty.

At the beginning of the century, however, the paternalistic legal authority of the trustees was more often in evidence than it is today. In times of crisis they could and often did exert their power in a highly autocratic way. Trustees of universities, being themselves educated men, are supposedly qualified for direct control of general educational policy; but the philanthropic sponsors of The Rockefeller Institute, a highly specialized technical institution, neither could nor would claim any such competence for the guidance of medical research. Indeed, the Institute was already, at their invitation, being operated by medical men of force and distinction, leaders in science as the Rockefellers and their associates were leaders in business. How were the talents of both groups to be put to full use without limiting the scope of either?

Welch's idea was to assure final authority to the Trustees by empowering them to appoint a Board of Scientific Directors, checked by the requirement to choose from a list nominated by the Directors themselves. The Trustees were to receive and account for the funds, the Directors to control the scientific program.[16] These wise proposals were never questioned and were adopted in the bylaw of 1910. On the most critical point, namely, control of expenditures, the discussion was more prolonged. Apparently Holt's tentative draft gave the two boards joint authority over the budget, an unwieldy arrangement likely to break down under stress. Welch proposed that the Trustees should have full power over the details of the annual budget. For this stand his most recent biographer has somewhat harshly accused him of virtual treason to science, asserting that Welch was willing to throw away a unique opportunity to establish the right of scientists to control their research programs.[17]

Biggs and Prudden, however, vigorously dissented and carried the other Directors with them. "It would be within the power of the Trustees under these provisions," Prudden wrote, "to decline to support any or all phases of scientific work upon which in the judgment of the Scientific Directors the available yearly income should be expended, by refusing to approve the budget." He foresaw no such conflict of opinion under existing conditions, but if the time ever came when the two boards should disagree about the character and scope of the Institute's work, the ability of the Directors to lead and encourage investigators would be destroyed unless they had final control of the funds available for research. "One of the most depressing conditions," he continued, "under which most scientific men are working today . . . is the lack of a certain independence and the hopelessness of shaping their researches along the ideal lines, unless these can be demonstrated to others in power, but not always at the same viewpoint, to be urgent and promising."[18]

Welch's viewpoint was, in the first place, quite orthodox by collegiate tradition, and, in the second place, it reflected the easy unconcern of a professor and dean, with immense personal prestige, in a university whose trustees had been especially well taught, by Johns Hopkins's president, Daniel Coit Gilman, to divide authority with the faculties. Herter, Holt, and Prudden, on the other hand, professors in medical schools as yet academically insecure, and Biggs and Theobald Smith, accustomed to government institutions, had more reason to fear arbitrary or indifferent trusteeship. What they specifically wished to protect scientists against, we may suppose, was pressure from lay trustees for overly practical research at the expense of fundamental studies. As we shall see, the discussion resulted in a compromise by which the Directors obtained a controlling share in the allotment of expenditures.

This weighty question was still undecided in November 1907, when Rockefeller, Sr., announced to the expectant Board of Directors that he would give the Institute an endowment fund of $2,600,000 in stocks and bonds. This brought the whole question of trusteeship to a head, for the charter of 1901 did not grant the corporation specific authority to hold invested funds. Unable for this reason to transfer the funds directly to the Directors, Rockefeller adopted the expedient of including the funds in a large gift to The General Education Board, earmarked for the Institute as soon as it should be "qualified in law to receive the same."

In May 1908 the charter was duly amended to permit the Board of Directors to create, either by bylaw or by contract with the donor, a board of trustees empowered to hold investments. This action solved part of the problem of reorganization, but left unsettled the long-debated question as to who should control expenditures for research. Apparently Rockefeller was unwilling to give the Institute full command of the needed financial resources until the whole scheme of organization was complete. It will be remembered that early in 1907 the Board of Directors asked for an endowment fund of something like six million dollars. The gift of November 1907 provided less than half of that amount. Rockefeller cannily withheld the rest, not even announcing his intentions until the fiscal constitution of the Institute should be adopted and in force.

The question now was whether to create a separate board, or to convert the existing Board of Directors into a board of trustees by adding a few business men who should also act as a finance committee. The latter arrangement would merely have conferred trusteeship upon the very persons already conducting the affairs of the Institute, for Rockefeller, Jr., Gates, and Starr Murphy had frequently met with the Board of Directors when important matters of finance or policy were up for discussion. The die was cast, however, at a conference between Welch and the trio of Rockefeller, Gates, and Murphy in January 1910, in favor of an independent board of trustees to include two members of the Board of Directors, now to be renamed Board of Scientific Directors. This decision was made effective by a contract between Rockefeller, Jr., and the Directors, implemented by a bylaw, both dated October 15, 1910, which provided for a board of trustees of not more than nine members, to include a representative of the Rockefeller family to be nominated by John D. Rockefeller, Sr., or J. D. Rockefeller, Jr.; one member of The General Education Board; two persons to be appointed by one or the other of the Rockefellers during their lifetime, and afterward by the Board itself; three members at large to be elected by the Board; and two persons selected by and from the Board of Scientific Directors. The first board of trustees did not fill out the quota; its members were Rockefeller, Jr., Gates, Murphy, Welch, and Flexner. At Rockefeller's insistence, Gates was named chairman.

Now at long last, on October 17, 1910, the dedication day of The Rockefeller Institute Hospital, Rockefeller announced a further gift of $3,820,000 to the Institute. This, when added to the sum given three years before, made a total of $6,420,000, sufficient at current yields to produce the $290,000 annual income for which the Board of Directors had asked.

The problem of budget control was solved by making the annual budget subject to approval by a special committee of five, comprising three representatives of the Board of Scientific Directors and two trustees.[19] Prudden, the author of this plan, felt it a victory for those who wished to keep the direction of scientific research in the hands of investigators. "The Board of Trustees," he wrote later, "not the masters of scientific work through financial control, but friendly and informed councillors, has relieved the Directors of responsibility for the management of invested funds and of properties, but left science free to shape its own course."[20] Simon Flexner summed up the matter by saying that "At Prudden's revolutionary suggestion, Rockefeller and his advisers agreed to a delegation of power such as may never before have existed in an American philanthropic institution. The trustees agreed merely to take care of the funds, leaving the decision of how they were to be spent to a joint committee containing a majority of scientists."[2]

As it turned out, the lay trustees showed enthusiastic interest in the scientific program. Raymond B. Fosdick, who became a trustee and secretary of the Board, gives a vivid picture of one of its sessions: ". . . Gates and the younger Rockefeller listening with rapt attention as Dr. Welch or Dr. Flexner unfolded the intricacies of the current researches — JDR jr. taking in the story with quiet approval and a few crisp questions; Gates at the head of the table — with his shaggy white hair and with his necktie generally disarranged — flaming with enthusiasm, or with denunciation if any derogatory comments were reported which had been directed at the Institute."[21]

The joint budget committee worked well. The annual budgetary proposals were drawn up in two sections. The "Trustees' budget" covered such items as new buildings, reconstruction and refurnishing, maintenance and repair, insurance, and other overhead costs. The "Scientific Directors' budget" covered the distribution of research funds among the departments of the Institute. Both budgets were considered by the Budget Committee, with its three-to-two majority of medical scientists, and were submitted together for ratification by the Corporation, that is to say a joint meeting of the two Boards. The Trustees faithfully observed the spirit of this arrangement, leaving the scientific program to the Directors. These in turn assumed full responsibility for it, meeting four times a year to hear and critically review reports of the research work of the whole Institute. The research staff was entirely content with this way of managing the funds upon which their daily labors depended, and worked effectively under it for forty-three years.

THE ADVENT of The Rockefeller Institute was promptly followed, as might have been expected, by a number of proposals from other medical and scientific institutions hoping for mutual advantages from some sort of affiliation, or merely from proximity. In 1905 the City of New York and in 1908 the Presbyterian Hospital offered to erect general hospitals on part of the ground reserved by Rockefeller, Jr., for future use by the Institute. The Board declined both requests, declaring that the Institute should adhere to its original plan of erecting and controlling its own hospital, and should protect its land for that purpose as well as for expansion of the laboratories.[22] It would of course have been advantageous to have a good general hospital close to the Institute, but the lack was made up later when the New York Hospital and Cornell Medical School were erected just north of Sixty-eighth Street. In 1907 the Presbyterian Hospital asked the Institute to take over the work of its pathological laboratory, a request which showed a misconception of the Institute's aims. The Board softened its declination of the proposal by permitting E. L. Opie to be visiting pathologist to the Presbyterian Hospital for about three years.[23] In the laboratory which he developed there several good pathologists began their research careers.

Among these friendly approaches was a request from the Carnegie Institution of Washington for the location of a laboratory to be devoted to the work of W. O. Atwater and F. G. Benedict. These distinguished chemists were investigating metabolic chemistry and the caloric aspects of nutrition; and the Board replied that the Institute would be happy to have the Carnegie Nutrition Laboratory for a neighbor although the Institute could not provide a site upon its own land.[24] The Laboratory was finally established in Boston.

In 1907 the Rockefellers, now fully confident of the Directors' wisdom in medical affairs, turned to them for advice on an appeal for aid to the medical school of McGill University in Montreal, which had sustained heavy loss by the burning of two buildings. Welch, to whom the Board entrusted the preparation of its reply, sent Gates a long review of the state of medical education in America, setting forth the advantages to humanity that might come from wise gifts to medical schools. Outlining the qualifications a school should exhibit to warrant help, Welch said the Board was willing to advise on such a program but, before reporting on McGill, wanted to know whether Rockefeller and his advisers approved the general ideas he had set forth. According to Flexner, Welch was deliberately using the opportunity to influence the Rockefellers to support American medical education and investigation on a large scale, and was trying to get them to commit themselves in principle to such a program.[25]

The Rockefellers made no grant to McGill at this time and did not again ask the Board for advice about gifts to outside institutions. Welch's thoughtful report, however, must have helped to prepare Gates and Rockefeller, Jr., for their part in developing support of medical education and research a few years later through The General Education Board and The Rockefeller Foundation.

When the two Rockefellers were first thinking over the establishment of an institute for medical research, they were at the same time considering the problem of education of the Southern Negro. Their thinking broadened, as it proceeded, to cover the whole field of education for white people as well as Negroes. From these discussions grew The General Education Board, founded in 1903, which was devoted to the promotion of education throughout the United States without distinction of race, sex, or creed. Out of it was to come later (in 1923) The International Education Board.

In 1905, Gates, pleased with the progress of The Rockefeller Institute and The General Education Board, suggested to the Rockefellers the creation of a series of corporate philanthropies to promote a wide range of activities in science, the arts, agriculture, citizenship, and civic virtue throughout the world. The Rockefeller Foundation, Rockefeller's largest philanthropic enterprise, was incorporated in 1910. Four members of the Board of Trustees of The Rockefeller Institute, Rockefeller, Jr., Gates, Flexner, and Starr J. Murphy, were among the first trustees of the Foundation. The International Health Board, growing out of an early interest in hookworm disease on the part of The General Education Board, became an extensive division of The Rockefeller Foundation. The Laura Spelman Rockefeller Memorial Foundation, set up in 1923, operated for seven years in the field of social sciences and was merged with the senior Foundation in 1928. In the latter year also The General Education Board and The International Education Board, after making great and far-reaching contributions to the advancement of education, were merged with The Rockefeller Foundation. By 1952 it was calculated that Rockefeller's gifts to these various philanthropic organizations had amounted to nearly $450,000,000, and his vast contributions to human welfare had become part of the cultural history of our time.[26]

The obvious lack of enthusiasm on the part of the Board of The Rockefeller Institute about serving as an advisory committee and possibly a grant-making agency on a national scale perhaps averted an assignment that might have spread their energies too widely and distracted their attention from the affairs of the Institute. As the Institute grew and the staff found more ways to develop its work, Flexner's administrative duties became very burdensome. It is astonishing that he was able to lead an extensive program of investigation, publishing about a dozen scientific papers each year from 1906 through 1911 in his own name or with colleagues, while conducting the daily business of the laboratories in all its detail, and editing with Opie's help the *Journal of Experimental Medicine*. At the same time he was constantly on the watch for new staff members, and was engaged in a running fight with the antivivisectionists, as will shortly be described.

Early in 1909 the Board authorized Flexner to look for an administrative assistant, and in May 1910 Jerome D. Greene, thirty-six-year-old graduate of Harvard Law School, sometime secretary to the Harvard Corporation, was appointed business manager. Greene not only succeeded at once in rescuing Flexner from many administrative duties but also promptly won the confidence of Rockefeller, Jr. Resigning in 1912 to join the latter's personal staff, he had a distinguished career as banker, internationalist, and trustee of practically all the Rockefeller philanthropic boards. Making him one of its own trustees, The Rockefeller Institute continued to profit from Jerome Greene's wisdom and experience for many years.

Flexner found a successor to Greene in Henry James the younger, son of the distinguished psychologist William James and nephew of

Henry James the novelist. Like his father, Henry James the younger did not find at once the best outlet for his talents and, defying the American preference for consistency, experimented with several occupations. He practiced law in Boston and tried his hand at forestry; at The Rockefeller Institute also he was feeling his way toward a career. A cautious, precise administrator, he was too independent to enjoy working under others. During World War I he enlisted in the American army as a private, because he was unwilling to claim the privileges of an officer, and only later went abroad to direct relief activities. On returning to the United States after the war, he did not resume his post at the Institute, but engaged in administrative work and writing. His two-volume biography of President Eliot of Harvard won a Pulitzer Prize. James was an officer of the Carnegie Corporation and became head of the Carnegie-endowed Teachers' Insurance and Annuity Association. He was a trustee of The Rockefeller Institute from 1929 until his death in 1947. In 1919 James was succeeded as business manager of the Institute by Frank A. Dickey, registrar of Columbia University, who died after less than a year in office, and then by another Harvard man, Edric B. Smith, whose long service will be mentioned in later chapters.

MOVING TO THE commodious new laboratory building on York Avenue caused scarcely a ripple in the work of the four Members of the Institute and their associates. Flexner meanwhile was trying to find men qualified to round out the staff. To his own division of pathology and bacteriology and Levene's division of chemistry, a laboratory of physiology and experimental pharmacology was added in June 1907, under the leadership of Meltzer. The Board had in mind several other possible new lines of research, including cytology, medical zoology, epidemiology, and vital statistics, but preferred to look for men with ideas, whatever their precise specialties might be, and to build the staff around them rather than first to set up new laboratories in predetermined fields. Meanwhile, the most pressing need was for additional investigators of senior rank in the existing divisions. Levene and Flexner in particular wanted such men working beside them. Otto Folin, Swedish-born research chemist at McLean Hospital, Waverly, Massachusetts, was approached in 1906, but President Eliot captured him for Harvard instead, blandly apologizing to Herter when the two met on vacation at Seal Harbor.[27] The minutes show that as late as 1910 the Scientific Directors were thinking how to recapture Folin, but in the end he was left to continue his notable career at Harvard.

To lead bacteriology in his own division, Flexner tried to find an American colleague, offering the place in 1907 to Frederick G. Novy, professor of bacteriology at the University of Michigan, who only a year before had followed up Schaudinn's discovery of the cause of syphilis by finding a similar parasite, the spirochete of American relapsing fever. Novy chose to remain at Ann Arbor, and for lack of other eligible Americans Flexner had to look to Europe. Constantin Levaditi of the Pasteur Institute of Paris had made himself known by work on the organism of syphilis; Charles Nicolle, former associate of Emile Roux at the Pasteur Institute of Tunis, was pioneering brilliantly in the field of virus diseases. Both these bacteriologists had given Flexner reason to hope they would join the Institute for a couple of years at least, but both declined when actually invited.[28]

All four of these men who were unsuccessfully approached in 1905–1907 were stars of the first rank, just at the height of productive research careers. Except Levaditi, they were all forty years of age or more, and already occupying responsible executive posts which they were unwilling to exchange for full-time research in the young Institute in New York. Flexner, not discouraged by these setbacks, kept up his search. A few years later, when still another well-established European scientist, Franz Knoop of Freiburg, Germany, declined a post at the Institute, Flexner wrote to a friend, "I am convinced that there is just one way to keep up and not go backwards, and that lies in trying for the best man, who may decline to come, rather than go for men less good, who you know will accept your invitation."[29]

While Flexner was trying in vain to draw these rising men from France and Germany, another no less brilliant European was unknowingly on his way toward membership in The Rockefeller Institute. Flexner first met Alexis Carrel in the spring of 1905 when the young surgeon, casually visiting New York, saw the Institute buildings under construction, and, stopping to look at them, came upon the Director inspecting the work. A year later Flexner offered him a fellowship.

Carrel was born in 1873, near Lyons, to wealthy bourgeois parents. After studying medicine at the University of Lyons, he began, while a hospital surgeon, to devise techniques for closing wounded blood vessels without the risk of obstructing clots, and for rejoining arteries and veins end to end after they were cut across, a feat impossible by contemporary surgical methods. He told an associate many years later that his attention was directed to these problems by the death in 1894 of Sadi Carnot, President of France, from hemorrhage from a blood vessel severed by the assassin's knife.[30] Gifted with exceptional ingenuity and dexterity, Carrel soon made notable progress. Not only did he develop great skill with his superfine needles and miniature clamps, but he also worked out ways to avoid infection of the blood stream and clotting of blood in the vessels, which were the chief obstacles to success. He failed, however, in the stiff examinations required for a teaching post in the surgical clinics; or perhaps he was not allowed to pass, for his self-assurance and his positive religious views, expressed in the anticlerical atmosphere of the Lyons medical faculty, had already begun to make him enemies.

Carrel's French biographer states that a newspaper article he wrote, averring that he had personally witnessed the miraculous cure of a dying girl at Lourdes, was criticized, on one hand, by a radical-socialist politician as mere credulity and, on the other hand, by a prominent churchman as too scientifically restrained in its expression of faith.[31] He himself retrospectively attributed his lack of promotion to the intellectual rigidity of the Lyonnais medical men.[32] At any rate he left France in 1904 on a long journey to Montreal and the American West. Soon settling down in Chicago, Carrel received a minor appointment at the University of Chicago, with laboratory facilities in the department of physiology. There he resumed his brilliant experiments on the suture of blood vessels, taking every opportunity to publish his results and to speak about them at medical meetings. A lecture at the Johns Hopkins Medical School in 1905 made a great impression. Flexner, who no doubt received word of this success through his Baltimore friends, finally determined to invite Carrel to the Institute, after reading a short article in which the French surgeon described the transplantation of a dog's kidney by an operation in which its artery and vein were effectively joined to corresponding vessels in the dog's neck, the kidney continuing to function in its new situation.

Although the Institute had made no plans for experimental surgery, such unheard-of technical achievements as Carrel's demanded the support of a research institute, for they seemed to open the doors to a future era in surgery, when damaged organs might be replaced by healthy ones, obtained, perhaps, from volunteer donors or from the bodies of persons accidentally killed. In time — who could say? — such organs might be kept alive under refrigeration, ready for use. Flexner, of course, expected no miracles; perhaps Carrel did, for had he not seen one at Lourdes? Mystic that he was, he consciously felt himself to be an instrument of God's work. During his travels in America, he had written in a letter to his mother, "What gain is it to be applauded, admired, courted, compared with this one aim of not being disobedient to a heavenly vision?"

Carrel joined the Institute just as it moved to York Avenue. With its admirable facilities at his disposal, he continued his experiments on blood-vessel surgery and soon showed a far-reaching constructive imagination. Before long the journalists discovered him and began to publicize his successive achievements — the transplantation of various internal organs, the repair and grafting of blood vessels, even the successful transfer of a whole leg from one dog to another. Such fame had its dangers, for to the general public some of these experiments, however justified as trials of technique, must have seemed more spectacular than useful.

An incident that occurred in 1909, however, provided dramatic evidence of the potential value of Carrel's experiments on animals and helped build his reputation for wizardry in blood-vessel surgery, for which in 1912 he was awarded the first Nobel prize for medicine that came to America. A premature infant, son of a New York doctor, developed on the third day of his life the dangerous disease melena neonatorum, in which blood oozes from the whole surface of the digestive tract from mouth to lower intestine. Two cases were on record in which babies suffering from this disease had been saved by blood transfusion, but the only practical method then known for this was to connect the radial artery in the donor's wrist with a vein of the patient by a small tube or cannula. This baby weighed only five pounds; its veins were extremely small, and a tube would have blocked most of the vessel. The father, who had seen Carrel at work on animals, appealed to him for help. Carrel suggested an attempt to unite the father's radial artery temporarily to the popliteal vein in the infant's leg by stitching the two vessels together end to end.[33] At the operation, as one of the assisting surgeons noted, the baby's vein had the diameter of a matchstick and the texture of wet cigarette paper. To suture its cut end to the donor's artery seemed almost impossible, but as the urgency of the operation became every minute more apparent, Carrel persisted in the attempt and succeeded in completing the junction. As soon as he removed his clamps from behind the line of attachment, the blood flowed freely from father to child, and the baby's color changed within a few minutes from a waxy pallor to a healthy red. Complete recovery followed.[34] Rockefeller, Sr., learned about this dramatic scene through a memorandum sent him by one of his associates, presumably Gates, and was so deeply impressed that he told the story in his book, *Random Reminiscences of Men and Events.*[35]

The next major appointment brought to the Institute a man who stood in complete contrast to Carrel in temperament and in ways of working. Jacques Loeb, born in the Rhineland in 1859, began his university studies in philosophy but soon abandoned them for medical school and research in physiology. As a very young man he had become convinced that science rather than metaphysics holds the key to the understanding of life and mind, which he considered to depend entirely upon physical and chemical reactions. Loeb's mechanistic conception of life, upon which he founded his whole career, was no mere negation of faith, nor rejection of sentiment; it was a religion to which he dedicated all his powers. His yearning for an explanation of human life and conduct in scientific terms naturally led him to study the behavior of animals, beginning with the reactions of the lowest creatures, such as the spontaneous turning of protozoans toward food or toward light. Loeb's mechanistic theory of such tropisms was the first of his great achievements.

Loeb was at the Marine Station in Naples in 1891 when he received a call to Bryn Mawr College. He came to America greatly relieved to be quit of the uncongenial military and political atmosphere of Germany, and happy to adopt the country of his wife, Anne Leonard of Easthampton, Massachusetts. After a year at Bryn Mawr, he accepted the chair of physiology at the newly founded University of Chicago and proceeded to spend most of his summers in Massachusetts at the Woods Hole Marine

Biological Laboratory, where in 1898 he started a famous course in general physiology. In 1902 he was called to the University of California, which built a seaside laboratory for him at Pacific Grove.

While at Chicago Loeb became acquainted with new theories on the physical chemistry of ions, that is to say, atoms of chemical substances in solution, bearing free electrical charges. To cite a simple example, in ordinary dry table salt (sodium chloride) each sodium atom bears a positive charge and each chlorine atom a negative charge. When the salt is dissolved in water, the charged atoms or ions are relatively free to move, under the influence of thermal and electrical forces. Perceiving the enormous importance of this concept for understanding what goes on in animal tissues, Loeb plunged into a series of experiments on the physiological functions of ions. Investigations of this kind must of course begin with the simplest available biological systems. Loeb chose to make many of his experiments on eggs of marine animals, especially sea urchins' eggs, which are plentiful, easily handled, and in a certain sense simple in organization and reactions. Normally the fertilized eggs undergo a precise sequence of cell division by which they develop into embryos. By altering the salt concentration of the sea water in which the eggs were developing, Loeb could change the pattern of development, causing them to produce Siamese twins, or other more extreme embryonic abnormalities. Still more striking was his discovery that unfertilized sea urchin eggs could be made to divide and develop into embryos if exposed for a time to solutions containing certain salts in higher concentration than in sea water. This astonishing result showed that the action of the sperm cells in starting development of the egg is merely a physical-chemical triggering of a potency inherent in the egg cell. Loeb had thus brought one of the most fundamental phenomena of animal life, hitherto unexplained, into the realm of physical chemistry. He had taken a long step forward in his search for a mechanistic explanation of life processes.[36]

The promptness with which the Directors of The Rockefeller Institute recognized the importance of Loeb's new approach to physiology shows how keen and broad was their search for talent. As early as December 1901, at the end of the first year of the grants-in-aid program, Christian Herter tried to see Loeb at a scientific meeting in Chicago, and failing to meet him, wrote to ask if he would be interested in financial aid. Loeb's reply, prophetic in its vision of things to come, may well have helped to broaden Herter's concept of the Institute's possibilities, and through him to guide the Directors toward creating a division of basic or general physiology.

> My recent work [he wrote] on the antitoxic effects of the valency and the electric charge of ions opens up, if I am not mistaken, a new field in the pathology and possible therapeutics especially of nervous and possibly mental distress. But the blessings may go beyond this and include phenom- ena of fermentation and secretion . . . Such work as well as that on the prolongation of the life of the unfertilized egg might be considered as falling within the scope of an institute like that of Rockefeller. I feel more and more that the more original the lines are which are taken up in such an Institute the more it serves its purpose . . . Work on bacteriological lines and on the problem of immunity should not be neglected yet I feel that one should, if possible, welcome in this country any independent start which seems to open up fertile fields . . . It has been my ambition to put biology on its own feet in this country — as far as my limited ability allowed me to do — and to free our young men from the idea that we must be imitators of the Europeans instead of independent thinkers and work- ers, if not leaders. Especially a new Institute cannot put the ideas too high at the beginning.[37]

During the next seven years the Board kept its eyes on Loeb, and when in 1909 they were ready to set up a division of experimental biol- ogy, they invited him to join the Institute. Because the question of full endowment had not yet been settled, the Board had to ask Rockefeller for a special gift to equip and support the new laboratory. This was promptly granted, and Loeb was appointed as of July 1, 1910, with a sal- ary second only to Flexner's.

Outside the Board of Directors and even within it, voices were raised to ask whether an institute for medical research had any business taking on an investigator who had directed his attention almost exclusively to sea urchin eggs and similar low forms of living matter, with basic aims that precluded him from considering anything so complicated as the human body. Herter, Flexner, and Welch, chief proponents of this radi- cal appointment, had, for example, a very lukewarm response from Theobald Smith. What was the relation, Smith asked, of Loeb's field of work to the Rockefeller idea of "medical research"?[38] Loeb gave his own answer to these doubts in a letter to Flexner during the negotiations for his appointment:

> The question [he wrote] is whether or not the R. I. desires to add a new department, namely that of experimental biology — the latter on a physico-chemical instead of on a purely zoological basis. In my opinion experimental biology — the experimental biology of the cell — will have to form the basis not only of physiology but also of general pathology and therapeutics. I do not think that the medical schools in this country are ready for the new departure; the experimental biology in the zoological departments will be one-sided and remain so. The only place in America where such a new departure could be made for the cause of medicine would be The Rockefeller Institute or an institution with similar tendencies. The medical public at large does not yet fully see the bearing of the new science of experimental biology (in the sense in which I understand it) on medicine.[39]

When the Board of Directors installed Jacques Loeb as a Member of The Rockefeller Institute, they committed themselves, once for all, to the principle he so clearly stated. The Institute's definition of the key words in its title, "Medical Research," was henceforth to include any kind of investigation that might contribute to the understanding of health and disease, no matter how widely it ranged, from the body of a suffering man to subatomic particles. The Directors may not have realized at the time how broadly tolerant also was the commitment they were making with regard to the philosophy as well as to the scientific principles of the Members. They had received into the Institute both Carrel, the believer and mystic, whose interpretation of the meaning of human life was to express itself in books entitled *Man the Unknown, La Prière,* and *Le Voyage à Lourdes,* and Loeb, the rationalist, who would shortly write *The Mechanistic Conception of Life.* Within these laboratories, capacity for discovery was to be the only test of acceptance.

HOWEVER MUCH the new ideas of ionic cell physiology might offer for the distant future of medical research, there was dire need in the immediate present for the less abstract work of the bacteriologist and immunologist — the inexact business of groping in the dark for weapons against a widespread and mysterious disease. Infantile paralysis, striking New York with epidemic force in 1907, was killing and crippling children at the very gates of The Rockefeller Institute. This disease, more accurately known as poliomyelitis, because its attack is by no means limited to infants, was first clearly recognized as a special disease by Jakob Heine of Cannstatt, Germany, in 1840. Earlier medical literature, studied in the light of his description, contains recognizable descriptions of poliomyelitis as early as 1799; no doubt it existed previously, but was not distinguished from the generality of paralytic disease in children. There is some reason to think that poliomyelitis never became epidemic on a large scale before the late nineteenth century. In the 1880's, however, small outbreaks occurred in various parts of the world, and were followed by larger ones, especially after 1900. In 1907 serious epidemics broke out in Germany, in Austria, and on the Atlantic seaboard of the United States. New York City had 2,000 cases that summer, with at least 100 deaths. The helplessness of physicians against it deepened the terror it caused by the suddenness of its attack and by the heart-rending disabilities it left in many of the survivors. Although it seemed to be almost certainly an infectious disease, no one knew what caused it or how it was transmitted. Various attempts to isolate a germ responsible for the infection failed; bacteria found by one or two European investigators in the brains and spinal cords of children dead of the disease turned out to be mere contaminants of the cultures. Nobody succeeded in transmitting the disease to animals.

When the 1907 epidemic struck New York, Flexner hoped to duplicate his recent success with cerebrospinal meningitis by transferring poliomyelitis to animals, perhaps even by employing an immune serum against the unknown paralyzing agent as he had against the meningococcus. During this outbreak, he was unable to secure material from a fatal case and could only utilize cerebrospinal fluid drawn for diagnostic purposes from a living patient. This he injected into various animals, including monkeys, placing it in the spinal canal and also in the abdominal cavity. Not one of his animals developed either fever or paralysis. Success in this necessary step toward understanding the disease was first attained the next year by a European bacteriologist, Karl Landsteiner of Vienna. In November 1908, at the post-mortem examination of a little boy in the Wilhelminer Spital, Landsteiner prepared an emulsion from bits of the brain and spinal cord and inoculated two monkeys by injection into the abdominal cavity. Both developed paralysis and died; their spinal cords showed, under the microscope, the same nerve-cell damage that occurs in human victims of poliomyelitis. Landsteiner tried to pass the disease from these monkeys to others, but failed. He and the boy's physician, Wilhelm Popper, published their findings on May 25, 1909, and in a few weeks their achievement was known to pathologists all over the world.

Flexner promptly requested physicians in the New York area to send spinal cords from fatal cases of poliomyelitis, and in September two specimens arrived. With his assistant Paul A. Lewis, he inoculated monkeys with the infected tissue by injection, under anesthesia, into the brain. These animals developed typical poliomyelitis and died; from them Flexner and Lewis at once successfully infected other monkeys. Having thus trapped the disease for study, by establishing it in laboratory animals, they could proceed to investigate the nature of the infectious substance. Within a few weeks they found that they could draw it through a porcelain Berkefeld filter; in other words, it must be a filtrable virus, one of those living organisms so much smaller than ordinary bacteria that they cannot be seen with the optical microscope. Though little understood at the time, similarly minute agents were already known to be the cause of foot-and-mouth disease, yellow fever, and a dozen other acute diseases. In February 1910 Flexner and Lewis announced that they had transmitted the disease from monkey to monkey by dropping the virus-containing tissue suspensions into the nasal passages. With another assistant, Paul F. Clark, Flexner found that the housefly could harbor the virus, and for many years this was thought to be a possible means of spreading the disease.

Some of the inoculated monkeys used in these various experiments recovered from their attacks of poliomyelitis. From them the experimenters learned another fact of cardinal importance: animals that survive one attack are immune to reinfection, having in their blood something that can neutralize the live virus. Progress stopped, however, at this point. Blood serum from immune monkeys, unfortunately not highly potent, was in any case too scarce a commodity for wholesale use, and Flexner had no large animal capable of furnishing serum with which human patients could be protected or treated. Moreover, the virus could not be made to grow outside of animal bodies. There was to be an agonizingly long wait of two score years before a succession of workers learned how to grow this and other viruses in tissue culture in quantities sufficient to produce vaccines for human use.

This bafflement was a great disappointment to Flexner, whose hopes remained high until the spring of 1911. In March of that year, in the heat of a campaign against antivivisectionist legislation, the newspapers quoted him as saying that the way to prevent infantile paralysis had been found and that a cure was not far distant. Even the first part of this statement was, to say the least, premature; six weeks later, when reporting his work to the National Academy of Sciences, he spoke much less optimistically, saying that "the control of infantile paralysis today must be by prevention, since no specific remedy for it is known."[40]

Yet Flexner had forged an essential link in the long chain of investigations that would give real promise, forty-five years later, of ultimate victory over poliomyelitis. The fact that very able rivals were running neck-and-neck with him during these two years of rapid progress by no means diminishes the merit of his achievement. Landsteiner's first breakthrough had of course opened the field for anyone equipped to enter it. Constantin Levaditi of the Pasteur Institute of Paris—who had declined a post at The Rockefeller Institute two years before—promptly offered Landsteiner the use of his laboratories and a stock of monkeys. Planning their experiments by correspondence, the two bacteriologists succeeded with monkey-to-monkey transmission only a few days after Flexner and Lewis. Similar success was achieved within a few weeks by two other workers, one in Berlin and another in Vienna. Thus four separate laboratories independently discovered the transmissibility of the disease in monkeys. Landsteiner and Levaditi proved the virus to be filtrable, again only a few days later than Flexner and Lewis. They also independently observed the immunity of monkeys which had recovered from experimental infection, but like the American workers failed to produce an immune serum or a vaccine.[41]

The two groups, in Paris and Vienna and in New York, of course kept each other and fellow workers elsewhere informed of their progress by prompt publication. Their rivalry, though sharp, aroused no personal jealousy, as such scientific competition sometimes does; a dozen years later Landsteiner joined The Rockefeller Institute at Flexner's invitation, and spent the rest of his career there with great distinction.

IT WAS inevitable that the enemies of experimentation upon living animals would attack The Rockefeller Institute as soon as they became aware of its leadership in experimental investigation. Antivivisectionist sentiment had gained strength in America following the movement's victory in England in 1876, when Parliament passed an Anti-Vivisection Act seriously hampering medical research. Founded upon the character- istic British traits of fondness for pet animals and hatred of cruelty, the movement was reinforced by a tendency among nineteenth-century evan- gelicals to believe that man's animal companions possess immortal souls.[42] Other protests came from the ranks of those who opposed vacci- nation, or who believed in the reincarnation of human souls in lower animals. Passage of the British act was achieved by ill-informed, heavily propagandized public opinion swaying the votes of parliamentarians who, educated chiefly in the humanities, were not well prepared in 1876 to appreciate the arguments of biology and medicine. In America the movement had progressed less successfully. In 1897 Senator Jacob H. Ballinger of New Hampshire introduced an antivivisection bill in Con- gress, against which William H. Welch led a brilliant and successful attack. Similar attempts to control laboratory investigation by legislation were made in several of the state legislatures not long thereafter; and in New York a bill restricting experimentation on animals was defeated in committee early in 1907 only by the efforts of a group of prominent physicians.

The first rumble of an approaching storm involving The Rockefeller Institute broke in October 1907, just after it had acquired an animal farm in the village of Clyde, New Jersey. Scarcely had the place been cleaned up and fitted with cages and corrals when a journalist from the New York *Herald* appeared to look it over. A few days later he printed a six-column article about the farm, which was factually accurate and ostensibly fair, and even quoted a prominent New York surgeon, Carl Beck, on the scientific and religious justification for experiments on ani- mals. On the other hand, the writer introduced over and over the pro- vocative word "vivisection," emphasized the alleged secrecy of the Insti- tute's negotiations for the farm, and hinted that stolen dogs were being sold to the laboratories in New York City. Giving a frank warning of the impending attack, he wrote, "The establishment of a hundred-acre farm to raise animals for vivisection is certain to attract universal attention, not only from scientific men in sympathy with the movement [*i.e.* animal experimentation], but from the antivivisectionists throughout the world. It is by no means improbable that the Rockefeller Institute and its ani- mal farm will become the antivivisection storm centre of the world."[43]

This reporter's newspaper was all too ready to help raise the tempest he had forecast. Its owner, James Gordon Bennett, Jr., was a great fancier of small dogs, frequently being accompanied, even in his office, by a troop of Pekingese or Pomeranians. He was already an antivivisectionist; and, moreover, as a popular magazine boldly stated, he held a grudge against the medical profession because the New York County Medical Society had forced him to drop certain medical advertising it deemed improper.[44] Bennett knew, too, the business value of a sensational newspaper campaign.

In February 1908, the New York Antivivisection Society held a mass meeting at the Carnegie Lyceum, presided over by Mrs. Diana Belais, "a well-meaning, ignorant, reckless and muddle-headed agitator."[45] She had gathered together a good many substantial citizens, including the pastor of a prominent New York church, an assemblyman who had an antivivisection bill ready for introduction in Albany, two celebrated actresses — Clara Morris and Minnie Maddern Fiske — and the famous opera singer Emma Eames. The warm-hearted, impulsive people of the stage have always been readily swayed by sentimental appeals; a great actor, George Arliss, was to join the Society a few months later. The meeting adopted by acclamation a resolution addressed to John D. Rockefeller asking him "to reconsider his programme and restrict vivisection in the institute bearing his name."[46]

By the end of February 1908, the New York and New Jersey legislatures had antivivisection bills on their dockets, and the existence of a campaign was mentioned for the first time at a meeting of the Board of Directors of The Rockefeller Institute. In March Flexner spoke against the bills before the legislative committees at Albany and Trenton. The *Herald* led newspaper agitation for the bills; the *Times, Sun, Evening Post, Tribune,* and *American* opposed them throughout four years of public contention, not only in leading articles but by printing from time to time news items about medical discoveries at the Institute. The foremost American humorous weekly, the former *Life,* carried on a running attack against animal experimentation for several years. The depths to which it descended, and the viciousness of the antivivisectionist attitude at its worst, are illustrated by this magazine's comment on a news item it quoted from a daily paper about a shipment of monkeys received by The Rockefeller Institute for the study of poliomyelitis: "Children and monkeys are the 'material' preferred by the vivisectors. Children are found in the orphan asylums, babies in maternity hospitals, and the above extract explains the monkey supply."[47]

Notable among the national magazines, *Collier's Weekly* fought fire with fire in a series of sharp editorial comments on Bennett and the *Herald* ("a newspaper hungry for sensation"), on *Life* ("the friendly but insane weekly"), and on "the muddle-headed Mrs. Belais."[48] In a series of articles by professional men, *Collier's* supplemented its sarcasm by responsible accounts of current medical research.

The Board of Directors of The Rockefeller Institute prepared for the coming fight at first only by defensive actions, reinforcing by a written order the rule, already tacitly accepted, that the director of the laboratories must approve all experiments on animals; and giving Carrel, whose experiments on organ transplantation were under particularly heavy fire, a trained nurse to insure care and comfort for his dogs during and after operation.[49] Flexner also arranged an interview with a prominent newspaper writer in which he explained and defended experiments on animals.[50]

An international antivivisection congress held in London in the summer of 1909 encouraged the American leaders to make new efforts against the Institute. A woman living near the farm at Clyde, whose husband was politically influential, petitioned the New Jersey Board of Health in November 1909 to declare the farm a public nuisance. Such wild stories were spread about alleged experimentation at the farm that whenever Carrel's convalescent dogs bayed at the moon, sensitive neighbors thought they were yelping from the pain of an operation. Late in November somebody set fire to the barns, and a few days later the owner of an adjacent farm, who had helped fight the first fire, lost his own barn to an arsonist. Because the incendiary, whoever he was, had caused the agonizing death of several cows and calves, as well as of many chickens, the antivivisectionists could not gloat over his acts; and the *Herald* had to explain them as the work of someone whose mind had been unhinged by reports of animal suffering.

In December 1909 the affair reached its most serious stage, as far as the Institute was concerned, when the *Herald* printed a long affidavit of a former employee of the Institute's animal house, a Mrs. Kennedy, narrating in a most exaggerated way a series of alleged cruelties she claimed to have witnessed. The *Herald*'s articles became more and more vehement, and antivivisectionists tried to bring pressure on Rockefeller, Jr., through members of his Bible class at the Fifth Avenue Baptist Church.[51] Faced with another bill in the state legislature, the Board of Directors decided upon a determined counterattack. Flexner swore to an affidavit accusing Mrs. Kennedy of attempting to bribe a fellow employee to testify against the Institute, and of herself trying to sell animals for experimental use. He followed this with a powerful and dignified letter to the *New York Times,* a tightly knit polemical masterpiece.[52] The 1910 bill was killed in committee, but the fight was resumed the next year. In March 1911, Flexner led his heaviest battalions into the fray, taking with him before the committee Walter B. James, professor of medicine at Columbia University College of Physicians and Surgeons, William H. Park of the New York City Board of Health Laboratories, and Walter B. Cannon, noted physiologist of Harvard Medical School. Once more the legislature refused to hamper medical research by a law restricting the use of animals.

This was the New York Antivivisection Society's last serious threat to the Institute's work. The deluge of sentimentality and misrepresentation, ineffectual against the bulwark of informed public opinion, at last receded. By 1911 the public's confidence in the Institute, and in medical research in general, had been built up by successive announcements of forward steps in the fight against disease, steps such as Flexner's serum against epidemic meningitis; his work on poliomyelitis, exaggeratedly reported by the press but, at the very least, hopeful; and Carrel's remarkable transplantations of whole organs. Furthermore, the opening of the Institute's hospital in 1910 emphasized its zeal for human welfare. For ten or fifteen years more Flexner kept on the alert, deputizing Peyton Rous to represent the Institute's views and to expound the general cause of research before legislative committees in Albany. Thenceforth the legislature consistently rejected the yearly offering of a bill against experimentation on dogs, designed as the entering wedge for further restrictive legislation. In the long run, the antivivisectionists helped the cause of science more than they hurt it at the time. By inducing men like Welch and Flexner to explain their aims openly and boldly, this unfortunate controversy taught the public to appreciate the achievements of medical science and to support experimental medical research.

CHAPTER FOUR

The Hospital in Its Early Years

Planning the organization; Herter's hopes. Rockefeller's additional gifts. Cole appointed Director; his new ideas; full-time research. Opening of the hospital; its unique equipment. Additional endowment. First staff of the hospital. Diseases chosen for study: pneumonia, syphilis, heart disease, poliomyelitis, celiac disease. Establishment of the research ideal in clinical medicine

THE FOUNDERS OF The Rockefeller Institute for Medical Research had in mind from the very first that the Institute would create a hospital of its own, closely integrated with the laboratories. Herter implied as much to Welch in the letter of March 15, 1901, in which he broke the news of Rockefeller's intention to found the Institute; and in January 1902 Simon Flexner, not yet appointed head of the laboratories, wrote to Herter as one director to another, in the exuberance of his hopes:

> We shall be closely watched by other hospitals in this country as well as by the general profession at home and abroad. Everything will lead to bring the Institute and Hospital into prominence; their close association; the large and growing endowment; the ideals for which they stand, and the good beginning made by the Institute. I think that we can start well. We shall be without traditional hindrance and shall have the world's experience, gathered at first hand, as a heritage.[1]

Flexner went on to say that he considered Herter the best man for chief physician of the projected hospital and that the rest of the Board agreed with him. Herter was willing to take the post, and his manner of living and working left him free to do so. Although he had chosen to study chemical pathology in his own private laboratory and had no need to build up a time-consuming private practice, he had given attention to clinical medicine and had even written books on the subject. He was fa-

miliar with the problems presented by human illness as well as with the
rapidly developing knowledge of bacteriology and biochemistry which
the Institute aimed to apply to the study of disease. Herter and Flexner,
already close friends, continued to exchange ideas about the hospital
during the spring of 1902. When Flexner had drafted his plan for the
organization of the Institute—which, he must have known, was to be a
test of his fitness for the Directorship—he had suggested the kind of hospital the Institute should have, saying that the Institute should never
lose sight of the immediate problems of human disease. "In order that
these problems be not neglected," he wrote, "there should be attached to
the Institute a hospital for the study of special groups of cases of disease.
This hospital should be modern and fully equipped, but it need not be
large. It should attempt to provide only for selected cases of disease."[2]

When the Board of Directors submitted to Rockefeller their fully
thought-out plan and program for the Institute as part of a report on the
first year's operations, they included Flexner's statement on the hospital
almost word for word.[3] No immediate action followed, for Rockefeller's
policy was to see one phase of the enterprise well under way before starting another, and until 1907 the Directors were far too busy with the laboratories to give consideration to a hospital. Herter, for whom this was a
matter of special concern, continued to urge it upon his fellow Directors, even though illness was beginning to sap his energies. In the summer of 1902 he passed through a period of severe despondency, ascribed
by his friends to grief over the recent death of his young son, but in retrospect it seems probable that the slowly developing disease of the nerves
and muscles, of which he died eight years later, was already beginning to
weaken and depress him.[4]

He went on, however, with his work, continuing to give earnest attention to the Institute, and as late as December 1902 wrote to Flexner
that he still hoped "to try the experiment of looking after the hospital if
the Board feels it to be a desirable thing for the Institute."[5] By 1906, he
was again ill and so depressed that he wrote to Flexner expressing doubts
of his ability to direct the hospital and even proposing to resign from the
Board. Welch and Flexner during these years did not realize, any more
than Herter himself, that he was organically ill, for they wrote to him as
to a friend who needs only spiritual encouragement. Welch, in his kind
but fundamentally impersonal fashion, urged him to pull himself together; Flexner, often considered a cold and reserved man, gave Herter,

as the illness progressed, the utmost sympathy and compassion. In 1906 he wrote that he still thought Herter qualified to direct the hospital if he felt equal to it.[6] Without knowledge of this tragic personal situation, it would be difficult to reconcile an acknowledgment of Herter's very considerable influence in determining the character of the hospital with his gradual relinquishment of an active part in its operation.

In the "Estimate for the Endowment of The Rockefeller Institute" which the Board of Directors presented to Rockefeller early in 1907, they repeated their plea for a hospital:[7]

> At the present time the conditions prevailing in the hospitals where large numbers of patients must be cared for, are such that adequate individual study of patients is impossible. The hospitals are of necessity places where traditional methods are applied rather than where new methods are originated. In a hospital affiliated with the Rockefeller Institute patients could be studied with an unprecedented degree of thoroughness . . . Treatment, instead of being largely experimental, would gradually become a matter of certainty. The principles of treatment thus established by the thorough study of a few patients would become applicable to the many . . . At the present time there probably exists nowhere in the world the most advantageous affiliation of laboratories and hospitals such as is here proposed.

In February 1907 Rockefeller authorized the preparation of plans for a hospital and the securing of bids, though he made no commitment as yet about paying for the building.[8] Things now moved rapidly. In June a committee on the hospital, consisting of Herter, Flexner, and Holt, presented a preliminary plan for a fifty-bed hospital, equipped with laboratories independent of those already existing in the Institute. Ten of the beds were to be set aside for infectious diseases. An outpatient dispensary would not be needed. Emphasis was placed on a good diet kitchen under expert management, because the committee realized that the subject of feeding in hospitals was in a "surprisingly undeveloped state."[9] The following May, after a careful review, Rockefeller promised to give another $500,000 for the hospital, and to permit the use of $150,000 remaining from his earlier pledges.[10]

By this time it was clear that Herter could not undertake the directorship of the hospital and another leader must be found. Two young men of conspicuous ability, Theodore C. Janeway of New York and Rufus Cole of Baltimore, were considered by the Board. Welch favored

Cole as best representing the new movement toward laboratory study of disease; Herter and the other Directors concurred. Before the decision was made final, Welch, learning that Cole had just been offered the professorship of internal medicine at the University of Michigan, risked telling him that The Rockefeller Institute was considering him, and Flexner sent him a set of blueprints of the proposed hospital. Impressed by the aims of the Board, Cole decided to stake his career upon the small research hospital in New York, as yet unbuilt and unendowed, rather than on the secure but less adventurous post at Ann Arbor.[11]

Born in Ohio in 1872, Rufus Cole had gone to college at the University of Michigan and studied medicine at Johns Hopkins. After his internship at the Johns Hopkins Hospital, he rose to be resident physician, a post which under the policy of that institution was tenable for several years and gave its incumbent almost professorial prestige, as indicated by the faculty rank of Associate in Medicine. His notable shyness, which gave him more the manner of a scholar than of a medical man, masked a persistent and determined character. Cole had done excellent work in clinical bacteriology; his improvements of the technique for growing the bacillus of typhoid fever from the patient's blood helped to establish the standard blood-culture diagnostic test for that disease. On October 10, 1908, he was elected Member of the Institute, in charge of scientific and medical conduct of the hospital, and on November 28 he was named Director of the Hospital and (somewhat redundantly, it seems) Physician to the Hospital. At the same time Herter also was appointed Physician to the Hospital and Member of the Institute.[12]

The position thus conferred upon Cole indicated a concept of the hospital program quite different from that which the Board had envisioned earlier. Herter had proposed that attending physicians, representing the best medical talent of the city, should direct the care of patients, but not be full-time members of the Institute, although expected to give it priority over their private practice; and that a resident staff of young physicians perform the routine ward work and round-the-clock service to the sick. Presumably, the scientific study of disease, for which the hospital was created, would be led by Herter himself and the staff of the existing laboratories, of whom at least two—Meltzer and Carrel—looked forward to testing and applying their ideas clinically. This scheme made research and care of the patient separate functions exercised by different sets of physicians. Herter's failing health denied him the opportunity to mature these plans, and, as he gradually withdrew from active participation in the project, a fresh influence sprang up from the direction of Baltimore.

When Cole was Resident Physician at Johns Hopkins, he served one year under William Osler before the latter left to become Regius Professor at Oxford, and then under Osler's successor, Lewellys F. Barker. Barker's appointment reflected a change that was taking place in American medicine. Osler had represented the best nineteenth-century British traditions of medical teaching. He was a masterly observer and interpreter of the manifestations of disease in the individual patient — in other words, a great diagnostician. His method and aims were well expressed by the epitaph he said he wished for himself: "He taught medicine at the bedside." There, and in his superb textbook, he expounded the natural history of disease, setting forth the signs and symptoms observed from the bedside and explaining them by information garnered from all available sources — from post-mortem examination of previous similar cases, from bacteriology and chemistry, from personal experience with the sick, and from medical statistics. He did not undertake or promote studies of the fundamental nature of disease, for which his clinic, and indeed all others outside Germany, lacked facilities. Osler, great clinical physician as he was, could not fully perceive how rapidly biology and chemistry were advancing to the aid of internal medicine. Those who did see the trend — chiefly workers in the preclinical sciences of anatomy, physiology, biochemistry, bacteriology, and pathology — held the opinion that serious medical investigation could be carried out only in their own laboratories, because clinicians had neither time nor training for such complex researches.

Unlike Osler, Barker came to his clinical chair by way of a professorship of anatomy and a career of laboratory research. Just before his appointment to Osler's place, moreover, he had paid a long visit to the great institute of internal medicine at the University of Munich. He was determined to follow the German example by introducing the university spirit into his own department of medicine, making research a major obligation of the professor and his staff. To this end he established, adjacent to his wards, research laboratories of biology, chemistry, and physiology. Before that time such laboratories as American hospitals possessed were intended only for diagnostic tests; those of Barker's clinic were to study disease itself. Barker chose Cole to be the first head of the biological laboratory of his clinic. In that capacity Cole carried on his pioneer studies of typhoid bacilli in the blood stream, studies which constituted the first systematic clinical laboratory research at the Johns Hopkins Hospital.

The general movement, of which Barker's program was one example, to turn the clinical services of teaching hospitals into true university departments, could obviously not be conducted by physicians busily engaged in private practice. The medical schools would have to create full-time salaried positions for teachers of the clinical subjects, like those already established for the preclinical sciences. Osler had opposed the full-time plan; Barker favored it wholeheartedly. Although not put into effect at the Johns Hopkins University until 1913, it was already being discussed and debated when Cole was called to The Rockefeller Institute. Cole saw in the Institute an opportunity to develop and lead intensive medical investigation in an environment pervaded by the research spirit. Free from the ordinary routine of practice and of the teaching of medical students, he could train young men who would ultimately carry the new methods to the medical schools and to other hospitals.[13]

Cole's suggestions to the Board of Directors about the organization of the hospital staff reveal his attitude on the questions of the full-time principle and of clinical research.[14] He outlined a bold though relatively simple plan, calling for a resident staff of young men of exceptional ability, able to undertake independent research. They were not to be mere assistants to the physician-in-chief nor to the visiting physicians; on the contrary, each would have full control of a ward, where he could study patients suffering with a disease in which he was particularly interested. Each resident would be provided with enough assistance to leave him time for research. Facilities for animal experimentation and laboratory tests would be at his disposal. Even the interns — junior members of the resident staff who in other hospitals carried the day-and-night routine of patient care — would be allowed time for research. The director would himself foster and lead the work of these men. There were to be no attending physicians from outside, as in Herter's proposals. The resident staff would care for patients along with its research work.

These plans were indeed novel, for in effect they made the hospital not an annex of the laboratories, but rather an independent department, in which Cole and his associates would constitute an organized group, comparable to the existing departments of the Institute. The formal designation of Cole as a Member of the Institute indicated tacit acceptance of his program by the Board; but the actual creation of a full-time medical service in the hospital, not only a new but also a very expensive step, required the approval of Rockefeller and his close advisers. Flexner talked it over with Gates, and then it was discussed at a special meeting of the Directors in January 1909. They supported it, recommending by unanimous vote that physicians holding appointments in the Institute should not practice medicine outside the hospital and should not accept fees for services.[15] The following month Rockefeller, Jr., assured the Board that his father would provide for the proposed salaried hospital staff in the general endowment which he was preparing to set up. It seemed probable, the son added, that his father would stipulate not only that members of the medical staff devote full time to hospital work, but also that patients never be charged for hospital care. Thus Cole was to have the means and the freedom to put his ideas into action.[16] Two months later the Rockefellers cheerfully granted an additional $100,000 for various alterations to the building plans, and in January 1910 they gave another $20,000 for equipment.[17]

The Hospital of The Rockefeller Institute was officially inaugurated on October 17, 1910. On the same day Rockefeller made the great announcement awaited by the Board of Directors since January 1907. He would give $3,800,000 to the endowment fund, bringing the invested capital to a total slightly larger than the six millions for which the Board had asked. Rounding out the events of this climactic occasion, the Institute announced that new bylaws creating a Board of Trustees had gone into effect that day. The Rockefeller Institute for Medical Research, at last in full possession of its financial resources, was now established as an independent foundation in perpetuity.

The ceremonies of the first day were attended by two or three hundred invited guests; on the next day, October 18, the hospital was open to the public, and about two thousand visitors inspected the wards and laboratories. They saw that the architects and builders had put up, as Prudden dryly wrote, "a strictly utilitarian structure . . . space and expenditure for artistic effect being strictly limited by the Directors."[18]

Among the visitors, only those familiar with older hospitals would have been struck by the most advanced aspect of the new building: a whole floor devoted to laboratories, with space and equipment far in excess of need for mere routine examinations and tests. Medical visitors were impressed by the unusually small wards of only six beds each, and by the ample access of daylight and fresh air. Equipment now commonplace in hospitals but new in 1910 attracted the eyes of newspaper men: glass partitions between beds in isolation wards; labyrinth entrances to X-ray dark rooms, excluding light but allowing free passage without need for doors; foot-operated faucets on surgical hand-basins. The equipment for hydrotherapy was the most advanced in the United States. The diet kitchen was unusual in its relative size and completeness.[19] The small building for infectious diseases had a special ventilating system, designed to avoid cross-currents of air passing from one patient to another, by drawing air separately from each cubicle. This was considered a notable forward step in hospital hygiene, but the emphasis on removal of noxious air was actually a survival of antiquated notions about the conveyance of infections.[20] The Board in fact had taken one step backward when the isolation wards, originally intended to be located in the main hospital building, were erected as a separate two-story pavilion. Apparently this was done to make possible the separate ventilating system opening through the roof; but the whole arrangement was unnecessary and was finally abandoned in 1951 when the isolation pavilion was converted into the present nurses' dormitory. Advancing knowledge of infectious diseases and their transmission made unnecessary the elaborate precautions against infection from the air.

The wards and laboratories, so amply equipped, were operated by an unusually well-trained staff. Nursing was done entirely by salaried graduate nurses. Cole chose to eliminate the burden of the usual nurses' training school, thus also protecting the staff from the inconvenience of working with inexperienced pupil nurses. Miss Nancy Ellicott, a graduate of the School of Nursing of the Johns Hopkins Hospital, became the first superintendent of nursing. Member of a prominent Maryland family and an accomplished sportswoman, Miss Ellicott had much of the spirit and talent of her great-grandfather's brother Andrew Ellicott, the mathematician and explorer who in 1789 made the first topographical survey of the Niagara River. Endowed with considerable mechanical ingenuity, she devised several mechanical appliances at Johns Hopkins, including a back rest for bed patients. Such versatility excellently qualified Miss Ellicott for her part in organizing a new hospital, and at The Rockefeller Institute her resourcefulness was often needed. She learned, for example, how to run the hospital's laundry machines and when necessary substituted for the regular operator. Withal she could on occasion charm the most sophisticated acquaintance. Henry James the novelist, visiting the hospital in 1912 under Jerome Greene's guidance, on being introduced to Miss Ellicott solemnly remarked, "I have been greatly impressed by the beauty and efficiency of this place, all of which, if you will permit me to say so, is admirably embodied in your own person."[21] With these personal gifts Miss Ellicott easily dominated the housekeeping and nursing staffs of the hospital, although not without minor conflicts of authority with the doctors and the business manager. A gentler though no less effective administrator, Miss Mary B. Thompson, also from the Johns Hopkins Hospital, was her able assistant.

Naturally, the opening of the hospital, combined with the sensational announcement of the $3,800,000 of additional endowment for the Institute, attracted widespread attention. The leading New York newspapers, warmly sympathetic, were carefully briefed when the Board of Scientific Directors had an important announcement to make. The *Times* summarized the aims of the new hospital in words that might have been (and perhaps were) supplied by Prudden:

> From the standpoint of the sick man or woman or child this will mean the enlisting of all known forces that can fight for his recovery — diagnosis, medical treatment, diet, and nursing, under conditions as favorable as the founder's generosity and the wisdom of his advisers could control. From the standpoint of medical science it will mean an almost unequalled opportunity for study — the study of selected cases, with freedom to concentrate all the resources of medical knowledge and the most approved scientific methods, if need be, on a single disease.[22]

Yet in spite of the enthusiasm, the Board's spokesman was aware also of an undercurrent of suspicion. In the darker corners of the human mind a lingering dread of the medicine man's incantations gives rise to strange imagining about what goes on in laboratories. New York City had its "Doctor's Mob" in 1788 when the anatomy teachers were accused of dissecting stolen bodies. The antivivisection campaign of 1907–

SIMON FLEXNER

Small bronze at left by Anna M. Hyatt, shows Dr. William H. Welch
en route to the Ming Tombs near Peking in 1915

CHRISTIAN A. HERTER

1909 exploited similar apprehensions. A hospital beside a research laboratory known to conduct experiments on animals was *ipso facto* suspect of experimenting on human beings. When briefing the reporters, the Board saw fit to point out specifically that patients were not to be used as guinea pigs. The newspapers were primed to say:

> It has been supposed that a hospital connected with an Institute for Medical Research would be one in which the patients were to be experimented upon, but the trustees wish it understood clearly that this is not the case. By filling the hospital with only three or four kinds of disease it will be possible for the staff to concentrate upon these for the purpose of study. The hospital would have no right and does not expect to take any liberties with the patients.[23]

Fortunately the greater public had no such fears. Before the opening day seventy persons had asked to be admitted as patients, and in the course of the next four months more than two thousand applications were received.[24]

Rufus Cole chose his first resident staff with the advice of Flexner. With remarkable wisdom they recruited a group of young men who were nearly all destined to reach high professional distinction. The first senior resident was G. Canby Robinson, a Johns Hopkins graduate with several years' experience in pathology as well as in clinical medicine. He had been resident physician at the Pennsylvania Hospital and director of the pathological laboratory of the Presbyterian Hospital of Philadelphia. Before moving to New York he had been in Munich for the summer, studying diseases of the heart in company with his friend George Draper, a graduate of the College of Physicians and Surgeons of Columbia University, who now also joined the Rockefeller Hospital staff. Homer F. Swift came from the New York University School of Medicine, where he had been teaching pathology and dermatology. Under the influence of his uncle, John A. Fordyce, a distinguished dermatologist, he was ready to begin the research on syphilis that occupied him for years. Henry K. Marks, graduate of Harvard Medical School and intern at Massachusetts General Hospital, had studied at Berlin, Munich, and Paris, on one of The Rockefeller Institute's fellowship grants. Alphonse Raymond Dochez, also from the fellowship group, was already on the research staff of the Institute and was now transferred to the hospital.

Francis H. McCrudden, a graduate of the Massachusetts Institute of

Technology and of Harvard Medical School, took charge of the chemical laboratories of the hospital. In January 1911 Francis W. Peabody joined the staff. He was a Harvard graduate, had been on the resident staff of the Massachusetts General and the Johns Hopkins hospitals, and had spent six months with the great German biochemist Emil Fischer. About the same time came Alfred E. Cohn, who had studied medicine at the College of Physicians and Surgeons and then gone abroad for postgraduate experience, working on the pathology of the heart and on heart disease with Sir Thomas Lewis of London. Two other men came that year: Arthur W. M. Ellis (now Sir Arthur, later Regius Professor of Medicine at Oxford), a graduate of Toronto University; and Florentin Medigreceanu, a young Rumanian, who had worked in chemistry at Berlin and at the Pasteur Institute. During 1912 Francis R. Fraser (now Sir Francis) of Edinburgh joined Alfred Cohn's physiological laboratory for a couple of years, and Frederic Hanes, a Johns Hopkins graduate with postgraduate training at Columbia, was on the staff for a few months.

Following out the basic idea of Flexner and Herter that the hospital should concentrate upon only a few diseases at a time, five were chosen for the first attack: poliomyelitis, lobar pneumonia, syphilis, heart disease, and intestinal infantilism. Concerning these diseases the investigators thought they might, with the aid of the laboratory sciences, break through the walls of current ignorance. The first three presented primarily problems of infection, but at different levels of knowledge. Poliomyelitis was deeply mysterious. Landsteiner's work of 1909 and Flexner's of 1910 had shown a filtrable virus to be its cause, but the virus had not been cultivated and the mode of its transmission was not known. Investigation would have to begin in the dark. Lobar pneumonia was better understood. The microbe that causes it, the pneumococcus, could readily be cultivated, and German investigators had just learned that there are several strains or types. The investigation therefore would concern both the biology of the disease-producing organism and the defensive reactions of the patient. Studies of syphilis were still further advanced. The specific germ, the *Spirochaeta pallida* (since renamed *Treponema pallidum*), was known, and Paul Ehrlich of Frankfurt had just found a curative drug, Salvarsan, or "606." In this case chemistry was coming to the support of bacteriology, and the Rockefeller investigators could apply the methods of both to their study. Heart disease of the familiar sort (valvular and myocardial) called chiefly for the methods of physiology, by which the action of the failing heart and circulation could be analyzed and compared with that of healthy persons.

Intestinal infantilism was on the list because Christian Herter wanted to study it. He had identified by that name (now no longer used) a peculiar form of malnutrition in infants, characterized by severe intestinal disturbances and retardation of growth that sometimes approaches dwarfism. Judging from the hospital records and photographs of children admitted in 1910–1911, this was what is now well known to pediatricians as celiac disease.[25] Herter thought that bacteriology and biochemistry could contribute to the understanding and relief of this obscure ailment, and with his excellent knowledge of both he was eager to lead the work. His health, however, was now rapidly failing, and in September 1910 his medical advisers at long last discovered that his illness was organic and hopeless. After Herter's death on December 5, 1910, at the age of forty-five, McCrudden carried on the metabolic study of "intestinal infantilism" for a couple of years. He and Helen L. Fales were the first to observe the excessive excretion of calcium salts by way of the intestines and the weakness of bone structure (osteoporosis) resulting from the calcium deficiency thus produced. Their observations fully explained the bone deformities and dwarfism of extreme cases of celiac disease, to which Herter had called attention years before.

As his own special problem Cole chose acute lobar pneumonia. This was so common in the nineteenth century that Osler called it "the captain of the men of death," using the phrase John Bunyan applied to "consumption" (tuberculosis). In the cities of the eastern seaboard it was primarily a disease of males, striking down not only the aged, but robust men in the prime of life. The pneumococcus, a somewhat peculiar bacterium, discovered by Louis Pasteur in 1880–1881, so inflames the lung that the air spaces fill up with consolidated blood and pus throughout one or more lobes, with consequent impairment of respiration. The heart also is often damaged by toxic action of the bacilli. In the early nineteen hundreds there was no specific way to combat the inflammatory and toxic effects of the pneumococcus and, consequently, more than twenty per cent of the patients died. Up to 1940 this was the commonest kind of pneumonia, but after that its prevalence declined, as compared with pneumonias produced by other bacteria and by viruses, which consolidate scattered patches of lung tissue rather than whole lobes. Yet in spite of this change lobar pneumonia was in 1957 still killing 13,000 people every year in the United States.[26] Eventually, it is hoped, penicillin and other antibiotics will eradicate it.

Cole's aim was to produce an immune serum against the pneumococcus by inoculating horses with gradually increasing quantities of the germs, thus eliciting in the horse's blood "antibodies," that is to say, chemical substances capable of destroying germs or neutralizing their toxic products. This was the method by which Emil von Behring had attacked diphtheria and Flexner had achieved partial success with epidemic cerebrospinal meningitis. These victories had raised high hopes that protective serums might be found against many more diseases caused by specific organisms, but time was to show that not all man's bacterial enemies are as easily fought by immune serum as is the diphtheria bacillus. Cole and the two juniors who worked with him, Dochez and Marks, ran into serious difficulties. As others abroad had already discovered, the pneumococci isolated from patients represented several strains differing in virulence. They found also that these strains, most unfortunately, differ sufficiently in their chemical nature to elicit somewhat different antibodies in the host's blood, therefore necessitating a different serum against each of the four types they had identified. By the end of 1912 Cole and Dochez had developed a serum for use against Type I, and were working toward one for each of the other types.

To ascertain the type present in a given case of pneumonia, they adopted an ingenious procedure. The patient's sputum was injected into the peritoneal cavity of a white mouse, where the pneumococci multiplied and in a few hours caused an inflammation which filled the cavity with fluid. The fluid, laden with pneumococci, was drawn off with a hypodermic syringe and mixed, in small glass vessels, with blood serum from a series of rabbits previously immunized with one or another type of pneumococcus. In that particular vessel which contained immune serum of the type corresponding to the patient's pneumococci, a telltale clumping of germs occurred. The test required one or two mice and about half a day's time. Selective treatment based upon this "typing" definitely lowered the mortality rate. The test was at once widely adopted. Breeders of white mice had a seller's market for many years, and in 1917–1919 when the concentration of men in military camps brought many cases of lobar pneumonia into army hospitals, there were scarcely enough mice in the country to supply the demand.

Further efforts to control lobar pneumonia called for analysis of the slight chemical differences that gave each strain of pneumococci power to elicit its own particular antibody. The problem would require long effort by a man who combined thorough knowledge of bacteriology with a talent for chemistry. Cole found such a man in Oswald T. Avery, who joined the staff of the hospital in 1913 and spent the rest of his career investigating the chemistry of pneumococci. With Dochez, already at work with Cole upon pneumonia, he formed a close professional association and lifelong friendship in which the two constantly shared aims and ideas. Avery and his associates soon located the specific immunity-inducing substances in the capsule that surrounds the bacterium, which is composed of polysaccharides, *i.e.*, sugars linked into very complex compounds, differing slightly in the various strains of pneumococci. The story of this work, by which Avery helped to found and lead a new branch of science, immunochemistry, will be resumed later. Here it will suffice to mention that scientific methods applied at The Rockefeller Institute Hospital developed the study of a disease in all its aspects from fundamental chemistry and biology to the treatment of patients.

The attack on lobar pneumonia begun by Cole and carried on by Avery and Dochez was one of the most elegant performances, from the standpoint of both theory and technique, in the history of bacteriology. As far as the cure of the patient is concerned, much of this work was made obsolete by the sulfa drugs and the natural antibiotics, which fortunately attack all strains of pneumococci with equal vigor. For years, however, the use of immune serum, such as that first developed at The Rockefeller Institute, was the only specific treatment of lobar pneumonia; physicians credited it with saving thousands of lives the world over. Even after the direct application of this work ceased, its benefits continue through the stimulus it gave to better study of acute lung disease and by its contributions to the epidemiology of pneumonia and to immunochemistry.

Homer Swift took charge of the studies on syphilis. The Rockefeller Institute had special reasons for its interest in this disease. As mentioned in the preceding chapter, Noguchi and Flexner had been the first in America to confirm Fritz Schaudinn's discovery of the specific parasite of syphilis, the microscopic protozoan called *Spirochaeta pallida* or *Treponema pallidum*. The Institute moreover had already helped to foster discovery of a curative drug. Henry Marks, while visiting Ehrlich's institute in Frankfurt early in 1909, reported to Flexner that lack of funds was holding back its work in chemotherapy. Ehrlich, as Flexner knew, had the idea that the spirochete of syphilis would not prove sensitive to immunity reactions and must be attacked by a chemical agent. This idea called for slow, expensive screening of hundreds of promising compounds to find one that would destroy the parasites without injuring the patient. On a recommendation by the Board, Rockefeller made a special grant of $10,000 to Ehrlich through the Institute.[27] The triumphant result, "606," or Salvarsan, tried out by Ehrlich's assistant Hata, was announced in 1910, just as the Rockefeller Hospital was opened. Ehrlich was of course favorably inclined toward the Institute because of this gift and wanted his new treatment to be tested and evaluated there.

A third reason for the Institute's special interest in syphilis stemmed from Flexner's success in reducing the death rate from epidemic cerebrospinal meningitis by injecting immune serum directly into the spinal canal. This gave a hint for the treatment of syphilis of the central nervous system, a most intractable form of this protean disease, producing locomotor ataxia, general paresis, and other grave disorders of the body and mind. Here too the possibility existed that the parasites might be attacked in the very tissues they had invaded. Homer Swift and Arthur Ellis found that Salvarsan, injected into a vein, failed to get into the subarachnoid space around the brain and spinal cord in an effective amount. It was too irritating to the nervous system to be injected directly into the spinal canal. Swift and Ellis therefore worked out an ingenious method for combining the arsenical compound with blood to make it tolerable to the sensitive nervous tissues. First they injected a solution of Salvarsan into the patient's veins, and then after a few hours obtained the serum, now heavily laden with the drug, by bleeding him. The serum was then injected into the spinal canal. A young member of the hospital staff, Alan M. Chesney, who shared in this study, soon afterward returned to Baltimore, where he has had a long and distinguished career in the medical study and care of syphilis and as the devoted dean of the Johns Hopkins Medical School. The Swift-Ellis treatment proved beneficial in many cases of tabes dorsalis (the form of syphilis characterized by locomotor ataxia) and in some other cases of syphilitic damage to the nervous system.

G. Canby Robinson and George Draper led the work on the heart and circulatory system. At that time it was possible to diagnose fairly well the nature and extent of the damage underlying heart failure resulting from one of the commoner cardiac lesions, such as the failure of a damaged valve to close completely, narrowing of the passage at the site of one of the valves, general weakness of the heart muscle, or occlusion of a coronary artery. There was, however, no accurate means of discovering how much these conditions impaired the power of the heart to pump blood, nor to what extent the patient's physical activity had to be limited. The two young men applied standard physiological methods to these problems, using the variations of pulse rate and of blood pressure during exercise and rest. They made some progress in this way, but soon acquired a novel instrument with much sharper diagnostic powers. This was the electrocardiograph in its first crude form employing the string galvanometer.

Only seven years before, in 1903, Willem Einthoven of Leyden invented this very sensitive device for registering electric currents by photographing the deflections of an exceedingly fine thread suspended between the poles of a strong electromagnet. It was capable of responding to the tiny currents produced by the muscular contractions of the heart. When these were led to the galvanometer from various points on the body the pattern they traced could be interpreted to show the site and extent of damage to the heart. The Rockefeller electrocardiograph, set up with the aid of Horatio B. Williams, a physician attached to the Columbia University physiology department, was first used on March 5, 1911. It was at this time that Alfred E. Cohn, one of the few Americans with experience in electrocardiography, was added to the staff. The Rockefeller instrument was the third such apparatus in New York City and the fifth in the nation; thus the Institute shared in the beginnings of electrocardiography in America.

Nowadays the electrocardiograph, a self-contained electronic device, is wheeled to the bedside; in 1911 Robinson and Draper's huge galvanometer required a whole laboratory. It was fastened to a wall, and wires running through the hospital from wet sponges bound to the patient's trunk and arms connected him to the instrument. By means of a portable telephone the doctor at the bedside gave instructions to the operator at the distant "heart station." This team worked mainly by making careful comparison of the electrocardiograms of cardiac patients with the signs and symptoms noted by the older diagnostic methods, and with the post-mortem findings in patients who died. This was exploratory work, useful chiefly in learning how to use the electrocardiograph for precise diagnosis. In addition, Robinson, in order to investigate the nature and cause of certain types of heart failure, studied experimental disturbances of the heartbeat which he produced by electrical shock applied directly to the heart in dogs. In the long run it was Cohn who carried on extended research on heart disease in the Rockefeller Hospital. Draper, always eager for new experiences, left in 1912 to enter practice in New York City, and later became professor of medicine at the College of Physicians and Surgeons. Robinson was called to St. Louis in 1913 to help reorganize the Washington University medical school, of which he later became dean.

High hopes attended Cole's choice of poliomyelitis as one of the five diseases for intensive study. It seemed to present exactly the kind of problem The Rockefeller Institute was prepared to deal with effectively. Skillful bacteriologists ought to be able in short order, it seemed, to isolate the mysterious infectious agent, even though, as they knew by 1910, they were dealing with a filtrable virus instead of a bacterium. Yet even if they produced a curative serum or vaccine, it could not be used against this peculiar disease without further information obtainable only by intensive clinical investigation. Poliomyelitis usually begins as a mild general illness, without any specifically characteristic sign or symptom; a few days later the sudden onset of paralysis reveals that the spinal cord has already been seriously damaged. To forestall this, the physician would have to recognize the disease in its first stage. Early diagnosis was also necessary for preventing spread of the infection from child to child in the home, and from house to house. Obviously, the hospital could make a crucial contribution to the recognition of poliomyelitis in the earliest stage by describing every symptom that keen observers could detect.

The opportunity came in the summer of 1911, when infantile paralysis broke out again in New York. The isolation building was filled all summer with patients, most of whom developed severe paralysis. This was before the invention of effective respirators or "iron lungs," and when, in some of these children, the respiratory center in the brain was involved, the physicians could only stand helplessly at the bedside and watch the little patient die of suffocation. Francis Peabody, A. R. Dochez, and George Draper gave their full time to the study of poliomyelitis that summer, and from these scenes of suffering and grief wrought out a monograph on the clinical picture of the disease that ranks among the classics of descriptive medicine. Rufus Cole recognized the necessity of this emergency service and praised the three physicians for carrying out their poignant task so well, but it was after all, he felt, merely another competent study of the natural history of disease. He would have been happier if his young men could have devoted their time to more fundamental investigations.[28] The exact knowledge obtained was not immediately useful, for the laboratories were unable to produce a remedy against the effect of poliomyelitis virus in time to use what the hospital men had learned about early diagnosis. Even today it is not possible to head off paralysis once the infection is established in the nervous system. As Flexner realized in 1911, the fight against poliomyelitis would have to be won by prevention, and not by cure.

The study of human illness can never be entirely impersonal as is most other research. To their patients the staff showed themselves as humane as they were scientific. Gates, always delighted by good reports from the Institute, sent Flexner a friend's message about one of the earliest patients: "My dear sister left the hospital with real regret. She said that if she were not going back there for treatment she believed she would have broken down and cried when she left. No words could express her deep feelings toward them all." To this Gates added, "Think of that! Your hospital organization must be of the choicest quality." A few years later, trying to persuade Rockefeller, Sr., to entrust himself to the hospital for a medical checkup, Gates wrote (as if it were still a matter of remark that men dedicated to research could also be kind and considerate doctors), "The physicians are extremely polite, gentle, and courteous, and the nurses are the very paragons of their tribe."[29]

Canby Robinson, the first senior resident, years later recorded his recollections of life in The Rockefeller Institute's hospital during the two and a half years in which he lived and worked there. He portrays a serious group of young men linked by common interest in clinical research, and working together in great amity. "Life in the hospital was full of joy," he wrote. "A few patients in whom we had special and intensive interest; laboratories such as none of us had ever before seen in any clinic; varied interests both within and without the realm of medicine; the East River with its great span of light at night, and its lapping waters; a blazing hearth about which we gathered after dinner." Sir Arthur Ellis wrote to Robinson from Oxford in 1943, "I have often thought what a remarkable act of faith it was, that we should all have been there consciously attempting to fit ourselves for full-time posts in medicine, when no such jobs existed anywhere."[30]

They did not all secure full-time posts, but nearly all won medical professorships or research posts of equivalent rank. Robinson was to be successively head of two medical schools, Vanderbilt and Cornell; Ellis became professor at London Hospital and later Regius Professor at Oxford; Fraser was the first full-time professor at St. Bartholomew's, London; Cohn had a fine career in The Rockefeller Institute, and Swift came back to it from Presbyterian Hospital, both rising to be Members; Draper and Dochez held chairs in Columbia University, the latter in time being elected a trustee of The Rockefeller Institute; Peabody reached the chair of medicine at Harvard before his untimely death at the age of forty-six; Hanes became professor of medicine at Duke University, and McCrudden professor of applied therapeutics at Tufts Medical School. Thus almost all of the group went to the top ranks of academic and scientific medicine. Medigreceanu died in World War I, too soon to show his full powers; Marks, after a short career as a practicing neurologist in New York City, turned novelist and settled in Paris.

Rufus Cole led his brilliant group of house officers by personal example rather than by executive pressure, avoiding the creation of a hierarchy. While he managed the hospital successfully, Cole was more interested in research than in administration. The young physicians profited from his ideals by working at his side.

Cole's effort to create a research group out of his resident staff at first set them apart from the laboratory men in the older division of the Institute. In view of the general state of medical education in this country at the time, it was open to doubt whether young physicians could carry on research worthy of the high level already set in the adjacent laboratories. To establish the qualifications of the able group he had assembled, Cole felt strongly that they should work independently upon their own problems; otherwise there was a risk that the hospital would be only a place where pathologists, bacteriologists, and physiologists could test ideas developed in other laboratories and obtain materials for chemical and metabolic studies. Such use of the hospital would have required a pattern of organization much like that originally drawn up by Herter, in which the junior hospital residents were to be medical attendants rather than investigators.

When in 1911 Cole's attitude was questioned in the Board of Scientific Directors, he gave Flexner a forthright statement of his position. Men who were studying disease clinically, he wrote, had the right to go as deeply into its fundamental nature as their training allowed, and in The Rockefeller Institute's hospital every man who was caring for patients should also be engaged in more fundamental study. It had required some energy and effort, he continued, to get the men to adopt this view, but they were all now convinced of its soundness, and he hoped that some of them, at least, might share in the revolution, or evolution, of clinical medicine that was bound to come. Of course, wrote Cole, collaborative studies by the hospital and Institute laboratories might be extremely valuable, but unless the hospital first accomplished something independently, the other laboratories would never respect its work. Cooperation must develop spontaneously.[31]

The young men of the hospital staff well knew that Cole had established their right to a place in the ranks of investigative science. When they went away to help build other centers of research and teaching, they took with them the inspiration his stand had given them. Thus the Hospital of The Rockefeller Institute, probably more than any one other institution, fostered that evolution of medical science in America which Cole first prophesied and then fostered. In the university clinics of this country, where once only a few pioneering physicians attempted the basic investigation of disease, today many hundreds are at work. Science and the healing art are now marching hand in hand.

CHAPTER FIVE

The Rising Tide of Research

Inflammation; the first virus tumors; discovery of spirochetes in the paretic cord and brain. Chemistry of "complex derivatives"; nucleic acids; ribose. Physiology: magnesium inhibition; artificial respiration, intratracheal anesthesia. General physiology: chemistry of the duration of life; antagonistic salt action; electrical activity of protoplasm. Tissue culture. Infant metabolism and nutrition.

THE FALL OF 1910 found The Rockefeller Institute in full activity. Thirty scientists were now at work in the laboratory department, and the eight hospital physicians had promptly filled their wards with patients in five categories of diseases under investigation. The Institute's *Journal of Experimental Medicine* provided for publication of the numerous scientific reports that were flowing from both groups and from other sources. Rockefeller's latest and largest gift had made the enterprise financially secure, and the administrative machinery was running smoothly under the new Board of Trustees and the Scientific Directors. At the end of the year Christian Herter died of the intractable disease that had long wasted his strength; Theodore C. Janeway, who had been considered with Cole for the directorship of the hospital and was now professor of medicine at Columbia, took Herter's place on the Board of Scientific Directors.

In spite of executive duties which ever grew more exacting even with an admirable business manager to help him, Flexner continued to lead research work. He alone, as yet, among the Institute's staff, was prepared to carry on investigations on human infectious diseases in a manner which captured the public imagination and won the confidence of the founders of the Institute, needed to assure its permanency. In his laboratory, however, Flexner had to depend more and more upon co-workers and assistants. Meanwhile two of them had left, James W. Jobling and Eugene L. Opie, the first two of a long line of men who carried the Institute's influence into the medical schools. Jobling, who had worked closely with Flexner, went to the Michael Reese Hospital in Chicago in 1909, on his way to a career as professor of pathology at Vanderbilt and later at Columbia.

Opie's brilliant independent work resulted in 1910 in a call to a chair at Washington University, St. Louis, six years after that school had first tried to secure him. One of the first at the Institute to apply chemical methods to the riddles of pathology, Opie had devoted himself while there to investigating the role of protein-digesting enzymes in the process of inflammation. In a series of papers from 1905 to 1911 he showed that the white blood cells which swarm into a region damaged by infection, where an abscess or exudate is forming, carry proteolytic enzymes that not only attack the foreign organism, but also clear away the accumulated debris as the infection subsides. Against them the blood and tissue fluids provide anti-enzymes, which prevent them from damaging or destroying the surrounding tissues. The progress of the inflammatory process depends, at least in part, upon the outcome of this chemical warfare in the tissues. By pitting the antagonist substances against each other, in experiments upon animals and also by observation *in vitro,* that is to say in test tubes or other laboratory vessels, Opie was able to observe the contest and evaluate the outcome. His papers are basic to present-day understanding of the subject, and on some difficult questions still give the last word.

When Jobling left, Flexner wanted someone to take over and expand the work on cancer which had led, as mentioned in Chapter 3, to the discovery and perpetuation of the Flexner-Jobling rat carcinoma. He offered the post to a young pathologist, Peyton Rous, trained at the Johns Hopkins Medical School and instructor for two years at the University of Michigan. Rous was reluctant, for there seemed to be no hope of fundamental discoveries in the field. Pathologists had studied numerous forms of human malignant tumors under the microscope without finding their cause and for years had been transplanting animal tumors with no better success. When Rous left Johns Hopkins, his master, Welch, had told him, "Whatever you do, don't commit yourself to the cancer problem."[1] But

Flexner was irresistible and Rous accepted the call, joining the Institute in 1909.

Never was such a challenge more promptly taken up. Within a few weeks after he began work, the young man, by a series of revolutionary discoveries, had reopened the whole question of the cause of cancer. One day a breeder of chickens brought to Rous's laboratory a hen with a large lump on its leg. Rous sectioned a bit of this tumor for microscopic study and found it to be a connective-tissue cancer of the type called spindle-cell sarcoma, which in mammals and man is often highly malignant. When Rous inoculated other chickens with small portions of the tumor, it proved to be transmissible, at first only to fowls of the same pure breed, but later, growing more malignant, to almost any chicken. Seeding itself through the whole body by way of the blood stream, it set up secondary growths, ultimately killing the affected bird. It exhibited, in short, the typical behavior of a malignant tumor.

Rous ground up some of the malignant tissue in salt solution and passed it through filter paper, which is quite sufficient to strain out cancer cells, yet the filtered extract still produced sarcoma when injected into chickens. Next he passed it through an earthenware filter that held back not only the tumor cells but also small bacteria added to test the filter. The filtrate still carried the power to induce sarcoma in healthy chickens. Without doubt, a virus, too small to be seen with the microscope, was causing the tumor, just as similar viruses were already known to cause foot-and-mouth disease, rabies, and — as Flexner had recently shown — poliomyelitis.

The virus of chicken sarcoma could be grown only in living chicken tissues, evidently depending upon them for its ability to reproduce itself, but Rous and his assistant, James B. Murphy, demonstrated in two ways that the virus is a separate entity. First, Rous succeeded in killing the cells, by storing tumor tissue in glycerine or by exposing it to ultraviolet radiation, without destroying the virus. Murphy afterward did the same by freezing and drying the malignant tissue. His demonstration that the virus could still be transmitted by the dried material was the first successful application of the process of lyophilization, now widely used in biological research. Second, Rous showed that chickens inoculated with the virus-infected tumor cells exhibit two kinds of resistance: the usual antagonism to the cells of another individual, noted in all grafting experiments, and also a specific resistance to the virus itself, resulting from the production of antibodies similar to those produced against harmful bacteria. Once harbored within living cells, the virus is protected against this specific resistance. Later Rous and his assistants discovered several other chicken tumors, each caused by a distinctive virus, and Rous showed that such a virus could give rise to tumors while revealing no other sign of its presence.

In order to learn whether the age of the host influences the development of chicken sarcoma — as it does that of non-malignant grafts — Rous and Murphy implanted the tumor in chick embryos, where it grew with far greater rapidity than in adult fowls. The virus itself, moreover, gave rise to tumors on the embryonic membranes of the developing chick. This was the first use of embryos of any kind for the maintenance of grafted tumors and as a medium for growing viruses. Thus Rous's work was not only significant for the study of cancer; it also provided a starting point for later investigations of the general principles of virus growth and infectivity. The successful cultivation, decades later, of many disease viruses, and the production of vaccines against them, stem from this pioneer work of 1912. Somewhat later Murphy found independently that rat and mouse tumors, which would grow only in adults of the species in which they originated, would grow also in chick embryos. Still later other investigators showed that human tumors would do the same, and thus chick embryos implanted with tumors are nowadays used by thousands in the search for substances that will kill cancer.

Naturally the demonstration that a filtrable virus is the cause of a malignant tumor of a kind well known in human pathology set up a world-wide discussion among cancer investigators, some of whom leaped to the conclusion that all cancer is of viral origin. Half a century later there is still no certainty about the cause of malignant disease in its totality. New discoveries pointing to a viral origin of human and mammalian cancer are offset by the continuing failure to recover viruses from most kinds of malignant tumors that confront the physician. Meanwhile, to this day, no discussion of the subject is possible without reference to the discoveries of Peyton Rous, made from 1909 to 1914.[2]

Flexner's senior laboratory associate after Opie left was the young Japanese pathologist brought with him from Philadelphia, Hideyo Noguchi. Conscious of his provincial education, willing to slave away his days and nights in the laboratory to win himself a great name in the world of science, Noguchi was fast succeeding in that aim, through his own talents and Flexner's affectionate guidance and patient teaching.[3] Noguchi was much interested in immunology, then a very live subject because of the growing use of antitoxic sera, and when he felt that he had done all he could with the problem of snake venom, set for him in 1900 by Flexner and Weir Mitchell, he turned to highly technical problems of complement fixation and the immunology of syphilis. Flexner did not approve of this, perhaps feeling that Noguchi, better at practical experimentation than logical analysis, might lose his way in the maze of current immunological theory. Furthermore, he had a greater project for Noguchi, in continuation of their joint work of 1905 when the two had so promptly confirmed the presence of Schaudinn's spirochete in syphilitic sores. Flexner wanted Noguchi to cultivate this spirochete, and a colleague recalls that one day Noguchi came to him in despair, because the Director would not buy a goat that he needed for his immunological work. "He won't give me a goat! Why won't Dr. Flexner buy me a goat?" he burst out.[4] There is even a legend that Flexner, finding Noguchi's laboratory table clandestinely laden with serum tubes, took his umbrella and swept them all to the floor — an implausible tale, symbolic at best, for Flexner was not an impulsive man nor given to smashing valuable equipment.

After publishing his work on immunology, Noguchi began his efforts to cultivate *Treponema pallidum*.[5] He was not the first to try. Five or six European laboratories had attempted the feat immediately after Schaudinn's discovery of the germ, but without success. How to begin was Noguchi's first problem. Spirochetes could not be cultivated directly from a syphilitic sore, swarming with bacteria that would quickly outgrow them. The syphilitic poison will, however, grow and multiply in a rabbit's testicle while the contaminating bacteria largely die out, leaving a more or less pure culture of spirochetes. Noguchi followed this up in characteristically hectic fashion, inoculating rabbits with ten different human strains, setting up hundreds of culture tubes filled with many kinds of nutritive media, sampling the cultures on thousands of microscope slides. At last some of the tubes became clouded with the growth of an organism looking like typical *Treponema*. Almost all the cultures were, however, still contaminated with bacteria. To get rid of these,

The first laboratory buildings of The Rockefeller Institute
at Lexington Avenue and East Fiftieth Street

THEOBALD SMITH

Noguchi ingeniously made his cultures in an inner tube of earthenware (a Berkefeld filter tube) suspended in an outer glass tube of the culture medium. The active, sinuous spirochetes, he found, could wriggle through the pores of the filter while the less motile bacteria stayed behind. Out of the ten strains kept going in rabbits, six were at length cultivated in this way. When Noguchi injected portions of the culture into the testicles of fresh rabbits, seemingly typical syphilitic orchitis developed.

Noguchi's report of 1911 still reads convincingly, but subsequent workers have never succeeded in growing the true parasite of syphilis by his (or any other) method. He had certainly grown *in vitro* a spirochete obtained from syphilitic tissue. It remains an open question whether he had really succeeded, by his peculiar skills that no one else could duplicate, in cultivating *Treponema pallidum,* or had merely grown one of the harmless saprophytic spirochetes closely resembling it in form and movement, which inhabit the mouth, genital orifices, and other moist regions of the body. Eighteen years after Noguchi's announcement and a year after his death, two qualified investigators summed up the whole story. Having vainly tried to cultivate *Treponema pallidum* by Noguchi's method and by all the methods of thirty other workers, their verdict was that although Noguchi's cultures are more likely to have contained *Treponema pallidum* than most of the others, his claim cannot be accepted so long as no one else can verify it. There the matter still stands a half century after Noguchi published his work.[6]

To another syphilis problem Noguchi made an all-important contribution. Two grave diseases of the central nervous system, general paresis and spinal tabes ("locomotor ataxia"), were generally thought to be late results of chronic syphilis, so regularly had that disease preceded them. In textbooks such as that of Osler they were termed parasyphilitic diseases. The connection was not proven, investigators having looked in vain for the spirochete in the brains and spinal cords of persons dying of those diseases. Noguchi brought to the quest no new method, but only his own high-strung determination, persistence, and visual acuity. Collecting 200 brains from cases of general paresis and twelve tabetic spinal cords, he made innumerable sections — staining them by various methods in batches of 200 each — and tortured his eyes through long nights at the microscope, intently looking for the tiny spiral threads that could too easily hide themselves among the interwoven fibers of the brain. Working at home all one night in 1912, he at last, as dawn approached, came upon the organisms in one of his slides, sparsely scattered through the substance of the brain. Greatly excited, he left his microscope on the dining table and hurried through the streets to call Flexner out of bed at 5 A.M. Coming with amused tranquillity, Flexner shared Noguchi's excitement when he too saw the spirochetes.[7] Once Noguchi knew where to look in the paretic brains, he found the spirochetes quite readily again and again; in the tabetic spinal cords they were also found, though never easy to see. Thus Noguchi had proved conclusively that general paresis and tabes dorsalis are indeed late stages of tertiary syphilis of the brain and spinal cord respectively. For this achievement the Association of American Physicians gave him in 1925 the first award of its prized Kober Medal.

Three other of Flexner's early assistants left for important posts elsewhere. Wilfred H. Manwaring, with Flexner from 1906 to 1913, devoted himself to the fields of phagocytosis and of immunity, in the latter of which he became a distinguished authority during his long incumbency of the chair of bacteriology and experimental pathology at Stanford University. Richard V. Lamar, at the Institute from 1907 to 1913, chiefly studying the pneumococcus, became professor of pathology and bacteriology at the University of Georgia's medical college. Martha Wollstein, recipient of one of the early grants-in-aid, joined Flexner from 1907 to 1921, publishing a variety of studies on pathogenic microorganisms; after leaving she was for many years pathologist to the Babies' Hospital and an associate professor at Columbia University, winning a considerable reputation as a pediatric pathologist.

IN THE biochemical laboratory on the second floor of the main building, Phoebus Levene was at work on a half-dozen problems at once. His was a one-man division until 1907, when competent young assistants and Fellows began to gather round him. Among them were G. W. Heimrod, Walter A. Jacobs, Gustave M. Meyer, Donald D. Van Slyke, and Frederick B. LaForge, all of whom except Heimrod carried on long careers in chemistry. Heimrod lost his eyesight in a laboratory accident in 1909, two years after he joined the Institute, and worked under that great handicap until his death in 1917. When Levene began his career, the major kinds of chemical constituents of living organisms had been identified but by no means fully analyzed. As he himself outlined contemporary knowledge in an early paper, "The principal elements are proteins, carbohydrates, fats, and their complex derivatives, nucleoproteins, glycoproteins, lipoids. There are also enzymes, and finally the products of cell activity, hormones and extractives."[8]

In a very general sense the fats, carbohydrates, and proteins provide the substance and form of the bodily machine, its basic moving parts, and the crude fuel with which it operates. Their chemical structure was already fairly well understood. The compounds that Levene called "complex derivatives" were, however, much less known. They provide materials sensitive to stimulation from outside and inside the body, insulation for the intercommunicating system of nerves, high-energy fuel for quick movements, and specialized chemical agents for organizing the tissues and transmitting hereditary traits. The task of biochemists of Levene's generation was to isolate and understand these substances, and to work out their interactivities. He himself had been devotedly doing just this for seven or eight years before he joined the Institute, and would go on doing it for thirty-five years more. Leaving his art-filled home, daily, for the laboratory, he worked there till evening, "a small figure surrounded by large pieces of apparatus," lifting a heavy bottle or handling a big Büchner funnel as willingly as any technician, speaking English, French, German, or Russian as needed for the guidance of assistants and guest investigators.[9] Never changing his main objective, but turning from one kind of "complex derivative" to another and back again, he mastered and applied new methods as they came in from organic and physical chemistry. In his forty-seven years of active work, alone or with his assistants he published more than seven hundred papers. Most of these were relatively brief reports on specific topics, but at rare intervals he took advantage of some special occasion to present a clear, well-ordered summary of his results.

In the temporary laboratory on Fiftieth Street Levene had continued his studies, begun at the State Pathological Institute, on the nucleoproteins, substances known to exist in the nuclei of cells and therefore supposed to take part in such important life activities as cell division and fertilization of the egg. German chemists, separating the nucleoproteins and nucleic acids, found the latter to be themselves complex compounds of phosphoric acid, nitrogen-containing bases (purines and pyrimidines), and sugarlike carbohydrates. To analyze them called for step-by-step splitting apart of the compounds by various chemical means, and identification of the resulting products, a task requiring great chemical erudition and technical ingenuity. With an early assistant, Walter A. Jacobs, and later Donald D. Van Slyke, both of whom attained eminence as biochemists, Levene rapidly succeeded in identifying the specific purine bases and sugars found in several important nucleic acids, thus establishing their complete structural formulas. Emil Abderhalden of Halle, author of a famous textbook of biochemistry, wrote to Flexner in 1910, "The greatest joy during the past few months has come to me over the wonderful works of Levene, Jacobs and Van Slyke on nucleic acids. Such a great result of systematic work in so short a time has seldom occurred."[10]

These results have been absorbed, often anonymously, into the textbooks and the basic thinking of the succeeding generation of chemists and physiologists. The conclusions of a pioneer like Levene in a very complex field could, however, hardly prove entirely correct in the light of subsequent investigation. Because of his great authority, certain erroneous deductions, about chemical linkages within the nucleic acid molecule, seem to have delayed later progress until methods more searching than his were applied.[11] But men now working on the chemistry of genes should remember that Levene and Jacobs first discovered that the five-carbon sugar of one of the two most important nucleic acids is *d*-ribose, and that Levene, with his assistant Louis A. Mikeska and guest worker Takajiro Mori, later identified deoxyribose in the other. Students of the source of energy in living tissues should recall who it was that first isolated and named adenosine, basic ingredient of the fuel upon which many biological activities depend, from the firefly's glow to the human heartbeat.

During these years also Levene with Gustave Meyer began to investigate the burning of sugars in the tissues, finding an intermediate substance suspected to be methylglyoxal or an analogous compound between the sugar and lactic acid. This pointed the way to discovery of the now well-known role of pyruvic acid in glycolysis. Levene and Van Slyke studied the constitution of the proteins and of the amino acids of which they are composed, with special reference to gelatin, casein, and egg albumin. Van Slyke, already an inventor of apparatus, devised a method and special glassware for determining the amounts of nitrogen in amino acids by freeing the nitrogen and measuring it as gas. About 1913 Levene and his assistants began an extensive investigation of the composition of lipoids — compounds containing fatty acids — in the brain and other tissues, leading to better purification and classification of these substances.

In summary, Levene had opened an attack, continued throughout his long career at the Institute, upon almost all the derivatives of fats, carbohydrates, and proteins then available for study. "So long as Life continues," he once said, "the human mind will create mysteries and biochemistry will play a part in their solution."

Samuel J. Meltzer, head of the laboratory of physiology and pharmacology, was the oldest of the Institute's scientific investigators. First appointed for part time only, he soon devoted himself entirely to research and in 1907, at the age of fifty-six, was made a full Member. Meltzer's career linked the Institute's work to the great days of German physiology, for as a student at Berlin he had listened to the lectures of Helmholtz and Du Bois-Reymond and had written his doctoral dissertation under Hugo Kronecker. Settling in New York City in 1885, he built a successful medical practice; by sacrificial effort he also managed to carry on a continuous program of research, at night and during spare daytime hours, with such facilities as he could find in the city's hospitals.

Notably combining a knowledge of clinical medicine with experimental physiology, he made it a lifelong mission to foster sympathetic understanding between laboratory workers and practitioners and to put medical practice on a physiological basis. Though never called to a professorial chair, he won an odd sort of influence on a larger platform by active, hard-working participation in an incredible number of medical and scientific societies. Just before he joined The Rockefeller Institute, he brought together the experimental physiologists and zoologists of New York in the Society for Experimental Biology and Medicine, still affectionately called the "Meltzer Verein" by those old enough to remember him. A few years later he organized a group of ambitious young practitioners into the Society for Clinical Investigation, called "Young Turks" to distinguish it from the older, more staid Association of American Physicians. In these and four other professional societies which he headed at one time or another — those of the physiologists, the gastroenterologists, the thoracic surgeons, as well as the Federation of Biological Societies — Meltzer, looking like a burgomaster, with his stocky build, florid face, and sweeping mustache, presided with autocratic vigor and solemn enthusiasm, saying exactly what was in his mind. In numerous other organizations, including those of the biochemists and the pharmacologists, he served faithfully as councillor or as mere rank-and-file member. However eremitic other Members of The Rockefeller Institute might choose to be, as long as Meltzer worked there it would never lose touch with physicians and biologists outside its walls.

Because of his age and early training, the lines of investigation Meltzer brought to the Institute and developed there represented the culmination of nineteenth-century physiology, rather than the new phase, based upon physical chemistry, that men like Jacques Loeb were inaugurating. In some respects, indeed, Meltzer's ways of thinking went back to an even earlier kind of speculative physiology. Certain observations he made when working with Kronecker at Berlin led him to form a general theory about life processes, which assumed that every excitation — of nerves, muscles, heart, stomach, and intestines — is accompanied by a corresponding inhibitory impulse. "The phenomena of life," he wrote, "are the result of a compromise between two antagonistic factors, the fundamental forces of life, excitation and inhibition." Nowadays it would be said that there are many and various inhibitions, but no general principle of Inhibition with a capital "I." In the late eighteenth century Meltzer might have based a whole "system of medicine" upon his inhibition principle, as, for example, William Cullen, John Brown, and Benjamin Rush did with similar generalizations. Instead, throughout a lifetime, he ceaselessly put his hypothesis to the test of experiment.

The very first work he did at The Rockefeller Institute, with his daughter Clara Auer, seemed to fit his general theory. Working with adrenaline less than three years after J. J. Abel of Baltimore first purified that hormone, the Meltzers discovered that its excitatory action upon the blood vessels and the iris is much enhanced by cutting off the connection of those structures with the sympathetic nervous system, as if inhibitory pathways were thus interrupted. However biased his preconceptions, Meltzer was always exact and objective in describing his results. Out of the work with adrenaline came the useful "frog's iris test" for very small amounts of this substance in body fluids, and also the practical knowledge that drugs injected into muscles are absorbed much faster than if merely put under the skin.

Years earlier Meltzer had chanced to observe a peculiar effect of magnesium salts, which also seemed to illustrate his principle of inhibition. At the Institute he and his assistant (and later son-in-law) John Auer followed this up with investigations reported in a series of twenty-five papers. Magnesium sulphate, they showed, when injected subcutaneously in suitable doses, produces unconsciousness and complete muscular relaxation, from which the animal recovers miraculously if given an injection of calcium chloride. Following up this observation in many varied experiments, Meltzer believed that in magnesium he had found the chemical element in the body which is specifically concerned with inhibition. Regardless of theory, this work definitely added magnesium to the list of metallic elements, sodium, calcium, and potassium, that control the functional activity of protoplasm. Always eager to apply his results, Meltzer hoped that magnesium sulphate could be used as a surgical anesthetic. Although this proved impracticable, he had the satisfaction of seeing his discovery widely used to diminish muscular spasm in desperate cases of tetanus, eclampsia, and similar grave conditions.

In much of the work on the physiological action of magnesium and other salts, Meltzer was assisted by D. R. Joseph, who in 1912 left the Institute to join the faculty of Bryn Mawr College and a year or two later became professor of physiology at St. Louis University. Israel S. Kleiner worked with Meltzer from 1910 to 1919, largely on experimental diabetes and sugar metabolism. In 1919, only three years before the discovery of insulin by Banting and Best, Kleiner prepared a crude emulsion of pancreatic tissue which lowered the blood sugar of animals with experimental diabetes. That same year he left the Institute to begin a long career as professor of biochemistry at the New York Medical College.

Because the chief danger in the use of magnesium in surgery was the risk of inhibiting the respiratory center of the brain, Meltzer and Auer studied the currently available methods of artificial respiration. They hit upon the idea of keeping the lungs inflated by a stream of air blown through a tube inserted into the windpipe by way of the mouth or nasal passage. By this means the blood is aerated without breathing movements of the chest; by including ether or some other anesthetic vapor in the air stream, an animal or human patient can readily be kept under surgical anesthesia. This invention was immediately taken over by the surgeons for important uses. In the first place, it solved a great difficulty in operations about the face and throat, by getting the anesthetist and his ether mask out of the surgeon's way. Better still, it was the simplest practical method for keeping the lungs inflated after the chest was opened. The only means thoracic surgeons had formerly had to avoid collapse of the lung was to place the patient and surgical team in a cumbrous low-pressure chamber, filled with pipes and gauges as in a submarine. Henceforth they could work in an ordinary operating room, keeping the lungs inflated by air under suitable pressure through a Meltzer-Auer tube. Alexis Carrel began at once to use the method in experimental thoracic surgery, and within a few years it was adopted by hospitals everywhere. Thus Meltzer's work facilitated the achievements of modern chest surgery, with its bold attack on tumors and localized tuberculosis of the lung, its still more sensational "blue baby" operations, and other surgery of the heart and central blood vessels.

Another of Meltzer's theoretical generalizations won more acceptance among scientists than did his inhibition principle. In a lecture in 1906 he took over the engineers' concept of "factors of safety" to describe the reserve powers possessed by living mechanisms, thus calling attention to the general biological law of adaptation of the organism to environmental stresses. In 1910 he made another suggestion so fundamentally useful in medicine that its origin has been almost forgotten. Auer, with Paul A. Lewis of Flexner's laboratory, had published a study of anaphylactic shock in the guinea pig, showing for the first time that the cause of death is spasm of the bronchial muscles. This observation led Meltzer to propose the hypothesis, now universally accepted, that bronchial asthma is a phenomenon of anaphylaxis, that is, of sensitivity to foreign proteins.

Meltzer was ill for some years in later life and, as an American with both Russian and German associations, was grieved and distraught by the war of 1914–1918. Resigning his post in 1919, he died in 1920.[12] Auer left the Institute in 1921 for a professorship at St. Louis University; the other principal assistants — Joseph, Kleiner, and T. S. Githens — had already gone elsewhere, and Meltzer's laboratory was dismantled.

Jacques Loeb joined The Rockefeller Institute in 1910, bringing with him the research program he had started at Chicago and California, as narrated in Chapter 3. Even before accepting his appointment he had vigorously stated his conviction that the future of medical research and of biology in general depended upon learning how the basic constituents of protoplasm are put together and how they interact. This kind of physiology cannot deal, as Meltzer's did, with the whole body nor with organ systems, such as those of respiration and digestion, nor even with simpler complexes, such as a group of muscles with their nerves and blood vessels. Loeb's questions were directed at the smallest independent elements of the body, the cells. What constitutes them, and what forces hold them together? What sort of boundary surrounds each cell, separating it from its neighbors and from the tissue fluids? What forces of diffusion, osmosis, absorption govern the movements of water, salts, and organic substances in and out of the cells? Are these forces and conditions the same that operate in respect to small physical objects, such as the electrical charges on ions, the valency of atoms, the size of molecules? What are the effects, in living protoplasm, of changes in temperature, of oxygen supply, of acidity and alkalinity?

Because he could not work upon all of these questions at once, Loeb first followed the lead most obvious at the beginning of his work, devoting himself largely to the study of the fundamental properties of protoplasm as affected by ions. He brought this program with him to the Institute, and continued it, with gradually broadening outlook, for the next eight or nine years. His grand discovery of artificial parthenogenesis suggested a strange new question. The egg cells of all animals, once they are shed from the ovary, are destined to early death unless fertilization gives them continuing life and the impetus to develop. Now that Loeb had induced division of the ovum by chemical stimulation, perhaps he could learn how to save an unfertilized egg from dying. Like many of his apparently specialized inquiries, this one had long-range philosophical implications; Loeb was asking whether death is a necessary consequence of growth and development. The experiments were, as always in his laboratory, very simply planned, with nothing more complicated in the way of apparatus than dishes and test tubes in which he exposed the living eggs of sea urchins or minnows to various salt solutions, or to changes of temperature or of oxygen supply.

One experiment, done in 1916 with J. H. Northrop, yielded a definite fact, if not about death, at least about the duration of life. Keeping groups of fruit flies (*Drosophilae*) at various temperatures from 34°C down to 9°C, Loeb and Northrop found that the average life span of the flies doubled roughly with every 10° decrease of temperature. This "temperature coefficient of the duration of life" is of the same order of magnitude as the temperature coefficient of the rate of chemical reactions. The finding obviously suggests that life proceeds by chemical reactions and that death comes when these are completed. These reactions must pertain to the whole organism or to certain special cells, not to cells of every kind, for, as Carrel was demonstrating with his tissue cultures, many cells when removed from the body can go on living and multiplying indefinitely.

While testing the fate of eggs in different salt solutions, Loeb discovered that the eggs of marine animals soon die if taken from the sea and placed in distilled water containing exactly as much sodium chloride as there is in sea water. Used alone, the sodium chloride is toxic; evidently the other salts found in sea water somehow neutralize this toxicity. In the 1880's Sidney Ringer of London had observed a similar countereffect of calcium and potassium, but Loeb's new observations greatly broadened the concept of "antagonistic salt action." With an able assistant, Hardolph Wasteneys (later professor of biochemistry at the University of Toronto), who joined him in 1910, Loeb followed up this problem, finding that the addition of all sorts of salts with bivalent or trivalent cations, such as calcium and magnesium, in the right proportions, counteracted the toxicity of salts with monovalent cations, including sodium chloride. Here again Loeb had raised a very large question, that of the relation between salt ions and the behavior of proteins in the cell. His own experiments could not fully answer it, yet they stimulated other people to work, for years to come, on the physiological significance of ionization and the shifts of ions in living tissues.

The permeability of cells — that is, the capacity of salts and other dissolved substances to enter and leave them — is evidently an important factor in controlling cell activity. A current hypothesis held that the cell membrane is composed of lipoid (fatty) substances; but since inorganic salts are not soluble in lipoids, they would not be expected to pass through such a membrane into the cells, unless very slowly. Loeb's experiments demonstrated that cells are in fact quite readily permeated by potassium and other salts present in the tissues, and from the details of his observations he conjectured that proteins of the globulin type form an important element of the cell membrane.

Loeb had long wished to look into the electrical phenomena of living tissues. It was known that the differences of potential across cell membranes, and the "action currents" that are set up in a nerve when it is stimulated and a muscle fiber when it contracts, are associated with different concentrations of ions inside and outside the cell. Loeb hoped to go beyond this to learn how the electrical potentials are involved in the actual functioning of tissues; but his distrust of any but the simplest apparatus caused him to postpone that effort until in 1911 he found an assistant, R. H. Beutner, who had experience with the necessary galvanometers and other special equipment. In the next three years, until Beutner left to join the Austrian army, they measured electric currents set up in plant tissues immersed in salt solutions, obtaining indications that such bioelectrical phenomena are explainable by ordinary physical laws pertaining to non-living materials.

In 1918 Loeb founded the *Journal of General Physiology,* published by The Rockefeller Institute, under the editorship of himself and W. J. V. Osterhout, then professor of botany at Harvard. Although his immediate aim was to provide for the prompt publication of the work that prolifically flowed from his laboratory, Loeb's new journal, like the Institute's first periodical, the *Journal of Experimental Medicine,* from the beginning welcomed articles by outsiders. After his death in 1924 the chief editorship fell to Osterhout, who moved to the Institute to succeed Loeb as head of the laboratories of general physiology. The editorial board has since been broadened by the addition of six distinguished physiologists from the Institute and other centers of research.

The unending exploratory search of Loeb and his associates frankly involved study of the simplest available living tissues, in experiments designed to avoid the inherent complexities of more highly organized creatures. Yet even this material, the protoplasm of marine eggs and plant cells, was complex beyond the understanding of his time. He was trying to apply laws drawn from the inorganic world of the physicist to living materials of imperfectly known constitution, under experimental conditions often not rigidly controllable. Naturally, the results were tentative and conjectural, serving largely to raise new questions for further experiment. Loeb's contribution, therefore, was not only his actual discoveries, important though they were, but also his influence upon younger physiologists the world over. Intellectually bold, outspoken, zealous as a missionary for the kind of research he knew to be essential to the full understanding of life processes, he did more than any other man in America to bring on the era of physical chemistry in biology and medicine.

Loeb expounded his interpretation of life and human behavior in three books, *The Mechanistic Conception of Life* (1912), *The Organism as a Whole, from the Physico-chemical Standpoint* (1916), and *Forced Movements, Tropisms and Animal Conduct* (1918). This scientist who in his youth abandoned metaphysics, because it gave no satisfactory answer to the question of free will, by no means reached through his experiments a complete explanation of life. He believed, however, that he had found enough to justify his hope that even human behavior might eventually be explained as the result of physical influences acting under natural laws upon sensitive living tissues. Loeb's mechanistic way of thinking did not lead him into philosophical pessimism or cynicism. Ever idealistic about human relations, hopeful of human progress, he even foresaw a better communal life founded upon biological insight: "Not only is the mechanistic concept of life compatible with ethics; it seems the only conception of life which can lead to an understanding of the source of ethics."[13]

OF ALL THE Institute's varied researches in the years from 1906 to World War I, Carrel's tissue culture work most vividly attracted public attention. Scientists saw in it an important new way of studying life processes; laymen were astonished and awed by the idea of living cells growing and multiplying in glass vessels in an incubator and even attaining the semblance of immortality by long outliving the creatures from which they were explanted. Carrel had good reasons for attempting to cultivate tissues outside the body. For years he had been interested in wound healing, wondering how cells of the skin, connective tissue, blood vessels, and nerves, leaving their places in organized tissue at the edges of a wound and wandering onward, reorganize themselves to fill gaps created by disease, injury, or surgery. How much of this constructive process, he asked, is carried on by the cells themselves and how much by the organizing powers of the body? The problem could at least be better defined if living cells could be studied away from the body, and even limited answers might suggest ways of speeding the healing of wounds.

For years also Carrel's extraordinary success in regrafting tissues, in patching vital arteries with materials taken from elsewhere in the body or from other animals, and in transplanting whole organs, including the kidney and spleen, had given him the hope that in the future surgeons might learn to keep human tissues and organs alive in storage, possibly even to grow them as replacements for damaged elements of the body.

Carrel's ideas came to a focus when the zoologist Ross G. Harrison of Yale, in a Harvey Lecture in New York in March 1908, reported experiments in which he had actually succeeded in cultivating cells outside the body. Harrison, studying the development of the nervous system, had come to grips at last with the biggest question in that field: By what possible means does the embryonic animal body construct the individual fibers of the nerves that connect its various parts? Some of these fibers — for example, those running from the spinal cord to the toes — may in adult man grow to three feet or more, yet each, whether long or short, issues from one particular nerve cell in the brain, spinal cord, or outlying ganglion. Of two suggested answers, both seemed highly improbable. Some embryologists supposed that each fiber grows out from its cell, even to great lengths; others conjectured that the fibers are formed from short lengths built by local cells and somehow joined end to end. Ross Harrison solved the problem by actually watching nerve fibers as they grew, unobscured by other tissue elements. This he did by cutting out a bit of spinal cord from a frog embryo and placing it in a clear drop of coagulated lymph on a hollowed-out microscope slide. In these preparations, which were in fact the first successful cultures of animal tissue, Harrison watched the living fibers sprout from nerve cells at the edge of the explant and grow out day by day as far as the clot allowed them to spread.

Greatly impressed by these observations, Carrel thought of going to New Haven to learn Harrison's methods in order to apply them to the tissues of warm-blooded animals, but at Flexner's suggestion he sent an assistant, Montrose T. Burrows, who had come to the Institute in 1909 directly from medical school.[14] In the spring of 1910 Burrows worked for several months under Harrison's supervision, beginning his trials with chick embryos, because embryonic cells could be expected to grow more actively than those of the adult. He improved upon Harrison's culture medium, clotted lymph, by substituting blood plasma (the fluid part of the blood freed of the red and white cells). Plasma, like lymph, clots on standing, and furnishes a delicate fibrinous mesh upon which the cells can grow. It is more easily obtained in quantity than lymph and forms a more uniform matrix. On this medium, incubated at a fowl's body temperature, Burrows grew cells from embryonic nerve tissue and skin. Some of his cultures included rudimentary heart tissue; these yielded the first — and totally unexpected — discovery of the Carrel tissue culture program. There had been a long-standing question whether the rhythmic beat of the heart arises within the muscle itself or is set up by nerve impulses from the spinal cord and the medulla. In the New Haven cultures muscle cells, developing from the explanted rudiments and freed from all nervous control, underwent spontaneous contraction, thus giving ocular proof of the intrinsic or "myogenic" theory of the heart beat.

After Burrows returned to New York, Carrel and he promptly cultivated the Rous fowl sarcoma, even carrying it from the first culture to a second, thus keeping the line of tumor cells alive *in vitro* through two generations. Withholding these results from publication for a time, they tried the still bolder experiment of cultivating tissues from adult dogs and cats. Explanting bits of highly organized structures, such as cartilage, kidney, and thyroid gland, they were excited to find cells growing out into the culture medium and arranging themselves into groups suggesting, at least in a rudimentary way, the structures from which they originated. In this interpretation Carrel's enthusiasm seems to have outrun his scientific judgment. What had actually grown in the various cultures of chick embryos and fowl tumors was largely, perhaps entirely, connective tissue and some of its derivatives, such as heart muscle and sarcoma cells. In all probability, the cultures of adult cat and dog tissues had also produced only new connective tissue cells. Although the photographs seem to show thyroid gland cells in the primary cultures, we can only surmise, from what was learned later, that the supposed cartilage and kidney cells, in these first crude, insufficiently nourished cultures, were in fact old cells already existing in the tissue before explantation.

When, in a paper published October 15, 1910, Carrel gave the impression that he had actually grown several kinds of highly organized mammalian cells, he met with outspoken disbelief. In November of that year he took his finding before a famous tribunal, the Société de Biologie of Paris, where he presented a paper on "primary, secondary, and tertiary cultures of the thyroid gland." One week later a well-known biologist,

A. Jolly, stated in the Society's *Comptes rendus* that he saw no evidence that thyroid epithelium had grown in a third-generation culture or even in a second. "It is a misuse of language," he wrote, "to apply the word 'culture' to these results."[15]

Carrel replied to his critics by a consummate piece of scientific enterprise and showmanship. Among the most sturdy of his cell strains was one derived from the heart of an embryonic chick. Carrel determined to keep this line of cells alive by repeated transplants until every doubter was overwhelmed by evidence that the culture had lived, grown, and multiplied. Dating the culture from January 17, 1912, he began to report progress in April, when it was 85 days old, having passed through more than thirty transplantations. In June, Albert H. Ebeling, then a technician, took charge of the cultures, assuming — whether or not he knew it at the time — duties as unremitting as if he had adopted a baby. Before the year was out Carrel had discovered a way to improve very greatly the growth of cells in tissue cultures. Recalling some experiments of 1909 and 1910, in which he had speeded up the healing of experimental skin wounds by poultices of crushed animal tissues, he added extracts of chick embryos to his plasma medium and observed considerably increased growth in the cultures. Thereafter, to the present day, all tissue culture workers have put embryo extract in their media, without knowing exactly how it contributes to the welfare of the cultured cells. Tentatively, they now suppose that the active principle is a ribonucleic acid of the sort originally analyzed by Levene and Jacobs at The Rockefeller Institute.

By February 1913 the culture had undergone its 138th passage and was more than a year old. In May 1914 the tissue, now in its third year, had been transplanted 358 times and, thanks to better and better techniques, was producing new cells at an increased rate. The total accumulation of new cells, had they all been kept, would have far exceeded the volume of the embryo from which the original explant came. Increasing vitality of the tissue now permitted the technicians to subculture it at longer intervals, finally only once a week. The culture became world-famous; the fact that it was called "the chicken heart culture" gave it a romantic aura for the press, even though the heart muscle cells it originally contained had long since died out, leaving only fibroblasts (connective tissue cells).

By 1921 Carrel could assert that the tissue had reached its 1500th generation.[16] In fact this strain of cells from a chick that never hatched outlived Carrel himself. Ebeling, long since appointed to the scientific staff, after taking his M.D. degree, as Assistant and later Associate, took the culture with him when he left the Institute to direct tissue culture work at the Lederle Laboratories of the American Cyanamid Company, where the cultivated tissue was used in testing the toxicity of germicides. There he and his assistants kept it going until April 26, 1946, two years after the master surgeon Carrel died in Paris, and thirty-four years after it was first explanted.[17]

This experiment, surely one of the most extraordinary in the history of science, with its demonstration of unending life force released from the mortal body, gave Carrel a vivid sense of closeness to Nature's secrets. It was, however, more than a mere *tour de force,* and it proved that Jolly in 1910 had been wrong in doubting Carrel's right to speak of "cultures." To the other part of Jolly's criticism, that the cultures of 1910 did not contain epithelial gland cells, Carrel could make no reply. Not until 1922 did Ebeling and Albert Fischer obtain flourishing cultures of epithelial cells; the early successes were with connective tissue strains only. The long-lived fibroblasts of the 1912 chick-heart culture provided, however, a more or less standardized cell line with which Carrel and his colleagues could not only try out improved techniques, but also study the structure of fibroblasts, their nutrition and growth rate, response to changes of temperature and oxygen supply, and many other physiological questions. In this phase of the work Raymond C. Parker, a former pupil of Ross Harrison at Yale, took a leading part from 1930 to 1939. Parker, now professor at the University of Toronto, is author of a standard work on tissue culture methods.

Carrel's chief contribution to science through the tissue culture work was that he and his associates established the possibility of cultivating tissues of warm-blooded animals, and devised the first techniques for such experiments. The work required perfect control of asepsis and great manual dexterity. Perhaps no one else in the world had the combination of hand skill, experimental technique, and standards of perfection which Carrel had developed through his experience with blood-vessel surgery. Other investigators, with greater powers of scientific analysis, not dreaming about growing whole organs nor concerned with metaphysical implications, would know better how to answer everyday questions of biology and chemistry by use of the tissue culture method Carrel had placed in their hands. It was to find application in many fields of medical science. Today, as it contributes to the study of cell structure and cell life, to the knowledge of cancer, to the understanding of viruses and the preparation of vaccines, the basic idea and most of the major improvements of technique stem directly from the pioneer work of Harrison, Carrel, and Burrows, followed by that of Ebeling and Parker.

IN 1910, the same year in which Christian Herter died, his hopeful vision of the chemical approach to diseases of nutrition took effect through his intimate friend L. Emmett Holt in an extramural enterprise at the Babies' Hospital of New York. Holt persuaded his colleagues of the Board of Scientific Directors of The Rockefeller Institute to grant a few hundred dollars for equipment and a salary for Angelia M. Courtney, a trained biochemist. The work of this little laboratory was planned and interpreted chiefly by Holt, who often sought advice from Phoebus Levene and Donald D. Van Slyke. It resulted in about thirty articles on the metabolism and nutrition of infants. These included the first reliable analysis of the minerals of human milk and some of the earliest assays of the blood chemistry of infants as well as comprehensive studies of their calcium metabolism and utilization of fats. When Miss Courtney resigned in 1920 to take a position at the University of Toronto, her assistant Helen L. Fales took over the work. In January 1923 Holt, now failing in health and strength, reported to the Board of Scientific Directors that he had terminated the undertaking. During the twelve years of its existence, laboratory work in pediatric medicine had taken root in many medical schools, Holt's friend and former colleague John Howland leading the way at Johns Hopkins. As his biographers remark, Holt, whose clinical training was limited to bedside observation and pathological description, had in his later years taken up the tools of the coming generation and used them forcefully and effectively.[18]

CHAPTER SIX

War and Peace

Growth of the Institute. Foundation of the Department of Animal Pathology at Princeton; Theobald Smith appointed its Director; its first researches. World War I: special investigations; blood preservation, Tryparsamide. Relation of the Institute to the general advance of medical science in the United States.

As THE YEAR 1914 with its mounting tensions began, Europe had cause to fear that the world's uneasy peace might soon break up, but few Americans could foresee that their country too would soon be at war. The Trustees and Scientific Directors of The Rockefeller Institute for Medical Research, rejoicing in the steady development of its scientific work under Simon Flexner's direction, were at work on large plans for additional buildings in New York and for a new department of animal pathology to be located in Princeton, New Jersey.

With a scientific staff now numbering forty-two, the Institute was already outgrowing its space and equipment. Including Rufus Cole, the Director, the hospital staff comprised ten physicians. Flexner's division of pathology and bacteriology, largest of the five laboratory groups, included two Associate Members, four Associates, four Assistants, and two Fellows; and each of the other Members, excepting Carrel, who then worked only with technicians, had a similar though smaller staff. Because of these increasing numbers the laboratories were becoming badly crowded, and the animal house, power plant, and administrative offices were already inadequate. The Board of Scientific Directors had tentatively planned that when the time for expansion arrived, the original laboratory building would be enlarged by wings extending toward the river; but Rockefeller, Jr., and Gates, looking ahead toward even further expansion later, now urged the construction of a separate new laboratory (the present Flexner Hall), new and more capacious animal quarters, and a much larger powerhouse on a new site at the southeast end of the grounds.[1] In June 1914 Rockefeller, Sr., gave the Institute $2,550,000 to be used for new construction and as additional endowment.[2] Fortunately, the buildings were completed in 1916 before war interfered with civilian construction. After the divisions of chemistry and of pathology and bacteriology moved to the new laboratory, the central structure (Founder's Hall) was altered and given over to experimental surgery, physiology, and experimental biology.

The Department of Animal Pathology at Princeton was a natural development of the original plan, although it came into being, as we shall see, through an unexpected proposal from outside the Institute. From the beginning, Flexner had urged and the Directors had agreed that The Rockefeller Institute should not limit itself to the study of human disease.[3] Pathologists and bacteriologists draw no line between human ailments and those of animals; experimental medicine is founded upon the essential similarity of disease processes throughout the animal kingdom. Pasteur studied the diseases of silkworms, as well as of man; his most famous works, those on anthrax and rabies, dealt with diseases that occur in several species of mammals besides man. Many of the most instructive discoveries of modern bacteriology concerned infections limited to animals and even to plants; for example, the first maladies found to be caused by filtrable viruses were the foot-and-mouth disease of cattle and the mosaic disease of tobacco plants. Indeed, by appointing America's most successful investigator of animal pathology, Theobald Smith, as one of its charter members, the Board of Directors of The Rockefeller Institute had implicitly accepted the principle that human pathology cannot well be studied apart from that of lower creatures.

There were few precedents for a research institute in animal pathology. The veterinary schools of Germany, Austria, Denmark, Holland, France, and Italy had been doing research for thirty years, but this was mostly practical work rather than fundamental investigation. The same was generally true of the agricultural colleges and state experiment stations in this country. South Africa had a true research institute, under the direction of Sir Arnold Theiler, which grew out of a government bacteriological laboratory, founded in 1903 in Onderstepoort, near Pretoria. The Russian Institute for Experimental Medicine, founded at

St. Petersburg in 1890, had laboratories for veterinary medicine. A German laboratory at Insel Reims, near Greifswald, had not yet extended its study beyond foot-and-mouth disease. In America the Bureau of Animal Industry of the United States Department of Agriculture had become, under D. E. Salmon's leadership, a very active center of research, in which Theobald Smith had taken a leading part; Smith's own recently organized Department of Comparative Pathology at Harvard was the nation's only other advanced research laboratory in animal pathology.

In 1913 a calamity a thousand miles away placed a problem of animal disease squarely before the Board of Scientific Directors of The Rockefeller Institute. An outbreak of hog cholera sweeping the Western states had caused a loss estimated at thirty to fifty million dollars, impoverishing many farmers and seriously affecting rural trade. James J. Hill, the powerful president of the Great Northern Railway, deeply concerned about the welfare of farmers in its territory and the business they produced, offered the Institute $25,000 for an investigation of hog cholera.

Flexner and Theobald Smith were appointed to consider the matter. Calling for more than the *ad hoc* investigation of one disease, they proposed the creation of a full-scale department of animal pathology. The Board of Scientific Directors, hesitant about undertaking so large a commitment without greater support than the sum pledged by Hill, were encouraged by the Trustees to go ahead, if necessary without his aid, and in April 1914 Mr. Rockefeller pledged another million dollars with which to begin the new department.[4] The Board hoped to secure Theobald Smith to lead it, but Welch predicted that he would decline. "No one gives up a Harvard professorship," he said.[5] However, with adequate support guaranteed, Smith accepted the appointment. The Board's caution in not undertaking the project without long-term financial support was justified, for Hill's money was never received. Apparently, Theobald Smith, always careful in money matters, preferred not to call for payment against the pledge until he was ready to begin his investigation, and when Hill died after a brief illness in May 1916 the gift lapsed. Nevertheless his proposal had been so effective a stimulant that the loss of a monetary contribution went almost unnoticed.

Theobald Smith became director July 1, 1914. The Institute had already bought a tract of farm land near Princeton, New Jersey, across

Carnegie Lake from the town and university. The original 425 acres were later increased to about 800. Smith chose Carl TenBroeck of Harvard as his first assistant, Ralph B. Little as veterinarian, and, as the fourth member of the staff, an entomologist, Rudolf Marchand of Leipzig, Germany. Little was temporarily put in charge of the small farm at Clyde, New Jersey, already used by the Institute for the serum horses and Carrel's dogs. In the fall of 1915 the others, using laboratory space generously provided by Princeton University, began the Institute's first research on animal pathology for its own sake. Theobald Smith had begun at Harvard an investigation of a disease of domestic turkeys, called "blackhead," which was ruining the business of turkey raising in the Eastern states. Having discovered a protozoan parasite that causes the malady, he resumed the study at Princeton, finding new strains of the parasite and seeking to learn how it spreads from infected to healthy birds. He had already concluded that some bird other than the turkey may constitute a reservoir of infection, and when Ernest W. Smillie, trained as a veterinarian, was appointed Fellow in 1916, Smith started him and a new assistant, Harry W. Graybill, examining sparrows, robins, and other common wild birds in search of the parasite. The outcome of this research, which saved the turkey-breeding industry, will be narrated in Chapter 11.

TenBroeck tested the immune reactions of Smith's *Salmonella choleraesuis,* the causal agent of paratyphoid fever in hogs. Marchand, a specialist on the biting flies that transmit certain animal and human diseases, studied the natural history of New Jersey deer flies. Papers reporting these researches began to appear in the *Journal of Experimental Medicine* as early as March 1916. That same year another investigator, Frederick S. Jones, a veterinarian trained in bacteriology, who had proved his mettle while associated with Peyton Rous since 1913, also began work with Smith, studying infections of the cow's udder (mastitis). Already known to be caused chiefly by common pus-forming germs of the streptococcus group, mastitis was a serious economic problem for dairy farmers. Before this work was well under way, however, the young veterinarian was off on a journey to Patagonia. A call had come to the Institute for someone to investigate sheep staggers, a disease that was decimating the chief productive asset of that far-off land. The Institute lent Jones's services, and in the late summer of 1916 he rapidly carried out a series of experiments in the field, proving that the malady was caused by grazing on a poisonous pampas grass, *Poa argentina*.

The Board of Scientific Directors was meanwhile making plans for the new buildings in Princeton. The first bids were far higher than the original estimates and there were other unexpected costs, so that even counting James J. Hill's still expected gift, the funds available would not equip and operate the department for longer than three years. The Rockefeller Foundation, however, responded to an appeal at the end of 1915 with an appropriation of one million dollars, thus doubling Rockefeller's earlier gift.[6] By the fall of 1916, the department was comfortably settled on its pleasant new site, in a large central structure housing laboratories of pathology, bacteriology, protozoology, and biochemistry. In addition there were buildings for the animals, including two for isolating those with infectious diseases. The farm was fully equipped for raising food for the animals. Several dwellings were remodeled, and others built, for the scientific and service staffs. Two years later, in spite of wartime hindrances, Smith had fully organized his group. There were six Associates, two Assistants, and four Fellows. The Director himself, TenBroeck, Jones, Little, Paul E. Howe, and J. Howard Brown were all at work on infectious diseases of cattle and hogs. They were aided by several juniors, four of whom — Smillie, Graybill, Laura Florence, and Marion L. Orcutt — were to remain with the department for a long time.

It was perhaps inevitable that this group of young, relatively inexperienced people, under the direction of a man of commanding personal experience and reputation, should devote itself at first largely to confirming and extending details of pathological and bacteriological knowledge about swine and cattle diseases on which their Director had previously worked. Smith was not temperamentally inclined, as he himself once stated, to start expensive and uncertain ventures in new fields. He had grown up in an era of very limited financial support for research, when the investigator of animal diseases had to work with problems and animals that were ready at hand.[7] Fifty-five years of age when appointed to head the new enterprise, he had reached the time of life when most scientists no longer begin radically new investigations. He probably felt, moreover, a certain pressure to justify the new department by making prompt and practical contributions to the prevention of diseases of domestic animals. Such indeed had been the expectation of James J. Hill, whose original offer had led to the foundation of Smith's department. There was in fact no need for Smith to go outside that field; his experience in such work provided enough unsolved problems to keep his department busy for a long time. Later the Princeton laboratories became the scene of great new discoveries; meanwhile, Smith's first effort was to cultivate research in which progress seemed certain.

THE OUTBREAK of World War I in August 1914 had at first very little effect upon the research workers of The Rockefeller Institute. A few staff members of foreign citizenship left at once for military service. From the hospital, Arthur Ellis went to join the Canadian Expeditionary Force; Gotthard Zacharias-Langhans returned to Germany and died in service. Reinhard Beutner of Loeb's department joined the Austrian army.[2] Before long, however, the conflict in Europe inevitably had its impact on the activities and emotions of other members of the Institute's staff, gathered from many nations and, like most scientists, strongly internationalist in outlook.

Even before the United States entered the war, some of the older men of European birth felt the strain of divided allegiance and suffered under the unreasoning intolerance of wartime. Samuel J. Meltzer, combining affection for the old Germany of his student days with fears that the world-wide brotherhood of scientific men would be permanently destroyed by the war, organized and promoted a society of physicians for international good will, called "Fraternitas Medicorum." It recruited many thousands of members in the United States and other countries, but collapsed when our nation entered the war.[8] Jacques Loeb, unable to relieve his personal tension in any such quixotic way, expressed it by an idealistic philosophy quite suitable for discussion in time of peace, but under the existing circumstances very bold. For example, in an address before a scientific meeting in December 1916, he declared that wars result from mob spirit, rooted in ignorance and superstition and fostered by statesmen unacquainted with scientific logic. Against these forces high-minded scientists must apply the results of the exact sciences to international relations, in order to diminish the danger of war.[9]

Alexis Carrel was more fortunate, for he could at once throw his talents into the service of his native land. In August 1914 he was on vacation with Mme Carrel at their villa in Anjou, where as a French citizen he received his mobilization order on the day that Germany declared war against Russia. After a few weeks of routine military service at Lyons, he persuaded the authorities to give him a special hospital where he could combine research with treatment. His chief hope was to find better methods to combat severe bacterial infections of lacerated wounds, certain to be a major problem in the military hospital. Influential Americans, notably the capitalist James Hazen Hyde, a great friend of France, and Henry James, business manager of The Rockefeller Institute, came to his support in negotiations with the French government and with interested organizations in America.[10] As a result, The Rockefeller Foundation granted $20,000 to the Institute for special war work, much of which was devoted to Carrel's program.[11] Henry B. Dakin, an experienced English biochemist, who had worked for several years in Christian Herter's private laboratory, continuing there after the latter's death, eagerly joined Carrel. The French government provided a hotel building at Compiègne, then very near the front lines, and a staff of French medical officers. Dakin was to search for substances which might prove antiseptic, and Carrel was to treat infected wounds with them.

Battle wounds are usually heavily contaminated with dirt and bits of clothing or metal and other debris, and are often so badly lacerated as to provide deep and intricate lurking places for septic germs. In World War I, particularly in its earlier years, the transport of wounded soldiers was often slow, giving time for bacterial infection to develop. Men frequently arrived at base hospitals in a highly toxic state resulting from widespread necrosis of injured tissues and extensive collections of pus in the wounds. Nowadays, antibiotics attack invading and rapidly multiplying organisms by way of the blood stream, but in 1914–1918 these agents were unknown. The only recourse, Carrel believed, was to apply antiseptic solutions directly, somehow getting them into the depths and crannies of the wound. Such solutions must be very critically compounded to be potent enough to kill the organisms, yet mild enough not to damage tissues.

After several months of preliminary trials, during which, it is said, Dakin tried two hundred substances, he produced a solution of sodium hypochlorite, buffered with sodium bicarbonate to keep it close to the natural balance between alkalinity and acidity characteristic of living tissues. Carrel then devised a system of radical surgical removal of injured tissue (*débridement*), followed by intermittent irrigation with Dakin's solution through branching rubber tubes inserted into the depths of the wound and left in place for days or weeks. Although the Carrel-Dakin treatment was the best available for the time being, Carrel himself did not regard it as ideal. Nevertheless, in his hands the results were remarkable. The treatment cleared up deep-seated purulent wounds, rendering them less toxic to the patient and freeing them from pus-forming bacteria so that they could be closed surgically. The method roused a great deal of controversy, especially among French surgeons, some of whom attacked it as ineffective, others as too drastic. Military surgeons, moreover, found it too elaborate for use at the front. Only in a protected, unhurried environment could they maintain the alkalinity of the solution and make frequent bacterial counts from the wounds, as required by Carrel. As the transport of wounded soldiers improved, so that they reached hospitals more quickly, there were fewer massive infections, and wounds could be closed at once after *débridement*. In time of peace there were still fewer occasions for combating deep purulent infections by so elaborate a method. Surgeons did not feel it necessary to maintain at their hospitals the special apparatus, the chemical and bacterial control, the supply of precisely buffered Dakin's solution, and the constant attention that went into successful operation of the Carrel-Dakin method at Compiègne and later in New York.[12] The method therefore did not take hold in civilian major surgery, though Dakin's solution was long used as a disinfectant for trivial wounds. More than twenty years were to elapse before the whole problem of wound infection was revolutionized by the discovery of penicillin and other antibiotics.

In the United States, meanwhile, the war was coming ever closer. Growing tension between this country and the Central Powers reached a peak with the sinking of the "Lusitania" in May 1915, but at that time Germany backed down. On February 1, 1917, however, the Kaiser's government announced the resumption of unrestricted submarine warfare, making it inevitable that the United States would soon enter the war. Even before President Wilson's address of April 2, 1917, calling on Congress to recognize the existence of a state of war, the Institute's governing boards had begun to discuss their responsibilities in the pending crisis.

One possible contribution was clear: teaching the Carrel-Dakin method to American medical officers. Flexner offered to set up a center for this purpose, and took Carrel, in New York on leave, to Washington to see the Surgeons General of the Army and Navy.

With a special appropriation from The Rockefeller Foundation, the Institute began a War Demonstration Hospital on June 1, 1917. Planned to imitate conditions near the front, the project also offered a good opportunity to experiment with designs for temporary hospitals based on European experience rather than on the installations that had heretofore served the Army's needs. Fortunately an architect, Charles Butler, was available after studying British and French military hospitals in France for more than a year and working with Carrel on plans for a proposed portable hospital behind the Belgian lines. The sixteen portable wooden buildings, occupying the whole southwest corner of The Rockefeller Institute grounds, were completed in six weeks — a remarkable feat, testifying to skillful planning and enthusiastic cooperation between architect, builders, and the acting business manager of the Institute, Edric B. Smith. The hospital comprised two wards of twenty-five beds each and an operating pavilion, with all necessary facilities and dormitories for the entire personnel.[13]

The War Demonstration Hospital was staffed by French and American military surgeons. The former, four in all, headed by Carrel, were sent by the French army from the group he had trained at Compiègne; the latter, together with a number of bacteriologists and chemists, were assigned by the Surgeon General of the U.S. Army. The first patients were civilians suffering from a variety of infected wounds; these were replaced, after American forces entered combat, by soldier patients sent home from France. Twice each month from August 2, 1917, to March 29, 1919, a new class of medical officers came for two weeks' instruction in the Carrel-Dakin method. In addition, specialists were given short courses in the chemical preparation of Dakin's solution and in the bacteriological testing and control of the surgical treatment.

Meanwhile, the rest of the Institute, both laboratories and hospital, took on so many wartime tasks that on August 24, 1918, the War Department commissioned it as U.S. Auxiliary Hospital No. 1 and U.S. Auxiliary Laboratory No. 1.[14] Practically all staff members who were qualified for commissions in the Medical Corps went into uniform, Flexner taking top rank as Lieutenant Colonel.[15] "I am mostly associated nowadays with colonels and majors," wrote Prudden in a letter describing the changes. "Nearly all of our leading lights have now gone over to the military, Doctors Cole and Van Slyke being the last of the old regime to succumb, and they are now awaiting their commissions."[16] The Stars and Stripes, flying daily from a flagpole newly erected in front of the main building, gave notice that The Rockefeller Institute for Medical Research was now a United States Army post.[17]

During these years Flexner was often away as consultant on Army medical problems, and the business manager, Henry James, also deeply involved in war work, resigned his post in 1917 to join the army. Administration of the Institute might have suffered greatly had not Edric B. Smith, James's capable assistant, provided continuity of experience, with the advice and guidance of T. Mitchell Prudden, who installed himself as unofficial counselor. Going daily to the Institute to help Edric Smith with current problems, and lending his authority as member of the Board of Scientific Directors when decisions had to be made, Prudden guided the Institute's business affairs with unassuming wisdom and, when the emergency was over, quietly dropped the reins he had so inconspicuously grasped. Frank A. Dickey, Registrar of Columbia University, was appointed business manager in place of Henry James, but died a year later. Edric Smith then took the post.

The chief task of the Institute, operating as Auxiliary Laboratory No. 1, was to conduct courses in bacteriology, clinical chemistry, and the techniques of pathology for medical officers and technicians. Flexner took charge of bacteriology, setting up a class laboratory on an unused floor of the recently completed North Building (Flexner Hall). The army sent each month a new class of 20 to 40 men and women, in all 480 persons. These students perhaps did not realize what an all-star faculty they had: Lieutenant Colonel Flexner; Majors Harold L. Amoss, Carroll G. Bull, A. R. Dochez, E. K. Dunham; Captain Oswald T. Avery; Lieutenant Peter K. Olitsky; and on the civilian side, Wade Hampton Brown, Rufus Cole, Hideyo Noguchi, Louise Pearce, Peyton Rous. Donald D. Van Slyke conducted the course in clinical chemistry, preparing 126 officers, enlisted men, and civilians, most of them college students majoring in chemistry, for the special diagnostic work of the military hospitals. Van Slyke's faculty group was almost as distinguished as Flexner's; even Phoebus A. Levene did not disdain the rank of mere instructor.

Early in the war cerebrospinal meningitis appeared in British army camps, first among Canadian and then among English recruits. Finding the serum treatment inadequate, British physicians suspected that drug firms were not putting out a reliable product, and turned to The Rockefeller Institute. With financial assistance from The Rockefeller Foundation, Flexner's laboratory developed a rapid method of producing antimeningitis serum, soon supplying large quantities to the Allied medical services. When the United States War Department requested the Institute to expand this service for the benefit of the American forces, Flexner and Theobald Smith with further support from The Rockefeller Foundation set up a special unit in Princeton, under J. Howard Brown, and large-scale production of serum was soon under way. By the end of the war, the New York and Princeton laboratories had furnished the huge total of 677 liters.

A considerable quantity also of antidysentery serum was made, at first for the French and later for the American army. Furthermore, Rufus Cole, who in the course of his regular hospital research program was making sera against the several types of pneumococcus, was able to supply our army and navy with a generous amount for diagnostic use. In addition, he accepted twenty-six army physicians as temporary interns at the Hospital of The Rockefeller Institute while they learned new methods of typing and treating pneumonia, before being assigned to the pneumonia wards of military hospitals. Alfred E. Cohn began a course of instruction for medical officers on diagnosis of heart diseases by the new methods of electrocardiography and X-ray measurement of the heart, but had to discontinue it when the army assigned him to overseas service.

One of the most ghastly surgical complications in World War I was the frequent contamination of wounds with the germ of gas gangrene, a spreading infection that destroyed tissues in the region of the wound so rapidly that even drastic surgery could not head it off. The organism which causes it, *Clostridium perfringens*, lives in the soil and was prevalent in the fields over which the war was fought. The Rockefeller Institute had a long-standing interest in this organism, for it was first clearly described in 1892 by William H. Welch (with H. F. Nuttall), and was for a time called *Bacillus welchii*. Simon Flexner, too, had studied it, comparing its virulence in various animals, and felt an obligation to reopen the attack against this murderous bacterial enemy. Carroll G. Bull, to whom he assigned the investigation, sought first to discover how the organism caused general prostration as well as local infection. Various explanations had been proposed, most of them based on the supposition that tissues damaged locally release toxins that poison the whole body. Bull and his assistant, Ida W. Pritchett, found, on the contrary, that the organism itself contains a toxin which is picked up by the blood stream. By inoculating guinea pigs, Bull produced active immunity against the germ. He obtained an antitoxic serum that protected guinea pigs for two to three weeks and, moreover, arrested the infection even after its establishment in an experimental animal. The work of Bull and Pritchett was not a complete answer to the problem of treating human victims of gas gangrene, but it was the first breakthrough in the ultimately successful scientific attack against the infection.

The Institute applied its resources also to other war projects. Peter K. Olitsky attempted to produce protective immunity against cerebrospinal meningitis by administering the antitoxin to healthy soldiers. Frederick L. Gates,[18] of Flexner's laboratories, made similar experiments with an antitoxin against bacillary dysentery caused by *Shigella flexneri.* John Auer of the division of physiology studied the effects of poison gases. Phoebus Levene lent his laboratory and the services of some of his young men for several pieces of special research requested by government departments. These included a method of making the analgesic drug barbitol (Veronal), antidotes to mustard gas, protection against vermin that attack furs used in making aviators' garments, and the preparation of rare sugars for use in the identification of bacteria.[19]

Another piece of research also illustrates the versatility of the Institute's resources. The war created an urgent demand for increased supplies of acetone, used as a chemical reagent in the manufacture of high explosives, and also as a solvent in making the "dope" used to stiffen and protect the fabric with which at that time airplane wings were covered. One method of obtaining acetone utilized a special bacterium that ferments starches. The bacteriologist A. Fernbach and the chemist Chaim Weizmann (afterward President of Israel) had developed such a process, using maize as its raw material, which was already furnishing large quantities of acetone; but it also yielded three times as much butyl alcohol, for which there was then no use. In response to a plea from the Council of National Defense, John H. Northrop of Loeb's division of general physiology began a search for a process yielding more valuable by-products. Several species of bacteria which would produce, in addition to acetone, the more valuable grain (ethyl) alcohol were known to exist, but were not available. Northrop and his assistants, therefore, obtained potatoes from various parts of the country, let them ferment spontaneously, and took cultures from those that produced acetone. Although they did not find the precise species they were seeking, they did turn up a previously unknown bacillus giving an excellent yield of acetone and ethyl alcohol, which they named *Bacillus acetoethylicus*.

The investigators then worked out a method for supplying the raw material and nutrient substances and for drawing off the products of fermentation without interrupting the growth of the culture. This seems to have been the first attempt to conduct such a process as a continuous operation. Northrop arranged for pilot-plant trials at a testing laboratory in Boston, and his team helped to set up experimental large-scale production at the plant of the Commercial Solvents Corporation in Terre Haute, Indiana. Shortly after the war, a process was developed for making ethyl alcohol synthetically, while butyl alcohol became commercially valuable as an ingredient of automobile lacquers. Consequently, Northrop's process could not compete with the older one whose by-product was butyl alcohol.

The most far-reaching and beneficent achievement of The Rockefeller Institute in World War I went almost unnoticed at the time, and was not even cited by Flexner in his report to the Corporation on the Institute's wartime activities. This was the discovery of a practical method of preserving whole blood for use in transfusion. Even before the United States entered the war, Peyton Rous and his associates, who had been studying blood proteins, were deeply disturbed by reports of wounded soldiers dying at casualty stations for want of some means of promptly counteracting the loss of large quantities of blood by hemorrhage. Direct transfusion from donor to patient, already in wide use in civilian hospitals before the war, could not be used under emergency conditions at the front.

Rous began several lines of research, trying, at first, to find an adequate blood substitute. With Oswald H. Robertson he studied the normal life span of red blood cells, and with G. W. Wilson he tested various solutions that had been used or proposed as blood substitutes. He saw that something more than mere replacement of fluid is necessary to restore exsanguinated bodies. There is no complete substitute for red blood corpuscles. Unfortunately, as everyone knew who had worked with blood, these cells are extremely sensitive to their environment; they did not withstand the substances added to prevent clotting and keep them in uniform suspension. Together with J. R. Turner, Jr., Rous began a search for a fluid in which the corpuscles might be preserved in good condition. By a series of logically planned experiments, wasting little time in false moves, they soon discovered that sugar solutions have a very high protective value. Starting with one of the standard physiological salt solutions (Locke's), plus sodium citrate to prevent clotting, and adding cane sugar at first, later dextrose, they achieved a mixture in which human red corpuscles survived intact for nearly a month.

With this done, Rous and Turner next experimented with stored rabbit's blood, to see whether it could save exsanguinated rabbits, and found that, after at least a fortnight of preservation in an ordinary refrigerator, it not only did so, but functioned well in the circulation of the transfused animal. Oswald Robertson soon made himself an opportunity to try the new preservative on the battlefield. With this aim in view he joined the U.S. Army Medical Corps in 1917 and managed to gain assignment to the Third Army, British Expeditionary Force. Close behind the front lines in Belgium, he built an ice chest out of packing cases and stocked it with flasks of human blood donated by the camp personnel and the walking wounded, and preserved in the Rous-Turner solution. This he used, even after preservation for as long as twenty-six days, in life-saving transfusions of severely wounded soldiers fresh from the front lines. His primitive installation was the world's first blood bank.

The achievement did not go entirely unnoticed by English surgeons, who saw Robertson's work at the front or who read his explicit, though unsensational, report in the *British Medical Journal* in 1918. After returning to The Rockefeller Institute in 1919, he received one day, to his great surprise, a packet containing the medal and ribbon of the British Distinguished Service Order.[20] Yet neither at the Institute nor in the medical world outside was the true magnitude of this contribution rec-

ognized. It was twenty years ahead of its time. Peace-time surgeons continued to use various techniques of transfusion directly from donor to
patient, until the demand for transfusion blood outgrew the casual
method of sending for a donor when needed and performing an operation on two persons at once. About 1937 the hospitals, faced with short-
ages of blood in time of need, began to set up blood banks using only
citrated blood, which lasted less than nine days. The Rous-Turner solution was not employed until imperative need for blood, during the
"blitz" in England, emphasized its value.

The extensive use of stored blood in civilian surgery is known nowadays to millions of people who have received a transfusion or given
blood for a friend or to the Red Cross. Public recognition of this beneficent gift to mankind came at last in 1953, when the Association of American Physicians awarded the Kober Medal to Peyton Rous.[21]

Rous's group did their work so well that almost no improvements
followed upon the original Rous-Turner solution. Various experimenters have modified it slightly, without obtaining any longer preservation
of the red blood cells. During World War II great quantities of blood,
stored in solutions closely based on the formula of 1917, were used to
save lives throughout the world, from the London blitz to the battlefields
of Iwo Jima and Okinawa.

THE INTRODUCTION of a curative drug for African sleeping sickness, discovered by a team of four working from 1914 to 1919 at the Institute,
must be counted a triumph of peace rather than of war, even though
Flexner chose to list it among the Institute's wartime accomplishments.
African sleeping sickness is caused by trypanosomes, microscopic blood
parasites somewhat resembling spirochetes. Although limited to those
regions of Equatorial Africa where the tsetse fly exists, it was in 1920 a
terrible scourge. The germs of this insidious, slowly progressive, and invariably fatal disease were widely disseminated among the population, at
least one half being infected in the worst regions. In the Belgian Congo
it was the most prevalent and severe of the diseases affecting the natives,
depopulating whole villages and causing incalculable loss of life and
productivity. The story of its vanquishing started, indirectly, a decade
earlier, in connection with another disease, syphilis.

In 1910 Flexner had followed with intense interest the results of Paul

Ehrlich and S. Hata's announcement of Salvarsan, an organic compound containing arsenic, powerfully effective in the treatment of syphilis. As related in Chapter 4, Flexner had secured a special grant from Rockefeller, Sr., for Ehrlich's work and had encouraged Homer Swift's early use of the new drug at The Rockefeller Institute Hospital. Salvarsan then came into general use, but the war in Europe had cut off its supply from the German manufacturers, and it was urgently necessary that the United States should produce an antisyphilitic drug of its own. W. A. Jacobs, later head of the Institute's laboratory of chemical pharmacology, had been engaged in an attempt to synthesize bactericidal drugs based on the antiseptic substance hexamethylenetetramine, to be described in the next chapter. Assisting in this work was Michael Heidelberger, who had joined him after a year's post-doctoral study abroad. Flexner asked these two to prepare Salvarsan in America. Other workers had tried this and failed, and it was widely rumored that Ehrlich had deliberately omitted some essential step from his patent specifications in order to prevent others from making the drug. Shortly before the United States entered the war, supplies of Salvarsan began to arrive in blockade-running German submarines, but by then Jacobs and Heidelberger had acquired enough experience in the chemistry of arsenical compounds to verify the patents and make Salvarsan. American manufacturers then took over their experience.

Flexner hoped that the Institute might contribute a still more effective and less costly treatment. Salvarsan and its successor, neo-Salvarsan, were not altogether satisfactory, even though they constituted the most conspicuous achievement of the new science of chemotherapy. With this hope was linked another: Ehrlich, turning his attention to African sleeping sickness, had produced arsenical compounds related to Salvarsan and possessing at least limited power to kill trypanosomes in the blood stream. A concerted effort to find new arsenical drugs, Flexner thought, might yield something useful against this disease as well as against syphilis.

In organizing this effort, Flexner assigned two members of his own laboratory, Wade Hampton Brown and Louise Pearce, to join two chemists, W. A. Jacobs and Michael Heidelberger. The pathologists prepared themselves to test the hoped-for new compounds by a thorough study of the various forms of trypanosomiasis as manifested in different animals. In rats and mice, they found, the disease is primarily a blood stream infection; in rabbits, the parasites invade various tissues, including the central nervous system, and cause a chronic disease resembling in many respects African sleeping sickness of man. Rats or mice, therefore, served well enough for preliminary trials to determine the effectiveness of a drug against trypanosomes in the blood; but the rabbit disease provides a better test of the drug's power to destroy the parasites deep within the nerve tissues.

Jacobs and Heidelberger, attacking the chemistry of the problem, knew that Salvarsan and its derivatives, which contain arsenic in trivalent linkage, are difficult to dissolve and rather unstable chemically, whereas pentavalent arsenicals are more soluble, more stable, and also more diffusible; moreover, one of them, Atoxyl, was known to have some slight anti-trypanosomal effect. The Rockefeller Institute workers therefore devoted their efforts chiefly to pentavalent compounds. Beginning with a few that were already available, Brown and Pearce studied first their toxic action, then their effect upon trypanosomes in the blood of rats and mice, and finally their curative action upon experimentally infected rabbits. Jacobs and Heidelberger meanwhile began to synthesize new pentavalent arsenical compounds, varying them as experience suggested. They introduced a methyl group at one point, for example, or an amide or some more complex side chain at another, until they had produced 243 arsenicals, all of which were tested in laboratory animals.

The very first of their new compounds, Tryparsamide, turned out to be a potent trypanocide, clearing all parasites from the blood of infected rats, mice, and guinea pigs in less than twenty-four hours. Administered to rabbits heavily infected with *Trypanosoma brucei* — which causes the disease nagana in both wild and domestic animals in Africa — and *T. gambiense* — which causes African sleeping sickness in human beings — Tryparsamide brought about prompt and lasting cures in more than 80 per cent of cases. In amounts sufficient to clear up the infection, it caused no toxic symptoms nor pathological changes, and repeated doses could be given. It was chemically stable. Being highly soluble in water, it was easy to administer, and permeated the tissues of the entire body, including those of the central nervous system. In short, it qualified as an almost perfect chemotherapeutic agent. None of its variants or derivatives, nor any of the other arsenicals synthesized by Jacobs and Heidelberger, excelled it.

Readers familiar with organic chemistry will appreciate the reasoning which led Jacobs to prepare Tryparsamide. Ehrlich had made certain arsenical compounds which were strongly trypanocidal, among them arsenophenylglycine. This substance was, however, highly toxic to experimental animals. Jacobs reasoned that if a carboxyl group ($-COOH$) forming part of this compound were converted into an amide ($-CONH_2$) the resulting drug would be less toxic. The derivative thus formed was Tryparsamide.

Colonial governments in tropical Africa were naturally eager to have the drug tried out. The Rockefeller Institute sent Louise Pearce in May 1920 to Léopoldville, Belgian Congo, trusting her vigorous personality to carry out an assignment none too easy for a woman physician and not without its dangers. There, for the first time, she saw human beings suffering with the dreadful disease that she and her colleagues had been fighting in the laboratory. A thorough test of Tryparsamide, made in collaboration with a local laboratory and hospital and with strict controls based on experience with the experimental rabbit disease, was highly successful. Early cases were almost uniformly cured with few relapses, and the majority of patients in even late stages of the disease were saved. Its one drawback, however, now became apparent. The drug has a toxic affinity for the optic nerve, and a small percentage of patients treated with too large or too frequent doses suffered from partial or, more rarely, complete loss of vision. Nevertheless, it at once became and still remains the standard remedy for the Congo type of sleeping sickness caused by *Trypanosoma gambiense*. It is, unfortunately, not as useful in the Rhodesian variety, caused by *T. rhodesiensis*, but this is much less common and occurs in a limited area.

Although Brown and Pearce found that Tryparsamide possessed relatively feeble power to kill spirochetes — in animals experimentally infected with syphilis — as compared with its effect upon trypanosomiasis, its special property of freely penetrating the central nervous system suggested that it might be effective against syphilis of the brain and spinal cord, and especially against general paresis, the most refractory chronic form. Such was indeed the result: injections of Tryparsamide produced dramatic improvement in many otherwise hopeless cases. When artificial fever was introduced a few years later as a treatment for syphilitic general paresis, combined use of fever and Tryparsamide arrested the disease in 80 per cent of the cases. Accepting the danger of damaged vision as a calculated risk, physicians used the drug until 1950, when penicillin replaced it entirely.

For her services at Léopoldville, Pearce received, after her return from the Congo, the Order of the Crown of Belgium. In 1953 the Belgian government, gratefully recalling the event of thirty-three years before, summoned her to Brussels to receive the King Leopold II Prize — a generous check — accompanied by a second decoration, the Royal Order of the Lion. Honoraria were also sent to the widow of Brown, who had died in 1942, to Jacobs at the Institute, and to Heidelberger, then professor of immunochemistry at the College of Physicians and Surgeons. The men were made officers of the Order of Leopold II. Thus was the discovery of Tryparsamide honored by the nation whose colonials had first experienced its benefits.

The Board of Scientific Directors as well as the physicians of the Tryparsamide research group were very much concerned about their responsibility for the purity and the potency of the manufactured drug. Foreseeing similar situations in the future, the Board in 1919 declared it the Institute's policy that all discoveries be made freely available to the public, subject to such precautions as might be necessary to prevent improper exploitation. To this end, the Board decided, the Institute might in certain instances protect discoveries by patents, and license their manufacture and marketing by suitable firms, but in no case accept royalties or other pecuniary benefits.[22] Under this resolution Tryparsamide was patented and a license granted to a responsible pharmaceutical firm; each batch made was subjected to biological tests by the Institute. This arrangement entailed a great deal of work, and a voluminous correspondence concerning patent rights and registered trade marks in ten or fifteen countries. After a few years, however, the Institute no longer found it necessary to implement its authority by controlling production.

Northrop's acetone process had already been patented at the direction of the government agency under whose authority the project had been placed. A few months later, Phoebus Levene produced, as a side issue of his chemical work, a substance in which toothpaste manufacturers took an unexpected interest.[23] In that case, the Board decided against patenting the discovery, and since then the Institute has relied simply upon full public disclosure through scientific journals as its only means of protection against exploitation. In this policy, the Institute is in accord with the general attitude of American physicians, who have long been reluctant to limit medical discoveries by legal restrictions.

WORLD WAR I did much to wipe out whatever provincialism still clung to the American medical profession. Men from different cities and schools working together at the front, in the base hospitals, and in laboratories and offices at home, could not fail to influence each other's professional ambitions and standards. Colonel William H. Welch, president of the Board of Scientific Directors of The Rockefeller Institute, and Lieutenant Colonel Flexner had ample opportunity to note, as they inspected the Army's medical installations, that the character and pace of American medical education and research were rapidly changing. Not even a war could prevent or greatly delay an advance now under way for several years.

At the beginning of the century, when the Institute was organized, there were, as we have seen, only about five universities in the whole country which could properly be designated as centers of medical research — Harvard and Johns Hopkins, the Universities of Pennsylvania, Chicago, and Michigan. In these, in individual laboratories of a half-dozen other schools, and in a small number of health departments and government laboratories, a few score research men conducted original investigations in anatomy, physiology, biochemistry, pathology, and bacteriology. The rest of the country's hundred medical colleges were still in the trade-school stage, some of them shockingly inadequate, a few striving to improve themselves.[24] The American Medical Association, well aware of this weakness, set up a Council on Medical Education in 1907 to grade the schools from "A" to "C," according to facilities, curricula, and standards of admission. Although the public knew little of this quiet step toward reform, some of the class "C" schools were at once driven out of existence, and many of the "C" and "B" institutions added trained full-time teachers to their preclinical departments. In 1910 Abraham Flexner's brilliant, widely publicized report, *Medical Education in the United States and Canada,* startled the public into full knowledge of the situation. The reform, thus greatly speeded, made itself felt at first chiefly in the preclinical sciences, for which a score or more of the medical schools soon possessed adequate research laboratories.

Not long after came an advance also in clinical teaching and research. In 1913 the Johns Hopkins University, aided by The Rockefeller Foundation, put full-time professors in charge of most of its clinics and gave them better research facilities. Within a few years several other medical schools, notably Washington University in St. Louis, Yale, and the University of Iowa followed suit with some or all of their clinical chairs. This resulted in a vast increase in academic appointments of all grades in both preclinical and clinical subjects. The country now had positions and facilities for several hundred medical investigators. As against five or six centers of medical research, there were by 1920 a dozen, and by 1925 eighteen or twenty rivaling the best European universities in facilities and productiveness. Furthermore, a number of research institutions had sprung up in the train of The Rockefeller Institute, some of which covered wide fields of medical research — for example, the Mc-Cormick Memorial Institute (1903) and the Sprague Memorial Institute (1911) of Chicago, and the Hooper Institute for Medical Research of San Francisco (1914). Others cultivated special areas, such as bacteriology, embryology, tuberculosis, cancer, and mental illness.

This expansion of research inside and outside the universities resulted in far more active interchange of men and information among American medical institutions than had been possible two decades earlier. The Rockefeller Institute, for example, until 1920 had necessarily drawn about half of its young American-trained medical men from either Harvard or Johns Hopkins; there were few graduates of other schools who sought or qualified for research posts. On the other hand, of those who left the Institute up to the end of 1920, only one fourth went to one of these two schools; new or newly expanded research centers looked to the Institute for recruits. Eugene Opie and two others went to Washington University, St. Louis, three went to Stanford, and four to the College of Physicians and Surgeons of Columbia University, at last taking its rightful place among the nation's medical schools. In 1921 three joined the reorganized Yale Medical School. By 1925 the Institute was represented on the faculties of Columbia, Yale, Johns Hopkins, Harvard,

Chicago, Pennsylvania, and Vanderbilt. In turn, it was recruiting from an increasingly wide group of universities.

The inevitable result was to lessen the contrast between The Rocke-feller Institute and the academic research centers. As Abraham Flexner pointed out in his report, an institute for medical research could not be fundamentally different from a university faculty of medicine. It was, he said, itself a faculty, somewhat specialized, happily circumstanced, freed from undergraduate teaching, but like the university medical faculty a cooperative group of workers devoted to training as well as investiga-tion.[25] In one way, however, the development of other research centers favored the Institute's distinctiveness, by lessening its burden of respon-sibility for work immediately related to medical practice and public health. With good research hospitals in many cities and an increasing number of public health departments equipped to investigate infectious diseases, the Institute could, with a good conscience, devote itself to basic studies in chemistry, biochemistry, and biophysics, as well as in physiol-ogy, pathology, and bacteriology; and the hospital was more than ever free to select its own fields of investigation.

The Rockefeller Institute retained a special character because of its independent status and the international origin of its staff. In such a place divergent temperaments and ways of working were freely toler-ated, differences of language and nationality counted for little. The In-stitute's laboratories and hospital still received about one fourth of their new recruits from foreign countries and sent a like proportion back to Britain, Europe, and the Orient. Scientists of many nations, sharing ex-periences and opinions gained all over the world, continued to work together with mutual comprehension and a common aim.

CHAPTER SEVEN

Men and Molecules

Life in the Institute. Simon Flexner as administrator. "Arrowsmith."
Biochemistry, chemical pharmacology. General physiology; proteins
as colloids. Physical chemistry, photobiology, biophysics.

AFTER WORLD WAR I, the Institute enjoyed a long period of calm, with no major changes of direction or policy until after Flexner's retirement in 1935. Members of the staff, returning in 1919 from national service or resuming their normal programs after diversion to the Institute's emergency research, easily stepped back into the peace-time life of the laboratories. Until 1921 the Board of Scientific Directors consisted of six members only. Herter's successor, Theodore Janeway, had died in 1918. The laboratories were still directed by their original heads. Meltzer's health, however, was failing, and his group was soon to be disbanded.

Each of the five laboratories was a little kingdom ruled over by the distinguished scientist for whom it was organized. How egocentric the command, how strict the direction, varied with the character and temperament of the Member in charge and with the nature and range of his interests. Flexner, with a group of wide scope including several mature people, left his senior men free to follow programs of their own. The others, accustomed to European methods, kept their staffs at work on problems in which the laboratory directors were personally interested. Jacques Loeb, exploring broad general ideas by very simply planned experiments, used chiefly assistants, with special experience in related fields of science, who could devise and operate recording apparatus or assist with the analysis of results. He did not discuss the work freely with them. Such assistants left when no longer needed or when they wearied of working under close direction. Two of them, however, John H. Northrop and Moses Kunitz, developed the programs assigned to them with such success that they became Members of the Institute. Carrel also, accustomed as a surgeon to prompt, unquestioning service, held his staff, most of whom were skilled technicians, strictly to his own program. Levene, too, used his young chemists largely for his own experiments. Flexner did not conceal from Levene his fear that they were not being trained for independent work. Against this charge Levene defended himself, with some justification, by pointing out that Van Slyke and Jacobs were leading independent research in the Institute, and three other former assistants were filling responsible positions elsewhere.[1]

It has often been said, by those whose memories focus on one or two specific leaders rather than on the Institute as a whole, that the several component groups were at this time isolated intellectually, seeking little help and inspiration from one another. In reality, the majority of the two-score scientists and physicians were happy in sharing ideas and experiences. Hideyo Noguchi, reminiscing in 1914 about the earliest days of the Institute, went on to say in his halting English, "The fine brotherly feeling has never left us. . . . There is such good fellow-feeling among the workers, and I think all the men who served under Dr. Flexner must have felt and must be feeling just so as I feel."[2] The workers in pathology, bacteriology, chemistry, and pharmacology consulted one another freely and visited each other's laboratories. Attendance at a weekly staff meeting to hear reports on current work was practically compulsory. The whole staff, moreover, met daily at lunch, where the workers of all ages mingled and there was no ban on shop talk. Younger men thought it a special privilege to sit at Jacques Loeb's table, for he was sure to discuss in lively fashion one of his projects or to elaborate some unexpected whimsy.[3] He was as ready to encourage keen young men in any of the laboratory groups as he was to criticize old-fashioned or unimaginative thinking. The inspiration he thus afforded his juniors reached far beyond the Institute's walls. A distinguished botanist, now a Trustee of the Institute, has recorded Loeb's gracious and encouraging response to correspondence in which, as a young and unknown beginner, he ventured to challenge one of Loeb's interpretations.[4]

Alexis Carrel, although he won almost fanatical devotion from some of his immediate helpers, held himself aloof from the general life of the Institute. Working largely by himself, he rarely consulted colleagues. His laboratory rooms, necessarily guarded against bacterial contamination, acquired the aura of a sanctuary where masked acolytes clad in black gowns and caps performed the aseptic mysteries of experimental surgery and tissue culture. Early in his career Carrel adopted black surgical gowns and drapes for the operating table to cut down glare and give better visibility to the tissues upon which he performed his extremely delicate operations. People from other laboratories, fearing to carry infectious germs into the laboratory, did not drop in for casual visits and never learned what was going on, except when specially invited. Even at the lunch table, Carrel did not fully unbend, often entering after the others were seated, wearing his surgeon's cap as a badge (some of his colleagues thought) of hieratic distinction. Many rumors about cloistral seclusiveness at the Institute can be traced to the behavior of this unique personage.

It was Simon Flexner who welded into a coherent whole this band of individualists with their separate concerns and their private staffs, giving the Institute a unified front to the Board of Scientific Directors and to the outside world. "The Rockefeller Institute is yourself. You are its mind," Carrel once wrote to Flexner.[5] Frederick T. Gates, speaking for the two Rockefellers and the Board of Trustees, said the same thing in his own exuberant way: "The spirit of this great Institute, the inspiration of it, the directing force of it, that spirit which, more than any other single agency, has wrought these great and beneficent results, is an embodied spirit. It has a local habitation and a name, and that name is Simon Flexner."[2]

Outright respect and admiration like this is never won by administrative fiat. Flexner, in fact, had made himself, without formal title, leader not only of the research staff but of the Board of Scientific Directors. The Board had originally thought of the Institute, in a vague way, as a group of enterprises — laboratories, hospital, department of animal pathology, perhaps a department of public health — not necessarily under a single leader. Flexner, as director of the laboratories, received the earliest command; by his talent for organization he kept command, without a specific directive, when the hospital and the department of animal pathology were created. Not until 1924, when some now forgotten issue arose between the laboratories and the hospital, did the Board, by amending its bylaws, formally declare him Director of the Institute as a whole.

It is not easy to describe how this self-contained, soft-spoken, slightly built man so quickly gained the confidence of the two Rockefellers and their aides, Gates and Starr Murphy; nor by what skill he led the experienced physicians and scientists of the Board of Scientific Directors and managed his heady team of research men. Estimates of Flexner vary in emphasis, for he showed different sides to different people. All agree on his intellectual powers. Raymond Fosdick, who often saw him in action in the board room of The Rockefeller Foundation, speaks of the ". . . steely precision of his reason. His mind was like a search-light that could be turned, at will, on any question that came before him."[6] A close associate in the laboratory wrote that "One of his best strengths was a logic far beyond that of most men, final as a knife."[7] It was agreed, too, that Flexner was an excellent business administrator. That he won the approval of Rockefeller, Sr., is sufficient attestation that he was enterprising and conscientious in his use of the Institute's resources. During the early years he felt especially responsible for the money entrusted to his care. A scientific executive who finds himself, like Flexner, directing large expenditures after struggling with an inadequate academic budget tends to be overcautious in small matters, thus stilling his own qualms while preaching economy to his associates. Then, too, his boyhood in an ambitious but poor immigrant's family had made him sensitive to the value of money.

Some tales of Flexner's minor economies are exaggerated or apocryphal. Gossip tells, for instance, that he once levied a twenty-five cent fine on a young man caught leaving a Bunsen burner lighted when not in use, and that he prescribed the exact width of a floor area along the animal house partitions to be dusted with insect powder. Pennies saved by minor economies were, however, spent without stint when liberality was indicated. "You need a vacation," he wrote to an Associate Member who had overworked on an emergency assignment. "You and your wife are to go to Bermuda for a month. The business manager has the money ready for you." The habit of attention to housekeeping details, developed when he was supervising construction and equipment of the laboratories, persisted for years. Flexner would be seen trying the doors at closing time, or inspecting the scrub women's work in dark corners. An elevator man needing a shave or an errand boy with dusty shoes was noticed and admonished later by his immediate superior, or sometimes on the spot by the Director himself.

Flexner's control of the staff rested upon respect for individuality and understanding of the scientific temperament. He knew that he was directing a group of exceptional men whose personal intensity inevitably raised problems for the administrator. In a confidential report to the Board of Scientific Directors, he wrote in measured words, naming nobody, "Such men, when numerously assembled under one roof, may give rise to situations which tax somewhat the administrative staff; but it appears nevertheless that with the high purpose mutually understood and appreciated and the exercise of a fair amount of human wisdom and tact, such a temperamental team is capable of working in close contact and with mutual respect and helpfulness over long periods of time." Leaving his more self-confident associates to follow their own devices, he provided for others moral support, direction, and even control when he thought it necessary. "The ablest men are often the most diffident and self-deprecatory," he wrote; "they require in many cases to be reassured and made to believe in themselves."[8] One of the foreign-born Members who needed such reassurance, at a time of special stress, got it and was grateful: "I did not think yesterday morning that my nerves could stand the strain much longer. I left your room after our little interview cured and happy. This was happening right along repeatedly . . . I value this growing — what shall I name it but affection — above all."[9]

Such consideration and solicitude for the welfare of people dependent, in one way or another, upon his leadership, extended from Member to new employee in the shops or animal house. He made himself acquainted with the families of staff and employees, gave sympathy and practical help in time of illness, and at times surprised them with special attentions, such as sending a book on child care to a young mother. He kept a sharp eye on the operating personnel and when he spotted a bright ambitious youth marked him for promotion and sometimes arranged special training for him. The present superintendent of maintenance, Bernard Lupinek, relates that Flexner, seeing him sketching a floor plan, promptly had him take a course in architectural drawing and thereafter saw to his advance.[10] Anthony J. Campo, purchasing agent and chief pharmacist, who began as office boy, was encouraged to study pharmacy. Several valuable administrative aides were thus started in lifetime careers in the Institute.

Naturally, Flexner generally got what he wanted from the staff on request or by friendly persuasion. William H. Welch once humorously remarked on the readiness with which everyone "consented" to do what Dr. Flexner asked.[11] Yet Flexner could act, at times, like an executive director rather than a friend or father. Naturally enthusiastic and outgoing, he had learned to restrain the show of affection in order to protect himself when firmness was necessary. "Dr. Flexner asked me to write the stuff up *immediately,*" wrote young Frederick L. Gates to Peter Olitsky, "and when he talks that-a-way, no sir, he don't mean maybe."[12] Even Members felt the full force of executive authority when they overran their annual budgets. Levene, more than once guilty of such an indiscretion, squirmed like a naughty boy under reproof.[13] Flexner's most impersonal side was shown in the execution of his policy regarding tenure of appointment. He firmly maintained the rule that only Members had permanent tenure. Men who did not seem likely to reach full membership, even if competent investigators, were permitted or advised to accept posts proffered by other institutions. In this way the Institute promoted medical education by serving as a training school, and if it risked occasionally losing a good scientist, it might hope to get him back later. Such moves were handled with formal courtesy and every kindness; Flexner, if necessary, looked up positions for men he wished to drop and, it is said, he sometimes got the Board of Scientific Directors to subsidize a new appointment elsewhere, to prevent temporary loss of income by the departing staff member. Frequently, such a move brought higher academic rank in a worthy institution, and the decision seldom rankled.

A question about Flexner to which diverse answers are given by those who worked under him concerns the extent to which he controlled their research programs. The answers differ because Flexner treated people individually. Once having chosen men of independent genius, like Carrel, Loeb, and Levene, or seeing such men develop within the Institute, like Rous and Northrop, to name only a few of many, he let them go their own way. To less certain men he gave needed attention. In his division of pathology and bacteriology, Flexner carefully shepherded juniors not ready for independent work, encouraging others to follow their own ideas. When the Institute was new, he closely watched the work of the staff, often visiting the laboratories, and urging on young workers by his enthusiasm for what they were doing. When he was sure of his man's competence, the pressure was light. One of the staff recalls telling the Director that he wished to leave pathology for physiology. Flexner approved, and added, "It will take you two years to find your way. I'll not expect anything of you until after that."[14] Noguchi was a special case. Flexner had assumed almost a parental responsibility for him and, as we have seen in a previous chapter, deliberately chose his line of work. Perhaps he pushed him too hard, as some thought, but Noguchi's burning ambition was sufficient to explain his pace, sometimes too rapid for balanced judgment.

The Institute and Flexner himself have been accused of capitalizing prematurely on some of the hopeful results of the early research. Certainly the newspapers, deeply interested in the work, made the most of it under sensational headlines. They had as yet no trained science writers, and tyros searched every number of the *Journal of Experimental Medicine* for a headline. Carrel and Noguchi, in particular, attracted publicity about which Flexner's friends were sometimes moved to banter him. When a London newspaper quoted him as asserting that the experimental surgeons at The Rockefeller Institute would soon accomplish the transfer of sound vital organs from lower animals to man, Sir William Osler dashed off a note from Oxford, signed with the pseudonym under which he perpetrated his sharpest practical jokes: "Dear Sir, Both my kidneys are worn out, my heart is used up and my liver has struck work. How much would it cost to have ones put in at your Institute? Edgerton Yorick Davis, Jr."[15]

Less easily amused critics of American medical institutions brought charges, implicitly directed at The Rockefeller Institute, against such centers of research. The most thoughtful critic, Hans Zinsser, complained of "premature publication . . . frequent ballyhoo of unimportant stuff as the work of genius . . . popular interest, unwisely exploited," ascribing the more serious delinquencies of this kind not to the scientists themselves as much as to "administrators and directors impelled by the desire for institutional advertising."[16] Zinsser, pointing thus at Flexner and his Board, was unjust to both. As early as 1908, when Flexner's anti-meningitis serum was much in the news, he expressed his displeasure with the newspapers to F. T. Gates, Chairman of the Board of Trustees, who replied,

> I am entirely in sympathy with your efforts to protect yourself and the Institute from the press. If I were in your place I would care more for the respect and confidence of 150 leading scientific men in this and other countries than for the good opinion of all Christendom besides put together. You will certainly have my most active co-operation in your determination to hold the Institute strictly to its business and to stop the ears of everybody about it from hearing any voice but the voice of science.[17]

If in spite of good intentions Flexner and the Board of Scientific Directors inadvertently exposed themselves to undue publicity, the indiscretion arose from the novel character of the enterprise and the pressure everyone felt to demonstrate to the public and to the founder of the Institute that progress was being made. His reassuring letter to Flexner notwithstanding, the ebullient Gates was eager for new achievements.

> Who has not felt the throbbing of desire to be useful to the whole wide world? [he asked at a dinner in 1914]. The discoveries of this Institute have already reached the depths of Africa with their healing ministrations . . . You announce a discovery here. Before night your discovery will be flashed around the world. In thirty days it will be in every medical college on earth. In sixty days it will be at the bedsides of the best hospitals and from these hospitals it will work its way to every sick room in the world that is visited by a competent physician.[2]

In the face of such naïve expectations, restraint must have been difficult. "The first years," Flexner said, "were nervous ones for all concerned in the actual work and I suspect the Scientific Directors did not escape this feeling of uncertainty which may be expressed by the slang phrase, the necessity of 'making good.' "[2] The antivivisection campaign of 1907–1910 intensified the need for an understanding press and public. In his zeal to justify experiments on animals, Flexner, as we have seen, was quoted as predicting quick benefits to public health, especially in regard to poliomyelitis. This represented, as Zinsser admitted, the growing pains of American medical science. Research institutes had to learn by experience and so did the press. Early in 1930, when a reporter for the *Herald Tribune* tried to find out something about Carrel's chicken heart culture, on its eighteenth anniversary, he complained that it had been sheltered from publicity for the past two years and he could get no news at all from "the large anti-publicity department of The Rockefeller Institute."[18]

In retrospect, adverse criticisms of Flexner as administrator, and of his Board of Scientific Directors, weigh very little against their immense achievements. However exuberant public pronouncements about The Rockefeller Institute and however severe its Director with those requiring guidance or restraint, those who labored within its walls knew that its work was being led quietly, humanely, and well, and that the organization being created would not be shaken by any transient ineptness of executives or investigators. The best testimony to Flexner's skill as director is that during his entire regime no full Member left to go elsewhere, except Eugene L. Opie, who was called to an important chair that especially appealed to his love of teaching.

Simon Flexner had come a long way since he was graduated from a proprietary school of medicine[19] and traveled to Baltimore for postgraduate training under William H. Welch. In those days, he himself said, he was "unformed, inexperienced, ambitious, over-strenuous and inconsiderate."[2] These, after all, are characteristics of eager youth. Time and self-discipline would cure them. Now he was an investigator known around the world, an astute executive, the influential friend of John D. Rockefeller's son and his almoners, unquestioned leader of pre-eminent scientists.

WHEN SINCLAIR LEWIS published in 1925 his famous novel about medical research, *Arrowsmith,* he thanked Paul de Kruif, not only for much of the bacteriological and medical material in the tale, but also for help in realizing the characters as living people and for his philosophy as a scientist. Readers acquainted with the career of Lewis's collaborator naturally looked for The Rockefeller Institute in the novel's setting, without finding it, however, in any literal sense.

Paul de Kruif, a pupil of F. G. Novy at the University of Michigan, joined the Institute's division of pathology and bacteriology in 1920 and stayed two years. His excellent work on bacterial mutations, as correlated with smooth (virulent) and rough (attenuated) colonies of the bacillus of rat septicemia, *Pasteurella multocida,* focused the attention of bacteriologists on that important subject. But the impetuous young man, already tempted to give up research for scientific writing, indiscreetly contributed an anonymous chapter on the state of American medicine to a critical book about civilization in the United States.[20] Declaring in this essay that our medical men were losing the personal touch as they became more scientific, de Kruif (not himself a physician) took issue with a statement by Rufus Cole, director of The Rockefeller Institute Hospital, that medicine is an independent, not merely an applied, science. Furthermore, he illustrated what he considered the unscientific quality of much research then done by physicians by an example drawn from the hospital's studies — not identifiable as such by the general reader but sufficiently obvious to the Institute's people, some of whom knew de Kruif had written the article. Flexner, discussing staff problems a few years later in a confidential report, said that there had been one case in which a scientific worker overstepped the bounds of fellowship: "Reminded of the original understanding under which he accepted appointment, he at once proffered his resignation."[8] Thus departing, de Kruif began his career as a writer, promptly making a great success with *The Microbe Hunters* (1926).

The "McGurk Institute," imagined by Sinclair Lewis and Paul de Kruif in *Arrowsmith,* was not a direct caricature of The Rockefeller Institute, which it did not resemble physically. "McGurk" represented some of the good and all of the bad things seen by the idealistic young consulting author in the medical institutions he had known, retouched by the novelist's imagination. Nor were any of the characters direct portraits, although some of the Rockefeller staff contributed bits of their personalities to the composite figures Lewis drew from de Kruif's memoranda. Jacques Loeb was mingled with F. G. Novy and perhaps also Moses Gomberg of Ann Arbor, in the benign, unworldly "Gottlieb." "Terry Wickett" largely reflected de Kruif's admiration for his friend Jack Northrop. "Tubbs," director of McGurk, and his suave, ambitious understudy "Rippleton Holabird" were pieced together from isolated traits of various individuals who interested or irked de Kruif, and were pointed up by Lewis. "Sondelius," the world-ranging public health expert, was an invention of Sinclair Lewis alone.[21] Nevertheless, *Arrowsmith* gives an instructive, if overwrought, picture of the motives, dilemmas, and exasperations of some men who work in a research laboratory — a picture, however, which plays down one notable type, the steady-going professional investigator, not inflated by success nor flustered by mistakes and concerned more with getting his work done than with outdoing or reforming his colleagues. The Rockefeller Institute had — and has — many such men, better subjects, perhaps, for the historian than for the novelist.

IN 1918 Phoebus A. Levene moved his division of chemistry into the building now called Flexner Hall, where he had not only more room for his chemical benches and apparatus, but also an office large enough for his extensive private working library, and ample wall space on which to hang a few favorite reproductions of modern paintings. In these quarters he resumed his ceaseless exploration of biological compounds, publishing alone or with assistants from half a dozen to thirty papers every year. Levene's investigations of the difficult group of lipoids (substances related to the fats, occurring especially in the brain and liver) helped bring order to a chaotic field, by reducing the group to three definite classes: the lecithins and cephalins, the sphingomyelins, and the cerebrosides. Levene prepared many of these substances in more highly purified form than had ever been done; he worked out the chemical structure of sphingomyelins and cerebrosides, found previously unknown components of the very complex lecithins and cephalins, and succeeded in synthesizing one form of lecithin.

Turning his attention to compounds of a quite different kind, the mucins and similar substances, Levene and his colleagues again brought light into a dark subject. Mucins take their name from the mucous secretion of the digestive and respiratory tracts, which protect, lubricate, and moisten surfaces exposed to food and air. Similar viscous substances occur widely in the body, serving to hold cells together and to bind water in interstices of the tissues. They lubricate joints and contribute to the cushioning effect of the skin. Levene found that they contain glycoproteins, compounds of proteins with carbohydrates classifiable as sugars. These latter are, however, by no means as simple chemically as ordinary sugars; they contain nitrogen, so placed in the molecule as to baffle the chemist's ordinary methods of ascertaining the structural formula. Aware that the major difficulty arose from the presence of asymmetric carbon atoms in the molecule, Levene saw that he could utilize the property of optical rotation of polarized light, characteristic of substances thus constituted, as a means of working out the exact configuration of the problematic compounds. In developing the method, Levene and his associates synthesized a very large series of relatively simple chemical compounds containing only one asymmetric carbon atom, from which they learned how to relate optical properties to chemical structure in the more complex sugars. Levene was one of the first investigators in this country to recognize the importance of rotatory dispersion for elucidating problems of configuration. The subject held his attention throughout his later years. At first appreciated by only a few chemists, the method has now, two decades after Levene's death, come into very wide use.

In this work Levene was aided by Alexandre Rothen, a specialist in the optical investigation of biological materials, who came to the Institute in 1927 from Switzerland. Rothen's subsequent career at The Rockefeller Institute will be discussed in later chapters. Louis A. Mikeska, a Yale-trained organic chemist, assisted Levene in studying many concurrent problems of organic structure from 1920 to 1930, when he joined the Standard Oil Company's research staff. He was associated with Levene and a guest worker, Takajiro Mori of Tokyo, in the important discovery, announced in 1930, that the sugar of thymonucleic acid is deoxyribose. In 1931–1932 a principal assistant of Levene in these studies on sugars was Russell E. Marker, who later made (elsewhere) very important contributions to the chemistry of the ovarian hormones. When Flexner's administration ended, in 1935, Levene was still at work. A later chapter will deal with research done in his last years before retirement in 1939 with the title of Emeritus Member.

As mentioned in earlier chapters, the researches of Paul Ehrlich and his co-workers at Frankfurt, which led to the discovery of Salvarsan in 1910, were closely watched at The Rockefeller Institute, which had secured financial help for Ehrlich's work. His investigations raised chemotherapy from mere exploitation of discoveries made by chance (as, for instance, the quinine-containing cinchona bark for malaria) to a new branch of medical science based on a logical procedure for finding drugs with which to attack disease-producing parasitic germs. His method, made possible by the parallel advance of bacteriology, pathology, and organic chemistry in the nineteenth and twentieth centuries, is well illustrated by the discovery of Salvarsan. Taking advantage of a clue provided by physicians who had found arsenic useful in treating syphilis,

Ehrlich synthesized a large series of arsenical compounds, testing each for its biological effects and letting the results of the tests dictate the choice of new substances to be synthesized.

To Flexner's mind, the success of Salvarsan urgently suggested similar efforts directed against other infectious diseases. A clue was offered, he thought, by hexamethylenetetramine (Urotropine), in use for twenty years as a urinary antiseptic. This drug readily pervades the entire body but is bactericidal only in an acid environment; to act in the brain and spinal cord, it would have to be modified so that it would release its germicidal component (formaldehyde) in the normally alkaline environment of the tissues. A clever organic chemist, Walter A. Jacobs, was in Levene's laboratory. Flexner promoted him to independent status within the division of chemistry and gave him an assistant, Michael Heidelberger, who years later occupied a chair of biochemistry at Columbia University. For a year the two worked intensively on the transformations of hexamethylenetetramine, making scores of derivatives, some of which proved strongly bactericidal for typhoid bacilli, streptococci, and other organisms. None, however, came into clinical use, presumably because they were less effective in tests on animals than in test-tube experiments with bacterial cultures.

During the latter part of World War I, Jacobs and Heidelberger were busy, as narrated in Chapter 6, with the chemical side of work on trypanocidal substances, finally preparing the drug Tryparsamide, which was so brilliantly successful in treating African sleeping sickness. After the war these two, with their pathologist colleagues Brown and Pearce, returned to the quest for a better antisyphilitic than Salvarsan. Modifying again some of the arsenical drugs they had prepared earlier, they found one which was quite effective against experimental syphilis, and not toxic to their rabbits. Under the direction of Edgar Stillman, a clinical trial was begun at the Hospital of The Rockefeller Institute. In a first series of a hundred cases, the new drug gave excellent results, but the next batch revealed undesirable side effects and the whole effort was abandoned. Thereafter, Jacobs and Heidelberger worked for several years on other potential bactericides, especially derivatives of cinchona, without obtaining compounds sufficiently free from toxicity for clinical use. In any such joint effort, the chemist may find himself in an awkward position: his program of investigation is subordinated to the pathologist's demand for new compounds required by his animal experimentation. Jacobs, as a chemist hampered by this limitation, felt that he could work more profitably along lines primarily dictated by chemical principles.

As his next field of research Jacobs chose the cardiac glycosides. This term, meaning simply "heart drugs containing sugars," conceals behind technical verbiage one of the most romantic subjects in chemical pharmacology. Readers familiar with the English countryside in June, with its lanes bordered by tall glowing foxgloves, may imagine the scene in 1776 when the Shropshire woman told William Withering that the leaves of this plant were good for dropsy. How effectively Withering followed this clue was related in 1785 in his celebrated *Account of the Foxglove,* with its handsome frontispiece of a full-flowered spike of *Digitalis purpurea.*

More ominous in its association with the glycosides is the stately Javanese upas tree, *Antiaris toxicaria:*

> Fierce in dead silence on the blasted heath
> Fell Upas sits, the Hydra-tree of death.[22]

Though less sinister in fact than in poetry and legend, the upas tree is the source of a potent glycosidal poison. Pursuing the subject further, one comes upon such exotic substances as the African arrow poison ouabain, product of various species of *Strophanthus,* a plant of the dogbane family akin to the lovely oleander, itself laden with a cardiac glycoside. Deadly to man and animals because of their toxic effect upon the heart muscle, some of these drugs given in very small doses strengthen the failing heart and regulate its beat.

Powdered foxglove and strophanthus leaves make good but inexact medicines. For precise control of the failing heart, modern physicians need the purified active principles. Knowledge of the chemical structure of the glycosides was therefore imperative; furthermore, with this information, pharmacologists might hope to get at secrets of the heartbeat by discovering just what happens within the heart muscle cells when the glycosidal drug acts upon them.

European chemists investigating digitalis, strophanthin, and a whole series of other such drugs found that each molecule contains one to four molecules of sugarlike substances linked to an aglycone, that is to say, "something-not-sugar." The aglycone is responsible for the drug action;

the associated sugars may affect the penetration and utilization of the drug. Many plants containing such substances belong to the dogbanes or Apocynaceae, among which various species of the genus *Strophanthus* are characterized particularly by a high glycosidal content.

When Walter Jacobs began to study this subject about 1922, these species could be distinguished from one another only with difficulty, a fact which handicapped chemical investigation. His work, with his associates Heidelberger, E. L. Gustus, R. C. Elderfield, and others, brought order into the field through accurate chemical characterization of the strophanthus glycosides and through obtaining their physiologically active aglycones in the pure state. Working out the chemical composition of one particular aglycone, strophanthidine, Jacobs discovered that its complex molecular framework of 23 carbon atoms contains four carbon rings, and he suspected, therefore, that it is related chemically to cholesterol, a common lipoid in plants. This was the first hint of a relation between the cardiac glycosides and the steroids, a family of substances containing the adrenocortical and sex gland hormones. Gradual recognition by pharmacologists and chemists of this relationship has been very helpful in advances along a broad front in this field of organic chemistry.

In the 1930's, having largely clarified the chemical structure of the strophanthus glycosides, Jacobs shifted to the study of alkaloidal drugs, beginning with ergot, another drug with a long history. Lyman C. Craig, now a Member of the Institute, began his career there as an assistant in this work, which will be described in a later chapter.

DURING THE WAR Jacques Loeb had busied himself with several uncompleted investigations of earlier years. In 1915, for example, he extended in a spectacular way his famous experiment on artificial parthenogenesis in sea urchins, by producing living tadpoles from unfertilized frogs' eggs stimulated chemically. To the layman, fatherless offspring of a vertebrate animal constituted a far more compelling demonstration than did the primitive sea urchin; to biologists, the new experiment re-emphasized the general validity of Loeb's mechanistic theory of embryonic development.

In previous researches, Loeb had been observing the responses of an extremely complex material, the protoplasm of living vegetable and animal cells, to the action of very simple inorganic agents normally present in cells and body fluids, such as the salts of sodium, calcium, potassium, and magnesium. He had studied such phenomena as the induction of cell division by hypertonic salt solutions, the death of cells from antagonistic salt action, and the generation of electrical potentials in tissues, largely from the viewpoint of the external agents. Now, in the last phase of his research career, he turned his attention to the properties of protoplasm itself, the basic seat of life processes. Characteristically, however, he did not begin with protoplasm in the living organism, but with proteins in their simplest available form — as they exist, for example, in gelatin. Solutions of such proteins, even after extraction from the tissues, retain certain properties of especial interest to the physiologist, namely, viscosity, osmotic pressure, the maintenance of electrical potentials, a tendency to swell in dilute solutions of acids and alkalis, and to coagulate under the influence of heat and certain chemical agents. Many of these peculiarities result from the fact that in plant and animal tissues the proteins exist as colloidal suspensions consisting essentially of a fluid medium packed with very fine particles. Although these peculiar properties individually appertain to many non-living and even inorganic substances, the association of all of them with proteins suggested that they play a special role in life processes. Attempts, however, to explain their vital functions by familiar principles of ordinary chemistry and physics had been in vain. The role of proteins in living tissues was to be solved only by the methods of physical chemistry, which Loeb applied to the vital characteristics of protoplasm.

His first approach was to put little collodion bags filled with gelatin into fluids which reproduced in a simplified way the natural environment of cells in the body — dilute solutions of sodium chloride and of such other salts, acids, and alkalis as occur in living tissues — and then to measure the behavior of the gelatin as he varied the concentration of the inorganic agents. What he and his associates discovered can be most easily explained by first summarizing his general conclusion: some of the most puzzling peculiarities of proteins can be accounted for quantitatively by assuming that the latter behave according to a concept of physical chemistry called "Donnan's equilibrium principle" after one of its discoverers, F. G. Donnan of London. This principle, announced in 1911, was derived from laboratory experiments with salts and chemical dyestuffs, but Loeb perceived at once that it applies also to a situation that occurs frequently in living tissues. It states in mathematical form what happens when solutions containing substances composed (as are proteins) of very large molecules, mixed with small molecules, such as those of ordinary salts, are confined within membranes of semipermeable material, such as collodion, cellophane, or the surface membranes of animal or plant cells. In brief, the large molecules cannot diffuse through the fine pores of the membrane, whereas the salts pass freely in either direction. By electrostatic attraction, the trapped large molecules hold some of the salt on their side of the membrane, causing an unequal distribution of salt ions in the two spaces, according to a ratio which can be calculated from the quantities of the dissolved substances. As a result, a difference of electrical potential now exists between the two surfaces of the membrane and can be measured with a galvanometer.

Loeb saw at once the importance of Donnan's principle for biology, and so also did an eminent European medical scientist, Leonor Michaelis, who was to join The Rockefeller Institute some years later. Michaelis experimented at times with living tissues but devoted himself mostly to the study of artificial membranes of dried collodion, developing general mathematical expressions for permeability and membrane potentials. Loeb and Michaelis were in touch by correspondence. Although both men deliberately chose a very simple experimental design, aiming to deal with their materials as would a physicist with nonorganic objects, in two important features Loeb's experimental conditions resembled those existing in living tissues: the collodion bags in which he enclosed the gelatin served as a large-scale model of the surface membrane that surrounds the protoplasm of a cell; and his exact regulation of the acidity or alkalinity of the solutions resembled that which exists in the animal body.

An English worker had already shown that Donnan's equilibrium principle could explain one of the most striking properties of the simple protein, gelatin — its ability to take up water with consequent great swelling. Loeb found that changes in the viscosity and the osmotic pressure of gelatin can be explained quantitatively in the same way. He supported this explanation by observing that variations in the acidity or alkalinity and the salt ion concentration of protein solutions are accompanied by electrical changes. If the swelling of proteins in acids and alkalis is actually a Donnan equilibrium effect, there must be a difference

The laboratory of P.A.T. Levene, about 1909

Left to right: Walter A. Jacobs, Donald D. Van Slyke, Gustave M. Meyer

Founder's Hall in 1906

Founder's Hall in the early 50's

A pathology laboratory in 1909, Eugene L. Opie at his microscope

of electrical potential between the gelatin inside the collodion sack and the fluid outside it, just as there was in Donnan's original experiments with inorganic substances. Loeb observed this potential and by exact measurement found its magnitude to accord with theory. Thus he demonstrated that several physicochemical characteristics of proteins, essentially concerned with life activities, are explainable by the theory of semipermeable membranes. David I. Hitchcock took part in much of this research, during Loeb's last years and afterward with J. H. Northrop. He left the Institute in 1926, for a post at Bryn Mawr College, shortly thereafter joining the faculty of Yale Medical School.

It is, of course, impossible in brief space to follow all the ramifications of this work from 1918 to 1924, or to consider the full implications of an investigation reported in no less than seventy published articles. It must suffice to say that by their experiments and conclusions, Loeb and Michaelis brought the concept of semipermeability of colloidal substances and protoplasmic surfaces, and the related phenomenon of membrane potential, from the realm of physical chemistry into biology and medicine. In this advance, Michaelis was the more precise mathematical thinker, Loeb the more practical experimenter with living tissues, and an effective propagandist. Loeb well summed up the objective of these years in the final words of his last book:

> Organisms have been defined as chemical machines consisting essentially of colloidal material capable of growing and automatically reproducing themselves. If this be true, advance in physiology will be chiefly a hit or miss game until science is in possession of a mathematical theory of the colloidal behavior of the substances of which living matter is composed. If Donnan's theory of membrane equilibria furnishes the mathematical and quantitative basis for a theory of colloidal behavior of the proteins, as the author believes it does, it may be predicted that this theory will become one of the foundations on which modern physiology will rest.[23]

Another generation has amply verified this prediction. It has become a commonplace in every branch of biology and medicine that semipermeable membranes exist wherever in a living organism there is a protoplasmic boundary: at the walls of capillary blood vessels, the surfaces of nerve cells, muscle fibers, and every other kind of cellular unit — even within the individual cells, between the general protoplasm and the surfaces of smaller elements, such as the nuclei and the tiny packets of essential enzymes known as mitochondria. This knowledge has become one of the foundations of modern molecular physiology.

Jacques Loeb died in February 1924, at the age of sixty-five, while the investigation was still in progress. He knew that his results were only a first approximation to the solution of a vast problem. Even before his own *Journal of General Physiology* could publish a formal obituary memoir,[24] his associates John Northrop and Moses Kunitz had begun to work out extensions and revisions of certain of his ideas in the field of protein physics, for which he would have been grateful. To present-day students, some of his experiments still look brilliant, others seem oddly planned; it is not always clear what he was about. Yet most of the world's physiologists now follow his lead in detecting, defining, and measuring the chemical interchanges and physiological activities that originate or are regulated at the myriad boundaries and surfaces within tissues and cells. Because of Loeb's insistence that it is the duty of science to seek a mechanistic explanation of life, reinforced by his own experimentation and vigorous propagation of his views, his work has had wide influence on today's thought in biology and medicine.

THE MANTLE of Jacques Loeb, prophet of general physiology, fell upon the worthy shoulders of W. J. V. Osterhout and John H. Northrop. Osterhout, who had come from a professorship of botany at Harvard University, was already connected with The Rockefeller Institute, as a member of the Board of Scientific Directors (appointed in 1920) and as a co-founder of the *Journal of General Physiology*. In 1922, while still at Harvard, he received a Rockefeller Institute grant of $10,000 to carry on research on marine plants in Bermuda. He became head of a laboratory of general physiology at the Institute in 1925.

Osterhout's assistants and other associates in Bermuda included at various times W. C. Cooper, Jr., M. J. Dorcas, E. B. Damon, and A. G. Jacques. In New York his helpers were E. S. Harris, Jr., S. E. Hill, S. E. Kamerling, J. W. Murray, and W. M. Stanley. Lawrence R. Blinks, one of Osterhout's Harvard pupils, joined him at the Institute from 1926 until called to Stanford University in 1933. Marian Irwin joined the staff as Associate in 1925 and worked independently until 1933, when she resigned and married Dr. Osterhout.

Osterhout was unusually well trained, for a botanist in his day, in mathematics, physics, and chemistry. He was a stimulating teacher, illustrating his lectures with the simplest apparatus. He and Loeb had been in close intellectual contact for many years. His research interests, however, were self-acquired before he met Loeb. As an instructor at the University of California in 1896 he began wondering about the relation of cell life to salt concentration, through observing marine plants in San Francisco Bay clinging to ships which had traveled back and forth between fresh and salt water. When the ship's load was lightened, moisture in and on the plants exposed at the water line was concentrated by evaporation until the plants were covered with crystals of salt; yet their tissues lived and kept on growing through successive extreme changes of osmotic pressure accompanying these violent alternations of salinity.

When Jacques Loeb went to the University of California in 1902, Osterhout discussed these observations with him, and had his attention called to the phenomenon of "antagonistic salt action" which Loeb had studied. Animal cells living in the sea or in the body of an animal are constantly exposed to a solution of sodium chloride which, weak as it is, would actually harm them if that salt were not balanced by potassium and other salts also present. In like manner, a pure solution of potassium, or calcium chloride, equal in strength to that in sea water or in an animal's body fluids, will be toxic to the cells unless balanced by sodium in proper concentration. Osterhout tested these effects in aquatic plant tissues and found them strikingly similar to those which Loeb had observed in animal cells. Applying exact quantitative methods, he noted that antagonistic salt action depends in some way upon changes in the permeability of protoplasm; when the tissue is exposed to a single salt, it may develop an increase in permeability which does not occur in a balanced solution.

With these experiments Osterhout began a lifetime study of the physico-chemical properties of plant cells: the ionic composition of their protoplasm, their permeability to salts and other substances, and the manner in which these characteristics are related to their osmotic and bioelectric behavior. To the investigation of these physico-chemical functions of living tissues, he added a study of irreversible processes — for example, coagulation and the excessive permeability associated with injury and death of protoplasm, as well as its recovery from injury. His book *The Mechanism of Injury, Recovery and Death*, published in 1923, in which he discussed the subject mathematically, has had much influence on the development of general cellular physiology. Osterhout later suggested that the physical changes associated with injury of protoplasm depend largely on the amount of water in the non-aqueous surface layers of the cytoplasm.

Quite early Osterhout saw the advantage of working with large plant cells from which sap can be obtained for analysis without contamination, and on which electrical measurements can be made by applying electrodes at two or more points on the surface or by inserting them into the cell. In 1920 he began to use a fresh-water plant, *Nitella flexilis,* which has individual cells several inches in length. Not long afterward he discovered the advantages of the marine plants *Valonia* and *Halicystis,* whose cells may become larger than a pigeon's egg.

Osterhout and his associates showed that *Nitella* cells can conduct an impulse resulting from electrical stimulation in the same way a nerve does, though more slowly. This gave great insight into the mechanism of nerve conduction. He was one of the pioneers in measuring the membrane potential of a cell by an electrode inserted into it, a technique now widely used by physiologists working with large animal cells.

The cells of *Valonia* have the property of accumulating potassium in a far higher concentration than in the sea water around them; those of *Halicystis* contain a cell sap of similar constitution to sea water. Such observations, analyzed by refined technical methods, led Osterhout to emphasize selective permeability as a major factor in tissue function. The ability of cells to accumulate certain salt ions in higher concentration than that of their environment depends upon the properties of their protoplasm, particularly that of their surface layers. These properties Osterhout studied in detail. His findings contributed greatly to the concept that the peculiar characteristics of the surface membranes depend upon the presence of non-aqueous layers containing carrier molecules capable of transporting ions into the interior of the cell, where they are set free by metabolism. To illustrate the operation of carrier molecules, he devised an ingenious cell model, which, like the living cell, is capable of accumulating ions.

His observations on the electrical potentials in his huge plant cells led him to conclude that they result from different speeds of diffusion for the sodium, potassium, and chloride ions migrating through the surface layers. This aided the understanding of similar but less accessible phenomena in animal tissues — for example, the conduction of nerve impulses, of muscle contraction, and the rhythm of the human heart.

It is difficult to characterize such work as this for the general reader, for Osterhout worked toward basic principles symbolized by physico-chemical models. What such a mind contributes is a way of thinking about the puzzles of nature, rather than a mere set of facts. Subsequent investigators may sharpen the observations, revise or even reverse the statement of a particular fact, but the way of thinking, if sound, is built into the structure of scientific method. This has been true of Oster-hout's work, which he still carried on in his ninth decade. Though too profound to make easy headlines, it affects the thinking of every physiologist studying the contraction of muscles, the kidney's power to excrete water while holding back salts, the transmission of nerve impulses, and indeed any other physico-chemical function of living tissues.

JOHN H. NORTHROP's research in general physiology was of a quite different character from that of Osterhout. Northrop had early demonstrated great ability as an investigator. Soon outgrowing the role of assistant to Loeb, he began about 1919 to work independently on the digestion of proteins by pepsin. Just after Loeb's death he was made a full Member of The Rockefeller Institute, but had no desire to fill Loeb's precise role in the New York laboratories. Tall and sturdy, an out-of-doors man fond of hunting and fishing, he detested city life and in 1926 got himself transferred to the Department of Animal Pathology at Princeton, where he could look out upon green fields.

The study of enzymes became Northrop's chief interest as a graduate student. His doctoral thesis on the chemistry of starch was a step toward the study of a starch-digesting enzyme, invertase. A little later, at the Institute, Loeb's theories concerning the colloidal properties of proteins, and in particular their behavior under varying conditions of acidity and alkalinity, suggested experiments on pepsin and trypsin, two enzymes then available that can work outside the body. Crude extracts of the stomach lining containing pepsin and of the pancreas containing trypsin had long been used to digest proteins in laboratory flasks and were even administered as medicine. The special characteristic of an enzyme (or ferment, as many of them are called because they take part in fermentation processes) is that it can initiate a specific chemical re-action. Pepsin, for example, starts the splitting of proteins in the stom-ach; rennin initiates the coagulation of milk; ptyalin, from the salivary glands, converts starches to sugars.

Knowledge of the chemical nature of these indispensable agents of life processes had become more and more necessary. Physiologists were learning that enzymes are at work not only in mass processes, such as di-gestion of food, but also in local chemical reactions throughout the body, where, in immense variety, they preside over innumerable specific re-actions by which nutritive substances are broken down and utilized, energy supplies built up and put to work, and waste products eliminated by chemical degradation. What is the chemical structure of the powerful digestive ferments, pepsin and trypsin, Northrop asked himself, and how do they act when they split proteins into lower compounds? For sev-eral years, he studied the influence of many chemical and physical factors on the process of peptic and tryptic digestion. He answered an old riddle of physiology — why do the digestive enzymes not attack the tissues of the body that produces them? — by showing that enzymes cannot pass the surface membranes of living cells. He was also the first to show that energy applied in the form of X rays can activate trypsin, that is, can con-vert the non-digesting form of this enzyme within the cells of the pan-creas to the active protein-splitting form found when it is discharged into the intestine.

Puzzled by abnormal changes of activity observed in some of his ex-periments with pepsin and trypsin, Northrop concluded that the en-zymes were being activated by some of the products of digestion. For further work on the kinetics of digestion, he needed the enzymes in pure form, and his studies on pepsin gave him hope that he could isolate it chemically. The European chemists Wilstätter and Pekelharing had car-ried several enzymes to a fairly high degree of purification. Their best preparations responded to chemical tests for proteins, but there was al-ways the possibility, as long as the purification was not quite complete, that the protein might be present as an impurity. Wilstätter, in fact, claimed that the active substances in his preparations were neither pro-teins, carbohydrates, nor fats, but entirely new and unknown com-pounds. In 1926, however, J. B. Sumner of Cornell University prepared in crystalline form a protein enzyme of vegetable origin, namely urease, which breaks down urea into ammonium carbonate.

At that time, Northrop was on the verge of a similar success with pepsin, and in 1930 he was able to announce the preparation of crystalline pepsin, the first animal enzyme to be isolated in this way. The last step of Pekelharing's method had yielded an amorphous precipitate possessing considerable enzymatic activity, which Northrop had repeatedly tried in vain to crystallize. Finally, he noticed that this precipitate dissolved if warmed to body temperature (37°C) and reappeared upon cooling. These are good conditions for the formation of crystals. Northrop therefore prepared a highly concentrated suspension of the precipitate in a beaker, warmed it to 37°C, and allowed it to cool to room temperature. The next morning the beaker contained several grams of beautiful crystals in the form of double six-sided pyramids. The enzymatic activity of these protein crystals was five times that of the best commercial pepsin. Northrop calculated that one ounce of his crystalline pepsin would, under favorable conditions, digest about one and one-half tons of boiled eggs in two hours, or would clot 600,000 gallons of milk or liquefy 10,000 gallons of gelatin. Improving his method of preparation, he could easily obtain a half pound of pure pepsin crystals in two days. He now possessed the means for a thorough study of the properties of pepsin and the conditions under which it acts in the process of digestion.

Because Sumner's and Northrop's results differed from those of Wilstätter, the latter's great authority delayed acceptance of their work more than a decade. Meanwhile Wendell M. Stanley's discovery — based partly on methods Northrop and associates developed — that tobacco mosaic virus is a crystallizable protein reinforced the earlier work on urease and pepsin. In 1946 the Nobel Prize for chemistry was awarded to the three American investigators, half to Sumner for showing that enzymes could be crystallized, half to Northrop and Stanley jointly for the isolation of pure enzymes and viruses.

Northrop and his colleague Kunitz had begun to work on trypsin, the chief proteolytic enzyme of the pancreas. They ran into serious difficulties because trypsin, far less stable than pepsin, breaks down so rapidly that slow cooling would not crystallize it. Finally they succeeded in crystallizing the inactive precursors of trypsin and chymotrypsin from beef pancreas, then in activating the enzymes and recrystallizing them in active form. This was made possible by their discovery that a trace of trypsin itself would catalyze the formation of chymotrypsin and act as an autocatalyst in the activation of trypsin.[25] Following this up, Kunitz subsequently purified and crystallized several other enzymes related to trypsin, while Northrop and he continued the less dramatic but scientifically important investigation of the functional properties of these essential chemical agents of the body. Tenaciously pursuing this line of investigation, Kunitz (made a full Member of the Institute in 1949), between 1939 and 1952, achieved the purification of a number of very important enzymes which take part in forming and utilizing energy-rich compounds in the tissues, including crystalline ribonuclease and deoxyribonuclease from the pancreas, and hexokinase and pyrophosphatase from baker's yeast. We shall see later how all this experience of the Institute's biochemists with the purification of proteins facilitated other great accomplishments, including the purification of bacteriophage and the crystallization of diphtheria antitoxin by Northrop, and the crystallization of tobacco mosaic virus by Stanley.

WHEN DUNCAN A. MACINNES came in 1926 from the Massachusetts Institute of Technology to take charge of a laboratory of physical chemistry, he was The Rockefeller Institute's first senior investigator trained in a physical science, rather than in a biological field such as medicine, physiology, or biochemistry. By appointing him an Associate Member with independent budget, and a few years later adding another laboratory of physical chemistry under Leonor Michaelis, the Institute broadened its scope even more than Jacques Loeb had urged when in 1910 he accepted his appointment as Member. Loeb, and later Osterhout, had brought general physiology, which in their hands was physical chemistry applied to living matter, to an influential place in the Institute. Workers in other laboratories were beginning to utilize its principles. In the hospital, Donald Van Slyke and his associates were applying the concepts of physical chemistry to the study of the blood. Paul de Kruif had sought Northrop's collaboration in studying the agglutination of bacterial suspensions; Lecomte du Noüy was measuring the surface tension of blood serum. Osterhout brought MacInnes to the Institute because he saw that it was necessary to set an example of research in the physical sciences and to encourage day-to-day consultations on the basic problems of physical chemistry underlying all experimentation on living tissues.

MacInnes was especially prepared to deal with the current central problem of general physiology—ionization and its physical concomitants. Osterhout's work on the permeability of cells to salt ions, and on such resultant phenomena as the production of bioelectrical potentials and the conduction of impulses by protoplasm, called for precise understanding of ionization theory. The classical theory of Arrhenius, used by physiologists in analyzing their results, represented a salt in solution as only partly ionized, but this concept did not explain all the observed facts. Physical chemists, including MacInnes, had come to believe that strong electrolytes, such as the chlorides of sodium, potassium, calcium, and magnesium, the principal salts of living tissues, are completely dissociated into ions when in aqueous solution.

The experimental work was in large part designed to test the "interionic attraction" theory of Debye-Hückel and of Onsager, whose papers appeared in the early nineteen twenties. According to this theory, the properties of solutions of electrolytes, that is, acids, bases, and salts, are determined by the electrical charges, dimensions, and concentrations of the ions. Study of these parameters of ionization involves very precise measurements of electrical conductance, ion mobilities, and the potentials of galvanic cells, for which MacInnes and his assistants devised much new apparatus. MacInnes, Malcolm Dole, and Donald Belcher designed a greatly improved glass electrode for precise measurement of acidity and alkalinity, which is now universally used in determining the acid-base balance in living tissues. Within a couple of years MacInnes was surrounded by an outstanding group of young men, two of whom are still with the Institute. Theodore Shedlovsky worked with him on the conductance of salt solutions and on cell potentials, achieving values of such high accuracy that they are still in wide use two decades later as a basis upon which to calculate quantitative experimental results in related fields. L. G. Longsworth joined them in the determination of the relative motion of the ions of salts by an ingenious "moving boundary" method which will be described later.[26] By the end of Flexner's directorship, this group had achieved by joint work a triumphantly precise confirmation of the interionic attraction theory. From then on the program broadened as MacInnes's colleagues developed their own special lines within the common field of interest. In the succeeding period, to be discussed in Chapter 14, MacInnes, Longsworth, and Shedlovsky followed more or less distinctive lines of research, all aimed at applying the basic principles of physical chemistry to living tissues, in which ionized salts in solution, protein molecules, and other charge-bearing particles play a fundamental role.

LEONOR MICHAELIS was fifty-four years old and a renowned man of science when in 1929 he joined The Rockefeller Institute after a varied experience on three continents.[27] Born in Berlin, he was educated at a humanistic *Gymnasium* where there happened to be a small chemical and physical laboratory. Turned thus toward science in spite of classical schooling, he studied medicine, wrote a successful textbook of embryology, and spent a year with Paul Ehrlich at Frankfurt, where he made an important discovery in cellular biology, the vital staining of mitochondria with the dye Janus green. For four years he practiced medicine as a hospital physician. Appointed bacteriologist at a municipal hospital in his native city, with limited equipment and resources Michaelis accomplished between 1905 and 1914 a remarkable series of researches in biochemistry and biophysics. In this work he demonstrated great ability to see a problem in quantitative form and to express his results mathematically. He discovered the dependence of enzyme activity on hydrogen ion concentration simultaneously with Sørenson, whose prior publication took precedence in the literature.

In 1913 with a student of his, Maud L. Menten, Michaelis published a widely read paper proposing that in enzymatic catalysis a complex is formed between the enzyme and the substrate (the substance on which it acts) and that the rate of the reaction is determined by the concentration of the complex. Analyzing mathematically and testing in the laboratory ideas originally brought forward by Victor Henry, a French physicist, he introduced a factor representing the affinity of the enzyme for its substrate, which has become known as the Michaelis constant. Michaelis's formulation did not receive real recognition until the 1930's, and it has been fully verified only since the end of World War II. Today the Michaelis concept is accepted by virtually every enzyme chemist.

Michaelis also investigated the inhibition of enzymes by antagonistic chemical substances or "enzyme poisons," a subject now of consequence in many branches of biology, from the most abstruse cell physiology to insecticides. The English chemist Hardy had shown that if the experimenter studying any given protein in solution gradually changes the reaction of the solution from acid to alkaline or vice versa, he will arrive at the "isoelectric point" characteristic of that particular protein. At this point the protein molecules bear equal numbers of positive and negative charges. The protein is then electrically neutral; its solubility is at its lowest, and it is readily precipitated by alcohol, salts, or various other substances. Some proteins precipitate spontaneously at the isoelectric point. This principle is, obviously, important in the purification of proteins, in the laboratory and in industry. Michaelis developed it in a quantitative way, showing how the solubility, viscosity, and precipitability of proteins depend upon the electrical charges on their particles. He also pioneered in the technique of electrophoresis, which uses a strong electric field to move charged particles along a tube from one electrode toward the other, to determine the isoelectric points of various proteins. Jacques Loeb's work on the physical and chemical behavior of proteins was largely based upon these studies. During these productive years Michaelis published three books, on oxidation potentials, hydrogen ion concentration, and mathematics for biologists and chemists, which were translated into English and other languages and have had an important influence in twentieth-century science.

Before World War I Michaelis had won a world-wide reputation by his publications, without having obtained an important academic post in his own country. The prevalent anti-Semitism in German universities was no doubt a factor in this lack of official recognition, for he would have been eminently successful as a teacher. In 1921 the postwar German government gave him the title of "Professor Extraordinarius" in physical chemistry applied to medicine and biology, but without salary, budget, or laboratory. He therefore accepted a temporary professorship in Japan for three years, during which he did the important research, already mentioned in this chapter, on the permeability of membranes and the origin of potentials across membranes. A lecture tour in the United States led to a resident lectureship for three years at the Johns Hopkins University and then to membership in The Rockefeller Institute. The Institute thus acquired a Member with wide experience in biology, chemistry, and medicine, and gifted also in mathematics, languages, and music.

At the Institute, his chief studies dealt with the reactions involved in oxidation and reduction of organic substances, processes constantly occurring in every living tissue. Going deeper than the usual chemical approach, Michaelis attacked the problem at the fundamental level of the electron shifts that take place between reacting molecules. He proposed the hypothesis that oxidation and reduction reactions take place in two steps, with the temporary participation of free radicals bearing unpaired electrons, rather than of intact molecules of the reacting substances. He supported this concept by plotting the electrical potential generated in such a reaction, which changed, as the reaction progressed, in a manner fitting his expectation. To many chemists this idea was unacceptable; the first paper in which Michaelis stated it was rejected by a leading American journal. Within a few years, however, the same journal made him its referee for papers on that subject. He had converted the majority of organic chemists to his views by experimental proofs of the most recondite character, depending upon the paramagnetism of the compounds in question. This later phase of his work will be described in another chapter. The incident discussed here is sufficient to show that Michaelis was thinking well in advance of most contemporaries in his field.

Among the assistants who took part in various phases of the research on oxidation and reduction, several went on to academic posts — John Runnström at the University of Stockholm, E. S. Hill at Washington University, M. P. Schubert at New York University. Schubert also made notable contributions to the chemistry of sulphur compounds involved in oxidation-reduction reactions. Carl V. Smythe, who aided Michaelis in the study of iron compounds concerned in oxidative processes in the tissues, became head of an industrial research laboratory.

Another line of research, almost equally abstruse, had an amusing practical application. In 1933 Michaelis and David R. Goddard, a postdoctoral fellow in his laboratory (now professor of botany at the University of Pennsylvania), asked themselves how the fungus parasites of ringworm and similar diseases are able to digest the dry hard protein (keratin) of the skin surface. In the course of their studies they found that the crystalline structure of keratin depends upon the integrity of certain disulfide bonds, and that if these bonds are ruptured by reduction the remaining protein is amorphous and subject to digestion by the proteolytic enzymes trypsin and pepsin. After publication of these results, K. V. Linderstrøm-Lang of Copenhagen and one of his students investigated the destruction of wool by the clothes moth and found that the insect is able to reduce the disulfide bonds and thus break down the keratin. The cosmetic industry, learning about the reducing agents found effective in these experiments on wool and hair, employed them in "dry permanent waves," and one of the Institute's most subtle investigations acquired commercial importance.

To single out only these two lines of work does injustice to Michaelis and his assistants, but sufficiently suggests the example of research by which he quietly stimulated other workers throughout the Institute—an example reinforced by the inspiring atmosphere of his laboratory and by his lively discussions at staff meetings. The two divisions of the physical chemistry laboratories, led by the imaginative Michaelis on the one hand and by MacInnes, precise master of instrumental techniques, on the other, strongly supplemented each other and reinforced the influence of Loeb and Osterhout. At present the concepts of physical chemistry developed by these men are being applied in almost every laboratory in the Institute.

The record of research in physical chemistry during this part of the Institute's history would be incomplete without mention of Henry S. Simms. He came in 1920 as an assistant to Levene in the biochemistry laboratory and transferred to Princeton in 1926, leaving in 1931 for an academic career which ultimately took him to a professorship of biochemistry at Columbia University. At the Institute Simms served as a collaborating specialist in a score of investigations on various aspects of lipoid chemistry, salt antagonism, and the dissociation of salts and proteins, chiefly in the laboratories of Levene, Northrop, Kunitz, and F. S. Jones.

IN 1922 Flexner created a subdivision for the study of what he called photobiology. He had been impressed by the relatively recent discovery that rickets can be cured by exposure to sunlight, a finding which reemphasized the long-known beneficial effects of light in wasting diseases, such as tuberculosis. Knowing also that great advances were being made in the physics of the action of light, by students of photographic chemistry, he felt that The Rockefeller Institute should investigate the way in which energy, in the form of light, acts upon living tissues. To lead the work, he appointed Frederick L. Gates, eldest son of F. T. Gates, president of the Board of Trustees, who had joined the Institute in 1913 immediately after graduating from the Johns Hopkins Medical School. A brilliant student, and very ingenious at devising new methods and apparatus, Gates worked at first on bacteriological problems in Flexner's division, associated with Peter Olitsky in investigations on the bacteriology of dysentery and of influenza. Flexner now sent him to the University of Chicago and Johns Hopkins for a half year to prepare for work on photobiology. To collaborate with Gates on the chemical side, he appointed Oskar Baudisch, a European-trained specialist in photochemical synthesis, and Lars A. Welo.

Gates began at once to study ultraviolet light, known to be the effective portion of the solar spectrum in the light treatment of rickets, although the nature of its beneficial action was quite unknown. To simplify the problem, Gates used bacteria as the living material in his earliest experiments. With the aid of accurate thermocouples of his own design for measuring energies available at different wave-lengths, he worked out the action spectra — the relation between various wave-lengths of ultraviolet light and their action, stimulating or destructive according to the circumstances, upon bacteria, bacteriophages, viruses, and enzymes.

The little group Flexner had tentatively organized did not fuse into an effective unit. Baudisch and Welo worked on quite different problems, and Gates's studies were too new to make much impression at the time. Because of an obscure illness, which caused his untimely death a few years later, it was thought he might profit by a change of scene, and he transferred his laboratory to Harvard University in 1929. His work at the Institute on the action spectra of ultraviolet light, continued at Cambridge, was the first definitive study of the subject, and biophysicists now recognize Gates as a pioneer in this field.[28] When in 1936 Northrop made his remarkable discovery that a bacteriophage, regarded as a living biological agent, could be isolated as a chemical substance of protein nature, Gates's determination of the wave-lengths of ultraviolet light which are destructive to bacteriophage served as evidence that Northrop's protein and that of the bacteriophage were identical.

The work which Flexner had called photobiology fully deserved the title of biophysics, but that name had some years before been conferred upon J. B. Murphy's cancer studies, to be discussed in Chapter 9, apparently because he and his assiduous colleague, the physicist Harry Clark, were using X rays to stimulate and inhibit lymphocyte action in experimental cancer. A new subdivision of the Institute, formally designated as biophysics and opened in 1927 under Ralph W. G. Wyckoff, undertook to study the biological applications of X-ray crystallography. This was a new method of studying the atomic structure of chemical elements and compounds, developed in 1912 by Max Laue of Berlin and Sir William Bragg of London. It was based on the fact that crystalline materials act as diffraction gratings for X rays by virtue of the regular spacing of their atoms or molecules, exactly as closely ruled lines on a glass plate produce a visible spectrum by diffracting ordinary light. Thus any crystalline substance will deflect an X-ray beam passing through it, and produce on a photographic film a regular geometric pattern characteristic of the kinds and arrangement of atoms or molecules of which it is composed.

Wyckoff was the outstanding American pioneer in the use and refinement of this new method of analyzing crystalline substances. He had begun work at the Geophysical Laboratory of the Carnegie Institution of Washington in 1919, immediately after taking his Ph.D. at Cornell. His most important early contribution was to put the determination of crystal structures on a rigorous basis by applying the mathematical theory of space groups. Lecomte du Noüy, Carrel's brilliant associate at Compiègne during the war and for a few years thereafter in New York, worked briefly with the young physicist in Washington. When he reported that Wyckoff saw a possibility of determining, by X-ray crystallography, the structure of complex organic substances, even proteins, Flexner brought Wyckoff to the Institute as Associate Member in charge of the subdivision of biophysics.

It would have been hopelessly difficult to begin with the enormously complicated protein molecule. Since hemoglobin, the iron-containing respiratory pigment of red blood cells, was one of the proteins toward which the work was pointed, Wyckoff began studying the ammonium chlorostannates, salts far simpler than hemoglobin but, like it, containing nitrogen and complexly bound iron in a highly symmetrical arrangement.

With seven X-ray machines already at his command in 1928, Wyckoff added an X-ray spectrometer of his own design and developed a new cold-cathode tube. In X-ray crystallography he was assisted for several years by Robert B. Corey. Working on the structure of the amino acids, organic substances of which the proteins are composed, they laid a foundation for future studies on the structure of proteins themselves. This study has been carried on with great success by Corey at the California Institute of Technology. Wyckoff's investigations of the collagen of connective tissue, gelatin, and other fibrous proteins, carried out with improved techniques of his own devising, yielded new and useful details about their structure. With Alice H. Armstrong and others, Wyckoff determined new and more accurate values for the X-ray–scattering powers of many atoms, including oxygen, carbon, and nitrogen, information greatly needed for studying the structure of organic compounds. He was quite close to Carrel's group during his stay at the Institute and with them explored the effect of X rays on cells in tissue culture, being among the first to utilize ultraviolet light to secure finer resolution in microphotography.

At about the same time as F. Holweck and A. Lacassagne in Paris, Wyckoff and his associates made really quantitative measurements of the lethal action of X rays and of electrons on microorganisms, and proposed a theoretical explanation of these effects. Always enjoying a challenge to develop new apparatus for special problems, Wyckoff ingeniously constructed a time-lapse microscopic motion-picture camera with which he photographed the life cycles of bacteria. Next he was fascinated by the possibilities of the high-speed centrifuge as a means of isolating individual proteins and other relatively heavy molecular aggregates, for example viruses, from tissue extracts and other fluid media.

Experimental efforts to develop the centrifuge method were already being made, not in a division of the Institute itself but in the laboratories of the International Health Division of The Rockefeller Foundation, housed on the upper floor of the North Laboratory (now Theobald Smith Hall). Here Johannes Bauer was attempting to adapt the so-called spinning-top centrifuge of Herriot and Hugenard for study of the yellow fever virus. To advance the project, the Foundation laboratories brought to New York Edward G. Pickels, a gifted graduate student at the University of Virginia, under Jesse W. Beams, pioneer in the design of high-speed centrifuges. Pickels was able to combine the good features of both the French and the American (Beams-Pickels) machines and perfect what came to be known as the air-driven ultracentrifuge. The instrument was never produced commercially in the United States, but until it was replaced by a motor-driven type, all the ultracentrifuges at the Institute were built in its instrument shop from Pickels's plans. These machines included not only those used by Wyckoff, and later by Stanley's group at Princeton, but also one operated by Alexandre Rothen in his physical chemistry laboratory (see Chapter 14) and, with modifications, one built later by P. G. Ecker for the same laboratory.

Wyckoff joined Pickels in designing certain features of the air-driven ultracentrifuge and immediately began to use it for biological investigations. Observing that hemoglobin, the oxygen-carrying protein of the blood, spontaneously crystallized under the intense gravitational effect of the machine, he went on to develop methods which are still in common use for the ultracentrifugal purification of viruses. Wendell M. Stanley of the Department of Animal and Plant Pathology at Princeton had by this time begun his work on purification of the virus of tobacco mosaic disease which will be discussed in Chapter 12. Wyckoff suggested to him that they should try, in this new way, to get virus preparations less altered by manipulation than those he had begun to obtain by chemical methods. Their immediate success with tobacco mosaic led, during Wyckoff's last two years at the Institute, to the isolation, purification, and physiochemical characterization, jointly with Stanley and others at Princeton, of several plant viruses. This led Joseph W. Beard and Wyckoff to the purification of the rabbit papilloma virus, the first animal virus, other than the much larger vaccinia (cowpox) virus, to be obtained pure in appreciable quantities.

The application of physical methods to biological research was of course not limited to Wyckoff's laboratory. Peyton Rous's use of the electromagnet to isolate macrophages, to be mentioned in Chapter 8, was an example of practical biophysics. The philosophical and versatile Lecomte du Noüy, interested during his stay in Carrel's laboratory in the properties of blood serum as a factor in wound healing, invented an instrument for measuring the surface tension of serum and other fluids, which was so simple and reliable, in contrast to other available apparatus for the same purpose, that it was widely adopted and remains in extensive use.

When Wyckoff left the Institute, almost two years after Flexner's retirement, the biophysics laboratory was discontinued and for a long time there was no research formally designated as biophysics. When Herbert S. Gasser, Flexner's successor as Director, brought to the Institute, before Wyckoff's departure, his important investigations on the conduction of nerve impulses, he preferred to designate the work as physiology, even though it depended upon elaborate electronic equipment. In 1953, Detlev W. Bronk, newly appointed President of the Institute, and two Members long associated with him at the University of Pennsylvania and Johns Hopkins — H. K. Hartline and Frank Brink, Jr. — created a new division of biophysics, chiefly devoted to the electrophysiology of nerve conduction and sensory reception.

CHAPTER EIGHT

"Pathology Is the Fundamental Branch of Medicine"

Yellow fever, Oroya fever. Noguchi's fatal trip to Africa. Cerebro-spinal meningitis, influenza, foot-and-mouth disease. Experimental epidemiology. Experimental syphilis. Immunology: blood antigens, the Rh factor, allergy. Physiology: the gall bladder and the bile; pH of the tissues; lymph flow. Bacteriophages.

IN SPITE OF the steadily increasing importance of general physiology, organic chemistry, and physical chemistry at The Rockefeller Institute, Flexner's own division of pathology and bacteriology continued to be the largest of the laboratory groups. Throughout his directorship he regarded the investigation of the causes and characteristics of disease as the Institute's central purpose. When one of the Scientific Directors in 1933 suggested a physiologist as successor to William H. Welch on the Board, Flexner replied, "Pathology is far more important for us than physiology and pharmacology, and the background of medicine than general science. Our pathologists are all moving on; pathology is the fundamental branch of medicine."[1] Time was to challenge this judgment — an electrophysiologist succeeded Flexner in the directorship — but meanwhile the pathologists and, above all, the bacteriologists continued to carry on some of the Institute's most vivid activities.

In 1912 and 1913 Hideyo Noguchi, tirelessly following up his cultivation of a spirochete which appeared to be the germ of syphilis, applied his ingenious method to the isolation and cultivation of every kind of spiral organism he could find, those that are harmless as well as those that cause disease. Among them he grew the *Borellia* of relapsing fever, and the spirochete that is associated with the severe throat infection called Vincent's angina. Flushed with these achievements, he ardently tried to cultivate the virus of rabies and thought he had succeeded.

Flexner, desperately anxious to obtain a vaccine against poliomyelitis, urged him to work on that disease; and when Noguchi again produced what seemed to be a living culture, joined him in several publications on the subject. It is possible that there was some survival, even multiplication of the virus in their cultures; two such experienced workers could hardly have been completely deceived in thinking that the material had caused poliomyelitis when inoculated into monkeys. Flexner was better acquainted with the disease in these animals than anyone else in his time. Yet the work was never confirmed elsewhere, and when the real virus was grown, years later, quite different methods were found necessary, Noguchi's culture media failing to yield results. His habit of working with an almost unmanageably large assortment of culture tubes, not always labeled, was not conducive to precision. More enthusiastic than experienced in pathology, he sometimes mistook the lesions in his experimental animals for those characteristic of human disease. This type of error is historic in bacteriology. Studying virus diseases at a time when their manifestations were only beginning to be known, Noguchi unwittingly exposed himself to exceptional risks.

Noguchi's reports, following one another in rapid succession, began to win him notice abroad. He had been, with Flexner, first in America to confirm Schaudinn's discovery of the parasite of syphilis; he had proved its relation to general paresis and tabes dorsalis; he had presumptively cultivated it, and had certainly grown many other kinds of spirochetes, including some that cause important human diseases. Now, it seemed, he had even achieved the culture of rabies and poliomyelitis virus. When the Association of German Naturalists and Physicians invited him to address its annual assembly in the fall of 1913, his trip to Vienna was a triumph. The Association's president, Friedrich von Mueller, invited Noguchi to stop over in Munich for another lecture; Paul Ehrlich asked him to Frankfurt. From Paris he wrote to Flexner that he had demonstrated his pure cultures of various spirochetes and his rabies material to Elie Metchnikoff, A. Besredka, and many others at the Pasteur Institute. Metchnikoff, he said, "was much interested and said that I have the [rabies] virus grown."[2] There were similar demonstrations in

London at the Royal Society of Medicine, and in Copenhagen. To a Japanese friend Noguchi wrote that he had visited ten big cities, given eleven lectures, attended thirty-eight banquets as the principal guest. "I was given audience by two royalties . . . I have sat with great men of science and become intimate with them."[3] The Japanese peasant youth from Fukushima, who had changed his name to Hideyo, "great-man-of-the-world," was indeed greatly honored, in Europe and in America. Soon after his return to New York he was promoted, at the age of thirty-seven, to full membership in the Institute. This was the apogee of his career; there would be further discoveries and new honors, even adulation, but the fifteen years he had left were to play themselves out like the modern version of a Greek drama, in which a venturesome mortal, raising puny hands against the dark powers of ignorance and disease, was inexorably driven to a tragic fate.

The outbreak of war in 1914 cut Noguchi off from his newly acquired friends in Europe. About the same time he suffered his first serious illness, due to a valvular lesion with dilatation of the heart. He slowed down his work for a little while, tried to stop smoking, moved to an apartment house that had an elevator. Summoned to Japan in 1915 to receive the Imperial Prize of the Japanese Academy, he took occasion while there to get cultures of the spirochete of infectious jaundice (Weil's disease), recently identified by two Japanese bacteriologists. Back in New York Noguchi began work on cowpox, purifying vaccinia virus by a special method intended to facilitate the production of vaccine against smallpox, which never got into wide practical use. He returned also to another problem which he never solved, cultivation of the organism causing Rocky Mountain spotted fever.

In May 1917 Noguchi nearly died of typhoid fever complicated by intestinal perforation, and he recovered only slowly. He was still not quite well in July 1918, when the Surgeon General of the United States Army, William C. Gorgas, asked him to go to Ecuador as bacteriologist with a commission appointed to search for the unknown mosquito-borne agent that causes yellow fever. Arriving at Guayaquil July 6 with Arthur Kendall, chairman of the Commission, and three American nurses, he began work the next day. Noguchi's biographer, Gustav Eckstein, vividly tells the story of his three months at the yellow fever hospital.

The Ecuadorean doctors, eager to help, gave him access to patients who were suffering from a prostrating fever and jaundice, characteristic symptoms of yellow fever. Gorgas, and before him Schaudinn, had predicted that the cause of yellow fever would turn out to be a spirochete similar to that of infectious jaundice. A few days after arriving in Guayaquil, Noguchi found such spirochetes in the blood of a patient in the yellow fever hospital. Later he found the same germs in the blood, urine, or tissues in six more cases out of twenty-seven diagnosed as yellow fever. He was able to grow this organism, which he called *Leptospira icteroides*. Not having monkeys at hand, he inoculated guinea pigs (a species known to be susceptible to infectious jaundice), and produced a fatal disease characterized by fever and liver damage with jaundice. Finally, he made a vaccine from the cultures which he believed to contain the yellow fever organism, and inoculated a large number of military recruits who would be exposed to the disease when they went from the mountains to the infested coastal region for maneuvers.[4]

The citizens of Guayaquil, believing that their deadliest plague would now be conquered, tried to keep Noguchi permanently in Ecuador, and before he left showered him with compliments and honors. They gave him a gold medal and made him honorary senior surgeon of the national army with the rank of colonel. The hospital put up a bronze tablet in the room he had used, inscribed, "In this laboratory the eminent Japanese bacteriologist, Hideyo Noguchi, Member of The Rockefeller Institute, discovered the germ of yellow fever on the ninth of July 1918." At the end of the year Simon Flexner, in his presidential address to the American Association for the Advancement of Science, gave full credence to Noguchi's findings at Guayaquil. Confidently hoping that a curative serum would soon be found, he declared that yellow fever might be the first epidemic disease to be abolished by the conscious effort of man.[5]

Late in 1919, Noguchi, hearing that there was yellow fever in Mexico, set out for Mérida in Yucatan. The cases were few, but a guinea pig inoculated with blood from one of the patients died with jaundice and proved to have Noguchi's leptospira in its tissues. He returned to New York, but then, driving himself to the limit, in spite of his heart lesion, he went for three months in 1920 to Payta, Peru, to investigate an epidemic. There once more he recovered his spiral organisms from the blood of persons with yellow fever as diagnosed by the local doctors. In

June 1923 he made his fourth and last trip to Latin America, this time to the seacoast of Brazil at Bahia, where he saw no active cases of fever but got immunological reactions against *Leptospira icteroides* from the blood of convalescents. There was no doubt, then or since, that a disease existed which the local doctors took to be yellow fever, and that it was caused by the spirochete Noguchi had discovered and named. He knew immediately that his organism closely resembled the spirochete of Weil's disease, which could at times be mistaken for yellow fever. He seems, however, not to have given serious consideration to the possibility that the doctors who selected cases for him in Ecuador, Peru, Mexico, and Brazil might have been deceived by the similarity of these two diseases.

Theobald Smith, as well aware as any man could be of the difficulties involved in proving the association of a disease with its suspected agent, formally stated that, after rereading all Noguchi's studies on yellow fever in Latin America, he did not see how anyone could have drawn other inferences.[6] On the other hand, W. G. McCallum, experienced pathologist of the Johns Hopkins University, felt that in this, as in some of his other work, Noguchi assumed too easily that he was reproducing the human disease in animals. "At best," wrote McCallum, "the spirochetes never reproduced the disease in its characteristic anatomical lesions when injected into guinea pigs. We never could distinguish the results from those produced by the *Leptospira icterohemorrhagica* [*i.e.,* the organism of Weil's disease]."[7]

Strong doubt that *Leptospira icteroides* was the cause of yellow fever was expressed in Noguchi's presence at a conference in Jamaica, July 1924, by Aristide Agramonte of Havana, member of Walter Reed's U.S. Army commission that had proved the transmission of yellow fever by mosquitoes. "On the whole, his objections were very unreasonable," Noguchi wrote to Flexner, ". . . I am not certain whether these Havana men are really interested in scientific discussion or not."[8] Nevertheless, his confidence in *Leptospira* as the yellow fever parasite began to waver.

Before the final crisis, however, Noguchi did major work on two other infectious diseases, achieving brilliant success with one. Early in 1925 Telémaco Battistini, coming from Lima, Peru, to work with Noguchi, brought with him, packed in ice, a tube of blood drawn from a patient dying of Oroya fever. This disease, which exists only in mountainous regions of Peru, Ecuador, and Colombia, killed 40 per cent of all who fell ill with it before the era of antibiotics. It first came into prominence in 1870 when an epidemic caused 7,000 deaths. There is also another febrile disease, verruga peruviana, long known to the Indians, which occurs only in the same regions as Oroya fever. It is characterized by an eruption of large purplish warts lasting a month to a year with 5 per cent mortality. Peruvian doctors, noticing that verruga often occurred in persons who had recovered from Oroya fever, thought the two might be successive manifestations of the same infection. Knowing this, a medical student, Daniel Carrión, inoculated himself in 1885 with material from a verruga wart; thirty-nine days later he died of Oroya fever. He and his medical advisers did not keep full records, and his heroic act could not be accepted as proving the association of the two diseases. Among the doubters was a party from Harvard Medical School in 1913 which shared the suspicion of a Peruvian physician, A. L. Barton, that certain peculiar bodies which he had first seen in 1909 in the red blood corpuscles were the infectious organisms of Oroya fever. To this parasite they gave the name *Bartonella bacilliformis*.

Noguchi, aided by Battistini during the first few months of the investigation, seeded tubes of various culture media with the blood from Lima, and in some of them got pure cultures of *Bartonella*. Monkeys inoculated with this material came down with remittent fever and had *Bartonella* in their red blood corpuscles. When the germs were injected into the skin, the monkeys developed large red warty masses at the sites of injection. Noguchi then sent to Lima for verrucous tissue from human patients; this, inoculated into monkeys, gave them Oroya fever. Thus he had transmitted the fever from the warts and the warts from the fever. Finally, he showed that nine monkeys and a chimpanzee which had recovered from experimentally induced Oroya fever were immune to the *Bartonella* he had grown from the verrucous tissue. Proof was now complete that the two diseases are phases of the same infection.

To cap this achievement Noguchi undertook to discover the method of transmission of the disease. An entomologist living in Peru had suggested that a biting gnat of the genus *Phlebotomus* was the vector. R. C. Shannon of the International Health Division of The Rockefeller Foundation went to the fever-infested valleys and collected all discoverable species of biting and blood-sucking insects — more than twenty. When the living insects reached New York after Noguchi's death, two of his technicians, Evelyn B. Tilden and Joseph R. Tyler, tested them as he had planned, for the presence of *Bartonella*. Among the specimens, only *Phlebotomus* carried the germ of Oroya fever and verruga peruviana. The last five papers bearing Noguchi's name reported the concluding phase of this investigation conducted with impressive logic, speed, and finality. Its success alone would have justified a lifetime spent in the laboratory.

While all this was going on, Noguchi daringly undertook to look for the organism of trachoma, a great conundrum for bacteriologists, about thirty different organisms having been put forward erroneously by various workers before Noguchi's attempt. During a brief trip to New Mexico, where there were thousands of cases among the Indians with much resulting blindness, Noguchi inoculated a few monkeys and took to New York tissue from the granulated eyelids of five patients. Something turned up in the cultures which produced in monkeys a disease of the eyes — a granular form of conjunctivitis — believed by Noguchi to be the counterpart of human trachoma. Because of his reputation, his report stimulated a great deal of work which failed to confirm it. More than a dozen workers in several countries inoculated in all more than seventy human volunteers without causing a single verified case of trachoma. The active agent is now thought to be a large-particle virus related to that which causes psittacosis (parrot fever).

About this time reports began to come from the African yellow fever region that Noguchi's *Leptospira icteroides* could not be found in cases there. In 1927 a young Dubliner, Adrian Stokes from Guy's Hospital, London, in Africa for The Rockefeller Foundation's International Health Division, reported having transmitted the disease to rhesus monkeys by blood passed through bacteria-restraining filters. The agent must then be by definition a "filtrable virus," rather than a spirochete. Shortly afterward, Noguchi learned that Stokes had died of the disease while working with it. Grieved, disheartened, burdened by the thought that his efforts might have been vain, Noguchi resolved to go to West Africa, repeat Stokes's experiments, see whether he could recover *Leptospira* from yellow fever patients, and, if not, try to right his error by propagating Stokes's virus.

Friends at The Rockefeller Institute, noting signs of his damaged heart and knowing now that he had diabetes as well, urged him not to go. Flexner could have forbidden the venture; as Director he held the purse strings and, furthermore, the old master-pupil relationship still held between the two men. Not long before, after giving a well-received lecture at Washington, Noguchi had written to Flexner:

> Whatever my humble part may be in all these things it is of course due to you and you alone who are so patiently guiding the whole course of successive events in my life. I am getting to realize the meaning of all this more and more as I trod along in my years. Your patience make it possible for me to work in our renewing happy mood in spite of many difficulties and failures in my work.[9]

But however great the risk, Flexner could not deny this troubled man the opportunity to follow his quest to a final answer. Noguchi sailed for Africa in October 1927. At Accra on the Gold Coast, where he worked for five months with The Rockefeller Foundation's West African Yellow Fever Commission, he could not find *Leptospira;* convinced at last that his earlier work was wrong, he began to cultivate other organisms which he planned to carry home to New York. He developed a chill during a brief visit in Lagos, and on the coastal ship returning to Accra the illness deepened. Landing in a small boat through a heavy surf and a rainstorm, Noguchi, now feverish, was exposed for hours and wet to the skin. When the black vomit began, after a week in the hospital, he must have realized that he was dying of yellow fever.[10]

In the library of The Rockefeller Institute there is a superb bronze head of Hideyo Noguchi, made just before he went to Africa. From one viewpoint it depicts the confident, world-famous man of science; from another it looks like the lonely, tousle-headed youth from Fukushima who stood hopefully on Simon Flexner's doorstep one day in the fall of 1900.[11]

WHEN PETER K. OLITSKY came to Flexner's laboratory in 1917, he was well fitted, by training and interests, to render much the same kind of service as field bacteriologist and epidemiologist that Flexner himself had in his younger days. His first investigation for the Institute took him to the Naval Hospital at Portsmouth, Virginia, where there was an epidemic of cerebrospinal meningitis. A great increase in the proportion of seemingly healthy persons who were carriers of the meningococcus, observed by Olitsky in this epidemic, is now known to be a regular occurrence. In World War I he developed a useful method for identifying meningococci in the human nasopharynx.

The British colony of Hong Kong early in 1918 suffered a severe epidemic of meningitis with appallingly high mortality. Through Lord Reading, then Britain's Ambassador, Hong Kong officials called upon The Rockefeller Institute for help, and Olitsky, now a lieutenant in the Army Medical Corps, went to China. Arriving when the epidemic was waning, he had little chance to use the Institute's serum; but he carefully checked the work of the local bacteriologists. Confirming their identification of the organism, he determined its type, and trained the public health laboratory in Flexner's method of making a serum of high potency for use should the epidemic recur. Before leaving the Colony in July, he made a thorough epidemiological survey of Hong Kong, using the isolated, meningitis-free jail inmates as a "normal" population, which led him to conclude that overcrowding in the poorer native quarters was important in the spread of the disease. His vigorous report was gratefully received by the Governor, whose high regard the young American had won by his tact, courtesy, and obviously expert knowledge; and the Council of the Colony voted several million dollars to provide better housing at Kowloon for the dense Chinese population.

This was also the year of the great pandemic of influenza, and after Olitsky's return to New York he and his colleague Frederick L. Gates began a bacteriological study of this disease. Their findings did not support the prevailing view that the *Bacillus influenzae* of Pfeiffer was the infective agent, and they turned their attention to other microbes. Among the numerous organisms recovered from the throats of influenza patients, they found a new and peculiar germ which they named *Bacterium pneumosintes*. So small that, like a virus, it passes through a porcelain filter, this organism produced in rabbits one of the signs of human epidemic influenza in its early stage, reduction in number of the mononuclear white blood cells. It was, moreover, never found except in persons ill with influenza. In spite of these suspicious traits, Olitsky and Gates carefully avoided stating that *pneumosintes* caused the disease. Its significance is still a mystery, but it holds its place in the textbooks under the new name *Dialister pneumosintes,* as one of a class of little-known microorganisms indigenous to man and hence to be watched with special interest, even if not known to cause disease.

In 1924 there were outbreaks in Texas and California of foot-and-mouth disease, a very contagious and economically serious disease of cattle, pigs, goats, and sheep, which occasionally gets into the United States from infected regions of other countries. Upon the recommendation of Flexner, to whom Secretary of Agriculture Jardine appealed for advice, Olitsky was chosen to lead a Foot-and-Mouth Disease Commission created in 1925 by an Act of Congress. The disease spreads so easily and its virus is so resistant that the government then prohibited its experimental study in the United States. Olitsky and his colleagues, H. W. Schoening from the Bureau of Animal Industry and Jacob Traum of the University of California, therefore went to Alsace, where the disease was prevalent. L. Boëz, representing the Institute of Hygiene of Strasbourg University, joined them as consultant. During a stay of about a year, the investigators confirmed previous reports by isolating the virus and transferring it to guinea pigs, in which Olitsky kept it alive through more than ninety passages from animal to animal. As a result of their studies they were able to suggest practical measures for preventing the spread of the virus in fields and farm buildings. Man himself, they found, is the most important agent in spreading the disease, since stable attendants, milkers, and herdsmen carry the virus on their hands and clothing. The information gained in this investigation still constitutes a significant part of our practical knowledge about foot-and-mouth disease.

While at Strasbourg, Olitsky, Schoening, and Traum also studied an epidemic infection of horses and cattle, vesicular stomatitis, which resembles foot-and-mouth disease and had been confused with it. The three Americans were the first, along with W. E. Cotton of the Bureau of Animal Industry, to show that it too is produced by a filtrable virus. On Olitsky's return from Alsace, he investigated the virus with Carrel in the latter's laboratory, and in his own with H. R. Cox, P. H. Long, and J. T. Syverton he worked out its physical, chemical, biological, and immunological properties.

In the course of these varied studies Olitsky and his co-workers made a number of valuable collateral and incidental observations. Studies on dysentery bacilli, for example, showed that these organisms produce toxic substances of two kinds, one affecting the nervous system, the other causing the intestinal irritation characteristic of the disease. The neurotoxin and the enterotoxin have since been shown to differ in chemical constitution. Olitsky discovered microorganisms of two new genera, *Dialister pneumosintes* mentioned above and several species of *Noguchia,* a genus he named after his colleague. With Syverton he found a new species of *Salmonella* in mice. With Gates and Boëz he introduced new procedures for cultivating anaerobic bacteria. In 1923 Olitsky and James E. McCartney, a Fellow, were among the first to demonstrate that the common cold is caused by a filtrable virus.

As early as 1928 he began studies, which were to extend over many years, on neurotropic viruses, investigating simple herpes (the "cold sore"), the virus of which has the power to attack nervous tissue, occasionally in man but characteristically in experimental animals. As Flexner's directorship drew to a close, Olitsky, Syverton, Cox, and A. B. Sabin were actively studying the nature and physical characteristics of viruses that regularly or at times invade the nervous tissues, including the recently recognized virus of equine encephalomyelitis. This work, and also a very original and important investigation of disseminated encephalomyelitis, an experimental disease of mice resembling multiple sclerosis in man, will be discussed in later chapters.

Olitsky has been a generous teacher of young workers, giving more time to them than to himself, and helping them to independent careers. Beside those already named—Cox, Long, Sabin, McCartney, and Syverton—are D. C. Hoffman, I. J. Kligler, Ralph E. Knutti, and D. T. Smith. Other associates of later years who have gone on to positions of importance in virus research will be mentioned in Chapter 15.

The 1918 pandemic of influenza reminded the world how little science understood or could control certain infectious diseases. In the fall of the same year a destructive epidemic of mouse typhoid swept through one of the breeding rooms of The Rockefeller Institute. Simon Flexner's lifelong interest in the nature of epidemics was further heightened by these crises. Visiting the London School of Tropical Medicine about 1919, he saw there a team of investigators under W. W. C. Topley, who had begun to study "model epidemics" created in colonies of mice by introducing infected individuals in varying numbers on a predetermined schedule. Impressed by this experimental study of epidemiology, Flexner, in association with Harold L. Amoss of his division, began about 1920 to conduct experimental studies on the epidemiology of mouse typhoid, introducing the bacillus of the disease into previously healthy mice in isolated colonies or "mouse villages" and following its spread under varied conditions. When Amoss left in 1922 for a teaching post, Leslie T. Webster took over the program, in which he was assisted for various periods by a number of able young people including Henry W. Scherp, Geoffrey Rake, G. L. Fite, Ida W. Pritchett, J. Casals-Ariet, Horace L. Hodes, Caspar G. Burn, and Anna D. Clow.

The diseases first employed in the research were mouse typhoid, caused by a species of *Salmonella*, and infection with the pneumonia bacillus of Friedlaender. Following Topley's lead, Webster was able to cause at will explosive epidemics resembling those which occasionally devastate human populations, or to keep the infectious disease going in the mouse population with a more or less constant mortality rate, or with periodic fluctuations. Because it had long been supposed that such variations in the rate of infection depend upon changing virulence of the organisms, Webster and his colleagues developed precise methods of measuring virulence by infecting their animals with accurately counted numbers of microorganisms. With such control of methods and materials, Webster could answer, in regard to his mice, two large questions presented by epidemic disease. In the first place, his observations convinced him that sudden outbreaks are not to be accounted for by changes in the virulence of the organism. Far more important is the factor of varying exposure of susceptible animals to disease-infected carriers, as determined by the number of infected animals introduced into fresh populations and by the density of populations.

In these findings the English and American workers agreed. Topley's group, however, was inclined to consider that chance factors, interpretable only by statistical analysis of populations, determine which individuals will succumb to infection. Webster, on the contrary, continued his studies on the assumption that individuals differ by reason of inherited factors controlling their resistance.

Previous attempts to solve this question were open to the objection that the experimenters, by breeding from animals tested by exposure to a disease, had merely perpetuated the infection in a sub-clinical state and produced an active immunity in these animals, wrongly interpreted as a state of resistance. Guided at first in the unfamiliar field of inheritance by an accomplished young geneticist, M. R. Irwin (now professor at the University of Wisconsin), Webster adopted an ingenious method of selective breeding. Breeding for high resistance and high susceptibility was begun by testing litters with the infective agent, and, from these tests, choosing parents which had produced highly susceptible and less susceptible young respectively. The selected uninfected parents were then remated and their second litter was used as uninfected parents of the next generation. By this means susceptible and resistant inbred strains were derived from mice which had never been directly exposed to the infective agent. Webster thus succeeded in developing an inbred strain of mice in which 95 per cent proved to be highly susceptible to mouse typhoid, and another in which only 15 per cent were susceptible. When he then made up a mixed population of the two strains and exposed it to mouse typhoid, the individuals survived or died amid the crowd exactly as if still segregated in the breeding cages. Here was proof that the major factor determining whether or not an individual mouse succumbs to infection in the course of an artificial epidemic is its constitutional susceptibility to that particular organism, dependent upon its heredity. In subsequent experiments Webster's team showed that animals inheriting susceptibility to one kind of organism may be resistant to another and vice versa.

At this stage, although clear principles governing the experimental epidemics of mice had been established, little seemed to have been gained of practical use for human populations. If the English group somewhat pessimistically stressed chance factors in susceptibility, the Americans were not much more hopeful in pointing to genetic factors which are, practically speaking, distributed as if by chance through the established pattern of human mating. For Webster, hope of useful results from his work lay in understanding how the genetic mechanism operates to make the individual susceptible or resistant. Assisted by Howard A. Schneider, he began in 1940 to study the effect of various diets on the susceptibility of his contrasted pure lines of mice, but found their constitution so fixed by genetic selection that no experimental dietetic treatment could alter it. Schneider thought they must study hybrid populations in which gene selection had not gone to so powerful an extreme, such populations in fact as that exemplified by the human race. His further investigation of chemical and dietetic aspects of host susceptibility belongs to a later chapter.

Webster, made a Member of the Institute in 1934, devoted himself from 1937 until his death in 1943 to a study of certain neurotropic virus diseases, which partially grew out of his epidemiological work. One of these diseases was rabies. In 1937 Webster and Anna D. Clow succeeded in propagating its virus in tissue culture, though a Japanese worker, K. Kanazawa, anticipated their report by a month. Webster also worked out a mouse test for measuring the immunizing power of rabies vaccine, and with the assistance of J. Casals developed a new vaccine which proved more reliable in protecting dogs than others then available. For all this work he received a gratifying acknowledgment in the last months of his life, when the Dog Writers' Association voted him its 1943 award for "meritorious work on diseases of dogs"[12] — a contrast to Flexner's bitter experience with certain dog lovers thirty-five years before.

MEANWHILE THE Institute's study of syphilis took a new turn. Wade H. Brown and Louise Pearce had become interested in experimental syphilis in laboratory animals when, with Jacobs and Heidelberger, they worked on experimental chemotherapy. Aiming at a cure for that disease, as well as for trypanosomiasis, they tested the potency of arsenical drugs in syphilitic rabbits. At this time, less than ten years after E. Bertarelli of Parma first transferred the disease to rabbits, knowledge of the experimentally induced infection was extremely limited and in no sense sufficient for accurate evaluation of the action of antisyphilitic compounds.

Brown and Pearce spent about six years studying the disease as thoroughly as possible. Contrary to a general impression, they found that syphilis introduced by local inoculation, as, for example, by the standard method of injecting infectious material into the rabbit's testis, does not remain local; the spirochetes begin at once to disseminate themselves, largely by way of lymphatic vessels. Reaching the lymph nodes into which the testicular lymphatics drain, they ensconce themselves, multiply, and remain indefinitely. Spreading still more widely through the blood and lymph vessels, they create typical syphilitic lesions in sites remote from that of the original inoculation. Although the lesions, as a rule, eventually regress and heal, active spirochetes remain in the lymph nodes for life; with the disappearance of visible manifestations, the infection becomes latent. The persistence of latent infection in human cases, after initial and subsequent lesions heal, was reproduced and, to a certain extent, explained by the observations of Brown and Pearce.

Inoculation of a lymph node of a recovered rabbit into the testis of a normal rabbit reliably showed whether the gland was latently harboring spirochetes, and thus could be used to test the efficacy of antisyphilitic treatment in a laboratory animal. Alan M. Chesney (later dean of the Johns Hopkins Medical School), who had worked previously with Swift and Ellis, joined the group for several months in 1922, studying the course of experimental syphilis. In their animals Brown and Pearce produced syphilitic lesions of many organs and tissues, notably of bone, skin, and eyes. In short, they found that the disease in rabbits pursues a course not unlike that of human syphilis in the first year or two after initial infection, but does not later produce the degenerative nervous lesions that constitute its worst terror for man. To their remarkably complete description of experimental rabbit syphilis, set forth in a score of papers, these tireless observers added a great deal of information about the relation of age, sex, pregnancy, and other factors to the spread or localization of the infection, and about the influence of various factors that made experimental syphilis of rabbits much like that of human beings in many respects. Their work supplied valuable facts and methods for students of immunity in human syphilis and for those engaged in treatment of syphilitic patients.

KARL LANDSTEINER, pathfinder in immunology, was fifty-four years old when appointed a Member of The Rockefeller Institute in 1922, and fifty-five when he began to work there. Universities generally look for younger men to fill important vacancies or organize new departments. Promotion to a full professorship is rare after fifty. An older man, administrators fear, may be too firmly set in his ways, or will have exhausted the ability, so needful in a teacher, to tolerate inexperience and crudeness in his pupils. The Institute, concerned only with education at the doctoral level or above it, several times risked an appointment at fifty or later, gaining, in full and productive maturity, three scientists to whom life at the Institute meant at long last freedom from academic routine, financial insecurity, or political pressure. Samuel J. Meltzer and Leonor Michaelis, as we have seen, well repaid the courageous judgment that

brought them to the Institute in the sixth decade of life; Karl Landsteiner also flourished in New York, building a new structure of discovery
on foundations laid long before in Vienna.

Landsteiner has already appeared in these pages as the first to transmit poliomyelitis to monkeys, a feat promptly repeated and extended by
Flexner, which started experimental investigation of that disease. His
real bent, however, was toward the chemical study of biological processes,
especially those of immunology. While still an assistant in Vienna University's Institute of Pathological Anatomy, he did his first famous work
on human blood groups (1900–1903). It was known that the blood of one
species is generally incompatible with that of another, so that if an animal's blood is transfused, for example, into a man, the foreign corpuscles
break up or clump in his veins with disastrous results. That the blood
of some human beings is similarly incompatible with that of other persons was known so well in the latter half of the nineteenth century,
through fatal transfusion, that transfusion was seldom attempted early in
the twentieth. The nature of this incompatibility within a species was altogether unknown.

As so often occurs in biological research, Landsteiner came upon the
problem indirectly. Imagining that the blood serum of sick persons
might act deleteriously upon the cells of other people, he mixed such
serum with a healthy person's blood and found that, in some instances,
the red blood corpuscles clumped. He learned also that the serum of a normal person will, in many instances, agglutinate another's blood. Finally,
he and his associate Jansky found that every human being belongs by inheritance in one of four major blood groups. Their great discovery explained the incompatibilities which had caused fatalities in human blood
transfusions, and taught physicians and surgeons to match the donor's
and the recipient's blood before attempting transfusion. Nowadays the
blood groups are familiar to millions of people who have successfully
given or received blood. Landsteiner suggested using the blood groups to
determine paternity in doubtful cases, and raised questions about the
origin of these groups which led other investigators to study the inheritance and distribution of blood types among the races of mankind.

From 1908 to 1922 Landsteiner was engaged in research and teaching, as pathologist to the Wilhelminer Hospital of Vienna. In the hard
days after Austria's collapse in World War I, national poverty and despair

worsened the conditions for research, and the advance of communism threatened Landsteiner's security. He therefore gave up his post and obtained an appointment at low pay in a small Dutch hospital at The Hague, where he did routine pathology in a one-room laboratory, with a nun and a manservant as his only helpers. In his spare time he continued his researches in basic immunology. Flexner learned of his situation and late in 1921 offered him membership in the Institute, where he began work in the spring of 1923. It was characteristic of his enterprise and ambition that along with his personal effects he brought to New York a large barrel of tar, of a sort that had been found rich in cancer-inducing hydrocarbons.[13] His hope of using it for discovery was realized when he and James B. Murphy employed it to produce experimental sarcomas in fowls. Landsteiner later gave the remaining contents of the barrel to Peyton Rous, who for many years has used it to produce experimental cancer in rabbits.

About 1912 Landsteiner, who for years had been seeking a chemical explanation of immunity reactions, found at last a good lead. The basic fact in immunology is that when a foreign substance of a certain kind, an antigen, gets into an animal's blood stream, it elicits an opposing substance, an antibody. If the antigen consists of blood cells of another species, they will clump or dissolve; if of bacteria, they may break up or dissolve; if of an unorganized protein, combination with the antibody may cause serious chemical or physiological disturbance in the living animal. Agglutination of the blood of a transfused human patient by that of a donor of a different blood group exemplifies such antigen-antibody reactions.

Landsteiner was at first baffled by the difficulty of analyzing antibodies, for the antigen-antibody precipitates occur in amounts so small that he could not weigh them. Turning his attention, about 1912, to the chemistry of antigens, he found the going easier, because he began with known substances which he could obtain pure and in quantity. Most proteins will act as antigens; it had been supposed that all antigens are proteins, and the high specificity by which each such substance calls out its own individual antibody was believed to depend upon peculiarities of protein structure. Following the lead of E. P. Pick of Vienna, Landsteiner, and a chemist associated with him in Vienna, produced artificial antigens by combining relatively simple substances with proteins, finding to their surprise that the simple substance, though itself unable to provoke an immune reaction, could, when joined with the protein, elicit a specific antibody against the combination. Such a simple substance — for which Landsteiner coined the term *hapten* — could dominate the reaction so strongly that the antibody it called into being would react with another protein, if that were combined with the same hapten. This discovery was of great value because it widened the range of substances which can act as antigens.

At The Rockefeller Institute, Landsteiner had his laboratory equipped for chemical research and, as far as he could, chose assistants trained in that field. Freed from routine, he worked, if possible, more intensively than ever, allowing neither himself nor his assistants a moment of idleness. Among the compulsions of this man of somber genius was a tendency to doubt the correctness of his own work until he had queried and retested his results over and over; even when he had conquered his own doubts he needed the support of outside acceptance. Casual callers from a neighboring laboratory were sometimes surprised to have him, with almost pathetic humility, hand them a manuscript for criticism. It is said that he withheld from publication most of the results of six years' research on the antigenic properties of protein digests, because he was not quite sure what the latter contained. His assistants naturally suffered with their chief in his insecurity and perfectionism. Although he willingly heard their suggestions and hypotheses, he kept them at work on his own problems and usually insisted upon himself making critical readings at the climax of an experiment. He assumed that the others were there to assist him, not to be trained for independent original work.

Shortly after Landsteiner came to The Rockefeller Institute, Oswald Avery and his associates in the Institute's hospital discovered that specific immune reactions elicited by various strains of the pneumococcus depend upon the chemical nature of non-protein substances, polysaccharides, formed in the capsule of the bacterium. This unexpected finding suggested that the polysaccharides were behaving, in accord with Landsteiner's theory, as if they were haptens associated with the proteins of the pneumococci. Following out this clue with experiments to be described at length in a later chapter, Heidelberger, Avery, W. F. Goebel, and their assistants brilliantly demonstrated the soundness of the new chemical immunology created by Landsteiner. Utilizing the bacterial polysaccharides as haptens, they produced in the test tube synthetic antigens, which called forth immune substances in rabbits as if they had been made by a living bacterial culture instead of by the chemist.

Landsteiner limited his own studies at the Institute to two main subjects, the antigens of the blood and the immunological specificity of the proteins. With his assistants, J. Van der Scheer and C. P. Miller, Jr., he looked into the blood-serum specificities of apes and monkeys and of hybrids between mammalian species, such as the mule. With Philip Levine he studied the agglutinating substances in human blood, adding to the well-known groups A, B, AB, and O, a new series of blood factors detectable by immunizing rabbits against human blood containing these specific agglutinins. On the whole, the new factors (the first of which he designated M, N, and P) are not antigenic in man and, unlike factors A and B, do not render the blood incompatible for transfusions.

These advances in the study of blood antigens drew renewed attention to Landsteiner's earlier work on the four major blood groups, already part of the working knowledge of the medical profession, and it was for that original discovery that he received the Nobel Prize for Medicine in 1930. He would have preferred, it is said, to have had his work with haptens thus recognized.[14]

Continuing the study of blood, Landsteiner and his fellow workers discovered another factor of great importance for blood transfusion therapy and in human childbearing. In 1936, Alexander S. Wiener began to study the evolution of the agglutinogen M of Landsteiner and Levine's new M-N blood types, by observing their presence in the blood of monkeys, apes, and man. At first, he worked independently at the Jewish Hospital of Brooklyn, though in frequent consultation with Landsteiner. Later, Landsteiner and Wiener continued the work together and, as a step in their analysis, began injecting the red cells of rhesus monkeys into rabbits, in order to produce sera with distinctive immunological properties for use in differentiating human bloods. In this way they found a new antigen, present in the blood of about 15 per cent of human subjects whatever their blood group (A, B, AB, or O). Landsteiner and Wiener named the new factor "Rh," from rhesus.

At first this new human antigen appeared to be of only academic interest. A few years later, however, Wiener, studying bad reactions following blood transfusions, detected an antibody, to which he gave a temporary name, which occurs with the same frequency as does the Rh factor. When this coincidence dawned upon Landsteiner and Wiener, they realized that the new factor was indeed Rh, and that it might be involved in serious clinical disturbances. In 1940, therefore, they published their original findings, while Wiener and H. R. Peters described in full the role of Rh in transfusion difficulties.

Philip Levine, who had left The Rockefeller Institute and was at the Newark Beth Israel Hospital, reported in 1941 with R. E. Stetson a case they had begun to study in 1937, of a recently pregnant woman who suffered a severe reaction at her very first transfusion with blood that should have been compatible if only the standard blood groups were involved. Levine conjectured that this woman, while carrying her child in utero, had been immunized by some unknown factor in the fetal red blood cells. Shortly thereafter he found in several other women, also transfused for the first time, the same specific agglutinin for an unnamed blood factor in fetal blood. Women so immunized were subject to mishaps in childbearing; they often miscarried, or their babies soon after birth developed a serious disease, fetal erythroblastosis, characterized by destruction of the red blood cells. Learning of Landsteiner's and Wiener's Rh factor, Levine perceived that this was the antigen responsible in the cases he and his co-workers had studied. Such immunization may be developed in an Rh-negative pregnant woman who is sensitized by her own infant in utero, if the infant inherits the Rh factor from an Rh-positive father. By small leaks of blood cells from fetus to mother across the placental barrier, or perhaps by diffusion of submicroscopic blood-cell fragments, the factor gets into the maternal blood stream. The mother thus builds up, in successive pregnancies, agglutinins against her own infant in utero which not infrequently cause grave damage to the fetal blood-forming tissues. The extension by Wiener of his work with Landsteiner, when he discovered that the Rh factor may cause serious reactions following transfusions, and Levine's work of associating it with fetal erythroblastosis, has made the Rh test a necessary part of prenatal care, giving warning of threatened erythroblastosis in time for the physician to avert or treat it.[15]

In 1928 Landsteiner achieved a further step toward the understanding of anaphylaxis. This is a form of immunity in which the body becomes sensitive to an antigen which, unlike the antigenic products of pathogenic organisms, does no harm when first it enters the body. When, however, the sensitizing dose is followed by a second or later dose, various tissues react against the foreign substance, sometimes with violent physiological disturbances. Seeking the cause of this phenomenon, Landsteiner, with J. Van der Scheer and Merrill W. Chase, approached the chemical problem of protein specificity in two directions. By digesting proteins with pepsin they obtained split products which, although considerably simpler than the whole protein molecule, would still cause specific sensitization. Working in the other direction, by synthesizing proteins from the peptide fractions, they found specificity just beginning to appear when the synthesized chemical structure reached the relatively complex level of a pentapeptide.

Allergy is a kind of sensitization akin to specific immunity, hitherto unexplained by the principles of immunology. In allergic reactions such as those of hives, hay fever, asthma, certain cases of eczema, and local reaction to drugs, the time and cause of the original sensitization may be obscure. Landsteiner and J. L. Jacobs discovered that certain simple substances known to produce the allergic state in industrial workers can serve as haptens after introduction into the body through the skin, by attaching themselves to one or another of the natural proteins. Merrill Chase of Landsteiner's group was able to transfer the allergic state to normal guinea pigs by inoculating them with living cells from animals previously rendered allergic to simple compounds. This kind of allergy comes very close to the passive immunity long known and used for protective inoculation against various bacterial diseases; Landsteiner and his colleagues had in fact done much to bring together, into one picture, the phenomena of ordinary immunity, anaphylaxis, and allergy.

Landsteiner's career at the Institute extended a few years beyond the end of Flexner's directorship; becoming Member Emeritus in 1939, he went on working until he died suddenly in 1943. His last years were spent in advanced speculation and subtle experimentation, aided by Alexandre Rothen. They aimed to relate the specificity of antibodies to the pattern of their molecular structure, for by this time protein chemists were beginning to develop a coherent picture of the protein molecule. One of the greatest of them, Linus Pauling, was in close touch with Landsteiner's work, to which he traces some of his own ideas. Thus the work begun at Vienna, and continued at The Hague and New York, went on without interruption after Landsteiner's death, through his former associates and through colleagues elsewhere. He left a consistent record of successful investigation of major problems over a long period; and this in spite of a career twice broken by emigration from one country to another and of a mind often troubled by pessimism and self-doubt. There are military heroes, it is said, who go into battle trembling with fear; this was a hero of science who fought without optimism, unable to exult in his superb achievement.[16]

PEYTON ROUS's successful wartime effort to find a way of preserving blood cells for transfusion, described in Chapter 6, naturally directed his thought to the life cycle of the circulating red corpuscles. His associate O. H. Robertson, before leaving for France in 1918, had completed a study of the effects of repeated transfusions upon the activity of the bone marrow, where red blood corpuscles are formed. The marrow normally functions at a constant rate, supplying new corpuscles to replace those lost daily by wear-and-tear of the circulating blood. Robertson found that if he produced a superabundance of red cells in a rabbit by successive transfusions with blood from other rabbits, its marrow, no longer stimulated by the normal need for new corpuscles, ceased to produce them. After a few weeks, however, the animal reacted against the strange blood and destroyed it so rapidly that a severe anemia ensued which further transfusions did not relieve. The animal had built up antibodies against the strange blood, which destroyed its red cells and dispersed their vitally necessary hemoglobin. Soon, however, the blood-forming tissue in the recipient's bone marrow, no longer inhibited by the plethora of donated blood, reacted to the anemia by again making new cells and in such quantity as rapidly to restore the normal state. Robertson's analysis of this process explained why patients suffering with pernicious anemia often remained persistently anemic despite repeated large transfusions. Physicians learned from his work that in pernicious anemia with sluggish bone marrow small transfusions are preferable to large ones.

These and other studies on the fate of circulating red blood corpuscles led Rous and his group to study the fate of the blood pigment, hemoglobin, when the blood cells that carry it reach the end of their life span or are broken up by disease. Normally, the hemoglobin is broken down by metabolic processes, and most of the colored remnants are excreted by the liver into the bile. When the liver is damaged (for example, in yellow fever and Weil's disease), the pigment is retained in the body and the patient becomes jaundiced. Abnormal storage of hemoglobin derivatives occurs also in other organs after the breakdown of blood from various pathologic causes and is especially marked in a peculiar disease, hemochromatosis. Rous and his assistant Jean Oliver, who was to have a long career in pathology, reproduced this disease in rabbits by numerous blood transfusions during many months.

Rous's appointment to full membership in 1920 was followed by a turn in his activity. When he was studying the secretory function of the liver, he had perceived that the bile is by no means a finished product when it leaves the liver. Something further happens to it in the gall bladder, making it thicker and much richer in bile pigment. At that time most physiologists considered the gall bladder a passive organ, serving merely as a reservoir for bile and playing no significant role in digestion. So prevalent was this belief that surgeons freely removed the organ, not only when it was hopelessly damaged by infection but also when it contained only a few gallstones, and sometimes even when it was normal, in the course of an operation for disease elsewhere in the abdomen. Rous and an assistant, Philip D. McMaster (later a Member), worked out an ingenious method for comparing bile as it comes directly from the liver with that which has been for a time in the gall bladder. In dogs the bile ducts are so disposed that from one of them a portion of the bile can be collected as it comes from the liver, while the rest goes to the gall bladder. The outcome was as simple as it was instructive; the lining of the gall bladder, they found, removes water from the bile and thus concentrates it. An amount of water equal to nine-tenths of the volume of the gall bladder may be removed in less than a day. At the same time the gall bladder secretes a great deal of mucus into the bile which presumably facilitates passage of the thickened material through the common bile duct into the intestine.

Rous and McMaster's convincing demonstration revived a former conception of the gall bladder as an important organ of digestion. Evarts A. Graham, professor of surgery at Washington University, St. Louis, was led by this work, a few years later, to put the concentrating power of the gall bladder to an important practical use. Knowing that a dye, tetrachlorphenolphthalein, is secreted in the bile after injection into the blood stream, he had a chemist replace the chlorine with iodine to make the dye cast an X-ray shadow. When concentrated by the gall bladder, the dye became so opaque to X rays that gallstones could be seen amidst it with the fluoroscope, as had not previously been possible. Rous and Mc-Master's discovery was capped four years later by the anatomist E. A. Boyden, then at the University of Illinois, who showed that a meal rich in fats causes the gall bladder to empty itself suddenly into the duodenum, providing a considerable supply of concentrated bile which assists in the digestion of meat and other fat-containing foods. A diseased gall bladder neither concentrates nor discharges its contents in normal fashion. The diagnosis of biliary disease and the understanding of its symptoms have been greatly clarified by these discoveries.

McMaster's experience with the collection of bile from living animals enabled him to clear up, once and for all, a much-disputed and clinically important question in bile physiology. When liver function is impaired by certain diseases, a yellowish-brown substance called urobilin appears in the urine. This was known to be derived from the bile pigment bilirubin, but where and how the chemical steps resulting in the formation of urobilin took place was unknown. Many investigators supposed that it was produced by the liver; other conjectures had implicated almost every other organ of the body. With a young collaborator, Robert Elman (later professor of surgery at Washington University, St. Louis), McMaster devised an improved experimental technique which permitted collecting bile without bacterial contamination from the whole liver, or part of it. Alternately, the bile could be returned to the common bile duct and thence to the intestine. In these experiments, as in those with Rous mentioned above, dogs wearing a collecting bag protected by a wicker basket were able to run about for months and play like normal animals. Experiments in which the bile was by turns allowed to enter the intestine or kept from entering, by draining it off through lateral collecting tubes, showed clearly that, under ordinary circumstances, urobilin is formed only in the intestine from bilirubin in the excreted bile, and that it is never formed by the liver. These experiments, which incidentally fully explained how previous investigators were misled, have since been confirmed by many chemical and clinical workers.

In order to study other problems of liver function, McMaster and D.

R. Drury developed surgical methods for partial and total removal of the liver of animals, and were among the first to perform that intricate procedure so skillfully that the animals survived long enough — up to 60 hours — to show the effects of liver deprivation or insufficiency upon carbohydrate and fat metabolism. Another result of McMaster and Drury's work was the proof, announced simultaneously with similar conclusions by F. C. Mann of the Mayo Clinic, that fibrinogen, source of the fibrin that stiffens clotted blood, is produced by the liver.

Although this work of Rous's laboratory on the blood, liver, and bile has for convenience been discussed here under Pathology, it dealt with processes that go on in health as well as in disease. Rous's next inquiry went further toward physiology, as he sought to measure the intrinsic alkalinity and acidity of the tissues. This old problem was increasing in importance because of advancing interest in chemical exchanges within the body, which are of course influenced by the local acidity-alkalinity state (pH). A practical illustration of this has already been mentioned in connection with W. A. Jacobs's first work in chemotherapy, involving the failure of a well-known urinary antiseptic to inhibit bacterial growth in an alkaline environment. Available information on the subject was largely based on Michaelis's determinations of the pH of tissue extracts, already ten years old and known to be inexact because of chemical changes occurring during extraction. As Rous pointed out, this field of research awaited new methods.

In order to measure pH directly in the undisturbed tissues, Rous and McMaster, Drury, Frederick Smith, S. S. Hudack, and other associates utilized harmless indicator dyes which change color according to the pH, and which, on injection into the blood stream of an experimental animal, are distributed to all parts of the body, coloring the organs and tissues. Beginning with litmus, long used as an indicator in elementary chemistry, they later used aniline dyes of the phthalein group. Tissues with low metabolic activity, they found, tended to the alkaline side, active tissues to the acid side of the neutral (isoelectric) point of the blood. Matrix tissues (connective tissue, cartilage, bone) reflect the fluctuating reaction of the blood, whereas glands and other highly cellular tissues exhibit a more constant reaction. Striking changes in the acid direction accompany necrosis and even mere local stasis of the blood stream; a patch of freshly grafted skin, for example, if it remains alive, is quite acid as compared with the surrounding integument, until its blood supply is re-established. Rous was aware that the indicator-dye method had its own limitations; for example, the tissues may themselves affect the dye, altering the pH value at which it changes its telltale color. Yet the information he and his young men obtained was the best available for many years. For still greater accuracy the field had to wait again for new methods.

Led by Rous, the group went on to study the gradient of permeability along the finer blood vessels, by using vital dyes of differing diffusibility. They found that these dyes escaped most easily at the far end of the capillaries, where the blood enters the venules on its way back to the heart. This finding was wholly against contemporary opinion, but later workers have proved it valid. Hudack and McMaster went on to investigate the permeability of the lymphatic capillaries by means of dyes, boldly corroborating their observations on mice by numerous experiments upon themselves. They injected dye solutions into the skin of their arms so that for the first time the lymphatic vessels of the skin were made visible in living men. They concluded the first stage of their work with a report that strikingly re-emphasized the wealth of lymphatics in the human integument, well known to anatomists but somewhat neglected in pathology and medicine. As they showed, the most superficial lymph vessels lie so near the surface that, when skin is abraded or cut, microorganisms readily enter the lymph stream. A hypodermic needle inserted into the skin inevitably tears open the closely linked network of fine channels, so that every intradermal injection enters the lymph and may potentially reach the blood stream; and, as with small blood vessels, trifling injury to the lymphatics results in exudation, dye rapidly escaping into the tissue in both instances.

The technical methods developed for these studies have since been utilized by other students of lymph flow in man. McMaster's method of making the lymphatic vessels visible by injecting dye solutions has been used in human cancer patients, to trace the pathway of lymph drainage from diseased areas and to locate lymph nodes to which cancer cells may be carried to form metastatic tumors. Later work led by McMaster, on the physiology of lymph formation and flow, will be discussed in Chapter 15.

Rous's long experience with cells in the mass, that is to say in organized tissues and in tumors, naturally aroused his curiosity about various properties of individual cells, and led him into several incidental investigations which he conducted with striking ingenuity. In the first of these, conducted with F. S. Jones in 1915–1916, Rous sought to disentangle living individual cells from fixed tissues. Any attempt to separate them by dissection under the microscope was doomed to failure from mechanical damage; nor had anyone as yet found a chemical method of dissolving away the substances that bind the cells together, without killing their protoplasm. The way to success was to grow small tissue fragments in clotted plasma and, after the cells had spread out in this medium, to digest the fibrin strands of the clot with the pancreatic enzyme trypsin. The living cells resisted digestion just as the cells of the pancreas and the intestine resist it in the body; thus the cells of the culture were set free, unharmed, ready for study as individuals. With this method Rous and Jones investigated the phagocytic power of fibroblasts (connective tissue cells), showing that these cells protect ingested red blood cells and bacteria against antibodies in the surrounding medium, to which however they succumb when the fibroblasts die.

Many years later Rous, McMaster, and Hudack again utilized the trypsin method in an important investigation of the fixation and protection of virus particles by living cells, and in particular by the cells of tumors caused by viruses. Later, workers in Paul Weiss's laboratory of developmental biology, who again used trypsin as a gentle means of separating living cells, were surprised to find that the originator of the method worked in another laboratory of The Rockefeller Institute.

Another ingenious method of isolating cells was the use of a magnet to collect phagocytes (Kupffer cells) of the liver. These typical cells of the reticulo-endothelial system, lining the walls of the capillary blood vessels in the liver, are able to collect and withdraw fine particles from the blood stream. Using an iron compound, gamma ferrous oxide, which is light in weight but strongly magnetic, prepared by Oskar Baudisch of the Institute, Rous and J. W. Beard injected a suspension of the iron-containing particles into a rabbit's vein. After the phagocytes had taken up the metallic grains, the experimenters perfused the liver with physiological salt solution and passed the perfusion fluid, now laden with cells, over a rod of soft iron temporarily magnetized by a powerful electromagnet. After the cells became attached to the rod, it was demagnetized, letting the cells drop into a tube of culture fluid. In this way they isolated and maintained the Kupffer cells in pure culture, studying with great ease their unique characteristics and behavior under the microscope.

IN 1915 F. J. Twort of London first detected the activity of a hitherto unknown kind of parasitic agent, infecting not animals or the higher plants, but bacteria. F. d'Herelle of Paris, in 1917, independently observing the same phenomenon, brought it sharply to the attention of bacteriologists. These so-called bacteriophages are colonies of extremely small living particles which invade the bodies of bacteria and, multiplying there, cause the host cells to undergo lysis, that is, to break up or dissolve. Their action is revealed when the phage clears up a tube of broth swarming with bacteria, or eats out clear areas in a culture spreading on a gelatin-covered plate. Bacteriophages are now classified as viruses, because they depend upon bacteria for survival and yet harm them, exactly as the virus of poliomyelitis, injurious to human nerve cells, can live only in human or monkey cells, in the body or in a tissue culture. D'Herelle of course knew far less than this when he first wrote about bacteriophage. For some years bacteriologists remained uncertain whether this was a living substance at all, and whether it existed in only one form, attacking all bacteria, or in many strains, each specific for a given host. Interest in the phenomenon became acute because of the hope — not justified by the outcome — that bacteriophage might be used to kill pathogenic germs in an infected patient.

Rockefeller Institute bacteriologists were not slow to take up the problem. Martha Wollstein of Flexner's division, working in 1921 with a visiting Fellow, Leon E. Gratia of Belgium, isolated several strains of bacteriophage for study. In 1923 J. F. Bronfenbrenner began an intensive study of the physical and physiological characteristics of various bacteriophages. Assisted at first by youthful Fellows, Charles Korb, Elmer Straub, and Philip Reichert, he investigated the size of phage particles, their inactivation by alcohol, and their sensitivity to acidity-alkalinity changes. He was among the first to prove that there are many kinds of phage, each specific for one or another bacterial species. In 1927 Bronfenbrenner, Ralph Muckenfuss, and Donald Hetler succeeded in making motion pictures of bacteria containing bacteriophage; the film made clear for the first time the phenomenon of lysis by phage action.

At the Princeton laboratories in 1930 J. H. Northrop independently studied bacteriophages with A. P. Krueger, Associate in general physiology (later at the University of California). They carried the problem even farther into biophysics than had Bronfenbrenner, by studying the concentration of phage required for lysis, and the kinetics of the reaction between phages and bacteria. A later chapter deals with Northrop's return to this field after 1949, and his fruitful results.

This brief account of work on the bacteriophages illustrates the fact that much research is undramatic, yet valuable. Here were no striking discoveries nor spectacular conclusions, but only a series of technical reports, quickly absorbed into the growing stock of knowledge on the subject. Like the pieces of a jig-saw puzzle, once fitted into place they lost their individual significance. The findings of a lengthy study might not fit at all and might have to be pigeonholed until explained or corrected by future investigation.

Much of the research at The Rockefeller Institute, or any other laboratory, is of this sort — laborious, unexciting, and, even when successful, often relegated to anonymity. The reader of medical history — and the historian as well — eager to get on to more exciting achievements, may fail to see how little of such an effort is entirely lost. Bronfenbrenner's findings, shared with other workers elsewhere, helped to build up a consistent picture of the bacteriophages; Northrop's quantitative studies started him toward more fundamental discoveries about the chemical nature of this peculiar kind of living material; a half-dozen young collaborators were trained in advanced research, and one of them, Krueger, became a recognized authority in the field. The total yield of such an enterprise, if it could be calculated, might exceed that of a more spectacular success.

CHAPTER NINE

Cancer, Organ Culture, Cytology

Cellular reactions to cancer; role of the lymphocyte; heredity of cancer susceptibility; the "spreading factor"; a rabbit cancer; papilloma virus; Carrel's experiment with diets. Organ culture: the Carrel-Lindbergh pump. Chemistry and cytology of tuberculosis. Endocrinology. New buildings; changing personnel.

THE ROCKEFELLER INSTITUTE never put cancer research in the forefront of its program. All those who helped to found the Institute, both laymen and scientists, held the investigation of infectious diseases and physiological functions to be the primary aim. In these, they believed, lay the best hope of immediate progress; cancer was too complete a mystery for profitable attack, all leads toward its solution thus far having ended blindly. William H. Welch, President of the Board of Scientific Directors, warned his promising young pupil Peyton Rous not to stake his career upon so precarious a task as cancer research.[1]

Flexner, although he never proposed setting up a separate division for malignant disease, was not as pessimistic as Welch, for he took the gamble of putting Rous to work on the subject, within his own division of pathology and bacteriology. Later, when the Institute's membership included such distinguished investigators of fundamental cellular physiology and chemistry as Jacques Loeb and Leonor Michaelis, the cancer problem seemed to them even more formidable than the pathologists had thought it. Daunted by the complexities of apparently simple phenomena of life — movement of salts in and out of cells, conduction of the nerve impulse, transport of oxygen in blood and tissues — they saw immensely greater complexities in the problems of regulated growth, to say nothing of disorganization and malignancy. The attack on cancer, they felt, must rest on basic knowledge of cytology, chemistry, and genetics, not likely to be gained by study of fully developed malignant tissues running wild in the body of a human patient or a laboratory animal. Michaelis, disillusioned by two years of his own youth spent (not altogether unsuccessfully) in cancer research, told his assistant Granick, "The problem of cancer will not be solved in a cancer institute."[2] He may or may not have been right, but at least at The Rockefeller Institute it was strikingly true that advances in this field came from intelligent exploration of clues presented by chance rather than by deliberately planned research. Two instances of such alertness have already been discussed, namely, the discovery of a transmissible rat sarcoma by Flexner and Jobling, and of the first virus-induced tumor by Rous.

When in 1915 Rous turned from the cancer problem to work on blood preservation, his former assistant James B. Murphy was promoted to Associate Member and put in charge of cancer research.[3] Murphy soon developed a program, most carefully worked out, that stemmed from a familiar observation concerning the small round white blood cells, the lymphocytes. These play a great part in resisting transplants of foreign tissues, gathering locally in the tissues immediately surrounding the grafts as if to wall them off. Some years before, when he and Rous transplanted fowl sarcoma into embryos, they found that embryos lack the power of resistance to such transplants that is displayed, in greater or lesser degree, by all adult tissues except the brain. Recalling that the embryonic body and the adult brain have in common a lack of lymphoid cells, Murphy formed the hypothesis that lymphocytes have a specific role in resisting cancer. This idea could be tested by altering the activity of the lymphocytes, for example by exposing animals to heavy dosage with X rays, which kill off white blood cells. Working along this line with various assistants for many years, he accumulated a vast number of observations on the inhibition and stimulation of cancer transplants and normal tissue grafts by X rays, heat, hormones, and other agents known or suspected to affect tissue growth.

This exhaustive study of the biological reaction by which an organism responds to implants of foreign tissue was a mine of detailed information for subsequent investigators. It did not, however, confirm the initial hypothesis that lymphocytes have a protective action against tumors and grafts of normal tissues. The cause of their accumulation around grafted tissues that are faring badly, and their functional role in such circumstances, remain unknown.

Murphy's scientific career coincided with a changing attitude of the medical profession and the public toward cancer and related diseases. Blind terror and hopelessness were giving way to optimism based on the advance of scientific diagnosis and surgical technique, and research added its promise for the future. The times called for systematic education of the public to seek early diagnosis and treatment. The doctors, too, had to be kept up to date by organized instruction through national societies. Financial support had to be found for research institutions concentrating on cancer problems. At such a time Murphy's long experience, personal charm, and gift for executive leadership made him extremely useful. He took a notable part in the organization of American cancer research, as a board member of the Memorial Hospital for Cancer and Allied Diseases and the Sloan-Kettering Institute of New York, the Jackson Laboratory in Bar Harbor on Mount Desert Island, and the Roswell Park Memorial Institute of Buffalo. He also served the cause through effective lectures on the biological problems of cancer, and as a devoted member of research-promoting committees. Made a full Member of The Rockefeller Institute in 1923, he gave much time to these public efforts while carrying on his studies of factors regulating cell growth, with numerous collaborators, until his sudden death in 1950.[4]

Such a persistent and wide-ranging inquiry, even if it arrived at no comprehensive conclusion on Murphy's central problem, could not fail to open leads and provide new themes for the numerous workers associated with it. Waro Nakahara, at the Institute from 1918 to 1925, returned to Japan and later became head of a cancer research laboratory in Tokyo and the dean of cancer research in his country. R. T. Hance, cytologist, left to take the chair of zoology at Pittsburgh. R. G. Hussey, who assisted chiefly with the X-ray studies, became a professor of pathology at Yale.

Clara Lynch, who joined Murphy's group in 1918, made substantial contributions to the genetics of cancer, especially by her demonstration that susceptibility to the development of tumors, both spontaneous and induced by experiment, is heritable. When she began her work in this field, investigators of cancer were aware that the tendency to spontaneous development of tumors in various organs differs in different strains

of mice. As early as about 1907 E. E. Tyzzer of Boston, by selective breeding experiments with mice, produced a number of family lines with different incidences of spontaneous tumors, chiefly those of the lung. His
statistical analysis of the data also indicated that the differences were determined by heredity. This view was quickly confirmed by a number of
other workers. One of the best known and most assiduous of these,
Maud Slye of Chicago, made similar observations on other types of malignant growth. Acquiring vast experience in cancer pathology with regard to inheritance, she had, at that time, unfortunately committed herself to a dogmatic and untenable conclusion, later revised, that the
tendency to develop all spontaneous cancer in mice is transmitted by a
single recessive Mendelian gene. This idea was opposed to that of other
workers, notably C. C. Little of Bar Harbor. Leo Loeb of St. Louis
(brother of Jacques Loeb), in collaboration with A. E. C. Lathrop, studied the inheritance of cancer by crossing a number of strains of mice
with differing incidence of mammary tumor (of varied claims to genetic
homogeneity) and concluded that probably multiple Mendelian factors
were involved.

Lynch, on the basis of a series of crosses between female mice from
tumor strains and males from other sources, also took issue with Slye's
conclusion. In her mice, inheritance of susceptibility to mammary gland
cancer seemed to behave as if dominant rather than recessive, and probably to depend on more than one Mendelian factor. Thus, she helped to
keep open a question which has since proved to be complicated by factors unforeseen at the time, and which, though now more fully understood, is not completely elucidated to this day. She emphasized the fact
that susceptibility is inherited, not the disease itself. Susceptibility is,
however, variable in expression, its manifestations being dependent
upon many unknown influences; heredity is by no means the sole factor
in producing cancer. There is little evidence of genetic control of the
common types of human cancer, and persons in whose ancestry cancer
has occurred can be assured that the disease is not an inevitable consequence of their inheritance.

Lynch was among the pioneers in two areas of cancer research,
namely, tumors of the mammary gland and of the lung. Investigators
were recognizing that close inbreeding, such as brother-by-sister or par-
ent-by-offspring, would produce strains of animals with a high degree of

uniformity. Such material is of inestimable value in cancer research. Although a tumor may appear in a young mouse, it usually occurs in mid-
dle-aged or even older animals. There is no upper age limit. The fact
that a mouse dies without developing a tumor does not necessarily mean
that it was incapable of having one.

In the 1920's Lynch focused her attention on tumors of the lung,
which, unlike mammary tumors, commonly occur in both sexes; both
parents and all their offspring can therefore be characterized and used in
the analysis of experimental results. She was the first to use, in genetic
studies, strains of mice that differed markedly in the natural incidence of
lung tumor. No established lung tumor strains were generally available
when she began her work, though C. C. Little had established his DBA
strain and L. C. Strong of the Carnegie Institution was developing many
of the strains used today. Lynch inbred her mice so that the stocks became progressively more uniform. Two of her early strains, the BL sub-
line of Bagg albinos and the Swiss, to be spoken of later, are still maintained in various laboratories. During the inbreeding, it was noted that
two strains of separate origin already showed a significant difference in
incidence of lung tumors, a difference that was maintained. The existence of these differing strains, the results of crosses between them, and
collateral evidence of various sorts indicated that susceptibility to lung
tumor is genetically controlled.

A second advance in technology provided a way to produce malignant growths at will in laboratory animals, and gave Lynch a means of
testing the inheritance of induced as well as of spontaneous tumors. Two
Japanese pathologists, Yamagiwa and Ichikawa, had in 1915 succeeded
in producing malignant tumors in rabbits by painting the skin with coal
tar, and a third, Tsutsui, had since done the same with mice. Murphy
and Sturm at The Rockefeller Institute then showed that applying tar
to the skin over a period of four months (on various areas so that no
local tumors would arise) could produce, after a further lapse of time,
tumors in the mouse lung. Lynch, the first to apply this method to genetic studies of cancer, could use the species with which she was already
at work, and of which she had two strains which differed in the incidence
of lung tumors. When tarring was applied to the mice, the incidence of
lung tumors was increased. But there was still a difference between the
strains; the response appeared to be determined by the constitution of

the animals composing the group. A breeding test was carried out, and the mice of the first cross and backcross generations were subjected to tarring. In the first filial generation, the lung tumor incidence was almost as high as that of the more susceptible parent. The individuals resulting from the backcrosses showed a higher or lower incidence of lung tumor depending upon whether the second cross had been made back to the high or low line. As Lynch reported in 1926, it was evident that susceptibility to induced tumors was inherited.

In 1931 an experiment using different strains having spontaneous tumors, modeled on those done with tarring, with appropriate backcrosses, gave similar results. Susceptibility to spontaneous tumors also is inherited. In all these experiments lung tumors appeared in the first generation, though dominance was not complete and the mode of inheritance was evidently not simple. Sex had little influence on the incidence of lung tumor. Experiments by others a few years later (J. J. Bittner and C. C. Little, 1937; Bittner, 1938; H. B. Andervont, 1938–1939) using more highly inbred strains confirmed Lynch's finding that susceptibility to both spontaneous and induced lung tumor is inherited, and appears to be very nearly dominant. Different strains of mice were used by these experimenters, and their estimates of the number of genes concerned varied. Some of the findings pointed to a single gene. Andervont suggested that there are genetic factors controlling the degree of susceptibility, an idea afterward confirmed, as we shall see, by Lynch and others.

The idea that external agents could produce malignant change had been readily accepted, but it seemed to conflict with the proposition that susceptibility to tumors is influenced by heredity. Lynch's experiments resolved the conflict. A comparison of the backcross experiment involving tar tumors with a similar experiment involving spontaneous tumors showed that although the lung tumor incidence after tarring was higher than in the untarred mice in each group, the pattern of response was the same. The interplay of heredity and environment had been observed. In this case, the same genes appeared to be concerned in both types of abnormal growth. Later work by others has indicated that this situation does not hold for all incitants.

In the experiments with lung tumors, Lynch found no evidence of a maternal influence, such as prevailed with mammary gland tumors. J.

J. Bittner of the Jackson Memorial Laboratories, Bar Harbor, Maine, discovered that something in the milk of a mouse from a high mammary tumor strain affects the tumor rate of her offspring. The agent was later found to have the characteristics of a virus.

Experiments on various organs indicated that in any one strain of mice, susceptibility might be limited to a particular tissue. In 1933, using four inbred strains, Lynch found marked hereditary differences between the response of skin and lung to the tumor-inducing action of tar. The important fact appeared that although one strain had a high incidence of skin tumors, its lung tumor incidence might be low, whereas in another strain the situation might be reversed. In fact, almost every combination occurred, although in an individual strain suscep-tibility to induced lung tumor paralleled susceptibility to spontaneous lung tumor.

In previous experiments Lynch had found no correlation between susceptibility to spontaneous mammary tumors and tar-induced tumors of the skin. Spontaneous sarcomas are comparatively rare in mice. In 1935, by means of the tumor-inducing chemical 1:2:5:6-dibenzanthra-cene injected subcutaneously into mice of five strains, she showed that, although the strains differed in the incidence of lung tumors (spontane-ous and induced), they all responded with a high incidence of induced sarcoma. The conclusion was inescapable that tumor susceptibility is organ- or tissue-specific. When differing strains of mice live together in the same cage, each maintains its distinctive lung tumor incidence. Thus, there is in the mouse, and presumably in all mammals, a heredi-tary tendency to the development of distinctive tumors, depending on the breed, either spontaneously in response to unknown intrinsic fac-tors, or under stimulation by extrinsic carcinogenic agents. Interstrain differences with respect to susceptibility to tumors induced by tar were also demonstrated by other contemporary investigators. When the in-troduction of chemical carcinogens and other incitants supplanted the tedious and time-consuming method of tarring, it stimulated great re-search activity, and constitutional differences and the independence of susceptibility of tissues and organs were amply demonstrated.

Lynch incidentally made a useful contribution to animal research by introducing to this country in 1926 the Swiss mouse, so called not because it was indigenous to Switzerland but because Lynch brought some of them from a laboratory in Lausanne for use in her cancer studies. Eventually they served experimentally as a strain very high in lung tumor incidence. They are also used extensively in screening tests in the search for chemicals that might prove effective in cancer therapy. From the two male and seven female mice originally brought to The Rockefeller Institute, descendants have been bred commercially and in many laboratories. Unexpectedly, they were found to be excellent material for research on viruses, making possible, for example, a simple immunity test to determine whether yellow fever has been present in a human population within the life of the present generation. The Swiss stock has supplied a tremendous number — literally millions — of mice for use in a world-wide survey of the prevalence of yellow fever, by the International Health Division of The Rockefeller Foundation. In the field of genetics and infectious disease, Lynch, in collaboration with T. P. Hughes, used the Swiss as one of her strains to show by a breeding test that susceptibility to the virus of yellow fever was influenced by the hereditary constitution of the individual mouse.

FRANCISCO DURAN-REYNALS, a native of Barcelona, came from the Pasteur Institute in 1926 as assistant to Murphy, who set him to work on the factors governing the "take" and infectivity of vaccine virus. In the course of this study, using extracts of various organs as vehicles for the virus, he discovered unexpectedly that extracts of the testis greatly enhanced its infective power. Certain other organs, notably the kidney and brain, contain a similar but less potent "spreading factor." When he first described the phenomenon, in 1928, Duran-Reynals had no clear idea how the newly discovered factor works, but, in 1930, Douglas McClean of the Lister Institute, London, showed that in some way it increases the permeability of the skin, so that diffusible materials make their way through the dermis much more readily when the Duran-Reynals factor is present. D. C. Hoffman of Olitsky's laboratory and Duran-Reynals, not knowing of McClean's work, arrived at the same conclusion. Later, in 1937, Albert Claude and Duran-Reynals found the factor to be a protein. Finally, several workers elsewhere discovered that it is an enzyme, hyaluronidase, which acts by liquefying hyaluronic acid, a viscous mucopolysaccharide existing in the interstices of the connective tissue in the skin and elsewhere which acts as a barrier to the diffusion of fluids and finely divided solids through the tissues.

Discovery of the spreading factor opened up many fields of investigation, for it is related to physiological and pathological activities involving movement of fluids, bacteria, and many other materials through the tissues and the accumulation of fluids in edematous (dropsical) conditions and in injured joints. A review of the information gained and problems raised by this discovery, presented in 1950 in a symposium at the New York Academy of Sciences, occupies 150 pages.

Applying his experience with the spreading factor to virus-induced tumors, such as the Rous sarcoma and other fowl tumors, Duran-Reynals, after he left the Institute in 1938 to work at Yale, became a vigorous advocate of the virus theory of tumor causation.

During the early 1930's a wealthy philanthropist of Barcelona, Spain, named Roviralta, decided to emulate John D. Rockefeller by establishing a medical research institute in that city. Duran-Reynals was chosen to head it, and in 1935 went to Spain to recruit scientists for his laboratories and to bring them to The Rockefeller Institute for a year or two in preparation for their new tasks. Three such physicians, all trained in Barcelona, joined the Institute as volunteer investigators. Jordi Folch-Pi came late in 1935 to work at the hospital with D. D. Van Slyke; early in 1936, Jordi Casals-Ariet joined Leslie Webster's group, and Vincens Moragues Gonzales joined Leonor Michaelis. Duran-Reynals, returning to Spain in mid-1936 to organize the Barcelona laboratories, was caught for a time by the outbreak of the Spanish Civil War, which, unfortunately, put an end to the Roviralta project. He returned to the Institute and continued his work there until 1938, when he went to Yale University.[5] Casals and Folch were given positions on the Institute staff; their excellent investigative work is described elsewhere in this history. Moragues went to Creighton University Medical School, where he became professor of biochemistry. By the permanent residence of these four scientists in the United States, America gained, as so often has happened, from the political troubles of Europe.

Albert Claude, trained at Liége and Berlin, joined the Institute in 1929 and set himself, during his first years with Murphy, the very difficult task of identifying chemically the agent causing the transmissible

Rous sarcoma (chicken tumor 1). He succeeded in partially purifying the virus, but not sufficiently to characterize its chemical nature beyond the assumption that a protein was present. To this day it has not been obtained in a pure state. As will appear in a later chapter, this painstaking, persistent investigator went on to make a major contribution by way of a general study of the constituent elements of cells, introducing the electron microscope to the Institute and founding a group of cytologists who have continued to be highly productive.

In 1920, when Wade H. Brown and Louise Pearce had many rabbits with experimental syphilis under observation, they found in one of their male rabbits a small tumor of the scrotum, not syphilitic, but a malignant epithelial tumor or carcinoma, a cancer in the strict sense of the word. Taking advantage of this chance occurrence, they tried propagating it by inoculating bits of the original tumor into other rabbits. Succeeding in that attempt, they began a long experimental study of the tumor. It was the first malignant tumor of the rabbit to be propagated through more than one or two transfers. By the time Brown and Pearce first reported it, they had carried it through twenty successive transplants from animal to animal. They tried, of course, to transmit it by inoculation of cell-free filtrates, but this could not be done; the Brown-Pearce tumor was apparently not virus-induced like the Rous fowl sarcoma. In researches carried on for about six years, reported in ten articles in the *Journal of Experimental Medicine,* the two workers persistently studied the tumors from every aspect pathologists could envision, trying to understand the laws governing its transmission, "take," and spread in the host, and to find out why in some cases the tumors ceased growing or even disappeared.

The tissue never changed its fundamental biological characteristics through the long series of transplantations, except for a decidedly increased rate of growth. Its malignancy — that is, its tendency to spread to a fatal conclusion — unexpectedly fluctuated as the experiments progressed through successive transfers. Although the variability of tissue growing so wildly in unorganized masses baffled description of its behavior in precise terms, the investigators learned enough to conclude that the growth of this cancerous tissue obeys recognized biological laws. The outcome depends upon the innate growth capacity of the tissue, the resistance of the inoculated host to foreign cells, and the relative influence of particular methods and sites of inoculation. Because it had been so thoroughly studied, and was for many years the only available transplantable cancer of the rabbit, the Brown-Pearce tumor became well known in cancer laboratories all over the world, and serves today as test material in a wide range of experimental studies.

About 1934 Peyton Rous returned to cancer research, in which in 1909 he had made his first great success. He did so because a young colleague in The Rockefeller Institute, Richard E. Shope, had offered him for study a virus that caused a mammalian tumor — a generous gift, for the donor was well aware that work with this virus might bear on the riddle of cancer. Shope had found that a disease of wild cottontail rabbits, long familiar in the American Southwest and characterized by the growth of immense warts or papillomas of the skin, is caused by a filtrable virus. Domestic rabbits inoculated with the warty material developed even larger and more actively growing papillomas which often proved fatal. Yet these vigorous growths did not yield the virus, for, as Shope found, filtered suspensions made from such warts failed to reinfect other rabbits.

Supplied with infectious material by Shope, Rous and his assistants J. W. Beard and J. G. Kidd first ascertained that the virus-induced growths resembled the benign papillomas caused by tarring, in every respect except that the immediate cause of the latter was known. The investigators put the tumor through a remarkable series of tests. The virus would produce epidermal growths on the skin but it would not affect internal organs and tissues. Yet living bits of the virus-induced wart could be transplanted into the liver, a muscle, or almost any internal site and would there grow into large tumors. A finely ground suspension of the warty tissue injected into a vein was strained out by the lung and there, by its own proliferation, produced tumors of the same sort, exactly as happens when human cancer metastasizes to the lungs. When rabbits with vigorous papillomas were kept for several months, their cells often became cancerous, invading locally like epidermal cancers and distributing themselves through the blood or lymphatic vessels to form secondary tumors in distant organs. Because tars and other cancer-inducing substances cause papillomas on the skin of animals exposed to them, the Institute workers injected the Shope virus into the blood stream of animals carrying the tar papillomas. They found that the virus became localized in these benign tumors and caused them to undergo cancerous changes of bizarre character, through the interaction of the virus and the tar papilloma. Although none of these induced cancers ever yielded the virus, the affected rabbits developed strong immunity reactions against it, failing to develop warts after inoculation.

Here then was a virus that not only caused papillomas by its own action, which went on to become genuine cancers, but would also induce malignancy in concert with the cancer-inducing factor of tar. In the malignant growths of both sorts, the virus was still presumably present, though not recoverable from the tumor cells. Alexis Carrel, reading reports of this thoughtful, ingenious work, wrote to Flexner: "It is a masterpiece, of profound significance for our understanding of malignant tumors."[6] Yet the enigmas presented were too great for simple explanation. Rous could go no farther than to say cautiously that the observed facts pointed more than ever to viruses being the cause of cancer. Having been first, with his fowl sarcoma, to introduce this concept, he had brought it to the front again and was to keep it there, as a later chapter will show. We still do not recognize a single cause of all cancers, but at mid-twentieth century, as advancing knowledge promises to group together the hereditary gene substances, the functional nuclear material of plant and animal cells, and the filtrable viruses, all of which seem to consist essentially of nucleoproteins, we may look forward to solution of this great problem. To that outcome, through the work of the chemist Levene, the pathologists Rous, Murphy, Shope, Brown, and Pearce, and the virus investigators of the hospital (whose findings will be discussed in a later chapter), The Rockefeller Institute will have signally contributed.

FEW PEOPLE, even within The Rockefeller Institute, knew of Alexis Carrel's most elaborate venture into the field of cancer research. Both as a surgeon and as a speculative thinker, Carrel was fascinated by the problem of malignancy. His laboratory's command of tissue culture methods enabled him and his associates to conduct or to cooperate in a number of investigations of the behavior of cancer cells *in vitro* and of environmental factors in the culture media which affect their growth and multiplication. Finally, he developed ideas of his own about the cause of cancer and obtained from Flexner ample financial support with which to try them out. The story of this venture is almost wholly undocumented. In an authoritative account of The Rockefeller Institute published in 1930, Flexner rather vaguely mentions Carrel's view that hereditary and environmental factors affect the complete living individual, just as they had been found to affect pure cell strains and types in tissue cultures. These factors, Flexner wrote, are not outside the boundary of experiment and might actually be tested with a small, rapidly propagating animal, such as the mouse. Carrel, he said, was in fact making such tests in a specially constructed "mousery" at the Institute.[7]

Nothing else about the mouse colony seems ever to have appeared in the Institute's public or private reports; it is not once mentioned in Carrel's sections of the annual confidential reports to the Board of Scientific Directors. A brief passage in Soupault's biography of Carrel, apparently based on comments of favored visitors, is the only published description.[8] There was indeed a mousery of vast proportions, far from general view on an upper floor of the powerhouse. A member of the Institute's research staff, unaware of its existence and unexpectedly admitted, found himself in a city of mice, thousands of them, elaborately housed and cared for. Lars Santesson of Stockholm, then a Fellow, in a paper on tumors found in this colony reported a population of 14,000 mice.[9] A. H. Ebeling believes that at its peak the population reached 55,000; Soupault also cites this figure.[10]

The philosophy behind the mousery appears in the confidential report of 1928. Carrel had observed, he wrote, certain villages of French peasants and fishermen in which the annual death rate from cancer reached 4 to 6 per thousand, and others in which it was as low as 0.5 per thousand. The only reason he could think of for this great difference between people of identical race and way of life was the nature of their food. The villages with a high cancer mortality were those in which the inhabitants had modernized their diet and were eating white bread, margarine, and canned foods — including some possibly injurious substances — with few vegetables, and with less butter, milk, and eggs than in the traditional diet of the countryside. Carrel thought it likely that a faulty diet makes tissues susceptible to cancer. Although in his contribution to the confidential report he did not allude to experiments in progress, accounts of those who saw the huge mousery make it clear that its purpose was to test Carrel's ideas about a dietary cause of cancer. The possibility of hereditary susceptibility to malignant tumors, in inbred populations of certain of his French villages, seems not to have been taken seriously into account, although, according to Santesson and Ebeling, mice of four pure-bred lines were maintained in the colony.

Edric B. Smith, business manager of the Institute, recalled that in the air-conditioned, glass-roofed structure there was one room with a capacity for perhaps 5,000 mice, housed in boxes and glass jars. In part of the structure there were four large and deep bins containing soil in which the mice ran wild in burrows, under relatively natural conditions. Carrel even tried to grow various grains in these bins, to provide fresh food, but failed. The mice were variously fed, on purchased grains, or on canned foods to imitate the modernized village diet.[11]

This was a relatively expensive venture. The Minutes show that in 1928 about $70,000 was spent in constructing the mousery.[12] The cost of operation appears to have been over $20,000 per annum for five years. What actually came of this experiment, and when and why it was discontinued, are questions unanswered beyond an entry in the Minutes of June 4, 1932, implying that there would be no appropriation for it after 1933. One story current at the Institute has it that the mice in the big bins defeated the investigators by dying in their burrows so that they could not be examined post mortem; another that the records were too voluminous for analysis. Santesson and Ebeling published a few papers on mouse tumors; the confidential reports mention a few specific studies on physiological changes in mice, concomitant with changes in diet and with aging, by Ebeling and other assistants of Carrel. One thing is certain, that Flexner, usually enthusiastic about Carrel's achievements, let the episode pass without ever making a formal report on its scientific returns to his Board. To a member of his family he explained that he had authorized the experiment because he felt that when one of the Institute's productive investigators wanted to test a potentially significant hypothesis it was the Director's duty to support him, not to discourage the project on *a priori* grounds.[13] The records and preserved pathological material, left at the Institute when Carrel went to France in 1941, were by Mme Carrel's wishes deposited at Georgetown University, Washington, D.C., after his death.

CARREL's superb surgical experimentation had given him command of a technique for transplanting organs, but, unfortunately, he could not apply it to human patients. In the laboratory he was able to transfer the spleen or a kidney from one dog to another, reestablishing the blood circulation without clots or infection, although such transplanted organs did not function permanently at the new site. A surgeon bold enough to undertake any such replacement of human organs would be balked by the specific antigens in human blood and tissues, which make the tissues of one individual unacceptable to the body of another. The medical profession had long since learned this fact from disastrous attempts at transfusion before the discovery of the four major blood groups; and Carrel's colleague Landsteiner had shown that the incompatibility of organs is far more specific than that between blood groups. Almost imperceptible differences in individual protein and hapten chemistry distinguish each of us even from our parents and siblings. Today, more than a half century after Carrel's first transplantations of whole organs, surgeons usually venture to exchange a kidney only between identical twins, to save the life of a twin afflicted with severe nephritis.

Dreaming that it might be possible to cultivate new organs (not endued with a donor's incompatible antigens) from elemental tissues, Carrel took up mammalian tissue culture, as we have seen, immediately after Ross Harrison's first success with frog tissue. He and his colleagues quickly learned that, for the time being, it was difficult enough to keep even individual cell lines alive and reproducing themselves. But Carrel persisted, believing that experience with elementary routines of asepsis, composition of culture media, and control of physical conditions necessary for life *in vitro* would be useful when the time came for the culture of whole organs. As the work progressed, he became fascinated with the mystery of life as he saw it in simple terms of tissues growing in his flasks — tissues removed from the regulatory influences of other tissues and of the whole body. Problems of the biologist came more and more to the front in his thinking; those of the surgical technician receded. By the time Carrel was ready to attempt the culture of organs, he saw that, whether or not the treatment of diseased human organs by exchange or replacement ever became possible, the really important application of the method would not be in the field of surgery, but in physiology. Success would provide a new and more direct method for the study of phenomena such as nutrition, respiration, secretion, and the regulation of function.

Science might learn, Carrel said, "how the organs form the organism, and how the organism grows, ages, heals its wounds, resists disease, and adapts . . . itself to changing environment. The ultimate goal of the culture of organs is to obtain this new knowledge and to pursue it through the complexity of its unpredictable consequences."[14] Thus venturing into one of the most difficult fields in all science, after the fashion of an enthusiastic neophyte he raised all the great unsolved questions and hoped to solve them by a new method. For almost a century physiologists had been working on methods for keeping organs and fragments of animal tissues alive outside the body, in order to study their functions. Certain simple undertakings of this sort were easily possible. A frog's heart, for example, will beat for hours in an oxygenated solution containing the necessary salts in correct proportion, a little dextrose to provide energy, and a chemical buffer to keep the solution from becoming too acid. It stops either because of bacterial putrefaction or because of the slow deterioration of its proteins for lack of normally protective factors in the body.

The frog's heart walls are thin enough to be permeated directly by the oxygen, salts, and nutriment in the physiologist's bath. Thicker organs have to be supplied with these substances by perfusing the blood vessels with the aid of a pump. The first apparatus for that purpose seems to have been devised in the laboratory of the Leipzig physiologist Carl Ludwig, in the 1860's. With it one of his pupils kept a liver alive long enough to demonstrate that its metabolism continued outside the body, as proved by the presence of urea in the perfusion fluid. These early experiments showed that the perfusion works better if the fluid is pumped through the vessels in pulses like those produced by the heartbeat. With pumps designed for this purpose, physiologists kept alive isolated organs for a few hours, revealing much about the utilization of nutritive substances, the secretion of gland products, and the disposal of chemical wastes. The experiments were short-lived, often vitiated from the start by deterioration of the isolated organ; Carrel was aware that for continued survival and growth he would have to control many more factors. Artificial perfusion fluid must be free of floating particles that might plug capillary vessels 1/4000 inch in diameter; if blood was used it must contain no clumped corpuscles; temperature, acidity-alkalinity balance (pH), oxygen content, and osmotic pressure of the fluid, and the rate and pressure range of the pulse must be exactly regulated. Above all, the explanted organ must be completely protected against bacteria.

Perfect asepsis being the prime requisite, Carrel in 1929 had his technical assistant Heinz Rosenberger construct a sterilizable all-glass perfusion pump, operated by an external magnet. Although, as an extra precaution, he added Dakin's antiseptic solution[15] to the perfusion fluid, his attempts to maintain isolated kidneys with this apparatus failed completely because of bacterial contamination.

At this unhappy stage of the project an unexpected ally, Charles A. Lindbergh, volunteered his aid. The celebrated aviator tells the story in his preface to Carrel's posthumous book *The Voyage to Lourdes*.[16] In the summer of 1930 a member of Lindbergh's family, ill with pneumonia, developed "lesions on the heart." Unfamiliar with the meaning of this phrase, Lindbergh asked about the possibility of removing the lesions surgically, and was informed that an operation on the heart was impossible. Knowing little, as he says, about the biological aspects of the problem, but keenly interested in mechanical inventions, he wondered whether it might not be possible to construct an artificial heart which could maintain circulation, allowing a surgeon to stop the heart itself and operate upon it. A physician with whom he talked about this idea introduced him to Carrel. When Carrel described his difficulties with the perfusion apparatus, Lindbergh undertook to design a better pump, and was invited to work at the Institute as a volunteer in Carrel's laboratory.

This was only three years after Lindbergh's pioneer New York-to-Paris flight. He was still, to an embarrassing degree, the object of intense public interest. Although his first visit to Carrel at the Institute was meant to be incognito, word of it got about somehow, and windows overlooking the side entrance, through which Carrel had him enter, were lined with curious and admiring secretaries and technicians. Some of the senior Members were inclined to disapprove Carrel's introduction of an amateur to the select ranks of medical investigators; others feared sensational publicity; but, as the novelty of Lindbergh's presence wore off, the young man's modesty and discretion dispelled their objections and won him a place of quiet regard among the professional scientists. Asking for no official recognition, he was treated by the administration as

Carrel's personal guest. His presence went unnoted in the Minutes of the Board of Scientific Directors, and no one at the Institute would discuss the matter with newspaper men. When after a year's work he published a brief paper in *Science* about his first pump, a representative of that journal innocently told a newspaper reporter that the author was not Colonel Lindbergh, but a scientist of the same name at The Rockefeller Institute.[17]

The first Lindbergh pump consisted of a helical Pyrex tube mounted vertically on a motor-driven base, which swung the coil in a circle without rotating it, as a man waves a flag with upraised arm. Pressure being maintained by the head of the liquid, the motion of the tube caused the fluid to flow upward along the spiral to a chamber in which the explanted organ (heart, liver, spleen, etc.) hung from the tip of a fine cannula inserted into an artery. The pump did not develop adequate pressure and did not pulsate. It was difficult to avoid infection of the organ while placing it in its chamber. Nevertheless, Carrel reported that it maintained a flow of blood serum through a carotid artery for an entire month without infection. A second tentative model used gas pressure to carry the perfusion fluid to the organ chamber. This was simple to construct, but its long pressure tube was difficult to sterilize. By the end of 1934, after four years' work, Lindbergh was approaching a better solution, having hit upon a satisfactory way of transmitting power into a sterile system. He found that he could pass a fairly large flow of air through a glass bulb loosely packed with non-absorbent cotton which removed infective organisms carried by the air. Before applying the principle to his pump, he experimented with it by flowing air from the piped laboratory supply through such a bulb and into a flask of sterile broth culture medium, in which no contamination occurred during a month of continuous flow. Pulsating power so transmitted to the sterile portions of the perfusion pump was "soft," therefore better suited to living tissues than were the movements of a mechanical pump.

The final version, first successfully used in the spring of 1935, was driven by a stream of compressed air made to pulsate by a rotating valve. The pulses were transmitted indirectly to the "control gas," a mixture of oxygen, carbon dioxide, and nitrogen, which served both to circulate and to oxygenate the perfusion fluid. The organ chamber, fluid reservoir, and a pressure-equalizing chamber, constituting the perfusion pump proper, were in one piece made of Pyrex glass. The explanted organ was in contact only with glass and the nutrient fluid. The temperature, pulsing pressure, and rate of flow were precisely controlled from outside. The fluid could be removed and renewed aseptically and was automatically filtered while circulating. Carrel could prepare and install the kidney, heart, or thyroid gland of a small animal in less than twenty minutes. Lindbergh's remarkably ingenious design for all this required seventeen pages of descriptive text and seven full-page illustrations in the book Carrel and he published in 1938.[14] The Institute's glass blower, Otto Hopf, a genius in such work, constructed the chambers, tubes, and glass valves of this intricate one-piece assembly. Lillian E. Baker of Carrel's staff carried on a long research into the composition of perfusion fluids whose final formulas included, besides the salts, proteins, and energy-forming carbohydrates, a wide assortment of hormones and vitamins.

Beginning April 5, 1935, a whole organ — the thyroid gland of a cat — was successfully cultivated *in vitro* for the first time. After continuous perfusion for eighteen days part of the gland had broken down, but under the microscope much of its tissue appeared structurally normal, and fragments transferred to a tissue culture flask proved to contain living epithelial cells. During the next few years many other organs of rabbits, cats, chickens, and other small animals were tested in the Lindbergh pump. Hearts could be kept beating for several days. Ovaries increased in size, and fallopian tubes underwent peristaltic movement. Kidneys did not do as well, degenerating rapidly after the first day, but for a few hours at least they put out urine containing a higher concentration of urea than the perfusing fluid. Some slight evidence was obtained of more elaborate physiological activities persisting in explanted organs, including the production of insulin in the pancreas and antibodies by the spleen. Most of the experiments lasted about a week, but on one occasion a thyroid gland was cultivated for thirty days, with remarkably little change in the condition of its cells. In about a thousand experiments with the Lindbergh pump, Carrel learned much about the physiological needs of isolated tissues; for example, that many organs could not be oxygenated sufficiently for survival unless red blood corpuscles were present in the perfusion fluid, as oxygen carriers. Thus the fluids were gradually improved.

Carrel and Lindbergh first demonstrated their method of organ culture at a medical congress in Copenhagen in 1936. Albert Fischer of that city, a former assistant of Carrel at The Rockefeller Institute, shortly afterward set up at the Carlsberg Foundation Lindbergh pumps which were used by Harold Okkels in research on antihormones. Several other laboratories in Europe and America experimented with organ culture, but it was not widely used. As indicated by many of the narratives of research set forth earlier in this history, the biological sciences were already moving away from investigation of coordinated activities of the whole body and of organ systems, toward study of life processes at the level of the individual cell. For investigators interested in intimate details of cell structure and function, an organ can be observed no better when isolated than in the living animal. Biochemists, moreover, could study many of their problems with slices or minces of tissues surviving for a few hours, and were disinclined to undertake the laborious and expensive method of organ culture. Furthermore, the experimenters, lacking complete knowledge of the essential factors for life *in vitro,* were not able to reproduce perfect physiological conditions. Although Carrel's explanted organs survived surprisingly well, they almost always showed retrogressive or degenerative changes within a few days. Tissue spaces filled with edema fluid, arteries became calcified, connective tissues outgrew the more specialized secretory cells. Consequently, physiological processes quickly became abnormal. For these reasons the Lindbergh pumps, constructed between 1935 and 1938 and numbering many dozens, gradually dropped out of use.[18]

Nevertheless, there are important unsolved problems which can probably be best attacked by cultivating whole organs and embryos. In the study of metabolic chemistry, for example, culture *in vitro* of a whole organ would permit supplying it, over long periods of time, with selected nutritive substances free from unwanted products of other organs. The rapid degeneration and calcification of organs, resulting from imperfections of the Carrel-Lindbergh method, might, if slowed down in long-cultivated organs, teach something about degenerative diseases and the pathology of aging. Such hopes have kept the idea of organ culture alive, and have induced a few ingenious workers to attempt simplification and improvement of the Lindbergh pump and of the culture fluids.[19] This technique may some day come to the front again for purposes unforeseen or deemed incidental when it was introduced. Such has been the case with Carrel's earlier contribution, tissue culture, which for a time survived only as a means of solving highly specialized and limited biological problems, but which is now essential to the cultivation of cell-dependent viruses, such as that of poliomyelitis, and to the preparation of vaccines against them.

The newspapers soon found out that the young inventor at The Rockefeller Institute was indeed the aviator who had filled their front pages in 1927. Carrel, too, was already famous, and the spectacle of such men daringly attempting together the creation of an artificial heart made new headlines. Lindbergh's clear description of the first pump in *Science* in 1931 and of the final apparatus in the *Journal of Experimental Medicine* in 1935[20] gave the journalists accurate information, and the better newspapers restrained themselves fairly well in publicizing it. Carrel himself, though scrupulously factual in his published scientific articles, did not hesitate to express informally his hopes of what might later be done. He spoke of storing organs for transplantation and even of removing a damaged organ to a culture chamber temporarily for treatment. His aims, as well as his accomplishment, were of course recklessly exaggerated by the sensational papers, some of which went so far as to suggest that he planned to propagate human babies *in vitro,* or to keep an isolated human brain alive and thinking.

Carrel's vision of the future embodied no sinister design. He dreamed only that science, of the kind that could keep organs alive in a flask, joining with supernal forces as yet revealed only by religious faith, might ultimately extend the term of human existence, and even solve the mystery of death. Carrel had been at work, during the organ culture experiments, on an intense statement of his philosophy in *Man the Unknown.* When, shortly after the book's publication, he lectured at the New York Academy of Medicine, throngs of people stormed the doors and extra details of police had to be called out to keep order.[21] This was the climax of his popular fame. In 1938 he and Lindbergh presented the scientific world with a definitive account of their methods in book form.[14] The pump was exhibited in action at the New York World's Fair of 1939. Operated with Carrel's consent by two of his former technicians under the sponsorship of a pharmaceutical firm, it was the chief attraction in the Fair's Hall of Medicine, where large crowds witnessed the maintenance of a dog's thyroid gland and other organs.

When Carrel reached retirement age, July 1, 1939, Lindbergh discontinued his work at the Institute. Within a few months, both, in their separate ways, were drawn into the turmoil of World War II, and Carrel, hopelessly involved in the unhappy fate of his native country, left America February 1, 1941, never to return.[22]

IN THE earliest days of Flexner's administration, an editorial in the *Journal of the American Medical Association* expressed surprise that The Rockefeller Institute's staff included no investigator in the oldest of medical sciences, anatomy.[23] As time went on, someone at the Institute could always be found at work in the other preclinical fields into which medical research and teaching are customarily divided, namely, physiology, biochemistry, pharmacology, pathology, and bacteriology. Anatomy alone was not formally represented in any of its major divisions. This is easily comprehensible. In the first place, Simon Flexner and his Board of Scientific Directors no doubt considered that anatomy, then still devoting itself largely to descriptive study of normal tissues, had little claim to incorporation in an institute concerned chiefly with the experimental study of function and of disease. A brilliant renaissance of experimental and developmental anatomy, under the leadership of F. P. Mall at Baltimore, Charles Sedgwick Minot at Boston, and R. R. Bensley at Chicago, was only just beginning to make its influence felt during the Institute's first decade. Elsewhere gross human anatomy, long since almost completely worked out, offered little stimulus for research. Embryology was merely a study of developing form, largely irrelevant to the description of disease. Anatomical neurology, still merely descriptive, had little as yet to offer the experimenter as a basis for work, although later, under H. S. Gasser, electrophysiology of the nervous system, based on anatomical knowledge, became a major study at The Rockefeller Institute.

Among all the subdivisions of anatomy, that of histology and cytology — study of the general microscopic structure of tissues and cells — came closest to pathology, the main concern of the Institute at this period. The pathologists themselves, as already seen, contributed much to the microscopic anatomy of normal tissues, Carrel's group, for example, by describing fibroblasts and other cells in the living condition, Peyton Rous by his studies on macrophages (phagocytic connective tissue cells) and blood capillaries, and Rous's juniors, McMaster and Hudack, by observing the lymphatic vessels. Of the four anatomists who worked at the Institute during Flexner's administration, two, Florence R. Sabin and E. V. Cowdry, were welcomed mainly for their prospective contributions to the understanding of the cellular basis of certain major problems of pathology.

The Rockefeller Institute's only woman Member, Florence R. Sabin, joined Flexner's division of pathology and bacteriology in 1925. Born in 1871 in a Colorado frontier town, she spent the first part of her professional career at the Johns Hopkins University in Franklin Mall's department of anatomy. Her first extensive research, dealing with the origin and spread of lymphatic vessels in the embryo, and based on skillful injections of lymph channels, soon placed her in the front rank of American anatomists and is still quoted in textbooks of histology and embryology. Independent in spirit as in intellect, Florence Sabin enthusiastically joined the feminist movement of the early 1900's, campaigning for women's suffrage and taking every opportunity to show her interest in political and social reform. The medical students, unaccustomed to women professors, might have resented an "emancipated" woman in that role, had she not won their respect and affection by personal dignity, generosity toward young people, and a contagious enthusiasm for medical science which made her a superb teacher.

About 1917 Sabin, who had been promoted to a full professorship at Johns Hopkins, began an investigation which went on for about twenty years, on the development of blood cells in the embryo and in the adult bone marrow. Relegating the conventional use of preserved blood smears and sections to a subordinate place, she studied living cells under the microscope, applying recently discovered methods of staining them with non-toxic dyes. One of the results was the recognition of the importance of a hitherto somewhat neglected type of white blood cell, the monocyte, actively concerned in the process of inflammation. This cell she and her associates R. S. Cunningham and Charles A. Doan believed to be distinct from the other mononuclear white blood cell, the lymphocyte. Physicians as well as pathologists saw the value of these new methods for studying the pathology of inflammation, and of blood diseases in particular, fields which were stagnant at the time. In 1925 Flexner, who had known Sabin when she was a student and intern and had kept in touch with her during her career in the laboratory of his friend Mall, journeyed to Baltimore to invite her to join his division as a full Member of the Institute. Accepting the call, she took Charles Doan with her as her first assistant.

During her thirteen years in New York, Sabin worked chiefly on a problem in tuberculosis which interested her because it involved the behavior in disease of the very same cells she had been studying in normal structure and function. Under her lead the Institute participated in a large concerted research project sponsored by the National Tuberculosis Association.[24] The over-all aim of this project, which was initiated by the well-known tuberculosis specialist Esmond R. Long of Philadelphia and the Yale biochemist Treat B. Johnson, was to discover which of the chemical substances formed by the tubercle bacillus induce the various phenomena of cellular damage and immunity reactions characteristic of the disease. As one of the sponsors said, science could not hope to destroy all the tubercle bacilli in the world, but there might be a possibility of understanding the microbe's vital chemistry and that of the cells which it invades, and thereby of interfering with the relationship so as to arrest the destructive process.

When tubercle bacilli lodge in the tissues, they soon set up small areas of inflammation into which swarm great numbers of monocytes from the blood and the adjacent connective tissue. Ingesting the bacilli and damaged leukocytes, the monocytes enlarge, crowd against each other, and form a mass of so-called epithelioid cells, constituting a tubercle, the characteristic lesion of the disease. It had long been known that dead tubercle bacilli injected into the tissues will elicit tubercles; in fact, T. Mitchell Prudden, one of the original Directors of The Rockefeller Institute, had been the first, in 1891, to prove this indisputably. The next step was to discover those chemical constituents of the bacilli responsible for these local reactions and their sequelae. Under the leadership of a committee of the National Tuberculosis Association, two pharmaceutical firms, the H. K. Mulford Company and Parke, Davis and Company, grew enormous quantities of tubercle bacilli, from which Johnson and R. J. Anderson at Yale, and Long and Florence Seibert of the University of Chicago, separated the chemical fractions.

Anderson took charge of the water-insoluble substances, finding them to contain a whole series of lipids, waxes, glycerides, and polysaccharides. When Sabin and her associates Doan, B. K. Wiseman, K. C. Smithburn, C. E. Forkner, R. M. Thomas, and others injected the lipids and waxes into the peritoneal cavity of the rabbit, many of these substances caused ordinary inflammatory reactions, but one only of the lipids had a strikingly specific action, inducing typical tubercles. From this substance Anderson isolated a previously unknown fatty acid which he named phthioic acid, from the Greek word for consumption, *phthisis*. Injecting this into the peritoneal cavity, Sabin, Doan, and Forkner produced at will tubercles which they could observe at any desired state of development, and, using the method of vital staining which Sabin had mastered in Baltimore, they followed the whole process of transformation of monocytes into epithelioid cells, the subsequent development of the cell mass into a tubercle, and even, in a few experiments, the caseous degeneration which is the most important late phenomenon in the pathology of human tuberculosis.

The outcome of the joint effort was a fairly clear demonstration that the protein and carbohydrate derivatives of the bacilli, studied chiefly by Long's group, are responsible for the skin reaction to injected tuberculin, for the fever, and for certain general cellular reactions; the waxes determine the peculiar acid-fast staining properties of the tubercle bacilli and allied organisms; and the lipids produce the inflammatory reactions, one of them, phthioic acid, being largely or entirely responsible for tubercle formation. Subsequent investigators, however, have come to feel that the observed effects of individual bacillary constituents may not entirely explain the genesis and progression of the lesions produced by infection with living microbes. The dose of phthioic acid necessary to produce tubercles is far larger than the amount of living bacilli required for the same effect. Caseation rarely occurs in chemically induced tubercles. Furthermore, it is not certain that the chemist's fractions exist *in vivo;* Anderson himself and a group working with him, analyzing a large quantity of human tuberculous lung tissue, could not find either phthioic acid or the antigenic carbohydrates that had been isolated from cultures.[25] These questions remained unsettled, as investigators turned away from the infecting organism to study factors of the host's body which may influence the progress of lesions, such as allergic reactions to

Building the Power House in 1915

Flexner Hall construction, viewed from the East River in 1915

the tubercle bacillus and local variations of tissue nutrition and oxygenation. The discovery of antibiotics effective against the bacillus has still further pushed histopathology into the background as of chiefly diagnostic use in the study of tuberculosis.

During the same years Sabin and her colleagues explored many other problems presented by blood cells, bone marrow, and lymphatic system. Two of the young men in particular, Doan and Forkner, gaining extensive knowledge of the blood and lymph-forming tissues, put it to good use when, after leaving The Rockefeller Institute, each made his mark as a clinical hematologist.

Sabin's last important work at the Institute was an effort to test a long-standing hypothesis that the so-called reticulo-endothelial system is the site, or one of the principal sites, of the production of antibodies. For this purpose she ingeniously utilized a special antigenic compound synthesized not long before by Michael Heidelberger, a former worker at the Institute. The substance was a compound of egg albumen with a red dyestuff, forming a finely granular suspension. Injecting it into the veins or tissues of rabbits, Sabin found that, as expected, it was taken up and held by the special phagocytic cells in the walls of blood capillaries of liver and spleen, in the lymph nodes, and in the connective tissues, which constitute the reticulo-endothelial system. Thus captured, the antigenic substance was visible under the microscope because of its deep red color. The living cells, however, soon separated the dye from the protein, and just at the time when the colored granules disappeared from view, the blood stream began to contain an antibody against the albumen of the introduced compound. This result indicated that the antibody, chemically a protein of the globulin variety, was being formed in the reticulo-endothelial cells and delivered to the blood. Doan and Benjamin Houghton afterward repeated the finding at Ohio State University with similar cells in tissue cultures of the spleen. Although other possible sources of globulin antibodies, notably plasma cells, have not been excluded, this concept still has much experimental support and continues to hold its place in current teaching.

Retiring in 1938 at the age of sixty-seven, Florence Sabin returned to Colorado, where her good citizenship and zeal for reform soon brought her into the forefront of a movement to improve public health administration. When the reform was achieved and new health laws enacted, thanks, in good part, to her energy as a campaigner, she worked for the election of a mayor (Quigg Newton) who would enforce the Sabin Health Acts. When he could find no applicant qualified to be Manager of the Denver Department of Health and Charity, he insisted that Dr. Sabin take the post. At the age of seventy-six, and without previous administrative experience, she became chief health officer of a city of 300,000 people, successfully carrying on her duties for about four years. Amazed by such courage and versatility, and grateful for her services, the state of Colorado, after her death in 1953, declared her one of its two foremost citizens, to be commemorated by statues in the Capitol in Washington.[26]

Florence Sabin seems to have considered her last professional undertaking merely incidental, for she did not list it in *Who's Who in America,* esteeming Membership in The Rockefeller Institute the climax of her career. Nevertheless, to her scientific associates, her work in New York seems less characteristic than her teaching and research in Baltimore and her public service in Denver. In the laboratory she was a brilliant technician and keen observer, but not a rigorous experimentalist, for she was working with cells and tissues that could not easily be controlled and had to be described pictorially, rather than by quantitative formulas. Her investigations almost inevitably ended with a fringe of unprovable assumptions, for which she contended with a persistence that sometimes diverted attention from the painstaking, accurate observations on which they were based. Productive and happy though she was in New York, her great talents were more fully displayed to her medical students and — surprisingly — in public life than in a relatively cloistered environment like that of the Institute laboratories of her day. Teaching and inspiring a score of her country's best young histologists and hematologists, and guiding the people of Colorado toward higher standards of public health, she was a great scientific leader.[27]

Three other investigators trained as anatomists were at the Institute during Flexner's administration, but all of them, like Florence Sabin, applied their knowledge to problems of pathology and physiology. The first, Eduard Uhlenhuth, trained as a biologist in Vienna, and after 1925 anatomist at the University of Maryland Medical School, was a member of Flexner's division from 1914 to 1924. He studied the physiology of the thyroid and pituitary gland in salamanders. In these animals experimental operations are readily feasible, and the effect of the pituitary on growth and that of the thyroid on metamorphosis from tadpole to adult are striking phenomena, subject to experimental modification.

Edmund V. Cowdry, an experienced cytologist and for years professor of anatomy at the Peking Union Medical College, an enterprise of The Rockefeller Foundation, joined the Institute in 1921 and remained until 1928, when he was called to the chair of anatomy at Washington University, St. Louis. He applied his skill in the demonstration of minute structures within the cell (such as mitochondria and the Golgi apparatus) in a variety of exploratory studies on intracellular parasites of the *Rickettsia* group, which includes the causal agents of typhus and Rocky Mountain spotted fever. In 1925 he went to Pretoria to study heartwater, a disease of sheep, goats, and cattle, prevalent in that part of South Africa. The veterinary pathologist Sir Arnold Theiler had suggested that this disease is caused by a rickettsial organism; Cowdry confirmed this idea by finding the parasite, and secured evidence that it is transmitted by ticks. This was the first observation of *Rickettsiae* in any animal other than man. Besides this and other ventures in pathology, Cowdry while at the Institute made contributions to normal cytology, including a detailed description of the secretory cells of the kidney tubules, and a useful calculation of the surface area of the mitochondrial granules, now known to be, in effect, packets of enzymes engaged in chemical interchanges within cells.

In 1932–1933 Flexner invited one of the most distinguished American anatomists, Herbert M. Evans of the University of California, to spend a year at The Rockefeller Institute. He brought with him two medical biologists of his own staff, Miriam S. Simpson and Richard Pencharz. E. L. Gustus, an assistant some years before to Jacobs in chemical pharmacology, and Paul R. Austin, a young biochemist, joined the group for the year. With such a team, Evans was able to attack difficult problems in the field of pituitary hormones. The chief result was a demonstration that substances which increase or decrease the effect of certain hormones are present in the blood, urine, and other body fluids, and also in the pituitary gland itself. By their synergistic effect, these substances greatly strengthen the action of the gonadotrophic hormones produced in pituitary and placenta, which stimulate growth of ovary and testis. The well-known Ascheim-Zondek test for pregnancy, these workers found, depends

upon such reinforcement, for the very small amount of synergistic substance secreted by the pituitary gland of the test animal activates the
gonadotrophin in the urine being tested.

At the end of the year Evans and Simpson returned to the University
of California, continuing important work in the same field. The investigations of Uhlenhuth and Evans were the Institute's only ventures into
endocrinology during Flexner's administration, aside from Meltzer's
early experiments with adrenaline, and the clinical studies of diabetes
to be discussed in Chapter 10. Yet American anatomists were at this very
time taking the lead in endocrinology, especially of the pituitary gland,
ovary, and testis. Their work, based upon microscopic anatomy, was
opening the way for great advances in the physiology of the reproductive
system and of gestation. One can only speculate as to why the Institute
did not participate in this important movement. It is of course out of the
question, even in so large and well-supported an institution, to pursue
every promising line of research intensively. The outlook of the executives, the availability of suitable investigators, and financial considerations all influence the choice of topics for study. In any case, because
research in endocrinology and embryology was not continuously supported, The Rockefeller Institute had no such influence upon American obstetrics and gynecology as it has had upon internal medicine and
some branches of pediatrics and surgery.

Another field of medical biology into which the Institute did not enter seriously was that of the vitamins. Flexner, no doubt, saw the importance of the subject; at his suggestion, it is said, Phoebus Levene
worked from 1923 to 1926, with B. J. C. van der Hoeven and one or two
other assistants, on the chemical purification of vitamin B. They succeeded in concentrating the crude extracts then available, by absorption
upon silica gel, obtaining a preparation of greatly increased potency.
Their method, however, was soon superseded by others, and Levene,
whose heart was not in this kind of research, did not continue it.

GROWTH OF THE work in the laboratories, with increased scientific and
supporting staffs, began to crowd the existing buildings. In 1929 the
Trustees erected a building, now called Welch Hall, containing a handsome library reading room overlooking the East River, with ample book
stacks and offices for the librarians, and a large dining room, usable also

as an assembly hall seating two hundred or more auditors. In 1931 a seven-story laboratory building, now called Theobald Smith Hall, was erected to the north of the earlier group of buildings, and large additions were made to the animal house and powerhouse. No further changes in the main buildings were made during Flexner's administration. The buildings stood as they were at the end of 1931 until after the reorganization under President Bronk in 1953, except for the erection of greenhouses in 1937 and 1948, conversion of the original isolation hospital to nurses' quarters in 1950, and the addition of a new wing to the main hospital in 1952.

The three laboratory buildings now housed the six divisions — Pathology and Bacteriology, Cancer Research, Chemistry, Chemical Pharmacology, Experimental Surgery, and General Physiology — and two subdivisions, Physical Chemistry and Biophysics, whose work has been reviewed in this and two preceding chapters. By the mid-thirties these groups comprised twelve Members, six Associate Members, sixteen Associates, and about thirty-six Assistants and Fellows. Although it is in the nature of laboratory research everywhere to expand to fill all available room, workers at the Institute were not stinted for working space; each Member had at the disposal of himself and his associates a well-equipped suite, ranging from the three or four rooms occupied by a small group, such as that of Murphy, to the greater part of two floors used by Carrel. Variously located among the buildings were the offices of the business manager (Edric B. Smith), bursar (A. D. Robertson), superintendent of maintenance (Bernard Lupinek), and purchasing agent (Charles B. Spies). There were also the Library (Lillia Marie Donnell Trask), the Division of Illustrations (Louis Schmidt), the Division of Publications (Edith C. Campbell), the machine shop, glass blower, and other special services.

Simon Flexner, presiding over this great assemblage of laboratories with their administrative and service adjuncts, and also over the Hospital and the Department of Animal and Plant Pathology in Princeton, had behind him his Board of Scientific Directors, changing in membership as time passed but constant in its support of the Director. Flexner had assumed full leadership when he became Director of the Laboratories, overcoming a move during the first year, by Holt, Herter, and Biggs, which he considered an attempt to take charge of the Institute's affairs as a committee, with power over the Director.[28] His assumption of authority, achieved without leaving permanent scars, altered the role of the Board. No longer an organizing committee taking the initiative in executive actions, it became a consultative and advisory board, passing on questions and proposals laid before it by the Director.

Welch and Theobald Smith remained active almost until Flexner retired. Biggs died in 1923, Holt in 1924; Prudden, interested and helpful to the last in the day-to-day management of the Institute, as secretary of the Board of Scientific Directors, also died in 1924. W. J. V. Osterhout, elected in 1920 while at Harvard, served until 1926, retiring from the Board when he became a Member of the Institute. Eugene Opie, one of the earliest of the Institute's scientific staff (1904–1910), was a member of the Board for about three years, 1929–1932. To represent clinical medicine in place of Holt and Janeway, Francis G. Blake, professor of medicine at Yale and former staff member of The Rockefeller Institute Hospital, was elected to the Board in 1924. He filled his special role almost alone, for two other physicians chosen during this period, the pediatrician John Howland of Baltimore (1924–1926) and the internist Francis Peabody of Boston (1926–1927), died after serving only a year or two. Because of this succession of changes by death and other causes, there were only four Board members with long-continued service during the last phase of Flexner's directorship, namely Welch, Theobald Smith, Blake, and after 1926 Charles R. Stockard, professor of anatomy at Cornell Medical School. To these the Board in 1930 added James B. Conant; someone, presumably Flexner, had perceived that the young professor of chemistry at Harvard was a strong and wise man.

In this way, the Board's predominantly medical character had been modified in the direction of general science; of the three younger men active at this time, two (Stockard and Conant) were doctors of philosophy, not physicians.[29] In the Board of Scientific Directors, as in the research staff of the laboratories, the Institute's interests had broadened to include not only infectious diseases and pathology, which the founders had at first envisioned, but also a wide range of basic sciences extending to chemistry and physics. The Board continued to take a direct interest in the work of the research staff, perhaps not as intensive as that of the founding directors in earlier days, but far greater than lay boards of universities can hope to take. The Board members read the published results in their respective fields, visited the laboratories from time to time, and, in view of their scientific competence, did not hesitate to question Members of the Institute critically about their work. In administrative matters Flexner, advised by Welch, kept the leadership; one Board member during the last years of Flexner's directorship recalls no occasion when the group voted down a proposal earnestly advocated by Flexner.[30]

After Welch retired by reason of his last illness, in 1933, Flexner, now seventy years old, became somewhat less decisive, and members of the Board began to express themselves more vigorously on questions of major policy. Stockard, a forceful and sometimes opinionated man, whose post at Cornell Medical College placed him close to the Institute, took a particularly active role as President of the Board. Francis Blake, a calm spirit but firm when his independence led him to dissent from the Director's views, was to his chagrin not reappointed when his term expired in 1935. Other signs of disagreement on important administrative problems can be read between the carefully phrased lines of the Minutes of the Board of Scientific Directors. As the first Director's administration drew closer to its end, the Board was preparing for the exercise of authority which it had not claimed under his leadership. Yet all these men, themselves experienced in administrative affairs, whatever their attitude on individual questions of policy, retained high admiration for the wisdom, executive skill, and finesse with which Flexner had so long conducted the Institute. That its success had depended largely on his personal leadership had always been recognized by the Institute's principal sponsors.

As much as ten years before Flexner's retirement, Rockefeller, Jr., and Gates were asking themselves whether a change in the plan of organization might be desirable under a new administrator. At a conference in 1926 at which both were present, an unidentified speaker expressed fear that after the close of Flexner's regime the Institute might "sink into bureaucracy." By this he meant, apparently, that trustees and members of the Board of Scientific Directors might act in routine, unimaginative fashion and might even yield to pressure from spokesmen of special interests, such—one must suppose—as universities and professional groups with which these men were associated, or the other Rockefeller endowments (which were, in a sense, represented on the Board of Trustees); or perhaps even by succeeding generations of the Rockefeller family.[31] It was suggested, according to Gates, that members of the Board of Trustees and the Board of Scientific Directors should henceforth be chosen by a number of the great universities.

Reviewing the discussion in a letter to Rockefeller, Jr., Gates said that he had himself seen bureaucracy develop speedily in incorporated philanthropies which distribute money and whose directors are chosen on the representative principle. (Presumably he was referring to certain unidentified church boards and educational institutions with which he had been connected.) Of that evil, however, he had not seen the least trace in The Rockefeller Institute during Flexner's administration. Conducted by men sworn to serve the public interest through scientific work alone, it was under no pressure either to secure outside funds or to make appropriations to other institutions. Appointment of trustees or scientific directors by universities or other external agencies would introduce the very danger they wished to avoid. Gates had no fears for the future if the boards continued to be self-perpetuating and absolutely independent of outside influences. The Institute's freedom to conduct research unhampered had been protected not solely by Dr. Flexner's personality and character, but by its unique organization, independent endowment, and completely altruistic aims.[32]

CHAPTER TEN

The Hospital, 1913–1935

Pneumonia antigens and sera. Heart disease, protein denaturation. Rheumatic fever. Measles. Viruses: cowpox, psittacosis, louping ill, Rift Valley fever, choriomeningitis. Diabetes: treatment by under-feeding. Sprue and anemia. Physical chemistry of the blood and of the kidney; nephritis. Influence of the Hospital.

THE WORK OF a hospital never ceases. Although it has been convenient to divide the history of the Hospital of The Rockefeller Institute, during Rufus Cole's directorship, into an early period, described in Chapter 4, and a second period beginning about 1913, its work actually went on without interruption. Even World War I, which in one way or another affected the activities of almost every physician on the staff, did not greatly alter its general program.

The study of lobar pneumonia, led by Cole himself, had by the onset of the war reached a stage of direct use to the nation. There was reason to expect that pneumonia would be the principal cause of death among soldiers in army camps. Wherever in recent times large numbers of young men had been brought together — in the South African mines, for example, or in the construction forces of the Panama Canal — this disease had found many victims. Among U.S. troops concentrated on the Mexican border in 1916 it occurred in epidemic form. Cole and his team of senior associates — A. R. Dochez, resident physician, 1914–1915; Henry T. Chickering, resident physician, 1915–1917; and Oswald T. Avery, who had joined the hospital in 1913 as assistant — prepared a volume of the Institute's monograph series for the benefit of the medical profession. They set forth all they had discovered from practical experience about the existence of several types of pneumococci: how to distinguish them by serological methods, how to prepare an effective serum against Type I, and how to treat cases and prevent the spread of the disease.

Cole arranged with the Surgeons General of the Army and Navy to receive medical officers at The Rockefeller Institute Hospital as temporary interns. Remaining from six weeks to several months, they learned modern methods of diagnosis and specific treatment of pneumonia, and were later assigned to base hospitals in the United States and abroad. Cole himself led, with W. G. MacCallum, professor of pathology at Johns Hopkins, a commission for the study of pneumonia, appointed by the Surgeon General of the Army, which went to Fort Sam Houston, San Antonio, Texas, for six weeks early in 1918 to study the Army's pneumonia problem. Of the eight other members of this commission, two (Avery and Dochez) were from The Rockefeller Institute Hospital; Francis G. Blake had worked there, and Thomas M. Rivers later began a long career at the Institute. This intensive study of a wartime medical problem by a group of civilian experts, making recent research experience available to the Armed Forces, set an example of cooperation that was repeatedly followed in World War II.

When in July and August 1918 Eugene L. Opie, former Member of the Institute, went to Camp Funston and to Camp Pike to study epidemics there, Blake and Rivers joined his party. Blake participated in experiments in which Opie's group produced lobar pneumonia in monkeys for the first time, by injection of pneumococci into the trachea. Later that year, working at the Army Medical School at Washington, with Russell L. Cecil, later professor of medicine at Cornell Medical College, Blake continued his study of experimental pneumonia in monkeys, which helped to complete the proof that the pneumococcus is the specific cause of lobar pneumonia, and to distinguish that disease, once and for all, from bronchopneumonia, especially of the type that often complicates attacks of epidemic influenza.

After the war Cole's pneumonia workers resumed their studies in full activity at The Rockefeller Institute. They continued their efforts to produce effective curative sera against types of pneumococcus other than Type I, with which they had already been successful. From 1924 until 1930 Louis A. Julianelle, collaborating in part with H. A. Reimann, classified another organism often associated with pneumonia, Friedländer's bacillus, according to immunological types, as Cole and his earlier colleagues had done with the pneumococcus. In later years Julianelle was chief of a division of the New York City Public Health Research Institute, and Reimann became professor of medicine at Jefferson Medical College. Ernest G. Stillman, who joined the hospital staff in 1915 and remained until his death in 1949 at the age of sixty-five, devoted himself to studying experimental pneumococcus infections in mice and rabbits. An independently wealthy man of non-conformist temperament, Stillman (not to be confounded with his colleague Edgar Stillman) added variety to the life of the hospital by mild eccentricities and by divagations unusual in research men. He was, for example, an honorary medical officer of the New York City fire department and chief of the fire company in the suburban village where he lived. He would not take lunch in the doctors' dining room, but brought his own dinner pail and ate in the basement with the head painter and other friends on the service staff. Once in his later years Stillman enlivened a social function at the Institute, on a night of driving rain, by taking his post at the main entrance, dressed in yellow oilskins, and directing automobile traffic as guests came and went.

While the laboratory studies went on, general medical care of pneumonia patients presented many problems which the hospital was well equipped to explore. Alfred Cohn and a young man on the resident staff, R. A. Jamieson, studied the best ways of using the heart-regulating drug digitalis to combat heart strain resulting from impaired blood flow through the congested lungs. John Staige Davis, Jr., also on the resident staff, studied the use of morphine in pneumonia, to discover those cases in which it might promote freer respiration, by relieving the pain of the accompanying pleurisy, as well as those in which, because of extensive waterlogging of the lungs, it might dangerously depress the respiratory center. Alan M. Chesney, assistant resident physician, 1913–1917, took part in a study of treatment of the disease with ethylhydrocuprein (Optochin), a drug under trial at the time.

Robert L. Levy, resident physician, in 1919–1920 used the Institute's excellent X-ray equipment to make an exact study of the dilatation of the heart that often accompanies lobar pneumonia. This had been done only once before, in Germany, on a much smaller group of patients. Levy's findings, like those of Cohn and Jamieson, emphasized the value of digitalis in this condition. William C. Stadie, beginning a distinguished career in internal medicine, made a thorough study of the usefulness of oxygen in pneumonia. It had long been used, without much success, by inhalation from a funnel or mask. Stadie constructed a special chamber in which patients could be kept breathing a regulated concentration of oxygen. When patients who were literally blue in the face because of insufficient oxygen in the blood respired air containing 40 per cent oxygen, the cyanosis disappeared, respiratory distress was relieved, and samples of their arterial blood showed normal oxygen content. Some years later Carl A. L. Binger returned to this subject with the study of a much larger series of cases. Oxygen therapy was thus placed on a rational and practical basis. All these thorough investigations of the clinical management of a life-threatening disease were possible at The Rockefeller Institute Hospital because of the availability of selected patients and of complete laboratory facilities, utilized by competent men in an unhurried atmosphere of scientific inquiry.

As mentioned in Chapter 4, Rufus Cole placed the chemical investigation of the pneumococcus in the skilled hands of Oswald T. Avery, who came from the Hoagland Laboratory in Brooklyn where he had spent seven years in a variety of investigations. Avery, young as he was, brought with him the nickname of "Professor," later shortened to "Fess," earned by reason of his expository skill and the wise look of his sharp eyes surmounted by the bulky dome of his head. Cole installed him in a small private laboratory made over from a disused ward kitchen, and there he began a career of research on the pneumococcus that continued almost without interruption until his retirement in 1943.

Pneumococci are distinguishable from many other microorganisms because each individual germ is surrounded by a coating or capsule of clear material. There was already some evidence in the literature that the virulence of different strains of pneumococci is in some way associated with the presence of the capsule. Avery and his associates therefore aimed their main attack at this peculiar envelope of the bacterium. His first step, taken with Dochez, was to show that the germ-free blood serum and urine of pneumonia patients contained a substance having the same specific immunity reactions as those produced by the germs themselves. This substance could also be recovered from the capsular material of cultures of virulent pneumococci. To follow up the exciting implications of this find, an experienced chemist was needed, and in

1922 Michael Heidelberger, whose participation in the work on Tryparsamide has been recounted in Chapter 6, was transferred to the hospital staff for the new work. Two years later W. F. Goebel, a recent graduate in chemistry, joined the group.

By extracting the chemical ingredients of the capsule and testing them separately for their immunological reactions, Avery and his colleagues found that the differences in virulence and in immune reactions characteristic of the four known types of pneumococcus depend upon the presence of specific substances in the capsule. Up to this time it had generally been assumed that proteins alone are the determiners of immunological specificity. Now, however, when Avery, Heidelberger, and Goebel identified the specific substances of the pneumococcus capsule, to their surprise they found them to be carbohydrates. They were in fact polysaccharides composed, like starches, of linked sugar molecules.

Though this totally unexpected finding was at first greeted by wide skepticism, strong support came from Karl Landsteiner, now at The Rockefeller Institute on the laboratory side, whose discoveries on the chemistry of immune reactions have already been described (Chapter 8). The active carbohydrates of the pneumococci closely fitted the description of Landsteiner's haptens, for although themselves incapable of stimulating the formation of antibodies when injected into animals, they would react specifically with the immune serum produced by injecting an animal with the whole organism. In short, the specificity of the antigens of the pneumococcus is that of the polysaccharides in the capsule. Goebel carried the analysis a step farther by splitting the polysaccharides — immense polymers of linked aggregates with a molecular weight of several hundred thousand — into the small disaccharide molecules of which they are composed. The simple sugars thus isolated, he found, would combine with proteins to form specific antigens. The specificity of a given strain of pneumococci thus depends upon the disaccharides; their assemblage into very large polymers protects them from diffusing out of the capsule or being dissolved by the surrounding fluids.

Brilliantly following up these discoveries, Goebel and Avery attempted to imitate nature's processes by experiments in the test tube, and succeeded in building up compounds of proteins with simple sugars, which possessed antigenic properties similar to those of the more complex natural protein-polysaccharide compounds. Finally they were able to produce an artificial antigen by combining a common protein, such as the ordinary albumin of blood serum, with a specific pneumococcus polysaccharide. A compound of this sort injected into animals produced antibodies in their serum which reacted specifically against the polysaccharide in question, and protected them against infection with virulent pneumococci. The evidence was now complete that complex carbohydrates play a role in immunological processes as important as that of proteins. A very important consequence of this work is the explanation of virulence and immunity in terms of chemical components of the invading organism. In pneumococci the chemically important structure is the capsule, whereas in some other microorganisms it is another element of the cell, composed of quite different substances. These contributions of Avery and his group stand by the side of Landsteiner's discoveries in the foundations of the modern science of immunochemistry.

Were it not for the advent in the 1930's of the sulfonamides and later of natural antibiotics, which attack pneumococci regardless of their immunological type, we should still be depending upon the outcome of Avery's work in fighting lobar pneumonia. Doubtless, many refinements could have been achieved. In 1930, for example, Avery and R. J. Dubos were making a promising attack on Type III pneumonia, against which Cole's group had not been able to make a potent serum. Dubos grew a harmless soil bacillus in the presence of the polysaccharide from Type III pneumococcus capsules. The soil bacillus, adapting itself to this compound, produced a specific enzyme which could digest it, and this enzyme in turn had a remarkable protective effect against living Type III pneumococci in mice, rabbits, and monkeys. It seems almost a pity that such brilliant ingenuity was rendered pointless, as far as clinical treatment is concerned, by the powerful if less subtle antibiotics. It had, however, an important indirect outcome, as will be described in Chapter 19.

This summary of the striking achievements of Avery and his group necessarily omits many collateral researches. With Glenn E. Cullen, Avery studied the enzymes of the pneumococcus. With Theodor Thjötta and Hugh J. Morgan, he studied the nutrition of various bacteria and their need for accessory growth substances. With J. M. Neill, he looked into the oxidation-reduction powers of pneumococci. W. S. Tillett and Thomas Francis, Jr., were active for a time in the study of the carbohydrates. Not the least of Avery's claims to his nickname of "Professor" is the fact that every one of those men who worked with him for a few years went on to a professorship of bacteriology or medicine, or to full membership in The Rockefeller Institute. In 1946 when Avery received the Kober medal of the Association of American Physicians, he said that Rufus Cole had been his inspiration and guide, and ascribed the success of his laboratory to the fact that "Cole picked these men and all I had to do was to pick their brains." The younger men credit him personally, however, for their opportunity to do independent research. He did not assign them to problems, but left them to steep themselves in the interests of the group, giving them such assistance as they asked for.

All his juniors recall with amusement a kind of continuous seminar course which "Fess" conducted in the form of soliloquies, prose masterpieces polished by frequent repetition, by which he placed the interests of the department and the history of its research before successive newcomers to the laboratory. These discourses, which the young men called "the Red Seal Records," helped to maintain a remarkable unity of purpose in the group. As one of his most eminent pupils has said,

> Whatever the training of the listener — clinician, bacteriologist, immunologist, chemist — his attention was soon focused upon some aspect of the departmental problems to which his particular skill was well suited. And without ever being given a task, or even being asked to participate in the work, the newcomer thus became a part of the team. More important, he himself selected the area of work best suited to his own taste and gifts. . . . Avery did not select or train his collaborators. He created an atmosphere in which their potentialities had a chance to emerge from their unknown selves. His department was a nursery in which any form of genius could unfold.[1]

Avery conducted his own research with the least possible display of effort and with minimal use of the apparatus and mechanics of a laboratory. As he said of his lifelong friend and counselor, Dochez, he never let himself get so busy taking something out of one tube and putting it into another that he had not time to think of why he was doing it or what he was looking for. For Avery, R. J. Dubos remarks, an ideal experiment was one in which an inescapable conclusion resulted from observing a few cages of mice or a few test tubes in a single rack. Once his approach to a problem had been thoroughly discussed with his assistants, a critical experiment was set up, and from its results his imagination, in full action, would produce an exhaustive theoretical analysis and a new set of experiments.[2]

IN 1911, as recounted in Chapter 4, Alfred E. Cohn joined the hospital staff, bringing with him experience acquired abroad and in New York City in the use of the electrocardiograph, a new instrument for research on the heart and in the diagnosis of heart disease, which he introduced to The Rockefeller Institute Hospital.[3] When Canby Robinson left the Institute, Cohn was put in charge of the study of heart disease. This assignment he retained as he progressed through all the grades of the Institute's staff, becoming a Member in 1920. As a medical scientist Cohn was an explorer and recorder of phenomena, rather than a discoverer of principles. He belonged to that school of medico-biological observers to whom quantitative observation tends to be an end as much as a means. "If you walked with Alfred," figuratively remarked one of his friends, "you trod a measured way."

Given such a temperament, with ample facilities for electrocardiographic observation of human patients in the hospital and of animals in the laboratory, Cohn's contribution to medical science was a series of quantitative studies of the function and the disturbances of the heart. He mapped the size of the heart with X rays; studied the action of important cardiac drugs, including digitalis, quinidine, aconite, atropine, and others; wrote on the structure of the normal and aging heart muscle; classified heart diseases and compiled statistics of the various types. His interest in the effects of aging on the heart led him into a long experimental study of the changes with age in certain physiological characteristics, such as the heart rate, the hydrogen ion concentration of the blood, and the functional behavior of the blood vessels. This investigation began with chick embryos; in its later stages the hearts of dogs were also studied. The results, when compiled, put into quantitative terms some aspects of the orderly progression of changes in the physiological activities of the body as the tissues grow older.

One of the participants in this investigation was Alfred E. Mirsky, who came to The Rockefeller Institute in 1927, soon after taking his doctor's degree with Sir Joseph Barcroft at Cambridge University. Mortimer L. Anson, Mirsky's fellow student there and afterward a colleague

P. A. T. LEVENE

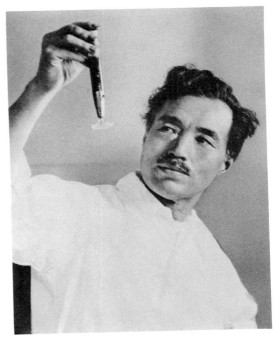

HIDEYO NOGUCHI

RUFUS COLE

ALEXIS CARREL

War Demonstration Hospital in 1917

at the biophysical laboratory of the Cancer Commission at Harvard, came to the Institute at the same time to join Northrop's laboratory of general physiology in Princeton.

When Cohn asked Mirsky to assist in the study of aging, by measuring the acidity-alkalinity balance (pH) of the blood of embryo chicks at successive stages of development, Mirsky and Anson needed a highly sensitive pH meter. Taking for this purpose the newly introduced glass electrode, they simplified its construction and adapted it to the work in hand. It is a curious illustration of the lack of contact at this time between the hospital and the two laboratory divisions, in New York and Princeton, that when only a little later Duncan MacInnes and Malcolm Dole began their valuable efforts to improve the glass electrode, and when in 1929 the two groups published their definitive papers only a month apart, neither seems to have been aware of the other's pioneering work on a technique that came into world-wide use.

At this time Cohn, much absorbed by his literary work, outside activities, and the intellectual friendships that meant so much to him, was not intensively pushing his research program. Mirsky, left free to follow his own interests, resumed with Anson a study of the denaturation of hemoglobin, which had already engaged them at Cambridge University and at Harvard. When hemoglobin, the oxygen-carrying pigment of the red blood cells, is treated with alkali, it is seemingly changed to a new substance, called hemochromogen, formerly thought to be a split-product of hemoglobin. This substance differs from hemoglobin in that although it can still take up oxygen, it can no longer release the gas. Anson and Mirsky found that the alteration does not result from chemical breakdown but from a physical modification (denaturation) of globin, a protein which forms part of the hemoglobin molecule.

Denaturation, which is brought about by heat, acids or alkalis, alcohol, and other agents, makes a protein insoluble at or near its isoelectric point, and ordinarily leads to its precipitation. The result, familiar to everyone who boils an egg, is coagulation. This had been supposed to be an irreversible process; boiled egg albumen, for example, could not be returned to its original state by any known means. Anson and Mirsky's study of hemoglobin, however, led them first to suppose and later to prove by striking experiments that the coagulation of this particular protein is indeed reversible. From this radically new finding they formulated the hypothesis that the coagulation of all proteins is potentially reversible, individual differences making reversal of denaturation relatively easy in some instances, difficult or practically impossible in others, *e.g.* egg albumen. From 1929 to 1935 the two investigators, jointly and separately, studied various chemical and physical characteristics of denatured proteins, hoping to explain denaturation in terms of the molecular structure of proteins. In 1936 Mirsky joined the eminent California chemist Linus Pauling in presenting to the National Academy of Sciences a structural theory of protein denaturation and coagulation which has considerably influenced subsequent investigation and theoretical analysis of the phenomenon.

Meanwhile Anson and Mirsky applied their experience to studies of the denaturation of protein enzymes, notably trypsin and pepsin, and contributed, through Anson's association with Northrop, to the achievements of the latter and his group in purifying and crystallizing various enzymes. A later chapter tells how Mirsky was led, by logical steps, from his studies of denaturation to a new field, the chemistry of cell nuclei and the chromosomes, to which he has made a distinguished contribution.

Among the many young members of the Institute hospital and laboratory staffs who were associated with Cohn, several made their mark in clinical cardiology and other branches of medicine. Among these are Robert L. Levy, J. M. Steele, Jr., and Harold J. Stewart of New York; Sir Francis Fraser of London; R. A. Jamieson of Toronto; and Fritz Lange of Munich. Others will be mentioned in a later chapter. The influence of Cohn's wide scholarship would doubtless be acknowledged also by associates whose careers developed in fields quite distant from that in which they were trained by him — for example, Henry A. Murray, Jr., professor of psychology at Harvard, and W. E. Ehrich, professor of histology and pathology at the Graduate Medical School of the University of Pennsylvania.

Cohn had a strong literary and philosophical bent. He was deeply interested in human personalities and in broad problems of the philosophy of medicine, the relation of research to practice, and the organization of educational and research institutions. He collected books assiduously, not only on modern and historical medicine but in many fields of art and literature. The example he set of a thoughtful, cultivated physician influenced young men who worked with him in the wards and laboratory, or who met him at lunch and at the hospital's journal club. To the outside world he represented the Institute effectively, through association with numerous distinguished friends in many professions and walks of life, to whom also he exemplified the ideal of a learned physician.

To THE ROCKEFELLER INSTITUTE's physicians, looking for diseases to conquer, rheumatic fever, a distressingly common and often crippling disease of children and young people, offered a hopeful prospect. Its relatively sudden onset, characterized by fever and often preceded by tonsillitis, suggested that it might be a bacterial infection, and as such it was eligible for the kind of combined clinical and laboratory study for which the Institute's hospital was well equipped. The idea that some sort of streptococcus causes rheumatic fever went back to the turn of the century, having been put forward in a famous, though not fully convincing, paper by F. J. Poynton and A. Paine, published in 1900 in the London *Lancet*. Since then dozens of investigators had worked on the difficult and confusing streptococcal organisms, and had, with varying degrees of plausibility, cultivated one or another from rheumatic fever cases. The hypothesis was attractive because antecedent tonsillitis is often caused by inflammation-producing germs of the streptococcus group.

Homer Swift began to interest himself in this when he was concluding his work at the Institute on the treatment of syphilis, recounted in Chapter 4. Beginning in 1914 during a brief stay at the Presbyterian Hospital, he and a colleague, Ralph Kinsella (later professor at Washington University, St. Louis), began bacteriological studies on rheumatic fever with an attempt to classify the various kinds of streptococci by comparing their cultural characteristics with their immunological properties.

The investigation was interrupted by World War I, but Swift resumed it when he returned to the Institute in 1919. Like all previous investigators, he was unable consistently to recover any one specific organism from patients with rheumatic fever, or to reproduce the disease in animals with any of the various organisms that had turned up in cultures from patients' throats and joints. All he could do for a time was to continue bedside study, using the best available laboratory methods, and to go on searching for clues by examining various tissues obtained from patients during the illness and after death. Enabled by the generous policy of The Rockefeller Institute to keep his young patients in hospital as long as the illness continued, he patiently studied individuals for months or even a year or two, recording every diagnostic and pathological sign. In this part of his daily work Swift found great satisfaction, for he was an excellent practitioner of medicine, winning the affection and confidence of his patients. He was, moreover, a thorough and systematic observer, much given to tabulation, graphing, and comparison of data from his cases. The nickname "Speedy" given him by younger members of his staff, playing upon his surname, was a comically inappropriate appellation for this deliberate, cautious, painstaking physician.

The cardiac complications of rheumatic fever had long been recognized as serious. Joining forces with Alfred Cohn, Swift and his assistants found that the new and sensitive electrocardiograph detected in rheumatic fever disturbances of the heart's function more serious than had generally been recognized. After the acute symptoms have abated, electrocardiograms may show abnormalities persisting for months, accompanied by a high white blood cell count and other inconspicuous signs of disease. Ninety per cent of heart disease in young persons, Cohn and Swift found, resulted from endocarditis (inflammation of the lining of the heart and the surface of its valves) associated with rheumatic fever. Their detailed description of these features of the disease, and the emphasis their study placed on its persistence as a chronic illness, alerted physicians to keep long and careful watch on their patients and to continue treatment much longer than had been customary, in order to avoid strain upon the heart and recrudescence of the endocarditis.

In the laboratory Swift and his colleagues made a wide exploration of the bacteriology of the disease, continuing his earlier work on streptococci but not limiting attention to that group. In the middle 1920's they looked for a virus, and were led astray for a time by picking up the peculiar and quite irrelevant "rabbit Virus III," to be mentioned again shortly. About 1930–1932 the physicians B. Schlesinger in England and Alvin F. Coburn at Columbia University drew attention to the possibility that one particular kind of streptococcus, the hemolytic variety (so called because when cultured on a medium containing blood it breaks down the red pigment) might be associated with this disease.

At this time bacteriologists, not only at The Rockefeller Institute, but also in many other laboratories, were watching with excitement the new findings of Oswald Avery's group concerning the chemical factors in the antigenic reactions of the various types of pneumococci. Swift's group therefore added the methods of chemical immunology to the classical bacteriological procedures already in use in their attempts to identify organisms associated with rheumatic fever. The antigens of streptococci, they found, were not polysaccharides like those found by Avery in pneumococci, but proteins, as would have been expected from the previous experience of immunologists.

Working along immunological lines from 1928 to 1933, Rebecca C. Lancefield of Swift's group produced a classification of hemolytic streptococci in several groups, only one of which (group A), she found, is pathogenic for mankind. Bacteriologists everywhere, their attention focused accordingly upon a limited and definable group of organisms, began to find a close association between Lancefield's group A hemolytic streptococci and rheumatic fever, which can generally be traced to an antecedent infection of the tonsils. The exact nature of the infectious process remains to the present time somewhat mysterious, for no one has as yet reproduced the disease in animals. Expert opinion favors a view that Swift began to hold about 1925, to the effect that the damage to the joints and lining of the heart in rheumatic fever results not from direct injury of tissues by the organisms, as in most germ-produced diseases, but from some sort of allergy-like hypersensitivity of the tissues to the streptococci. In this view Swift was not alone; such an idea had been crystallizing in the minds of others, and was promulgated by Hans Zinsser, for one, about the same time as by Swift. Christopher Andrewes, C. L. Derick, and Swift, following the clues of others on allergic reactions in tuberculosis, produced a state of hyperallergy, as Swift called it, in rabbits, by sensitizing them with streptococci. Between 1928 and 1932 Charles H. Hitchcock and Currier McEwen of the hospital staff worked actively with Swift in studies of the immunological relations of streptococci bearing upon the allergic theory of rheumatic fever. Upon such general evidence of disease-producing powers of the germs, and upon deductions from the immune reactions to streptococci exhibited by rheumatic fever patients, the allergic theory rested. Although the precise nature of the disease process remained imperfectly known, the studies of Swift, Cohn, Lancefield, and their associates greatly helped to define the cause of infection, the pathological process, the course of the disease, and the best methods of treatment available at the time. When at last the discovery of antibiotic drugs provided a more effective treatment, physicians were better prepared to use them than they would otherwise have been because investigators at The Rockefeller Institute and elsewhere had sharpened the diagnosis and the evaluation of symptoms.

MEASLES IS one of the most infectious diseases; 99 per cent of persons closely exposed to it for the first time acquire it. Although the fever and rash are not themselves dangerous, an attack of measles may be very serious, especially in young children, because it is sometimes accompanied by severe and even fatal secondary infection of the lungs. Until quite recently there were no means of controlling the illness in time to prevent secondary infection, except by isolation and good general care. Obviously, it would be better to prevent the original infection, for instance by protective inoculation. To produce a vaccine or serum it was necessary that the virus be isolated or at least obtained in usably pure form like that, for example, used in smallpox vaccination. In 1919, when The Rockefeller Institute Hospital began to study measles, the virus had not yet been cultivated and there was great uncertainty whether the disease could be transmitted to animals. Two medical officers of the U.S. Public Health Service, J. F. Anderson and Joseph Goldberger, stated in 1911 that they had given measles to monkeys by injecting blood from patients and also bacteria-free filtrates of such blood. Others attempting the experiment had frankly failed, or obtained inconclusive results. A respected investigator at Harvard, A. W. Sellards, tried again during an epidemic at Camp Devens, Massachusetts, in 1918 and, failing to infect either monkeys or human volunteers, expressed vigorous doubts of Anderson's and Goldberger's claim.

Francis G. Blake, who joined the hospital staff as Associate in 1919, after completing his wartime service at the Army Medical School, and James Trask, a recent medical graduate who was an assistant resident physician of the hospital, reopened the question by trying a different method of infecting monkeys. After all, little was known about the state and location of the virus in the patient's body; perhaps it was not present in the blood, as the previous experimenters had assumed. Blake and Trask thought it more likely to be found in the nasal and pharyngeal secretions of the patient, during the early catarrhal stage when the disease is highly contagious. It might be effective also, they conjectured, to introduce the supposedly infectious material by the ordinary route through which it enters the body, namely the upper respiratory tract. When the two young physicians, following this reasoning, placed material from the nose and throat of a measles patient in the trachea of a monkey, the animal developed measles, as nearly typical as could be hoped in a different species. After an incubation period of four to seven days the monkeys showed general signs of illness, evidenced by malaise and drowsiness; they developed conjunctivitis (pinkeye), a typical skin rash, and the telltale Koplik spots on the inner side of lips and cheeks. By passing the infectious nasopharyngeal drippings through a bacteria-retaining filter, the investigators ruled out the possibility that one or another of the bacteria in the throat was causing the disease, leaving a virus as the only agent that could be responsible.

Later, they infected monkeys with a suspension of ground-up skin and mucous membranes of the mouth of measles-infected animals, and with whole blood drawn between the seventh and tenth days after the original inoculations. Finally, they showed that monkeys which had recovered from experimentally induced measles were immune to reinoculation. Blake and Trask, though not the first to demonstrate the transmissibility of measles to monkeys, nor to show that the disease is caused by a filtrable virus, were the first to provide a solid background of experiment upon which further research could proceed. About fifteen years later, Harry Plotz of the Pasteur Institute, Paris, and Geoffrey Rake and M. F. Shaffer at the Squibb Institute for Medical Research, New Brunswick, New Jersey, cultivated the virus in tissue cultures and in chick embryos; but additional efforts to develop a preventive vaccine were rendered unnecessary by the development, during World War II, of methods for separating the proteins of human blood. It was found that blood proteins of one particular group, the gamma globulins, contain immune bodies against measles. These immune bodies are present in almost all blood donors, because practically everyone has had measles in childhood; consequently, the whole adult population automatically provides the wanted protective material in blood donated to blood banks.

Blake left the hospital at the conclusion of his experiments, having been called in 1921 to the chair of internal medicine at Yale. In 1924 the Institute appointed him a member of the Board of Scientific Directors, a post which he retained until 1935. Trask accompanied him to Yale, as instructor in medicine, and later became associate professor of pediatrics there.

In 1922 Cole called Thomas M. Rivers from the Department of Pathology and Bacteriology at Johns Hopkins, where he had also been trained in pediatrics, and put him to work in The Rockefeller Institute Hospital with a general assignment to study virus diseases. This was not yet an organized branch of medicine; there was no one to teach the young man, and he had to find his own way. It is not surprising, therefore, that his first efforts led in unexpected directions, yielding no solution of the problem he started to investigate, but turning up new leads from which he and his colleagues learned more about the general nature of virus disease than if the study had run smoothly.

Because Rivers had been a pediatrician, he was interested in chickenpox and chose that disease for his first work. His attempts to transmit chickenpox to monkeys did not succeed. His next step was to try infecting rabbits by inoculating the virus into the testicles. Other viruses had been propagated in this way, and Rivers hoped he could adapt chickenpox virus to the rabbit and build up the infection to a concentration which would yield a vaccine for the prevention of chickenpox in human beings. After four or five passages from one rabbit to another by intratesticular injection, the rabbits began to have fever and other signs of infection. Rivers naturally thought that he was propagating the virus of chickenpox; but when he made immunological tests with human blood serum, he found that his rabbit virus was not related to that of chickenpox. At about this time his colleagues C. P. Miller, Jr., Christopher Andrewes, and Homer Swift, attempting to transmit rheumatic fever in the same way, encountered an active agent that Rivers recognized as identical with his. In short, both of these groups had picked up a hitherto unknown virus that occurs in apparently healthy rabbits. Various collateral tests confirmed this hypothesis; for example, Rivers and Louise Pearce found that the new virus ("Virus III") had spontaneously infected the Brown-Pearce tumor mentioned in Chapter 9, being carried along in the tumor cells as they were inoculated into fresh animals. These experiences had a very salutary effect on virus workers at the Institute and elsewhere because they called attention to the existence of unsuspected viruses in the animal — and, presumably, the human — population, and emphasized the danger of confusion between the true virus of a disease and others that may be incidentally present in test animals.

Between 1927 and 1933 Rivers and several colleagues gained a great deal of experience with methods for producing smallpox vaccine by growing the vaccinia (cowpox) virus on a relatively large scale, using cultures of chick tissue to provide the living cells needed by the virus for its growth. The use of tissue cultures as hosts for the propagation of viruses had begun in Carrel's laboratory, the first virus thus cultivated having been that of the Rous sarcoma. The Rockefeller Institute's workers were, however, not the first to use the method for the cultivation of cowpox virus. As early as 1913 Edna Steinhardt, C. Israeli, and R. A. Lambert of Columbia University kept the virus alive for several weeks, probably without multiplication, in tissue cultures of the hanging-drop variety. In 1925 Frederick Parker, Jr., and R. N. Nye of Boston grew vaccinia in similar small cultures. Two years later Rivers, aiming to produce vaccine in quantity, joined Carrel in growing vaccinia virus in flasks of culture fluid containing fragments of living tissue, in sufficient amounts (two to eight cubic centimeters at a time) to justify their use of the word "fabrication" in the title of an article, published in French, describing their method. Subsequently, Rivers and his associate C. P. Li reduced this method to its simplest form by the use of tissue fragments suspended in flasks of Tyrode's solution, a physiological solution containing only the necessary salts and a buffer substance to keep the proper balance of alkalinity. This method has since been extensively used for the cultivation of all sorts of viruses and also of organisms of the *Rickettsia* group.

The vaccine virus cultivated by Rivers and his associates was successfully used for the vaccination of children, although it eventually became too attenuated to afford complete protection against smallpox. The work is historically important because it involved the first cultivation of a virus in tissue culture for use in human beings. But the years Rivers spent working on vaccinia virus had more than this practical aim. He was answering a major biological question: could viruses grow in culture media containing no living cells? The whole theory of the nature of viruses hung upon this question. Even at the Institute it had been thought that viruses may not be necessarily dependent for their existence upon association with living cells of higher organisms. Flexner and Noguchi, for example, had described the cultivation of "globoid bodies," thought to be living particles of poliomyelitis virus, in bacteriological media of the ordinary sort, free from living cells. Rivers's experience was entirely to the contrary. In cultivating vaccinia virus he failed to confirm the experiments of workers elsewhere who thought they were succeeding with cell-free culture media. In December 1926 he was ready to declare, in a paper at an important scientific meeting, that the filtrable viruses are obligatory parasites upon living cells. Realizing that he was about to contradict the previous work of the Director and of a prominent Member of his own institution, he took the manuscript to Noguchi, who made no comment upon it, and then to Flexner. When the Director had read it, he returned the draft to Rivers, remarking, "This is a free country, Rivers; you must publish what you think is right."[4]

In 1930 Rivers and George P. Berry, then assistant resident physician, undertook an investigation involving great personal risk. During the preceding two years there had been in many countries a widespread epidemic, in human patients, of psittacosis, or parrot fever, believed to have been introduced into Europe and North America by the trade in South American parrots. In man this disease was characterized by a violent pneumonia which killed about one in five of those who contracted the infection. In January 1930 the New York Board of Health warned the public that pet birds could transmit the disease to their owners. A National Bird Dealers' Association, hastily organized to protect the industry, issued a statement denying that psittacosis affects human beings.[5] The Board of Health laboratory assigned six workers to study the virus, but by March, four of them had contracted the disease, and when the chief investigator, Charles Krumwiede, coincidentally fell ill with an unrelated ailment, he discontinued the work and donated his stock of the virus to The Rockefeller Institute. At Flexner's invitation Rivers and Berry volunteered to continue the study, and a year later another assistant resident physician, Francis F. Schwentker, joined them. For two years their laboratory was the only one in the United States which ventured to deal with this exceedingly infectious disease.

Extreme precautions were of course taken. The scientists and caretakers who handled the infected parrots and test animals wore protective suits covering them from head to toe, with glass goggles in the helmets and rubber gloves attached to the sleeves. In spite of all efforts, the disease took its toll; Berry and Schwentker contracted it, both fortunately surviving after severe illnesses.

Krumwiede had transferred the psittacosis virus from diseased birds to mice; Rivers and Berry succeeded in infecting also rabbits, guinea pigs, and monkeys. In monkeys, they produced a typical pneumonia only if they introduced the infectious material into the trachea. Subcutaneous inoculation produced only a generalized fever. Because of this, Rivers was convinced, against the opinion of other workers, that human beings are infected by way of the upper respiratory system and not by bites or other local contacts with infected parrots. His conclusion was subsequently accepted by all experts on psittacosis. The most useful outcome of this courageous enterprise was the discovery of a quick method of diagnosing the disease in man, by injecting the infected sputum into the body cavity of a mouse. Rivers and Schwentker made some progress toward the development of a preventive vaccine against psittacosis, but the advent of antibiotics which controlled the infection rendered it unnecessary to continue such risky work.

In Scotland and Northern England there is a serious infectious disease of sheep known as "louping ill" from the gyrations of the sick animals. Rockefeller Institute workers became interested in this malady when they learned that mice and monkeys infected with it developed symptoms somewhat resembling poliomyelitis. In 1932 a bacteriologist, M. N. Finkelstein, associated with another institution, brought a specimen of louping ill virus from England to the Institute. Although its resemblance to the virus of poliomyelitis could not be confirmed, studies were continued in Webster's laboratory, to which Rivers supplied some of the active agent. Two physicians and a technician on Webster's staff contracted the infection and suffered illnesses resembling severe influenza from which all three fortunately recovered under treatment in The Rockefeller Institute Hospital. In this way, Rivers and Schwentker had the opportunity to study the first recorded cases of louping ill in man. Although they failed to isolate the virus from these patients, they proved the nature of the disease by tests in which immune serum from the recovered patients neutralized the virus injected into animals.

To this growing list of exotic virus diseases explored by Rivers and his associates, another was added in 1932. Rift Valley fever, a disease of sheep in British East Africa, causes the death of 50 to 95 per cent of the animals that contract it; in man it produces a mild febrile illness with practically no mortality. Infectious material was brought to the Institute for study, and a young pathologist who worked with it for several weeks was accidentally infected. His admission to The Rockefeller Institute Hospital gave Schwentker and Rivers the opportunity to observe the first human case of Rift Valley fever in the Western Hemisphere, and to study its immunity reactions. The patient unfortunately died of an unusual complication that developed when he had almost recovered from the acute stage of his illness.

The adage that chance favors the prepared mind was exemplified in 1935 when two cases of a previously unknown human virus disease occurred in the immediate environs of The Rockefeller Institute. One patient was a painter on the Institute's maintenance staff, the other a scientist in the Department of Animal Pathology in Princeton. These men underwent illnesses of several weeks' duration, resembling severe influenza with symptoms indicating meningitis. Rivers and T. F. McNair Scott of the hospital resident staff obtained an infectious agent from the spinal fluid of both patients, with which they transmitted the disease to mice, proving the infection to be due to a virus. The great experience Rivers had acquired since his bafflement with the rabbit Virus III now gave him full assurance as he worked his way through a maze of comparisons with other known viruses. In a prolonged investigation that was a model of logic and precision, Rivers and Scott tested their virus against every procurable virus known to have similar characteristics. It differed from all except one reported the previous year by Armstrong and Lillie of the U.S. Public Health Service, from mice suffering with a disease called lymphocytic choriomeningitis. A similar virus had later been found, by E. Traub, in mice in the animal colony of The Rockefeller Institute's Princeton department, where one of the two human cases had occurred. Consequently Rivers and Scott were the first to recognize the existence of lymphocytic choriomeningitis as a human disease. Other investigators have since found that a good many people have immune bodies in their blood against the virus; the disease apparently occurs not uncommonly in man, as one of the fevers that pass as grippe or influenza and are not specifically identified, because they are usually not severe enough to call for the necessary laboratory tests.

As Flexner's directorship drew to a close, Rivers, who had begun his untutored career as a virus specialist thirteen years before, with what might have seemed a futile experience with the elusive chickenpox virus, was now a master of experimental techniques, an authority on a wide range of virus-induced diseases, and a recognized specialist on smallpox vaccine. With his lectures and reviews, he had taken his place among the country's leaders in his field. He had, moreover, trained several younger physicians for important places in bacteriology, internal medicine, and pediatrics: Berry at Rochester, New York, and later at Harvard Medical School, as dean; Schwentker at Johns Hopkins; Scott at Pennsylvania; and, in later years, W. Paul Havens of Jefferson Medical College, J. E. Smadel of the National Institutes of Health, and Lewis Thomas of New York University.

IN HERTER's original plan for the work of The Rockefeller Institute Hospital disturbances of metabolism were given high priority. Facilities for controlling the metabolic state of patients, for providing special diets, and for making necessary tests were installed on a scale elaborate for the time. As mentioned in Chapter 4, Herter himself began chemical research on a then obscure metabolic disease of children, intestinal infantilism, or celiac disease. Francis H. McCrudden, a medical graduate of Harvard, continued this research when Herter's health failed, but resigned in 1913. After Herter's death Cole continued to list "certain types of disturbed metabolism" among the subjects chosen for investigation. One of the commonest and most serious disturbances, diabetes, naturally claimed attention, and in 1913 Cole brought to the hospital a young physician, Frederick M. Allen, who had made a promising beginning in diabetes research at Harvard Medical School. As Assistant, and later Associate, Allen was given independent status as an investigator, with ample laboratory space and materials, and a few beds in the hospital for diabetic patients.

His first goal was to produce experimental diabetes in an animal, so that he could conduct metabolic studies leading to better understanding and treatment of the human disease. It had been known for about thirty years that dogs could be made diabetic by total removal of the pancreas, but the disturbance produced was so severe and progressed to death so rapidly that it did not closely resemble the more chronic human disease. Allen found that by removing large portions of the organ, leaving just enough to support minimum utilization of sugar, he could produce diabetes that progressed slowly enough to permit experimental studies at leisure. Animals in this condition were observed for months, and even years, and did not come to autopsy until there had been time for the development of pathological conditions, in the surviving fragment of pancreatic tissue, characteristic of long-standing human diabetes. In this way Allen accumulated evidence that confirmed the association of diabetes with the islands of Langerhans, first demonstrated in 1901 by Eugene L. Opie, as mentioned earlier.

Through his painstaking studies of these diabetic dogs, in which the food intake was carefully controlled and the urinary excretion of sugar constantly measured, Allen came to the conclusion that not only the metabolism of the carbohydrates (starches and sugars) is disturbed, but also the utilization of the other major food ingredients, fats and proteins. Physicians were already aware that fat metabolism is affected in some cases of diabetes. When the body has exhausted its available carbohydrate, it draws upon fats, which are mobilized from their storage places and broken down, yielding energy for vital functions. There may even be an accumulation of fat in the blood (lipemia); this condition Allen duplicated in his diabetic dogs by giving them a diet rich in fats. Sometimes the fats are broken down so rapidly that fat derivatives of acidic nature (ketone bodies) are concentrated in the blood, upsetting the normally close balance of acids and bases in the blood and tissues. Such a state of acidosis causes wide physiological disturbance and finally brings about the diabetic coma with which, in the pre-insulin era, the disease often terminated.

It seemed to Allen that the diabetic patient must be relieved not only of his primary disability, that of failing to utilize normal amounts of carbohydrates; he must also be spared, as far as possible, the necessity of utilizing fats and proteins. In short, he must be placed on what Allen frankly called the "fasting or undernutrition treatment," calculated to provide only the minimum amount of carbohydrates to keep him alive and comfortable, and to furnish a relatively low number of calories in the total intake of carbohydrates, fats, and proteins. These conclusions were summed up in an imposing monograph of 650 pages by Allen, Edgar Stillman, and Reginald Fitz.[6]

To evaluate this program in the light of subsequent information would demand a long essay on fat utilization, a subject still not fully understood. Neither Allen nor workers elsewhere have succeeded in completely explaining how fat metabolism is involved in diabetes. His accurate control of the carbohydrate intake, coupled with strict limitation of the total food supply, was theoretically sound and practically the best that could be done in the pre-insulin days. Many patients were thus given a longer term of useful life, and some whose sugar tolerance was not greatly impaired were relieved of all symptoms and distress. Among these a good number were spared long enough to receive the benefits of insulin. Allen's scientific approach, incidentally, led him to test and discard various unsound treatments suggested by physicians of standing in their despairing efforts to deal with this disease, such as the oatmeal diet of the eminent German clinician Naunyn, and the use of alcoholic liquors as a major source of dietary calories.

Allen's persistent and accurate work, clearly reported in his papers and in numerous appearances before medical societies, won him a high place among specialists in diabetes and led to general use of his methods by American physicians. In 1918 he left The Rockefeller Institute to organize a special hospital for metabolic diseases, the Physiatric Institute at Morristown, New Jersey, where he continued research and clinical work. By coincidence, his departure from the Institute occurred almost at the end of the pre-insulin era. When in 1922 the Toronto group of Banting, Best, Collip, and McLeod announced the discovery of insulin, Allen was among the first to whom the new extract was made available for trial before it was distributed to the medical profession generally. With his long experience in the exact study and control of carbohydrate tolerance, he took a useful part in working out the best means for using the hormone in treating diabetic patients. The strict limitation of diet imposed by his undernutrition treatment could now happily be abated as insulin improved the patient's ability to utilize carbohydrates, reducing the demand upon his stores of fat which had in severe cases produced the ketosis and lipemia that Allen and others vainly endeavored to explain.

In 1933 the hospital created a special service for clinical hematology, the study of diseases of the blood-forming organs. Its leader was Cornelius P. Rhoads, who had been at the Institute since 1928, first in Flexner's laboratory, where he worked intensively on the virus of poliomyelitis, and later as pathologist to the hospital. In 1931 he devised and executed with marked surgical skill a method for explantation of the kidney in experimental animals, to make the renal vein accessible for procuring blood for chemical analysis. This was used effectively in Van Slyke's laboratories and elsewhere.

Rhoads was a member of a Rockefeller Foundation commission which made valuable contributions to knowledge of two tropical diseases in which anemia is a characteristic and serious feature. Led to Puerto Rico in 1931 by W. B. Castle of Harvard University, the commission discovered that in hookworm disease the administration of iron by mouth strikingly lessens the anemia and improves the patient's general health, whether or not the worms are removed. This treatment has been generally utilized in practical treatment of the disease, notably in the public schools of Puerto Rico. The commission also studied tropical sprue, the adult form of the celiac disease of children which Christian Herter had studied earlier. Sprue somewhat resembles a still more serious and widespread disease, pernicious anemia, in that it combines severe gastrointestinal lesions with a characteristic disturbance of red blood cell formation known as macrocytic anemia. The commission's intensive study reinforced the view, then much controverted, that sprue is a deficiency disease, and confirmed the curative value of feeding liver or a liver extract, first demonstrated by A. L. Bloomfield and H. A. Wyckoff of Stanford Medical School in San Francisco.

These conclusions brought sprue into even closer relation to pernicious anemia. Within the previous few years much had been learned about pernicious anemia, mostly by three investigators who shared the Nobel Prize in 1934. By his brilliant investigations on dietary factors in blood formation, George H. Whipple of Rochester, New York, had shown that liver is the most effective article of diet for treating anemia in dogs. George Minot and William P. Murphy (of Boston) then tried adding liver to the diet of pernicious anemia patients. Their spectacular success, followed by the later experiments and observations of a fourth worker, William B. Castle (also of Boston), suggested that pernicious anemia results from faulty utilization of a substance stored in the liver and essential to the production of red blood cells. This was at first called "extrinsic factor," but has since been chemically identified as vitamin

B_{12}. The pernicious anemia patient cannot utilize B_{12} because the stomach disorder characteristic of his disease deprives him of another substance, "intrinsic factor," which in some way facilitates its absorption.

When Rhoads took charge of the hematology service, he and a young assistant resident physician, David K. Miller, turned their attention to pernicious anemia, hoping to produce it in animals — something that had never been accomplished — in order to have experimental material for study. They knew that Joseph Goldberger of the U.S. Public Health Service had produced a related disease in dogs, "black tongue" — a sort of pernicious anemia without the anemia — by feeding a deficient diet. This work Rhoads and Miller readily repeated; but no matter how they further modified the dietary deficiency, they could not superimpose a significant failure of red blood cell formation upon the gastrointestinal symptoms. Damaging the stomach by a bad diet did not bring on anemia. Accordingly, they concluded that in the dog the intrinsic anti-anemia factor is not produced in the stomach lining; and that however profound the stomach disturbance in black tongue, it does not disturb blood formation in that species.

On the other hand, the hog's stomach must produce the intrinsic anti-anemia factor, because extracts of that organ (and also of hog's liver) were found effective in pernicious anemia. Rhoads and Miller put several lots of pigs on Goldberger's black tongue diet. As the stomach lining deteriorated, the pigs developed a disease strongly resembling pernicious anemia and also tropical sprue in humans. When the pigs were killed, their stomachs and livers contained no anti-anemia factor. Thus the hog had yielded information useful in analyzing the nature of human pernicious anemia which had not been obtained by previous experimenters using dogs, because the site of production of the intrinsic anti-anemia factor is not the same in the dog as in man. Through the work cited in this brief sketch, sprue can now be treated successfully and pernicious anemia to a large extent controlled, by the use of vitamin B_{12} and other vitamins and improved dietary care.

Miller, Rhoads's associate in all this work, went to the University of Buffalo in 1937 and became professor of internal medicine there. Rhoads, with various assistants from The Rockefeller Hospital staff, continued to study the anemias until 1940. He was then called to head an important neighboring institution, the newly created and endowed Sloan-Kettering Institute for the experimental study of cancer and kindred diseases, adjunct of Memorial Hospital.

WITHIN A FEW years after their hospital opened, Flexner and Cole saw clearly that internal medicine was moving rapidly ahead along chemical lines. To guide the Institute's part in this advance, the hospital should have, they felt, an experienced chemist on its senior staff, setting an example to the physicians by conducting researches of his own while acting as general adviser on chemical problems. The task would be exacting. To fit into the work of a research hospital, the chemist must develop an interest in medical problems and be temperamentally able to cooperate with physicians, to whom care of patients is the first duty. America had few biochemists qualified for such a post, and in 1913 Flexner offered the place, with a full membership in the Institute, to Franz Knoop, an internationally known biochemist of the University of Freiburg, Germany. When he declined the invitation, the post went unfilled until it dawned upon the Director that the right man was already at hand.

Donald D. Van Slyke had come to the Institute in 1907 to work on proteins and their components, at first as an assistant to Levene. When in 1910 Van Slyke took up the study of amino acids, his chief realized that he had found a field of his own and left him free to cultivate it. In this research, as mentioned in Chapter 5, Van Slyke showed his special talent for devising extremely ingenious and notably useful laboratory procedures, by developing a method and apparatus for the quantitative determination of amino acids. Cole, who spent a year in Levene's laboratory while the hospital was being built, had become well acquainted with the young biochemist and, like Levene, recognized his great promise. In 1914 Van Slyke and his associate Glenn Cullen moved from their quiet corner in Levene's laboratory to new and ampler quarters in the hospital. Their chief feeling at the time, as Van Slyke said later, was one of serious doubt that they could justify their existence in such a place. Neither had any conception of clinical problems, and both were utterly uncertain whether they could ever be useful to medicine. Their new comrades, however, took them into their closely knit group, eagerly sharing enthusiasms and problems.[7] Among those who welcomed them and sought their help was Edgar Stillman, an assistant resident physician of the same age as Van Slyke. Working on diabetes in Frederick Allen's team, he was deeply involved with the problem of acidosis, which he placed before his new colleagues with such eagerness that they joined him in investigating the underlying physiological conditions. These three were aided from 1915 to 1917 by Reginald Fitz (later professor of internal medicine at Harvard) and W. W. Palmer (later professor of internal medicine at Columbia University's College of Physicians and Surgeons).

The body normally holds its acidity-alkalinity balance within a narrow range by exact regulation of the hydrogen ion concentration of the blood and tissues. This is achieved mainly by three mechanisms. First, the blood itself contains buffer substances — proteins, phosphates, and carbonic acid — which by their chemical nature protect it against changes in the acid-base ratio. Second, respiration removes carbon dioxide, an acid-forming substance, and thereby affects the acid-base balance. Third, the kidneys normally excrete acids in excess of alkalis. If this latter function is seriously deranged, as in chronic nephritis (Bright's disease), acidosis develops. Beginning with the study of acidosis in diabetes, Van Slyke went on to apply the concepts of physical chemistry to similar phenomena in other fields of internal medicine. Perhaps without fully recognizing it, he had entered upon a lifetime study of the acid-base reactions of the blood, respiratory gas exchange, the transport of oxygen and carbon dioxide in the blood stream, the distribution of these gases and of electrolytes in the tissues, and the physical chemistry of kidney secretion. The results have affected the thought of every physiologically minded physician.

Van Slyke and Cullen began by defining acidosis in chemical terms rather than in descriptive medical language, so that this condition could be evaluated in a given patient by direct measurement of carbon dioxide and carbonates in samples of his blood. For that purpose Van Slyke devised an apparatus for the exact measurement of oxygen and carbon dioxide in solution in blood and other fluids, which is so simple, sturdy, and convenient that it took its place at once and permanently in the equipment of medical scientists. "The Van Slyke apparatus" is known in hospitals and laboratories all over the world.

In 1920 Lawrence Henderson of Harvard, a leader in the study of regulation of body processes, with F. C. McLean and H. A. Murray, began a study of the changes in the distribution of electrolytes between blood plasma and cells, resulting from changes in oxygen or carbon dioxide tension. Their investigations overlapped those of the Rockefeller Hospital group on acid-base balance and blood gases, and in 1921 Henderson, McLean, and Van Slyke agreed to transfer the problem to Van Slyke's laboratory.[8] McLean moved to The Rockefeller Hospital, joining a team that included Cullen, A. B. Hastings, J. H. Austin, and J. P. Peters, for the work required a number of investigators working at the same time on different portions of the same blood sample, each man executing one specific analytical procedure. The work also demanded more precise methods than were then available for measuring the changes that were being studied. This led to the further development of the Van Slyke method of blood-gas analysis, which lent itself to the measurement not merely of the two major blood gases for which it was originally intended, but of many other substances in the body fluids, including carbon monoxide, total and non-protein nitrogen, amino nitrogen, calcium, and sugar. A second by-product was the development of a theoretical general equation expressing the relation of the concentrations of hydrogen ions (pH) and potassium ions (pK) of buffer solutions to their effects. This equation is now used in measuring the buffering effects of plasma protein and hemoglobin in blood.

McLean, on leave from Peking Union Medical College during the construction of its buildings, returned in 1921 to his professorship of medicine there. Van Slyke joined him for a year in 1922 as visiting professor, continuing the work on blood chemistry with the collaboration of the Peking chemist Hsien Wu. Their results showed that the distribution of electrolytes in the blood, between red cells and plasma, conforms to the Donnan equilibrium and that the effects of oxygen and carbon dioxide changes on this distribution could be explained and predicted by physicochemical laws.[9]

Christen Lundsgaard, a versatile Dane (later a distinguished professor of medicine in Copenhagen), joined Van Slyke in 1917–1918 to study lung volume in normal persons and patients with tuberculosis and pneumonia, from which the two went on to an authoritative study of factors producing faulty oxygenation of the blood, as evidenced by cyanosis (blueness of the skin) in various diseases.

About 1923 Van Slyke took up the investigation of nephritis in its various forms, including especially Bright's disease, a subject for which he was admirably equipped. The study of nephritis had been at a stand-still for years, waiting for medical biochemistry to reach a point at which progress could be resumed. To facilitate Van Slyke's program, Cole added this disease to the list of medical conditions eligible for admission to The Rockefeller Institute Hospital, and assigned Edgar Stillman, with a group of assistant resident physicians, to care for and help study the patients. With these young men and his colleagues from the chemical laboratory, Van Slyke undertook the systematic evaluation of all the alterations of metabolism, blood chemistry, and urinary excretion that could be chemically measured in nephritis. The hospital physicians who participated in this study between 1923 and 1935 were — the list is long because many were on the staff only a few years — A. S. Alving, W. E. Ehrich, R. R. Hannon, G. C. Linder, Christen Lundsgaard, J. F. McIntosh, E. Möller, Irvine H. Page, and H. A. Salvesen. From Van Slyke's laboratory the workers included A. Baird Hastings, J. A. Hawkins, Alma E. Hiller, and J. Sendroy.

A quietly sociable man, warmly generous to the young people who worked with him, Van Slyke admitted them to close collaboration in the laboratory, but protected himself more or less subconsciously from the bustle of joint research by periods of intense abstraction from which he emerged with fresh ideas and often with the solution of a knotty problem. To work with him, as one of his juniors has said, was to participate in a sort of post-doctoral training program which produced desirable candidates for posts elsewhere. The notable contribution of Baird Hastings to the studies on acidosis marked him for eventual promotion to the chair of biochemistry at Harvard. Irvine Page began at the Institute his investigations on nephritis and hypertension which made him one of the chief American authorities on those subjects. Practically all of the others, as well as Van Slyke's earlier colleagues previously mentioned, went on to professorships of internal medicine or biochemistry or to other important posts in the United States and four foreign countries. Their influence upon the physiological and chemical study of medical disease has been incalculably great.

A recent writer on the history of nephritis, placing Van Slyke's name in a list of a dozen who have made lasting additions to knowledge, characterized his work as a contribution to the "natural history" of this group of diseases.[10] By this he meant that it described the complex dis-

turbances that result from impaired function of the kidneys. Description, however, in work like this can only be attained by precise analysis
of the chemical relations between the various vital processes that are affected in such diverse diseases. Results are expressed largely in mathematical terms. In no other branch of medicine, perhaps, is so much abstruse thinking brought to bear on the study and bedside care of the
individual patient. This was an immense task, for once the kidneys lose
part of their power to excrete nitrogenous wastes together with closely
adjusted amounts of water and salts, or fail to conserve the proteins and
carbohydrates, widespread interlocking disturbances of the bodily economy are inevitable. In a score or more papers Van Slyke and his colleagues examined the alterations of protein, fat, and carbohydrate metabolism in various types of nephritis; they continued the study of the
equilibria of the gases and salts (electrolytes) in the blood, and their
modifications in acidosis, a frequent concomitant of renal disease; and
they improved laboratory procedures for measuring nitrogenous substances in blood and urine. This part of the work led by Van Slyke was
characterized by completeness and accuracy, like all his investigations.
Every conclusion was so explicitly proved that he never had to withdraw
anything he had once committed to the record.

In 1931, with nine of his colleagues, he published a monograph on
the clinical course of different types of Bright's disease and the corresponding changes in the kidneys, based on findings in sixty-seven cases
studied in this comprehensive way. During the whole span of Van Slyke's
work on nephritis, from the time he began it until he retired in 1948, he
and his group studied about six hundred patients, of whom three hundred were under observation long enough to yield valuable information.

One of the most notable contributions of this work was the urea
clearance test, a method of estimating the performance of the kidneys,
introduced by Austin, Edgar Stillman, and Van Slyke. Urea, a chemically simple, easily filtrable compound, is the principal nitrogenous
waste substance in the urine. Failure to excrete it in sufficient amounts is
the most characteristic physiological result of renal insufficiency. Van
Slyke's previous studies had equipped him to measure urea in blood and
urine; a dozen years earlier he and Cullen had worked intensively with
urease, a ferment or enzyme that breaks down urea into ammonium carbonate. By a simple chemical procedure the carbonate could be made to

yield carbon dioxide gas, and thus Van Slyke could use his gas-analysis apparatus for determining the amount of urea in a sample of blood or urine. In such ways as this a keen investigator continually applies his experience to new problems.

The task was to discover the laws that govern the normal relation between the concentration of urea in the blood and the rate at which it is excreted. A French physician, Ambard, had proposed a theoretical formula for this relation; following up and emending his work, the Rockefeller Institute group set up as the unit of comparison the amount of blood that is cleared of urea per minute. This can be ascertained by comparing a sample of blood with one of urine concurrently excreted. The clearance concept proved to be exceedingly useful in clinical work and in laboratory investigation. Clearances of other substances, such as inulin (to measure glomerular filtration) and para-amino-hippurate (to measure renal blood flow) have subsequently been introduced by Homer Smith of New York University, and by other workers. These clearances, however, involve the use of substances which are not, like urea, ordinarily present in the body. The urea clearance test continues to be used in hospitals as one of the standard methods of evaluating kidney function.

The findings and experience of Van Slyke's laboratory and clinic became part of a great body of information on renal function built up by many workers, notably A. R. Cushny in Britain, A. N. Richards in Philadelphia, Homer Smith in New York, and T. E. Addis in San Francisco. Contributing greatly to the present concepts of renal physiology, the Rockefeller Institute investigators went even farther than their contemporaries in applying them to the study of Bright's disease. There can be little expectation that any discovery will produce a cure for chronic nephritis. The kidneys are already damaged when symptoms appear, and the physician's only course is to relieve further strain and lessen discomfort, by physiological methods. By such means he can often secure years of relative comfort and usefulness for his patient. If a crisis occurs, such as the development of severe acidosis or an episode of excessive vascular tension, he can deal with it best if he understands what is going on in the patient's blood and tissues. In acute nephritis and in other special forms of kidney disease, such as the nephrosis of infants and children, knowledge of the natural history of the condition may enable the physician to clear up the acute symptoms and avert permanent damage to the kidneys.

That physicians can now classify the different forms of renal disease to an extent not possible three decades ago, that they can plan the treatment of the patient and follow his progress by sound physiological methods, is the result of investigations of the kind in which Van Slyke and his colleagues took such a great part. To the leader of this work—the biochemist without medical training who in 1914 was not sure he could be useful to medical science as chemist to The Rockefeller Institute Hospital —the Association of American Physicians in 1942 awarded its prized Kober Medal for the contributions he had made to clinical medicine.

To create a medium for publication of the numerous papers in the field of clinical research coming from The Rockefeller Institute and various university hospitals, Cole in 1921 proposed to the Board of Scientific Directors that the Institute sponsor a new journal comparable to its *Journal of Experimental Medicine*.[11] When, instead, the American Society for Clinical Investigation undertook the sponsorship, the Board helped to launch the enterprise by an annual subsidy of $3,000 for five years beginning with the first volume in 1924, and thereafter continued to support it on a diminishing scale until 1936, when the *Journal of Clinical Investigation* no longer needed such assistance.

ALL THESE Rockefeller Institute studies of pathology, physiology, and chemistry in the living human being depended upon the cooperation of the hospital's patients. Every year, during this period, about 200 individuals on the average were admitted, on recommendation of their personal physicians. They came from every walk of life—rich men and poor, artisans and housewives, physicians, clergy and other professional people, a governor of the state, a mayor of the city, all chosen only because they were suffering from particular diseases in which the Rockefeller Hospital was interested. Readers who have personally experienced hospital care or a thoroughgoing series of diagnostic tests may well ask how willingly these people, many of them seriously ill, tolerated the intensive scientific study that accompanied their medical treatment. In 1910, when the hospital was opened, the Board thought it advisable to disclaim any intention of taking liberties with the sick for scientific ends. Yet it was always made clear to the patients (and their relatives) that the privilege of treatment by physicians specially equipped to deal with their diseases implied an obligation by the patient to undergo detailed study, involving more diagnostic tests than another hospital might consider necessary. At times these procedures produced a certain degree of discomfort or monotony.

Far from protesting, patients have always cheerfully accepted, and indeed welcomed, the opportunity to furnish information that might help others, whether or not it contributed to their own relief. Teaching hospitals attached to medical schools have had similar experience with regard to use of patients for instruction of students at the bedside; people quickly appreciate the fact that the attending physicians, on their mettle before their pupils, tend to observe and analyze the illness with particular thoroughness. This appreciation is, if anything, enhanced in the atmosphere of The Rockefeller Institute's hospital, where the patients sense the intensity of scientific interest in their ailments and often exhibit pride in sharing the efforts of such a distinguished institution. Moreover, they have found their medical attendants to be compassionate physicians as well as scientists. The records contain many expressions of gratitude, but no evidence of serious embarrassments or complaints arising from the scientific program.

The attitude of the hospital's patients and their families is poignantly expressed in two letters, differing from many others in the files only in the explicitness with which the writer, a sensitive artist subject to no professional bias toward science, appreciated the Institute's aims. When in 1938 the internationally admired and beloved operatic and concert singer Alma Gluck (Mrs. Efrem Zimbalist) died in the hospital, her daughter, the novelist and biographer Marcia Davenport, wrote to John D. Rockefeller, Jr.:

> The care and understanding that my mother received from The Rockefeller Institute were far beyond the realm of benefits for which one can express gratitude in words. But I want you to know that in a profound way I am filled with intense feelings of appreciation that my mother ended her life enabled, through your Institute, to be of further service (as she had already been of so much) to humanity. She derived profound satisfaction from the knowledge that in her way she was contributing to Dr. Rhoads's work and to the possibility that a means might eventually be found to treat or alleviate this hopeless disease.

To Rhoads she wrote: "I hope that my mother has been of the help to that work that she liked to believe she was."[12]

Everyone who served on the staff of the hospital testifies to the exceptionally friendly atmosphere and spirit of mutual encouragement that has always prevailed there, since the earliest years so warmly recalled by the first resident staff. For this, Rufus Cole was primarily responsible, for he had the great gift of encouraging and supporting his younger colleagues while providing constructive criticism and advice. Because most of the men were trained as physicians and were actively practicing medicine, the group was more homogeneous than was the laboratory staff, with its wider range of special interests. The sense of solidarity was perhaps increased also by consciousness of upholding the value and independence of clinical research. A journal club which Cole organized and conducted, until in later years Alfred Cohn took it over with equal devotion, provided a center of intellectual and social life, bringing together the workers of various ages and experience. The life of the hospital staff thus took on something of a family atmosphere and was conducted with an unusually cooperative spirit.

Summarizing the hospital's work to the year 1930, Cole pointed out that such an institution contributes to the advance of medical science in two ways. It may actually increase knowledge of disease, and it may, by example, influence medical thought and practice. He found it difficult to estimate the value of scientific contributions by the Rockefeller Hospital. The new knowledge could be enumerated item by item, he said, but the sum total of reported work would omit what might well be the most valuable result — the use of the findings as starting points for new investigations and new generalizations. The Rockefeller Institute Hospital, Cole thought, was especially likely to stimulate other medical investigators and suggest new ideas to them, because it provided for thorough study of disease in the individual patient and in selected groups, at the bedside and in the laboratory, to an extent heretofore unknown.

Cole found it even more difficult to evaluate the influence of The Rockefeller Institute Hospital on medical practice. Obviously, there had been great advances in the past two decades. When the hospital was founded, laboratory facilities in American medical clinics were almost nonexistent. By 1930 at least eight had well-equipped research laboratories, and several of these had interchanged staff members with the Institute. Already about thirty men formerly on the clinical staff of the

Institute were occupying professorial chairs of medicine in the United States, England, Ireland, Denmark, and China.

The hospital was also influencing the American medical profession through staff members who went into private practice, giving to many communities throughout the country medical care of the highest quality, as exemplified by the work of such men as — to name only Senior Residents — Robert L. Levy and the late Henry T. Chickering of New York, and Theodore J. Abernethy of Washington, D.C. To enumerate many others would be misleading, because a sharp line cannot be drawn between medical scientists and private practitioners, many of whom also teach in medical schools and do research. About fifty men had gone from the hospital into private practice during the entire span of its existence to 1953, half of them before Cole wrote his summary of accomplishments in 1930. The leaven of science, he felt, was already working in the American medical profession. There was a perceptible difference in the attitude of physicians; the best practitioners, not content with being skilled diagnosticians, were trying, more than in the past, to understand the diseases from which their patients suffered and to treat them by rational measures. Cole did not presume, of course, to distinguish between the influence of The Rockefeller Institute and that of the better medical schools in the creation of sounder medical practice in our country, but, in longer retrospect, it is now clear that the Institute's hospital, led by Cole, was in the forefront of this movement.[13]

CHAPTER ELEVEN

Infectious Diseases of Animals
1916–1935

Blackhead of turkeys; hog cholera; infectious abortion of cows;
mastitis; antibacterial properties of milk; pleuropneumonia-like
organisms; inheritance of resistance to tuberculosis; mad itch;
myxoma and papilloma viruses; swine influenza.

THE DEPARTMENT OF Animal Pathology, moving into its new buildings in Princeton in the fall of 1916, barely had time to settle down before World War I shook it up again. The Department was called upon to
house and organize the large serum laboratory mentioned in Chapter 6,
and the two veterinarians, Ralph B. Little and Ernest W. Smillie, spent
much time procuring, against heavy competition from military agencies,
the dozens of horses needed for serum production, and, afterward, taking
care of them in the stables. Two important members of Theobald Smith's
little staff of eight, Paul E. Howe and Carl TenBroeck, left for army service.

The Director was left with two Fellows and, in the higher ranks,
Rhoda Erdmann and Werner Marchand, both of whom, as Germans,
were as much liabilities as assets in the current state of excitement and
suspicion. By 1919, however, he had all his original staff again at their
regular posts.[1] He added to his own staff F. S. Jones, who had been with
him on loan from Peyton Rous's laboratory; transferred Little to the research staff; and promoted Smillie to be superintendent of the establishment at Princeton, a post calling for all the executive competence and
versatility the latter had displayed on the serum project.

Although Theobald Smith had declared that the diseases of domestic
cattle, because of their prime importance in the economy of every section

of the country, would be his Department's principal concern, the first discovery of great practical value had to do with a fatal disease of turkeys. Infectious enterohepatitis, or blackhead, has occurred everywhere in the world where turkeys are raised. As its technical name indicates, it is an infection of the intestines and liver. Its popular name derives from a darkening of the head, caused by disturbance of circulation. Blackhead was so widespread in the United States at the beginning of the twentieth century that turkey raising had been abandoned in regions where formerly it had flourished, and, everywhere, production was far below the level it should have reached with the land and feed available. Young birds were especially susceptible; breeders sometimes lost every bird in a hatching.

Theobald Smith took the first important step in understanding this disease in 1895, his last year with the Bureau of Animal Industry, when he discovered the infectious agent. Examining dead turkeys, he found swarms of a parasitic one-celled animal infecting the liver and the two ceca, blind pouches opening into the large intestine. He named the protozoan *Amoeba meleagridis* from the Latin word *meleager,* turkey. Its association with the disease has been amply confirmed, although protozoologists now consider it not an ameba but a flagellate, and call it *Histomonas.*

In 1913 at Harvard, Smith transmitted blackhead to healthy turkeys in the laboratory by feeding them minced cecal tissue containing the parasite, obtained from infected birds. But the way in which the infection spreads from bird to bird under natural conditions as yet eluded him. It was known that the soil of pens in which sick birds had lived was in some way infectious, but when Smith and his colleague Graybill, working in Princeton, fed healthy birds with grain contaminated with feces from sick ones, the disease was not transmitted. The investigators also found that chickens, though not susceptible to blackhead, could carry the parasite and contaminate the soil with their droppings. To explain why *Histomonas* in contaminated feces does not directly infect turkeys, they were forced to suppose that some other factor, perhaps a second parasite, takes part in causing blackhead. Two clues as to the nature of this supposed intermediary suggested themselves to Smith's logical mind: it must be something common to chickens and turkeys, and it probably lives in the intestinal ceca of these birds.

Thinking over all the possibilities these conjectures set before them, Graybill hit upon the correct answer, and his first experiment proved it. There is a nematode or roundworm, *Heterakis papillosa* (now called *H. gallinae*), which infects the ceca of turkeys, chickens, and some other birds. Graybill collected a quantity of these worms and chopped them up to free their eggs, which he kept a couple of weeks until the embryonic worms were nearly ready to hatch. When these embryonated eggs were fed to healthy turkeys, the turkeys somehow developed *Histomonas* infection and died of blackhead. The article Graybill and Smith published in 1920, presenting this find, by no means solved all the biological problems involved in so remarkable an association of three organisms — chicken, worm, and protozoan — working together to set up disease in a fourth, but it furnished all the information needed by turkey breeders, who had only to keep their young birds away from chickens and not let them live on soil infested with the worms. Within a few years most of the large commercial breeders were housing their flocks on wooden or wire floors in specially constructed turkey houses, totally avoiding the risk of infection from contaminated soil. Nowadays turkey breeding for the market is a flourishing industry; flocks numbering thousands are seen where in 1920 farmers had difficulty raising fifty a year.

As all the parts of this curious chain were linked together, it became clear that Smith was right in his original view that the protozoan parasite *Histomonas* causes the lesions of the disease. E. E. Tyzzer, Smith's successor in the chair of comparative pathology at Harvard, proved this a few years later when he produced blackhead in chickens and turkeys by inoculating them directly with *Histomonas* grown in cultures. Smith and Graybill meanwhile discovered how chickens keep the infection going. In chickens the histomonads cause only mild sickness, but continue to multiply in the intestine, so that the fowls become carriers, contaminating the ground with their droppings. Turkeys do not become carriers to any appreciable extent, because blackhead rapidly kills them off. Smith and Graybill supposed that turkeys pick up the protozoa directly from the ground or from fecal droppings of chickens, and that the roundworms play a merely incidental role, by irritating the lining of the ceca and thus aiding the histomonads to invade the host's tissues. Work on this subject in Princeton ceased in 1924 when Graybill left to join, a year later, the

California Department of Agriculture. Subsequently, Tyzzer found that the roundworms have a more important role than Smith and Graybill ascribed to them, for under poultry-yard conditions they effect the transfer from chickens to turkeys, acquiring the protozoa while in the chicken's cecum, and shedding their infected eggs in the chicken's fecal droppings, whence the eggs get into the ground and are picked up by the turkeys. Smith and Graybill, by detecting the association of the four species that participate in this complex pattern of disease production, even though they did not learn all the details, had found the key to prevention of blackhead in turkeys.

THE DEPARTMENT OF Animal Pathology had a vested interest in hog cholera, having come into being, as described in Chapter 6, because of J. J. Hill's alarm over the economic loss from this fatal epizootic disease of swine. If Hill's intended gift for a special investigation had materialized, Theobald Smith would have felt, no doubt, a moral obligation to devote much of his resources to study of the disease. Under the actual circumstances, he had only a desultory interest in it. He was, in fact, in a peculiar position.

As long ago as 1885 in a paper published jointly with D. E. Salmon of the Bureau of Animal Industry, he had reported having isolated a bacterium he named *Bacillus suipestifer* (renamed *Salmonella choleraesuis*), which he believed to be the causative germ of hog cholera. The find was quite generally accepted, and the organism holds its place in manuals of systematic bacteriology. In 1903, however, two other workers of the Bureau of Animal Industry, E. A. de Schweinitz and Marion Dorset, proved beyond doubt that the agent of the disease is not a bacillus, but a filtrable virus. The confusion had arisen because, in the first place, Salmon and Smith's bacillus is actually pathogenic for swine; although it does not cause hog cholera, it does cause another serious disease, paratyphoid of hogs. In the second place, *Salmonella choleraesuis* was often found in the intestinal tract of swine ill with hog cholera, where it caused a secondary infection. In this respect the illness resembles human epidemic influenza, in which a bacterial germ, the *Dialister pneumosintes*, discovered at The Rockefeller Institute by Olitsky and Gates, is often present in the patient's throat and lungs, though the disease is caused by a filtrable virus.[2] After de Schweinitz and Dorset's discovery of the virus of hog cholera, the Bureau of Animal Industry developed a protective serum.

By inoculating small animals at the Princeton laboratories, Carl Ten-Broeck tried to maintain the virus of hog cholera, to make it more available for laboratory study. A bit more successful than others who had tried in vain to do this, he kept the virus alive for a week, though not multiplying, in the albino rat. Meanwhile his colleagues Paul A. Lewis and Richard E. Shope sought more effective diagnostic tests. Thus the Department of Animal Pathology retained a general interest in swine diseases. Some years later when another epidemic sickness of hogs, swine influenza, began to cause serious losses, Lewis and Shope undertook an investigation which will be mentioned later. Shope, moreover, reviving the Department's concern with hog cholera after the lapse of nearly three decades, at a time beyond the scope of this history resumed active research on its epidemiology. He found that the virus is carried in a masked form by lungworms and that swine infected with such worms, but showing no signs of illness, can be brought down with hog cholera by various provocative stresses, one of the most effective being to feed embryonated ova of the roundworm *Ascaris suum*.

WHEN THE laboratories of the Department of Animal Pathology were opened in 1917, the dairy industry regarded infectious abortion (Bang's disease) as its most serious menace. Occurring in perhaps 20 per cent of dairy herds in the United States, it was causing a heavy loss of calves and a considerable reduction of milk yield, and it often resulted in permanent sterility of the infected cows. Although much work had been done in this and other countries, Theobald Smith saw many gaps that needed to be filled in our knowledge of the disease.

The problem presented itself, indeed, before his very eyes in the herds of an immediate neighbor, a famous dairy whose pastures adjoined the lands of The Rockefeller Institute. The history of the Walker-Gordon Laboratories and its herds is entwined with that of The Rockefeller Institute through two of the Institute's Scientific Directors, Christian Herter and Emmett Holt. Holt, in his efforts in the 1890's to secure a supply of pure milk for New York's babies, learned of the small and struggling Walker-Gordon Company, organized in Boston as a humanitarian enterprise, which was operating a model dairy and a laboratory for preparing milk for infants according to physicians' formulas. Herter, Holt, and one or two other New York physicians put up the capital in 1898 to start a branch of the company at Plainsboro, New Jersey, near Princeton. A score of the city's pediatric specialists formed a Walker-Gordon Milk Commission to support and advise the management. The enlightened and enterprising dairyman Henry W. Jeffers, in charge of the enterprise, soon made it commercially successful, and built up a combined farm, laboratory, and industrial plant distributing certified milk not only to the metropolis but to many other cities from Portland, Maine, to Washington, D.C.[3] When The Rockefeller Institute's Department of Animal Pathology was established on the Princeton side of its Plainsboro farms, the Walker-Gordon herds already numbered more than a thousand cows. Founded upon scientific principles, and guided by leading physicians, the Walker-Gordon Laboratories Company naturally welcomed the advent of Theobald Smith and his staff and gave them the privilege of using the herds for scientific study.[4]

The Princeton bacteriologists fortunately could begin their studies of infectious abortion with some knowledge of the germ that causes the disease. A celebrated Danish bacteriologist, Bernhard L. F. Bang, in 1897 isolated from infected cows a microorganism named by him *Bacillus abortus* (afterward reclassified as *Brucella abortus*). While still at Harvard, Theobald Smith had begun to study it, directing the work of a young assistant, Marshall Fabyan, who succeeded in infecting guinea pigs. In that species the organism produces a chronic disease something like tuberculosis. At Princeton several staff members worked on the bacteriology and immunology of the abortus germ; W. A. Hagan made a detailed study of the characteristics of the guinea pig disease, and a team made up of Smillie, Little, and Florence explored the value and limitations of tests of cow's blood for the presence of agglutinins against the organism. In this way the group acquired sufficient knowledge of the biology of Bang's disease to permit Smith and Ralph Little to undertake large-scale experiments on vaccination against the abortus germ. They were the first to perceive the advantages of preparing the vaccine from strains of low virulence. This discovery was shortly confirmed and extended by other workers at the University of Michigan and the U.S. Department of Agriculture Experiment Station at Bethesda, Maryland, and in time resulted in the world-wide use of one particular strain of *Brucella abortus* that possesses high immunizing power with low virulence.

In the very first year of these studies, however, Smith and his colleagues noted a number of cases of abortion due to infection of the placenta and fetal membranes, in which they could not demonstrate the presence of *Brucella abortus*. In the course of their five or six years of intensive work, about one in four of the cases of abortion they studied fell into this class. From most of these cases, Smith found, he could recover a totally different germ, a spiral organism which he named *Vibrio fetus*. Though he did not know it at the time, the same organism had been seen a few years earlier by British workers in cases of infectious abortion of sheep. Smith succeeded in cultivating the new germ in the laboratory and with it experimentally produced infection of the fetal membranes in two of four cows inoculated with it. The strong presumption thus obtained, that *Vibrio fetus* is responsible for not a few cases of infectious abortion, has been fully confirmed, and as the prevalence of brucellosis has been reduced by vaccination and sanitation of dairy herds, vibriosis has become more evident. It appears to be the principal cause of infertility in brucellosis-free cows. Subsequent investigators have worked out the way in which it is disseminated and have developed means for its elimination.

Theobald Smith was of course greatly interested in the discovery by Alice C. Evans of the U.S. Public Health Service, in 1918, that Bang's *Brucella abortus* is allied biologically to *Brucella melitensis,* the infectious agent of Malta fever, a disease primarily of goats but already known to be rather widely prevalent in human beings, and also to a third organism, *Brucella suis,* which is responsible for a febrile disease of swine. A long and confused discussion followed this finding, concerning the degree to which the three organisms are pathogenic for man. Smith, impressed by various differences in biological characteristics between the three organisms, doubted that the *Brucella abortus* of cows can produce Malta fever in man, but accepted the view that *Brucella suis* can do so. Longer experience has shown that all three of these species of *Brucella* can infect human beings, and that the bovine form is perhaps more often responsible than the others for causing the long-continuing and debilitating brucellosis, or relapsing fever, which attacks, by current estimates, about 10,000 persons every year in the United States. Fortunately, the major harm it does to cattle does not befall human patients; abortion due to infection with *Brucella abortus* is very rare in women. Human brucellosis is difficult to recognize clinically; immunological tests are required for positive diagnosis. In the development of such tests, and in the general advance in knowledge of this family of disease germs and their effects on domestic animals and man, the work done at Princeton takes high rank.

While Theobald Smith and his colleagues were studying infectious abortion in cattle, Little and Orcutt made a surprising observation on the transfer of agglutinins against *Brucella abortus* from a cow to her calf. They found that at birth the blood of calves born to immune or infected cows was free from *Brucella abortus* agglutinins if drawn before they had suckled their dams, but a few hours after birth it had somehow come to contain a relatively large amount of these immune substances. Testing the possible ways in which immunity could have been transferred under these peculiar circumstances, Little and Orcutt discovered that it was carried in the cow's colostrum, the secretion of the mammary gland that precedes the production of true milk during the first hours after parturition.

Colostrum from a cow with a positive agglutinin titer in her blood contains a high concentration of *Brucella* agglutinins. Testing successive blood samples from the newborn calves of such cows, Paul E. Howe of Smith's staff found that as soon as the calf begins to suckle, proteins of the euglobulin type, previously lacking in its blood, begin to accumulate there by absorption from ingested colostrum. These studies corroborated and amplified the earlier work of J. W. Famulener of the New York City Department of Health, who had pointed out that colostrum, though it contains far less fat than milk, has several times as much protein, which might be supposed to include immunizing substances. When he experimentally immunized pregnant goats against sheep's blood corpuscles, hemolyzing immune bodies appeared in the colostrum. The Princeton group had now shown that this principle operates in nature's fight against infections of the newborn, by supplying the necessary antibodies and proteins immediately after birth. Smith and Little were able to corroborate their findings by direct experiment. Depriving calves of colostrum, by taking them away from their dams, they supplied the natural antibodies and necessary proteins by feeding blood serum from normal cows.

In 1922, while Smith's staff were at work on the colostrum problem, J. H. Lewis and Gideon Wells of Chicago published chemical analyses of human milk showing as high a globulin content as cow's milk, and on that basis urged the necessity of breast feeding as a protection to the newborn baby. Subsequent studies elsewhere have shown that the human placenta, unlike that of the cow and other ruminants, permits transfer of immunizing substances directly to the fetus in the uterus. Transfer by colostrum is, therefore, only a supplementary protective factor in our own species. For this reason, the Princeton investigation, notable for its logic and conclusiveness, stands as a landmark in veterinary rather than in human medicine.

An unexpected observation made during this experiment revealed one of the causes of a form of nephritis, known as "spotted kidney," which Smith had observed while at the Bureau of Animal Industry without being able at the time to explain its cause. When some of the calves in the serum experiment developed spotted kidney, Smith traced the disease to a relatively mild infection with a common bacterium, *B. coli*. Although the calves had survived the period of serum feeding, they had, after all, not been fully protected against pathogenic organisms, because the amount of serum that could be given them was much too small to match the antibody content of the colostrum they would normally have obtained by suckling.

Another serious cause of economic loss to dairy farmers as well as of potential danger to consumers of milk was mastitis, infection of the mammary gland. The Princeton workers witnessed its ravages, for out of the Walker-Gordon herd, numbering 1,000 to 1,200 cows, the owners had to dispose of sixty-four animals in 1916 and seventy-one in 1917 because of diseased udders. This was a problem with which Smith's department, strong in pathology and bacteriology, was ideally qualified to deal; but F. S. Jones, who began work on it as soon as the laboratories were ready, knew that he was undertaking a complicated task. The lactating mammary gland of the cow, intensely specialized to produce milk in large quantity for a long time, with succulent gland tissue and rich blood supply, can be the breeding place of all sorts of microorganisms, introduced by contact with other cows, by the suckling calf, or by the milker's hands. Previous investigators of mastitis in Europe had found a score of different organisms in affected udders. To identify these germs precisely and determine which of them were actually responsible for damaging the milk-gland tissue was the task to be accomplished before that of finding ways to prevent infection. In 1918 Jones published in rapid succession a series of reports incriminating, chiefly, streptococci of both the hemolytic and the non-hemolytic type.

Interest in these bacteria was running high in medical circles at this time. Physicians interested in rheumatic fever, as has been noted in discussion of the work of Swift and Lancefield, were learning to classify the types of streptococci, and had discovered the association of one particular group of the hemolytic kind with rheumatic fever. That other kinds of streptococcus are the cause of septic sore throat and scarlet fever was becoming clear. Before Theobald Smith left Harvard, he and J. H. Brown and Marion Orcutt, studying a milk-borne epidemic of streptococcus sore throat, suspected that a milker, carrying the germs on his hands, had implanted the infection in a cow's udder, whence it was carried back to the human community in the milk. The question of human versus bovine origin of the organisms having been raised, J. H. Brown undertook to study the distinguishing cultural characteristics of streptococci from various sources. Jones and Little studied an explosive epidemic of scarlet fever occurring in a small New Jersey town in 1927, in which milk from an injured teat, *i.e.,* from a single quarter of one cow with hemolytic streptococcus mastitis, presumably acquired from a human carrier, caused 200 cases, 169 of which developed within a period of five days. By this time Rebecca Lancefield's method of differentiating the various types of streptococci was available and helped to prove that this cow was bearing germs of the type that causes scarlet fever. Little, Brown, and others elsewhere found that the streptococci most commonly associated with the severe contagious form of chronic mastitis belong to Lancefield's group B, whereas the human streptococci (group A) are much less commonly found. It is these latter, however, which are dangerous to human consumers of milk.

The laborious efforts of Jones, Brown, Little, and others at The Rockefeller Institute's Princeton department yielded a mass of valuable information rather than any one spectacular discovery about mastitis and its relation to milk-borne epidemics of human disease. The investigators, nevertheless, stand high in the roll of bacteriologists and pathologists of many countries who have built up the knowledge by which the number of milk-borne epidemics of scarlet fever and streptococcus sore throat has been greatly reduced, and an economic burden on the dairy industry considerably lessened.

Jones, while investigating mastitis, did not understand why the cow's udder, in which the germs of this disease are able to proliferate and create serious inflammation, is not more often invaded by pathogenic microorganisms. Many cows remained in the herd for years without developing udder disease. Yet their blood and milk contained no more agglutinins against mastitis-producing germs than did these fluids in susceptible animals. The inference was that the mammary gland and the milk produced there must contain some sort of bactericidal substance different from the specific immune bodies. The German bacteriologist Walther Hesse had shown in 1894 that the organisms of typhoid fever and cholera will not multiply in raw milk; and W. H. Park of the New York City Board of Health Laboratories had observed that in cool fresh milk the bacteria count drops for twenty-four hours after milking. A few subsequent workers attributed these effects, on partial evidence, to the presence of a special inhibitory substance. Jones was now prepared to study the phenomenon more precisely, using pure cultures of the mastitis streptococcus. He found definite evidence of a substance, not an agglutinin, which would inhibit the growth of the streptococci of mastitis and of human scarlet fever for four to eight hours or even longer. The substance was sensitive to heat, for boiled milk becomes an excellent culture medium for the same organisms. In 1929 Jones and H. S. Simms gave the name "lactenin" to this protective substance and, finding that it goes with the proteins of whey when they are precipitated, were able to prepare concentrated solutions containing two hundred times as much lactenin as skimmed milk.

At this point the study of lactenin lapsed for a time, but in 1951 it was revived by Armine T. Wilson, bacteriologist, former staff physician of The Rockefeller Institute Hospital, and pediatrician of the Du Pont Institute of Wilmington, Delaware, and his colleague Herman Rosenbloom. These workers learned a good deal about the chemical characteristics and mode of action of lactenin, though they could not purify it beyond the point reached by Jones and Simms. The reason why the group A streptococci that cause milk-borne epidemics become established in the udder, they found, is that lactenin is not active within the gland for lack of sufficient oxygenation. Once the milk is shed, the anti-bacterial potency develops in it, killing any streptococci that may be present, unless they are overwhelmingly numerous. This little-known agent, Wilson and Rosenbloom believe, is an important factor in preventing epidemics of milk-borne streptococcal diseases due to contamination of milk after milking. Lactenin is destroyed by the processes used in preparing canned and powdered milk, but not by commercial pasteurization.

JOHN B. NELSON, beginning his work as an Assistant under the direction of Theobald Smith, joined his chief in the study of an epizootic of paratyphoid fever in mice, caused by a bacillus of the *Salmonella* group, that broke out in the Department's animal house in 1924. Such an outbreak, occurring spontaneously in a colony of animals previously free from the disease, offered, they felt, an unusual opportunity to study the progress of an epidemic disease in a controlled population, and might throw light on the natural history of human disease. Following for several years the rise and fall of the acute epizootic, they observed its subsidence into an enzootic state with the appearance of healthy carriers and recurring incidence of a few cases. The two investigators had, occurring naturally, a situation comparable to that which Leslie Webster, studying epidemics at the New York laboratories (Chapter 8), was producing experimentally with bacterial infections of a type quite similar to the one that chance had presented to Smith and Nelson.

About 1932 Nelson, studying an acute respiratory infection, or coryza, of chickens, demonstrated for the first time in this country a microbe originally described in the Netherlands, and verified its causal relation to the disease. He then studied an unrelated coryza of chronic type. His findings became very important to the poultry industry when, a few years later, the chronic coryza occurred in explosive outbreaks, causing losses of millions of dollars, in the Delaware-Maryland-Virginia poultry-raising area east of Chesapeake Bay.

Because the very small filter-passing microorganisms which Nelson obtained from the nasal washings of infected birds could not be identified with any known type of bacteria, he called them simply "coccobacilliform bodies." In size they resembled the larger viruses causing smallpox and cowpox, but unlike the viruses they did not depend upon living cells for their maintenance. Nelson's first successful *in vitro* cultures were made with salt solution containing minced chick embryo tissues which yielded chemical substances that supported growth of the coccobacilliform bodies.

Workers at the Lister Institute of London had recognized the resemblance of organisms of this type to those causing epizootic pleuropneumonia of cattle, with which Nelson had never worked because it is so infectious that its study was prohibited in American laboratories. A number of related species, forming one of the most peculiar groups in the whole range of microbiology, are now classed together under the name of *Mycoplasma*. Those which cause respiratory diseases in chickens and turkeys have in recent years been widely studied in Europe and America.

Tuberculosis, one of the most important diseases of cattle, on which Theobald Smith had done pioneer work in the past, naturally claimed attention at the Princeton laboratories. In 1923 The Rockefeller Institute regained the services of Paul A. Lewis, who had effectively collaborated with Flexner in 1908–1910 in the investigation of poliomyelitis. Since that time director of the research laboratories at the Henry Phipps Institute for the study of tuberculosis, at the University of Pennsylvania, Lewis had collaborated with the geneticist Sewall Wright of the U.S. Bureau of Animal Industry in an intensive study of the inheritance of tuberculosis, using guinea pigs. Among a number of inbred lines of these animals developed by Wright, Lewis found several which differed greatly in their susceptibility to inoculated tuberculosis. Wright's mathematical analysis suggested that 30 per cent or more of this variation between families depended upon inherited factors; but what these might be remained unknown.

At The Rockefeller Institute's Princeton laboratories, beginning in 1923, Paul Lewis and Dorothy Loomis began to search for the heritable factors in low resistance to tuberculosis, first studying what they called "allergic irritability," by which was meant the relative capacity to be immunized, not only against tuberculosis, but against antigenic substances in general. Five years of breeding and testing pure lines of guinea pigs clearly revealed inherited differences in the ability to produce antibodies against foreign antigenic proteins and to resist infection with tubercle bacilli and other organisms. In Lewis's opinion the work supported the old concept, not then in favor, that there is an inherited "diathesis," or constitutional lowering of resistance to tuberculosis, which does not show itself unless the subject is exposed to infection. Modern bacteriology had disposed of the still older concept that the disease itself is inherited, and had even weakened the idea of an inheritable susceptibility, which the studies of Lewis, Wright, and Loomis now rehabilitated. In June 1929 this thoughtful research program was tragically ended when Paul Lewis, on leave of absence from the Institute to study yellow fever with a group of Rockefeller Foundation investigators, died of that disease at Bahia, Brazil.

Richard E. Shope, whose name, already mentioned in connection with the work on hog cholera, will reappear in this and later chapters, came to Princeton at Lewis's invitation to join a study of resistance to tuberculosis, which after three years of work had essentially negative results. Thereafter, he devoted himself chiefly to virus diseases.

In 1930 a veterinarian in Iowa called Shope's attention to an outbreak of a violent disease of cattle known as "mad itch," which causes such terrible itching that the infected animals bite at themselves in frenzy until, after an illness of thirty-six to forty-eight hours, they die, exhausted. Proceeding to the farm where nine cows in a herd of twelve were infected, Shope succeeded at once in transmitting the disease to rabbits by inoculating them with brain substance from a dead cow. He then passed the infectious material through a bacteria-retaining filter, proving it to be a virus. Later, he transmitted the disease to guinea pigs, rats, and mice, and showed that domestic pigs could acquire it by eating rats carrying the disease; but, although invariably fatal in other animals, the virus caused only a slight illness in swine. Nevertheless, it is highly contagious in pigs, spreading as a "silent" epidemic among them. When such latently infected swine are associated with cattle, Shope found, the virus spreads to the cattle in a fatal form. Accordingly, mad itch persists in the Midwest as a common infection in swine, but its presence is recognized only when it spreads from swine to cattle. Shope was able to prepare an antiserum capable of neutralizing the virus when administered with it, but could not develop an immunizing vaccine. As a final stage of this remarkably neat and rapid investigation, he proved the identity of mad itch with a disease, described in Hungary in 1902 as "pseudorabies," which still prevails in Russia and the Balkans.

While hunting near Princeton in November 1931, Shope killed a cottontail rabbit with a number of swellings under the skin of its paws. Taking the carcass back to his laboratory, he inoculated domestic rabbits with bits of the tumor tissue. In spite of the difference in species, the transplanted tumors grew and could be kept going by successive transplants. Furthermore, Shope succeeded in transmitting them by a filtered extract of the tumor tissue, thus adding another tumor of a mammalian species to the small list of those produced by filtrable viruses. It was a benign connective-tissue growth or fibroma; but in certain details of microscopic structure it resembled another, highly contagious and malignant disease of rabbits, infectious myxoma, first reported by G. Sanarelli in 1898 in South American rabbits, and accurately described between 1927 and 1930 by Thomas M. Rivers of The Rockefeller Institute Hospital. Myxoma also was known to be caused by a virus.

Shope now found the two viruses to be very similar, since domestic rabbits with the fibroma and cottontails which had survived the myxoma were each respectively immune to the other virus. Myxoma is, therefore, a highly virulent form of fibroma, the relation being very much like that between smallpox and cowpox. The two tumor viruses are in fact so closely related that in 1936 George P. Berry (who had gone from The Rockefeller Institute to the University of Rochester), working with several associates, actually transformed one into the other. The living Shope fibroma virus, together with a small quantity of the inactivated malignant Sanarelli virus, produced malignant myxomata when inoculated into rabbits. Evidently the addition of a non-living substance derived from the Sanarelli virus had conferred new powers upon the active benign virus. This striking result, difficult to explain at the time, has become more comprehensible with our increasing knowledge that the vital properties of these agents of disease depend upon the specific chemical structure of nucleoproteins, elaborate substances similar in fundamental pattern but capable of infinite slight variations.

Myxoma acquired general notoriety a couple of decades after Shope studied it, when a well-intentioned French landed proprietor, a physician, introduced the virus from South America to rid his fields of wild rabbits. Within a few years the disease spread through France and England and exterminated practically all the rabbits, destroying a valuable food source and upsetting the balance of wild life by removing the rabbits from competition with other denizens of woods and fields. Shope's fibroma virus, which confers immunity against myxoma, offers the only present hope of combatting this plague. The Pasteur Institute of Paris and commercial laboratories now distribute it for use as a sort of vaccine, looking toward the establishment of a myxoma-free rabbit population.

In 1932 Shope learned from friends in Iowa of another papillomatous disease, occurring in wild cottontail rabbits and characterized by the growth of huge hornlike protuberances or warts on the skin. From specimens of these papillomata sent to him in glycerin, and afterward from affected rabbits shipped alive to Princeton, he easily transmitted the new disease by inoculation of the warty tissue and by filtered tissue extracts applied to abraded skin. Later he was able, with some difficulty, to transmit the warts through a succession of domestic rabbits. E. W. Hurst, an English histopathologist (now with Imperial Chemical Industries) who was at Princeton from 1932 to 1934 studying the pathology of equine encephalitis, worked out for Shope the histology of the papillomata. Shope himself did little more with this particular find, but gave the papilloma virus to Peyton Rous, discoverer of the first virus tumors, who has since studied it for years with illuminating results that will be detailed in a later chapter.

In 1918 hog breeders in the Midwestern states were troubled by the outbreak of a highly infectious disease of swine, characterized by severe broncho-pneumonia very much like that which was occurring at the same time in the great epidemic of human influenza. The coincidence of similar epidemics, human and porcine, gave rise to a supposition that the swine had picked up the human infection, and led farmers and veterinarians to call the hog disease "swine influenza." In 1928 C. N. McBryde, W. B. Niles, and H. E. Moskey of the United States Department of Agriculture transmitted the disease by inoculating pigs with bronchial mucus or with diseased lung tissue from infected animals. Shope, in the same year and again in 1929, observed two epizootics of swine influenza in Iowa, in which practically 100 per cent of the animals in infected herds came down with the disease, with a mortality of one to four per cent. He and his chief, Paul Lewis, searching for a bacterial cause of the disease, recovered a bacillus (*Hemophilus influenzae suis*) resembling

Pfeiffer's influenza bacillus, which was then widely thought to be the causal agent of human influenza. Although *Hemophilus* was found in every case, to their surprise it would not reproduce the disease when inoculated into healthy swine. Shope then explored the possibility that a virus might be involved, and found that exudates from the lungs of infected swine, passed through a Berkefeld filter, did indeed cause an illness, but a very mild one, unlike the severe disease seen in the epizootics. Acting upon an improbable conjecture, Shope administered the bacillus and the virus at the same time, whereupon the animals amazingly came down with typical swine influenza characterized by severe pneumonia.

After Lewis died in 1929, Shope carried on alone for several years the analysis of this strange association of two agents in the production of a single, well-defined disease entity. The similarity of this disease to human influenza and also the resemblance of the bacterial component of the double infection to Pfeiffer's bacillus (which often accompanies the human influenza virus) led Shope to speculate that swine influenza may be an accurate replica of human epidemic influenza. At the time, however, there was no evidence of a virus capable of causing influenza in man. When two years later Wilson Smith, C. H. Andrewes, and Sir Patrick Laidlaw of the British National Institute of Medical Research isolated a virus of human influenza, they acknowledged the stimulus Shope's discovery had given them. It was demonstrated some years later that the human epidemic of 1918 had been due to the swine virus, a highly exceptional occurrence. Another strange turn taken some years later by Shope's study of swine influenza, which revealed the mode of spread of the disease on the farm, will be discussed in Chapter 16.

CHAPTER TWELVE

Parasitology, Genetics, Plant Pathology, 1916–1935

Protozoan parasites of insects; the Japanese beetle; parasitic worms in sheep. Inheritance of resistance to bacterial infections. Theobald Smith as Director characterized. Appointment of TenBroeck; study of equine encephalitis. Division of Plant Pathology organized; Kunkel appointed Director. Virus diseases of plants; plant tissue culture; crystallization of tobacco mosaic virus.

To the biologist the study of parasites is one of the most fascinating fields of investigation, however much the layman may shudder at the disagreeable aspects of infestation with protozoans, worms, or insects. It demands of those who undertake it wide knowledge in several divisions of biology, for the parasitologist must study not only the parasite but also the structure and habits of the host upon which it lives; and as he traces the relation of parasite to host often finds himself engaged in a thrilling piece of detective work. No one recognized more clearly than Theobald Smith the great importance of parasitology in animal pathology. His own work on blackhead of turkeys was a notable contribution to this field. He therefore made a special place for it in his department as soon as he could find a competent investigator. Rudolf Glaser, trained at Harvard, worked with the Bureau of Entomology of the United States Department of Agriculture from 1909 to 1920. Specializing on the parasitic diseases of insects, he became an excellent entomologist, bacteriologist, and protozoologist. He was among the very first to discover diseases of insects caused by filtrable viruses; his study of the wilt disease of the gypsy moth (1913) permitted virologists to include insects among the forms of life susceptible to virus diseases.

When Glaser came to The Rockefeller Institute in Princeton, he was experimenting with the bacterial diseases of grasshoppers. Observing that these insects, like higher animals, can develop immunity against bacteria that infect them, he ingeniously solved a difficult technical problem. Parasitologists had hitherto found it impossible to study in pure culture the protozoan parasites of insects, because in the bodies of host insects the animal parasites are accompanied by bacteria which inevitably contaminate the cultures. By deliberately inoculating grasshoppers and silkworm larvae with material containing both types of invading organisms, he induced immunity reactions which killed off the bacteria while leaving the protozoans alive. The latter could then be recovered from the temporary host and grown at will in cultures. Using another method, based on the geotropic migration of the organisms, Glaser and his technician Nicholas Coria cultivated the well-known "slipper animalcule," *Paramecium caudatum,* and certain other protozoans in the absence of bacteria, a feat never previously accomplished.

Another of Glaser's investigations had the practical aim of combatting that obnoxious pest of lawns, orchards, and gardens, the Japanese beetle. In 1930, working with Henry Fox of the U.S. Department of Agriculture, he discovered and described a small nematode (roundworm), which infects the grub of the beetle. This worm was afterward named after him *Neoaplectana glaseri.* Working with it for several years, he found a method of cultivating the worm *in vitro* and was able to keep the cultures alive indefinitely. The New Jersey Department of Agriculture, anxious to control the Japanese beetle, invited him to assist in establishing the parasite in regions where the pest was prevalent. Glaser and his associates developed methods by which the nematodes were grown by tens of millions weekly and transferred to the soil of areas infested with the grubs. This work, in which the U.S. Bureau of Entomology later participated, was the first large-scale use of nematodes in the control of an agricultural pest. Glaser's biographer, Stoll, a fellow worker in Princeton, regards its success as one of the most striking episodes in the recent history of parasitology.[1]

Norman R. Stoll, who joined the Princeton laboratories in 1927, began his work on the parasites of sheep after an intensive experience in human parasitology. For six years he had been a member of groups working on hookworm infection in the Caribbean Islands and Panama, under the auspices of the Johns Hopkins University School of Hygiene and Public Health with support of The Rockefeller Foundation, and in China under the auspices of the Peking Union Medical College. One of the major tasks of these investigators was to estimate the degree of infection of individuals in a given population. Stoll in 1923 developed for this purpose an effective method based on counting the number of hookworm eggs shed by individual human hosts of the parasite. He and other workers later applied the method to several other species of worms parasitic in the human intestine. This wide experience with the quantitative aspects of such diseases was now put to a new use in Princeton. One of the most serious parasites of domestic sheep is the twisted wireworm, *Haemonchus contortus,* which is ingested in forage grown in pastures infested with the larvae. The worms, coming to maturity, often in very large numbers, in the sheep's fourth stomach or abomasum, suck blood from its wall and cause a secondary anemia like that produced in human beings by hookworm. *Haemonchus* in sheep, like the hookworm in man, does not multiply within the host. Rather, it is the loss of blood due to accumulation of the parasites by reinfection from without which finally impairs health. In 1927 almost nothing was known of the cycle that takes place within the host. To study this, Stoll undertook experimental observations on sheep.

For a clean-cut test he needed young animals completely free from the worm, so that he might set up a precisely controlled initial infection. As it happened, such animals were uniquely available in Princeton. Theobald Smith and a colleague, E. R. Ring, assistant superintendent of the laboratory, while at work on the colostrum problem described in the preceding chapter, had found that they could raise lambs without contact with adult sheep, even their own mothers, by feeding them on cow's milk. A number of such lambs, completely free of parasitic worms, were available for Stoll's use. Inoculating them with a known number of *Haemonchus* larvae, he could follow the course of infection by his method of counting eggs in the fecal droppings and obtain a numerical estimate of the number of worms surviving in each lamb. The result, in brief, was that as the animals, pastured in an originally uninfested field, discharged the worms' eggs in large numbers and reinfected themselves by ingesting larvae as they grazed, the number of worms in the stomach increased sharply to a very large figure. The infection did not, however, ordinarily go on to a fatal result. After six to eight weeks the egg count suddenly dropped, because most of the parasites were shed from the stomach, and, from then on, even though these young sheep stayed in the same fields, they remained in excellent health. The process of self-cure was sometimes dramatically sudden, as when an animal apparently dying with a heavy infection was the next day quite lively and exhibited a sharp decrease in the output of *Haemonchus* eggs in its feces. Once self-cured, the animals were thereafter protected by an acquired immunity.

When Stoll subsequently tested the same lambs by feeding *Haemonchus* larvae to them in known numbers, they rejected the larvae administered. Evidently something had happened which closely resembled the development of immunity by animals or human patients infected with pathogenic bacteria. He found, however, that this self-cure and protection can be broken by serious illness or other disturbance of general health or nutrition of the sheep; for example, an animal whose infection was well under control might develop an overwhelming infection after a jaw injury which prevented mastication and thus impaired its nutritional state, or, again, as a result of acute bacterial disease. Moreover, if Stoll fed an excessively large number of larvae to a susceptible animal, the resulting accumulation of worms in the stomach could prove fatal by exhausting the animal before its power of resistance developed.

At this time no one working with parasitic roundworms had any idea that mammalian hosts could acquire immunity against such intruders. It was suspected, of course, from the hookworm studies, that some sort of control exerted by the body of the host must help to regulate the extent of infection, so that in most individuals in a human population constantly subject to reinfection the disease stops short of a fatal outcome. Stoll's demonstration of acquired resistance to a similar parasite of sheep was the first clear proof that a protective immunity affects the relations between roundworms and their hosts. A few years later he showed that this kind of self-cure and protection of the host applied not only to the blood-sucking wireworm *Haemonchus,* but could be demonstrated also with a roundworm of the domestic rabbit. M. P. Sarles, who came to Princeton in 1929 after studying dog hookworm in Baltimore, repeated Stoll's experiments on rabbits in a skeptical mood, his work

JACQUES LOEB

Department of Animal and Plant Pathology, Princeton, New Jersey; air view, about 1942

with dogs having led him to believe that some kind of resistance due to increasing age of the host was the significant factor in apparent immunization.

In a reminiscent review of these productive years, Stoll gives us a little picture of the excitement in such work, which so often fails to show itself in impersonally written scientific reports. As the two men worked side by side, Stoll expecting the rabbits to react as his sheep had, and Sarles maintaining his skepticism, the rabbits failed to show an accumulating resistance until they received the next to last dose of worm larvae Sarles had planned to give them. Then, they suddenly responded, to Stoll's satisfaction, by a reduction of the infection and self-cure. Later, Sarles and Stoll observed a similar resistance of cats, infected with a cat hookworm, to superimposed infection with fresh larvae. John E. Stumberg, a Fellow in Stoll's group, showed that this kind of immunity, like that against bacteria, is linked with the presence of proteins from the invading parasite in the blood of the host. Stumberg's untimely death in 1933 delayed completion of this chain of evidence, but an Australian investigator, D. F. Stewart, later demonstrated specific antibodies in sheep's blood, formed in response to antigenic worm protein, such as Stumberg had detected.

The experimenters naturally hoped to gain a clue to the production of a vaccine or some other kind of immunity-producing treatment. This hope was not fulfilled for many years. In spite of numerous attempts to extract antigens from the worms or to produce immunity by injections of larvae or otherwise, all Stoll's attempts failed to induce resistance to *Haemonchus*, except by feeding larvae. Only in recent years has he hit upon a method, to be described in another chapter, which suggests the possibility of vaccination against *Haemonchus*.

Meanwhile, beginning in 1935, Stoll published a series of reports on another sheep parasite, a tapeworm (*Moniezia*) which had turned up in 1927 in the course of his experiments with the wireworm. The basic problem here concerned the life history of the tapeworm, including the conditions of its survival in the free-living stages (eggs and larvae) in the pastures, the means of its spread from sheep to sheep, and the possibility of an invertebrate intermediate host. Stoll's very thorough studies, employing the quantitative methods which characterize all his work, yielded a great deal of essential information on the cycle of infection and reinfection. When, during the course of these studies, H. W. Stunkard of New York University discovered that a minute arthropod, a free-living orabatid mite, was the intermediate host in which the eggs first developed, the observations at Princeton helped to clarify the natural history of this association of sheep, mite, and worm.

George L. Graham, associated with Stoll from 1933 to 1947 (when he joined the School of Veterinary Medicine of the University of Pennsylvania), applied Stoll's quantitative methods to a very complicated problem in the life history of another roundworm, *Strongyloides*, related to the hookworms and wireworms. This genus greatly interests parasitologists because it is an intermediate form between free-living and parasitic species. In hookworms and wireworms, for example, each generation in the host requires a larval period of life in the open, but the larvae can only complete their development by getting back into the proper host (hookworm larvae by penetrating the skin, wireworms by being ingested). In *Strongyloides* the generation residing in the host gives rise to free-living stages which do not invariably return directly to the host for the true parasitic stage. They may pass through a free-living (heterogonic) generation with functional males and females which, in turn, produce offspring that must return to the host. (In some species, they may for a time continue further free-living generations.)

Graham chose an ingenious approach to the fundamental biology involved. He found that by infecting a laboratory rat with a single larva of the *Strongyloides* peculiar to rats he could often secure progeny from the resulting parasite in the gut of the rat. Using a closely inbred strain of rats as host material, he continued serial lines of such single-larva infections, establishing strains of rats carrying infective larvae derived from both the direct (homogonic) and indirect (heterogonic) cycles. The relative proportions of homogonic and heterogonic progeny appearing among the offspring of a single larva then gave him a view of what was occurring in this one *Strongyloides* species that was impossible to obtain from the usual type of infection by numerous parasites in one host. Graham's clear analysis of factors involved in this complicated life history is an important landmark in the biological investigation of these roundworms.

THE APPOINTMENT of John W. Gowen in 1926 to associate membership brought to the Department of Animal Pathology a man with experience in two new sciences — biometry and genetics — relevant to animal breeding and to the study of susceptibility to disease. Biometry, the investigation of vital phenomena by quantitative measurements and mathematical analysis of variations, became a recognized branch of biology in the late 1890's, largely through the efforts of two Englishmen, Sir Francis Galton and Karl Pearson. Genetics as an organized scientific discipline was still younger, in fact almost coeval with The Rockefeller Institute, for it was in 1900 that several botanists brought from obscurity the papers of Gregor Mendel and made them the basis of world-wide research on the mechanisms of inheritance. The study of inheritance in insects, notably the fruit fly *Drosophila,* which did so much to prove that hereditary genes are carried in the chromosomes of cell nuclei, was not in full motion until about 1910; the identification of Mendelian factors in mammals began about the same time.

Gowen's first professional appointment was at the State Agricultural Station, Orono, Maine, where Raymond Pearl was developing biometry as a tool for analysis of results in animal breeding. Stock farmers had, over the centuries, acquired considerable experience in selective breeding of domestic animals to improve desirable qualities — for example, speed in race horses, meat and milk in cattle, and wool in sheep. Standards for judging and selecting suitable breeding animals, and awards of merit at cattle and horse shows, were, however, usually based empirically on characteristics thought to be transmitted by inheritance, such as the configuration of the body or its parts — for example, in dairy cows, size and shape of the udder. After the turn of the twentieth century, biologists realized that knowledge of the principles of heredity and of biometric analysis must replace the empirical methods of selection in breeding.

Raymond Pearl, introducing this concept at the Maine Agricultural Station, secured from The Rockefeller Institute annual grants beginning in 1921, to support a study of the inheritance of milk production and its correlation with the conformation of the sire and dam, size of udder, and other physical characteristics. Gowen had charge of this study, which was based partly on data in herd books, records of cow-testing associations, and advanced registries of pure-bred cattle, and partly on a herd deliberately bred at the Maine Station by crossing animals with high and low milk yield and other contrasting characters. After joining the Princeton staff in 1926, Gowen continued work on this large project. Along with it, both at Orono and at Princeton, he studied the physiology of milk secretion. The results of his genetic analysis clearly pointed to inheritance as the main factor in keeping up a high milk yield, and de-emphasized the value of mere conformation as an indication of worth.

Gowen turned his attention also to the inheritance of disease and of disease susceptibility. He described an inherited disease (focal melanosis) of the fruit fly *Drosophila;* and he assisted Leslie Webster, by advising him and his associates on genetic procedures, in the investigation, described in Chapter 8, of the possibility that inborn factors of resistance to infectious disease may affect the spread of epidemics. The results of this work, together with that of Lewis, Wright, and Loomis on tuberculosis, mentioned in the preceding chapter, and of several bacteriologists elsewhere, confirmed the existence of hereditary differences in susceptibility to bacterial infections.

It next became important to discover whether the genetic resistance consisted of a single character, enabling the animal to withstand many kinds of infectious organisms, or a composite of independent characters, each enabling the animal to resist one such invader. Gowen and R. G. Schott, a Fellow of the Institute, investigated the question by choosing two strains of mice, which had already been found to show different grades of susceptibility to mouse typhoid (caused by a bacillus of the *Salmonella* group), and studying their respective susceptibility to a totally different disease, pseudorabies (caused by a virus). They found that the two strains were differentially susceptible also to the virus disease, but not to the same degree as to the bacterial infection. One strain more strongly resisted the virus, the other, the bacterial organism. Because of such experiments, it is now generally accepted that the genetic factors in resistance to infection are multiple, operating separately against either single organisms or closely related groups. Incidentally, this work of Gowen and Schott seems to have been the first extension to virus diseases of the theory of genetically determined susceptibility. To their finding, which was only tentatively presented at the time, Clara Lynch of the Institute's New York laboratories three years later added certainty, by proving a similar differential susceptibility of selected strains of mice to the virus of yellow fever.

In spite of his commitment to investigate the genetics and biometrics of domestic animals, as part of the program of the Department of Animal Pathology, Gowen continued research also on basic genetic mechanisms, for which he had been trained in his student years with T. H. Morgan at Columbia University. Almost every year he published a report on some aspect of gene action or chromosome pattern, or on a new mutant Mendelian factor, in the fruit fly. In 1937 he was called away from the Institute to become professor of genetics at Iowa State College. The Institute thus had nurtured at least one professional geneticist, and several of its other investigators did extensive work in genetics as applied to disease—Brown and Pearce, Chase, Louis Kunkel, Holmes, Lynch, Schneider, Swift, Trager, Webster—but basic genetic investigations did not gain a solid foothold in either the New York or Princeton laboratories. Such studies, developed chiefly in zoological and botanical laboratories, apparently did not appeal to the administration as part of a program then largely oriented toward pathology and physiology. Only years later, when gene action began to come within the grasp of biochemistry, was basic genetics to return to the Institute, under the leadership of Rollin D. Hotchkiss.

Another new concept that was beginning to affect medical thinking, that of the vitamins, received only slight attention in Princeton, doubtless because it also was too far from the Department's main interests. Some work was done on it by Oskar Seifried, who came in 1929 from a teaching and research post in veterinary medicine at Giessen, and returned to Germany in 1932 (later to become professor in the veterinary faculty of the University of Munich). Among a series of reports on animal pathology, based on research during his brief stay in Princeton, were three on the lesions caused in chickens by deprivation of vitamin A. There was no work on basic problems of vitamin chemistry and, after the departure of Seifried, nothing more was done even on the pathology of avitaminosis.[2]

The Department of Animal Pathology under Theobald Smith's direction was not, in fact, inclined toward new ventures leading beyond the existing program of work on infectious diseases of domestic animals. In his younger days Smith had won great personal distinction in this field, in which he saw enough unsolved problems to keep his staff busy for a hundred years. Since he came to the Institute in Princeton at the age of fifty-five, his long experience fitted him to work and direct his staff along these lines rather than to look for new lines of attack. His reluctance to expand the Department reflected a distaste for unnecessary additional executive duties, along with a strong sense of responsibility for the proper use of the resources entrusted to him. The ever-increasing cost of scientific investigation weighed upon him heavily and made him a cautious administrator, to which his temperament already inclined him. In daily routine it led him to insist on small economies which sometimes irked, sometimes amused the laboratory workers; in large matters he was not inclined to take long chances with money, materials, or men.

How deeply this austere, elderly scientist was troubled by expansion and changes, more or less forced upon his department by the policy of the Institute and by new trends of research, is shown by a passage in his confidential report of 1927 to the Board of Scientific Directors. Mentioning the addition of three new staff members — Gowen in genetics and biometrics, Stoll in parasitology, and Simms in chemistry — he wrote, "The orientation of these new staff members in their new environment should be watched with interest since none of them has been concerned either primarily or secondarily with problems of disease." This was scarcely true even of Gowen and Simms; to say it of Stoll, an expert on the detection and demography of hookworm infection, placed narrower limits on the scope of his department than even Smith would have drawn in a mood of less intense concern. (He subsequently followed Stoll's work on *Haemonchus* with interest and supported it liberally.) These appointments had no doubt been initiated by Flexner in recognition of the expanding scope of animal pathology; and still another burden upon Smith's resources had been imposed when Flexner moved Northrop and his group to Princeton from New York in order to keep that city-hating scientist in the Institute. "Besides these additions," Smith continued, "the Department has domiciled Dr. Northrop and Dr. Kunitz of the Division of Physiology and two assistants. . . . The pressure of the new staff for assistants and technicians is already being exerted, and if their demands are granted pathology and its auxiliary phases of bacteriology and immunology will represent only a small fraction of the entire activities . . . The original purpose of the Department should not be permitted to be submerged by the future organization."[3]

Smith's concern about his department arose not only from his wish to adhere to the program he thought most important, but also from a conviction that a research laboratory must not overtax its powers. In a letter to Simon H. Gage of Cornell University he once wrote, ". . . you and I know that research cannot be forced very much. There is always danger of too much foliage and too little fruit."[4] New workers billeted at the Department, new projects beyond its carefully defined scope, would, he felt, overstrain his controlled economy of intellectual as well as material resources. It was also both uneconomical and impolitic to duplicate research programs already undertaken at the Department of the Laboratories in New York.

For all these reasons Smith did not seek out radically new lines of investigation, and his program was limited mostly to extending (often brilliantly, as we have seen) research along the lines of his long experience. His general wisdom, however, was not limited to his own field. He enjoyed discussing all sorts of scientific topics and had an almost uncanny gift for asking significant questions. All who ever worked with him testify to his wide knowledge of pathology and bacteriology, and to the great breadth of his biological and philosophical outlook. For his senior associates he was an unfailing source of new ideas.

At a meeting of the Executive Committee of the Board of Scientific Directors in October 1926, Smith, then almost sixty-seven years old, told his colleagues it was time to look for a new director of the Department of Animal Pathology. The name of Carl TenBroeck, Smith's former colleague, was at once suggested. No one else seems to have been thought of then or later, and the Board began a cautious and lengthy series of steps that finally led to TenBroeck's appointment as Member of the Institute early in 1928 and as Director in April 1930.

TenBroeck, a medical graduate of Harvard in 1913, while still a medical student worked with Theobald Smith as a research assistant; then, briefly, in Christian Herter's private laboratory. After graduation he joined Smith's Harvard Department of Comparative Pathology, going with him to Princeton in 1914. There he worked, as already mentioned, on the hog cholera virus and on bacilli (*Salmonellae*) of the paratyphoid group. Five years later he accepted a call to the Rockefeller-supported Union Medical College of Peking, where he was professor of bacteriology and head of a combined department of pathology, bacteriology, and protozoology. In China he devoted his research chiefly to the tetanus bacillus, especially with regard to immunity reactions.

After settling down in Princeton and finishing up loose ends of research brought home from Peking, TenBroeck was drawn into a major problem. In 1933 he and a colleague, Malcolm Merrill (now director of the California Department of Public Health), recognized that a kind of brain fever of horses, which had broken out on farms along tidewater and salt marshes in Virginia, Maryland, Delaware, and New Jersey, was equine encephalitis. There had previously been similar epizootics elsewhere, and in 1931 K. F. Meyer and two colleagues at the Hooper Institute of San Francisco had isolated a virus from the brains of horses dead of the disease. TenBroeck and his Princeton associates also recovered a virus, much more virulent than the Western form and not quite identical with it by immunological tests. Both these viruses are occasionally responsible for epidemics in human beings, fortunately small in extent, but with a high mortality rate.

Various clues caused TenBroeck to suppose that the Eastern form of the virus is primarily resident in one or another species of birds living in the infected region, from which it is carried to horses and humans by an insect. Acting on this supposition Erich Traub of TenBroeck's staff succeeded in infecting pigeons with the virus, but after many passages its virulence became greatly attenuated, which suggested that that species is not the primary host. The general hypothesis, however, was strengthened when Captain (later General) R. C. Kelser of the Army Veterinary Corps found that the Western equine encephalomyelitis could in laboratory experiments be transmitted by the same mosquito (*Aedes aegypti*) that carries yellow fever. That species does not exist in the region where TenBroeck was working; looking for an insect present in the area which could be the vector of the Eastern disease, Merrill, TenBroeck, and C. W. Lacaillade, then a Fellow in Princeton, found that another mosquito, *Aedes sollicitans*, a denizen of the Eastern salt marshes, can carry the virus and might be the agent which transmits it from an unknown intermediate host, presumably a bird. Merrill and TenBroeck proceeded to show that the bite of a single mosquito can transmit the disease to a horse and, following up this clue, that the virus multiplies in the body of the mosquito, enabling it to inoculate its victim with far more numerous virus particles than it had acquired by biting an infected horse or bird. Such multiplication of a virus within its insect vector had previously been observed in a plant disease, but Merrill and Ten-

Broeck's demonstration of the multiplication of the equine encephalitis virus within the mosquito was the first of its kind in an animal virus disease.

Fortunately, none of The Rockefeller Institute's workers became infected with this very dangerous disease they handled for several years. When, over the years, TenBroeck's little group became scattered, its members took a working knowledge of equine virus diseases with them to widely separated parts of the world: Merrill became head of the California State Board of Health; Hurst became professor of experimental medicine at Adelaide, Australia; Erich Traub is director of the German Federal Institute of Animal Virus Diseases at Tübingen; Lacaillade took a teaching post, and later a professorship of biology at St. John's University, Brooklyn.

About 1926 the Board of Scientific Directors began to consider the creation of a division of plant pathology. William H. Welch, President of the Board, had long appreciated the possibility that study of plant diseases, at first sight very different from those of animals, might throw light on animal pathology. Flexner, in his biography of Welch, recalls that, more than thirty years before, Welch had read up on plant pathology in order to conduct at Johns Hopkins the examination of a Ph.D. candidate in botany, and that ever since Welch had followed new work in the field and kept in touch with those doing it.[5]

Because of certain recent developments, medical scientists were looking at plant diseases with new interest. The Rockefeller Institute's workers, having done so much to reveal the importance of filtrable viruses as causal agents of human and animal illnesses, had good reason to expect that plant viruses would offer valuable material for further study of the properties of these remarkable submicroscopic living entities. Incidentally, the first filtrable virus ever discovered was that of tobacco mosaic disease.

In cancer research also the plant pathologists might help. Erwin F. Smith of the U.S. Department of Agriculture had startled the American Association for Cancer Research in 1909 by pointing out the general resemblance of a plant tumor, the crown gall which affects many fruit trees and flowering plants, to human malignant tumors. Medical pathologists objected to his interpretation, saying that crown gall is no cancer, but only a kind of irritative response to a bacterium, *Bacillus* (now *Agrobacillus*) *tumefaciens*, which Erwin Smith had discovered in plant galls. When in 1911 Peyton Rous announced the discovery of a filtrable virus in his chicken sarcoma, Smith justly hailed it as substantiating his ideas about the infectious nature of the crown gall tumor and of malignant growths in general. This controversy was still active in the late 1920's. The Institute's cancer workers, receptive to any clues about the nature of malignant disease, considered what plant pathology might offer.

Early in 1931 the Board of Scientific Directors created a division of plant pathology in Princeton, under TenBroeck's general direction in a combined Department of Animal and Plant Pathology.[6] Louis O. Kunkel of the Boyce Thompson Institute for Plant Research at Yonkers, New York, was appointed to head the new division.

Kunkel, born in Missouri in 1884, had his professional training at Columbia University, where he took his Ph.D. in 1914. While a graduate student, he taught at Columbia and the University of Missouri. After a traveling fellowship in Europe, Kunkel became pathologist at the Bureau of Plant Industry in the U.S. Department of Agriculture, where he began to study virus diseases of plants. Because of this experience, the Hawaiian Sugar Planters' Association, faced with economic problems resulting from mosaic disease of sugar cane, appointed him associate pathologist in its laboratory. Returning from Hawaii in 1923, he was appointed pathologist at the Boyce Thompson Institute. Here he gathered together a group of young men trained in several fields of investigation that might contribute to the understanding of plant diseases. This group included the protozoologist Francis O. Holmes, who later accompanied Kunkel to The Rockefeller Institute as Associate Member; two others, C. G. Vinson and A. W. Petre, began under Kunkel's direction attempts to purify tobacco mosaic virus which Wendell Stanley afterward built upon at The Rockefeller Institute.

At the Boyce Thompson Institute, as in Hawaii, Kunkel made important contributions to the knowledge of mosaic diseases of tobacco, sugar cane, and Indian corn, and of a disease of asters known as "yellows," which he showed was caused by a virus. Virus investigators in the New York laboratories of The Rockefeller Institute knew his work, for he had been chosen, as an outstanding specialist on virus diseases of plants, to write a chapter on that subject in the influential book *Filterable Viruses*

(1928), of which T. M. Rivers was editor. This association perhaps predisposed Kunkel toward accepting the post in Princeton. William Crocker, his chief at the Boyce Thompson Institute, had warned him against it on the ground that he would be overwhelmed by the predominantly medical interests of The Rockefeller Institute.

After his appointment, Kunkel went abroad to visit European laboratories in his field. Settling in Princeton in 1932, he began active research with a staff of eight workers. Besides Francis Holmes, there was Philip R. White, one of the Fellows, who had also worked at the Boyce Thompson Institute. H. T. Osborn, the oldest and most experienced of Kunkel's juniors, had been an entomologist with the Hawaiian Sugar Planters' Association when Kunkel was there. Wendell M. Stanley, skillful in physicochemical methods as a graduate student at the University of Illinois and as Fellow with Osterhout in the New York laboratories, moved with Kunkel to Princeton as a chemist. The others — J. H. Jensen, W. C. Price, E. L. Spencer, and H. H. Thornberry — were recent Ph.D.'s or graduate students in botany and plant pathology.

Kunkel had been asked by the administration to make provision for studying plant diseases caused by bacteria and fungi as well as by viruses. When work began in 1932, however, investigation of plant viruses offered so many promising leads that Kunkel chose to capitalize his own experience of many years by putting his entire group to work on mosaic diseases, principally tobacco mosaic. This disease shows itself on the leaves of the tobacco plant, causing irregular spots of discoloration, as indicated by the name "mosaic." Plant pathologists knew that it is transmitted to healthy plants by contact with materials from diseased plants, and by the hands of field laborers contaminated by infected tobacco they chewed or smoked. Transmission by the bite of a species of aphid (plant louse) that frequents tobacco plants was also suspected, but never proved.

Various conjectures had ascribed the disease to wandering hereditary genes, to a parasite — such as a bacterium, a fungus, or a protozoan — to inadequate nutrition upon poor soils, or to excess chemicals or oxidative enzymes in the soil. In 1892 a Russian investigator, D. Ivanovski, found that the disease could be transmitted by inoculating a healthy plant with juice from a diseased one, passed through a porcelain filter. In 1898 M. W. Beijerinck, in Delft, independently made similar observations, and clearly stated the hypothesis that the causal agent is a living substance of submicroscopic size. He thus established the concept of filtrable viruses as the cause of disease, a concept already implied by Pasteur's investigations and ever since a central theme in plant and animal pathology. By the time the Princeton group went to work, dozens of virus-induced plant diseases were known. Numerous investigators in all parts of the world, among whom Kunkel ranked high, had investigated the modes of transmission of the different viruses, the spread of a virus through the affected plant, the susceptibility of different plants to the viruses of specific diseases, and the development of immunity. The nature of the viruses remained unknown. Agents too large to pass a porcelain filter had been ruled out, and genetic and nutritional factors had been proved unlikely. Some investigators were looking for a chemical factor, and others for a living virus.

Kunkel therefore again deployed his forces for an attack on the mosaic diseases along a wide front, as he had at Yonkers. Francis Holmes's experience as a protozoologist was no longer needed in the campaign, for protozoa had been ruled out as a cause of the disease; but Holmes had the technical knowledge necessary to study the infective characteristics of various strains of the disease-producing virus, and the powers of resistance of different varieties of tobacco and other susceptible plants. At the Boyce Thompson Institute, he had contributed a practical method for measuring the infectivity of mosaic viruses, by counting the local lesions following a standardized inoculation along the leaf of a plant. In Princeton, applying this and other methods to pepper plants, easily grown and readily susceptible hosts of tobacco mosaic virus, he obtained varieties that differed greatly in their susceptibility. Crossing such plants, Holmes found that resistance to the virus was inherited as a single Mendelian factor. In the course of this work he detected atypical kinds of viruses, such as attenuated strains able to produce only slight disturbance in the affected plants, and "masked viruses" producing no disease in one variety of plant but surviving there and able to infect another. By revealing in plant virus diseases peculiarities resembling those being found in animal and human virus diseases, this work helped to demonstrate the essential similarity of filtrable viruses throughout nature.

To determine how long the infected insect retains active virus, Osborn, the entomologist, studied another mosaic disease, that of pea plants, which is transmitted by an aphid. Price and Jensen worked on mutations of tobacco mosaic and cucumber mosaic virus. Price also studied the sensitivity of tobacco mosaic virus to heat, finding that in fresh juice the infectious material is quickly killed at 92° centigrade and slowly destroyed at 70°, which is within the general temperature range used to destroy bacteria in milk by pasteurization. Two of the other juniors looked into chemical influences on the nature and infectivity of the tobacco mosaic virus. Spencer found that a high concentration of potash in the soil restricts the spread of the virus in infected plants. Thornberry showed that by varying the acidity-alkalinity balance (pH) of infected plant juice he could change the filtrability of the infectious substance. K. S. Chester, who joined the group as Fellow in 1933, applied immunological research methods to the separation and classification of various strains of plant viruses.

One of these widespread efforts to feel out the nature of tobacco mosaic virus resulted in a notable advance in the technique of botanical research, useful far beyond the field of viruses. In 1932 Kunkel was supplying plants infected with tobacco mosaic virus to Carl Vinson, who was trying to purify the virus chemically at the Boyce Thompson Institute. The Director, William Crocker, objected to the assumption by Kunkel and Vinson that the plants in which they were growing the virus contained tobacco mosaic virus only. They could not fully rule out, he said, the possibility that, in spite of all precautions, a stray aphid might have brought some other virus into the greenhouse. It occurred to Kunkel that they could test Crocker's objection by growing virus in plants propagated aseptically in tubes or flasks or in tissue cultures. Plant tissue culture was in its infancy; the most significant attempt yet reported was that of William J. Robbins of the University of Missouri (now director of the New York Botanical Garden), who had been able to grow roots of Indian corn from excised fragments for a limited time *in vitro*.

As it happened, White, of Kunkel's staff, had also attempted the culture of root tissues while at the Boyce Thompson Institute. At Kunkel's suggestion he undertook in Princeton to cultivate tomato roots, because that plant, highly susceptible to tobacco mosaic virus, has much larger, more easily handled seeds than has tobacco. White obtained unlimited growth of excised tomato roots in a simple solution of mineral salts, cane sugar, and yeast extract. In these roots, growing in cotton-stoppered flasks, he cultivated several different plant viruses. As a means of obtaining pure tobacco mosaic virus for chemical study, the method was rendered obsolete by Stanley's investigations, shortly to be narrated; but White's work is regarded as a milestone in the history of plant tissue culture and the starting point of numerous investigations on the physiology of plant growth. The story affords an amusing comment on Crocker's fear that The Rockefeller Institute, with its predominantly medical interests, might limit the scope of Kunkel's group, for the beginnings of plant tissue culture of the type White developed can be traced indirectly to the Institute itself. Robbins, whose early technique White utilized and improved upon, records that his own pioneer cultures of corn roots resulted from his youthful attempt to test some of Jacques Loeb's experiments on regeneration of plants.[7]

Louis Kunkel, busy as he was in organizing his group and directing its research, found time to continue his own investigations of several virus diseases. Characteristically, he discussed these only at the end of his annual reports to the Board of Scientific Directors, first narrating the research activities of his juniors. He gave particular attention to the "yellows" infection of peaches, of which he was the most experienced student, confirming and extending his own discovery of its transmission by an insect of the leaf-hopper variety, and working out cross-immunity relations between several virus diseases affecting peaches. He also contributed to the subject of tobacco mosaic disease by studying a closely related virus, apparently a mutant strain of the tobacco mosaic, known as aucuba mosaic virus. Comparing the effects of the two on a large number of different host plants, he worked out in detail the differences in their infectivity and the lesions they produced. As Kunkel pointed out in a Harvey Lecture some years later, the discovery of new host plants experimentally infectible with various viruses often provided investigators with very useful material. When grown in a new plant species, a virus frequently behaved in a way more controllable for experimental study, or showed unexpected peculiarities helpful in distinguishing it from contaminating viruses. All this information proved to be pertinent to the chemical studies now to be described.

The foregoing pages indicate the setting in which young Wendell Stanley began his attempts to purify the tobacco mosaic virus and define its chemical nature. Kunkel, veteran of twenty years' research on plant diseases, twelve of them devoted to the viruses, had in his unassuming way stimulated and encouraged many newcomers to the field as he was now to foster Stanley's work. In Princeton his specialists could cover practically every aspect of the biology and pathology of the mosaic diseases, and were daily acquiring information that the chemist could use in testing preparations for infectiveness and specificity. The Princeton laboratories fortunately possessed also in Northrop and Kunitz two men whose work on the crystallization of enzymes, narrated in Chapter 7, had given them authoritative command of methods for separating and purifying proteins and related substances. That Stanley's search would take him into the difficult field of protein chemistry was obvious from the gropings of other workers during the past years. In 1916 H. A. Allard of the U.S. Department of Agriculture concentrated tobacco mosaic virus by precipitating it from the juice of infected plants with alcohol or acetone. Following this up, several workers, of whom the most persistent were Vinson and Petre of the Boyce Thompson Institute, got better and better preparations, by treatment with various agents known to precipitate proteins from watery solutions. Using lead acetate for this purpose, between 1925 and 1935 they gradually improved the yield of infectious precipitate, but like other workers did not secure a chemically pure substance.

Stanley went forward from this point with remarkable speed, even though, like every investigator feeling his way in a new field, he put a good deal of time into exploratory work not directly in the line of eventual success. In 1934, for example, Kunkel reported that Stanley had in the past year tested the effects of one hundred chemical reagents on the infectivity of tobacco mosaic virus, seeking clues to its chemical nature by discovering how to render it inactive. He spent much time also studying whether enzymes like pepsin and trypsin destroy the virus by digesting it. Meanwhile he continued his attack on the main problem of extracting the virus from plant juice, finally arriving at a chemical procedure utilizing one step of Vinson and Petre's lead acetate method, but based chiefly on methods for the purification of protein enzymes, developed and used successfully in Princeton by Northrop, Kunitz, and their associates.

After three years Stanley's efforts finally, in 1935, yielded a highly concentrated protein substance possessing the properties of the tobacco mosaic virus. This material, which took the form of small needlelike crystals, was extremely infectious. One cubic centimeter of a solution containing one part of the virus protein in ten billion parts of fluid would infect a tobacco plant. From such a plant a large quantity of virus of the same crystalline form could again be isolated after the disease had spread through its tissues. Anticipating objections that the crystals were not the actual virus, but contained some contaminant that was the real infectious agent, Stanley redissolved and recrystallized his protein fifteen times and still found it fully potent to produce tobacco mosaic disease. Now there came to his aid many techniques commanded by his Princeton and New York associates, by which he found that the virus protein had a constant chemical composition, a regular X-ray diffraction pattern, and a constant isoelectric point, and that, in a dozen other ways, it behaved in a uniform manner characteristic of a protein. The immunological methods his colleague Chester had learned to use strongly confirmed its identity with the virus as it exists in the plant. Aided by the biological experience of his other associates, Stanley isolated similarly virulent crystalline proteins from plants infected with aucuba mosaic virus and other viruses with which they were familiar.

No discovery made at The Rockefeller Institute, before or since, created such astonishment throughout the scientific world as did this. Crystals consist of molecules arrayed in a regular three-dimensional order definable in mathematical terms. A chemical substance in crystalline form stands forth as a veritable symbol of rigid mechanical structure, in total contrast with the complex, non-geometrical, highly mutable array of molecules and particles of various dimensions that characterizes living protoplasm. Yet here was a crystalline substance behaving as if it were alive, for it was able to reproduce itself in the plant, creating new substance of its own kind. Furthermore, if this was indeed the virus, the substance of the crystals must, like living organisms, be able to mutate, giving rise to slightly different strains, for tobacco mosaic virus living in plants has evidently, at various times in the past, given rise to numerous mutants. Stanley's find thus raised in a new and startling form the question, what is life?

We still have no clear-cut answer to this question, no rigorous criteria by which to distinguish living from non-living matter. Stanley in

CARL TENBROECK

FREDERICK T. GATES AND SIMON FLEXNER

his reports and lectures considered it unimportant whether the units of virus protein were thought of as molecules or as organisms; because of his training as a chemist he chose to refer to them as molecules.[8] As he pointed out, such substances represent a transitional state of matter, possessing some properties characteristic of living things and others of non-living materials. He and specialists he consulted estimated the molecular weight of the virus substance to be of the order of 17,000,000, greater than that of any other known protein; in other words, the constituent molecules of the crystals were extremely complex. A model of one molecule, such as organic chemists make from marble-sized balls representing atoms connected by rods representing the chemical bonds between them, would fill a good-sized room, and would consist of thousands of balls colored to represent individual atoms of carbon, hydrogen, oxygen, nitrogen, sulphur, and phosphorus. Such complexity confers far greater potencies for physical and chemical reactions with other ingredients of the host tissues, leading to replication and increase of the virus, and also far more numerous opportunities for mutation, than are possessed by the relatively simple compounds from which we derive our ordinary concept of a crystal.

Although Stanley's conclusion that tobacco mosaic virus is a crystallizable protein was soon confirmed in many laboratories, he met at first with vigorous skepticism on the part of those who held to the view that viruses were organisms differing from other infectious living agents only in size. Tensely concerned for the validity of his concepts, Stanley worked hard to confirm and expound them. After securing a mass of supplementary evidence, he took up the challenge by clear and forcible exposition of his findings in lectures given widely in America and Great Britain.[9] Support, of a sort which still further widened our glimpse into the chemical nature of life processes, came from English investigators who began to follow up Stanley's work as soon as his first papers appeared. F. C. Bawden and N. W. Pirie, then at Cambridge, working with methods based on Stanley's, within a year or two prepared crystalline viruses from tobacco mosaic and other plant diseases. They found, however, that the active substance is not, as Stanley had at first supposed, a simple protein of very high molecular weight, but actually a nucleoprotein — that is to say, a protein chemically combined with a nucleic acid, in this case of the ribose-containing variety identified by Levene at The Rockefeller Institute more than two decades before.

The significance of this seemingly minor refinement of knowledge of the chemical nature of plant viruses has grown more and more apparent with the advance of biochemistry. Today we know that many animal as well as plant viruses, including the peculiar viruslike parasites of bacteria known as bacteriophages, are nucleoproteins. We know also that complex organic compounds of the same kind are present in the chromatin of all cell nuclei, where they play an intimate role in the transmission of hereditary characters. Their structure, even more than that of the most complex simple proteins, presents to contiguous substances an enormous number of labile chemical bonds, well adapting them to participate in high-level chemical activities, even in such remarkable synthetic processes as the reduplication of genes and the self-reproduction of virus particles.

Thus the material of which viruses are made belongs to a group of substances now known to be involved in essential life processes. Stanley's achievement in fully purifying tobacco mosaic virus, and the further elucidation by Bawden and Pirie of its chemical nature, called the attention of biologists in many fields to the extraordinary properties of the nucleoproteins. Within a few years after the organization of the laboratories of plant pathology in Princeton, the combined experience of Louis Kunkel and the efforts of his young staff to understand the nature of plant viruses, capped by Stanley's chemical discoveries, had raised fundamental questions and stimulated biological investigation to a degree no one in the administration of The Rockefeller Institute could have foreseen. Further advances in this field, made at the Institute in later years, will be described in subsequent chapters. The award of the Nobel Prize in Chemistry in 1946 to Wendell M. Stanley (concurrently with John H. Northrop) was a recognition not only of his successful chemical work, but also of the philosophical importance of his isolation of a self-reproducing and potentially mutable agent in crystalline form—a link between living and non-living matter.

Flexner Retires; A New Director; Neurophysiology, Chemistry, Pharmacology, 1935–1953

Flexner retires; Gasser appointed Director. Changes in the Board of Scientific Directors and Board of Trustees. New directions of research. Research in neurophysiology. Biochemistry of protein components; structure of alkaloids; countercurrent distribution.

SIMON FLEXNER was so inseparable a part of The Rockefeller Institute that as he grew older neither the Trustees nor the Scientific Directors raised the question of his retirement. Year after year when he spoke of it they insisted that he should remain in active service, until in the spring of 1934, when he was seventy-one years old, he told them that he wished to retire as soon as a successor could be appointed.

Flexner could be well content with his achievement in three decades of single-minded devotion to his task. Looking about him as he went to his office every day, he could see the four chief buildings housing twenty-two active Members, with twelve Associate Members, about thirty Associates, and sixty Assistants and Fellows — a staff numbering more than one hundred and twenty, which he had built up from the twelve who began work with him in the temporary laboratories on Lexington Avenue thirty-one years before. On the library shelves were an even hundred volumes of bound reprints, *Studies from The Rockefeller Institute*, reporting the researches of those years, which merely to sketch in outline has required ten chapters of this history; and he knew that scattered through the heavy volumes were the records of achievement that placed

The Rockefeller Institute in the front rank of the world's scientific institutions. He knew too that its influence as a training center for the universities had been incalculable. One hundred and fifty-two persons had gone out from The Rockefeller Institute to become professors and associate professors in sixty-two American universities, colleges, and professional schools, and twenty to equivalent positions in seventeen foreign countries.

The Rockefellers had kept the faith upon which he staked his career when he took the directorship without a guarantee of permanent support. With generosity inspired by the Institute's success, they had built up an endowment which even in 1936 after the Great Depression amounted to sixty million dollars. The Founder, John D. Rockefeller, Sr., now ninety-seven years old, knew in his seclusion at Pocantico Hills that his benefaction had paid handsome dividends in scientific discovery and the control of disease. His son, who through a long career had kept the Institute in the forefront of his own wise philanthropic interests, was still active on its Board of Trustees, and a third John D. Rockefeller was now at his side.

At a special meeting of the Board of Scientific Directors, June 1, 1934, Theobald Smith, Charles R. Stockard, and Flexner himself were appointed to nominate a new director.[1] This committee, after the long and thorough consideration demanded by so momentous a question, and after considering the qualifications of several eminent men within The Rockefeller Institute and outside it, recommended the distinguished physiologist Herbert Spencer Gasser.

As of October 1, 1935, Flexner's resignation became effective, and his successor took office. Flexner wanted no fanfare to mark the end of his directorship. He was ready to turn over his duties to the new leader, although he continued working in a secluded room in one of the laboratory buildings. Once he stepped out of the Institute's affairs, he wrote some years later, administrative cares rolled off his back completely, and he never had a wistful or anxious moment over the change.[2] Only once more, in 1942, did he appear as a speaker before the Institute's staff; in that last lecture he talked about his teacher and friend William H. Welch, to whom he had owed his directorship.

Herbert S. Gasser, second director of The Rockefeller Institute, was born in Plattsville, Wisconsin, in 1888. After completing undergraduate studies at the University of Wisconsin and remaining there for two years as graduate student and instructor in physiology, he took his M.D. in 1915 at the Johns Hopkins University. Going then to Washington University, St. Louis, Gasser held various posts of rapidly advancing rank in pharmacology and physiology, becoming professor of pharmacology in 1921 at the age of thirty-two. During World War I his knowledge of the physiology of the heart and blood, acquired at the University of Wisconsin, qualified him to take part in an investigation of traumatic shock, led by Joseph Erlanger, professor of physiology at Washington University. Shortly before transferring from Erlanger's laboratory to the chair of pharmacology, Gasser dramatically entered the field of nerve physiology with a new method of studying the conduction of nerve impulses. Physiologists had long known that the signals that travel along nerves to convey sensation and to stimulate muscles resemble electrical impulses and can be recorded by electrical measuring instruments. The problem, however, was to find recording devices capable of reacting to impulses of very small quantity and extremely short duration, measured in fractions of a second. The string galvanometer and the capillary electrometer, fastest and most sensitive of such instruments available at the beginning of the century, were much too slow and insensitive to give a complete and detailed picture of a nerve impulse. The cathode-ray oscillograph, first described in 1897, was sufficiently quick if only it could be made sensitive enough by enlarging its readings of very small currents.

By 1921 the vacuum-tube amplifiers which had made radio possible were available to the physiologist. In that year, Gasser and a colleague, H. S. Newcomer, constructed an amplifier which considerably improved the sensitivity of the string galvanometer. Soon thereafter he used it with the oscillograph instead, with such good results that he could now record in detail and accurately measure single nerve impulses. During the next decade Gasser and Erlanger, working together in association with G. H. Bishop, used the new method in a fundamental study of the nature of nerve conduction. For this work and its continuation by Erlanger and Gasser separately in later years, they were in 1944 jointly awarded a Nobel Prize. Gasser interrupted his teaching at St. Louis to spend the years 1923 and 1924 in London working with the eminent physiologists Sir Henry Dale and A. V. Hill. Called to New York City in 1931 to be professor of physiology at Cornell University Medical College, he continued his research on nerve physiology with several associates. In New York he was an immediate neighbor of The Rockefeller Institute's staff and a colleague of Charles R. Stockard, professor of anatomy at the Cornell school, soon to become president of the Board of Scientific Directors of the Institute. These associations made known to a wide circle of new friends in New York that Gasser was qualified for a high place in the scientific world, not only by his international standing as a physiologist with broad intellectual interests and understanding of basic physical sciences, but also by his experience of fourteen years' successful administration of medical school departments. Regarding himself, however, as an investigator rather than an administrator, Gasser accepted the directorship of the Institute with some reluctance, under heavy persuasion by members of the Board of Scientific Directors and the Trustees.

Meanwhile the personnel of the Board of Scientific Directors had considerably changed. Charles R. Stockard in 1935 succeeded Theobald Smith as president. The physicians Warfield T. Longcope of Baltimore (1934–1952)[3] and Alphonse R. Dochez of New York (1935–1953), the physiologist Walter B. Cannon of Boston (1936–1945), and the pathologist George H. Whipple of Rochester (1936–1953) were new appointees. Following Stockard's death in 1939, Longcope became president of the Board, his polished, retiring manner in great contrast to Stockard's outspoken, downright way; and the Yale anatomist Ross G. Harrison (1939–1953) was elected to fill the vacant membership. With Gasser as *ex officio* member, this group at first maintained the same distribution of professional interests as in the latter years of Flexner's regime, having five members trained as physicians (of whom two were professor-practitioners of medicine, the others laboratory scientists) and two Ph.D.'s. When Detlev W. Bronk, then at the University of Pennsylvania, took Cannon's place after the latter's death in 1945, the proportion became four medical men to three trained in other fields of science, and so remained when the biochemist Vincent du Vigneaud of New York took the seat vacated by Conant's resignation in 1949. In contrast with the original Board of 1901, composed of seven doctors of medicine, the newer distribution reflected the growing alliance of the physical and chemical sciences with physiology, pathology, and bacteriology in the work of The Rockefeller Institute.

In another sense also the Board was becoming more broadly representative. The original group consisted of five residents of New York

City and two from other cities. After the death of Biggs, Holt, and Prudden in 1923 and 1924, New Yorkers were never again in the majority. From 1939 until 1949, there were only two local residents (Dochez and Gasser). The original Board represented only three cities; after 1924 there were always members from four or five. The Board of Scientific Directors tended more and more to resemble, in membership and in function, a university governing board.

The Institute's Board of Trustees was also assuming a more broadly representative character. Instituted in 1910 to provide for custody and skilled management of the endowment, and to share with the Board of Scientific Directors, through the Corporation, legal responsibility for the Institute, this group consisted at first of Welch as president of the Board of Scientific Directors, Flexner as director of the Institute, and three men from the Founder's family and business associates, namely, Rockefeller, Jr., F. T. Gates, and Starr J. Murphy. Those next added were also closely associated with the Rockefellers: Jerome D. Greene (1912–1932)[3] and the lawyers Raymond B. Fosdick (1921–1936) and Trevor Arnett (1926–1937). The next two, Charles W. Appleton (1928–1940), lawyer, and George Murnane (appointed 1928), banker trained as civil engineer, represented the world of business and civic affairs in general rather than Rockefeller interests in particular. Henry James (1929–1947), onetime business manager of the Institute, came to the Board as chief executive of the Carnegie-endowed Teachers' Insurance and Annuity Association. John D. Rockefeller, 3rd (1932–1950), and his brother David (appointed 1940) temporarily increased the family's representation, and from 1940 until 1950 there were three Rockefellers, father and sons, on the Board. John C. Traphagen (appointed 1936), banker, and Frederick Osborn (1938–1946), foundation executive and man of affairs, were, on the other hand, drawn from the general business community, as was Barklie McK. Henry (appointed 1947), the banker. Lindsley F. Kimball (appointed 1947) is an officer of The Rockefeller Foundation. Donald K. David (appointed 1950) is dean of the Harvard University School of Business Administration.

Although the Board of Trustees maintained its core of direct representation from the Rockefeller family and their close associates in philanthropic and business affairs, it gradually broadened to include experienced executives, lawyers, and bankers from outside this circle. During the last years in which two boards existed, there were four such members and three members from the Rockefeller group. The Trustees continued to elect to their board the director of the Institute and one other member of the Board of Scientific Directors. Gasser took Flexner's place in 1935. Stockard succeeded Welch in 1936; Whipple succeeded Stockard in 1939. During the forty-three years (1910–1953) of the Board's existence in its original form, it was made up almost exclusively of men whose work centered in New York City. Donald K. David is the only Trustee, other than *ex officio* scientists representing the Board of Scientific Directors (Welch and Whipple), ever chosen from another city. However widely the Institute's influence spread, however broad the territory from which it recruited its staff, Rockefeller, Sr., and his son and grandsons always considered it a New York institution. As long as there was a separate Board of Trustees with largely custodial functions, they looked only to the home city for guardianship of its endowment and public relations.

AFTER A SIMPLE installation ceremony for the new director on October 7, 1935, at a luncheon of the two Boards, Gasser and Rockefeller, Jr., were engaged by the press in an impromptu discussion of the Institute's apparent change of policy in selecting a physiologist to succeed a pathologist.[4] Prodded by reporters hopeful of enlivening their columns with some dramatic statement of new aims, both men frankly discussed the research program of the Institute, pointing out that a change of emphasis had long been in progress there as elsewhere. In the past thirty years, they said, research on infectious diseases had made remarkable advances; the time had now come to intensify investigation of fundamental life processes at the level of the cell and its constituents. The new director said firmly, however, that there would be no great changes in the Institute's staff for some time. Nor were there. The list of Members remained almost unaltered for several years, and the proportion of workers studying pathology decreased but slowly. It is of course impossible to classify investigators and their projects rigidly under one or another subdivision of medical biology; but the staff titles, taken for what they are worth in this respect, show that at the end of Flexner's regime half the Institute's investigators were called pathologists and bacteriologists, the other half chemists, physiologists, pharmacologists, and biophysicists. At the end

of Gasser's regime only one third were listed as pathologists and bacteriologists.

The following chapters will reveal the details of this change. Under
the new director the study of proteins and their derivatives begun by
Loeb and Levene was expanded until there were five or six laboratory
groups working on its various ramifications, by ever-advancing chemical
and physical methods. Gasser favored the research in physical chemistry,
begun when Osterhout brought Duncan MacInnes to the Institute, to
which Flexner had never given enthusiastic support. Gasser brought in
a group of biophysicists equipped to apply electronic methods to nerve
physiology. Within the older disciplines of pathology and bacteriology
he encouraged the use of new methods tending toward basic rather than
applied medical biology.

This broadening of the Institute's field was accompanied by gradual
changes in its inner structure, reflecting the new director's inclination and
facilitated by the retirement of several Members. During Flexner's regime, every Member had his own personal domain, each laboratory resembling an "institute" in the German sense of a research group under a
single dominating personality, with juniors devoting themselves to the
program of their chiefs. Upon the retirement or death of a Member, his
group would ordinarily dissolve and be replaced by another senior investigator with his assistants, in a different field. Under the new director,
however, as new fields of research and new techniques evolved, younger
men had more opportunity to develop special skills and interests, and
gained greater freedom to follow their own ideas. In several instances,
when a Member retired Gasser encouraged a senior associate to continue
and develop the program according to his own light. Gasser was quick to
recognize talent in young workers and was willing to take a chance on
them without requiring a mass of published work. One first-class research
article, he said, was often sufficient to reveal competence and originality.
A number of young men whom he brought to the Institute, though nomi-
nally attached to the laboratory of a senior investigator, were soon encouraged to work independently.

Consequently, the change in the Boards of Trustees and of Scientific
Directors, which was making them more like the governing boards of
universities, was paralleled by changes in the status of the research staff,
slowly tending to create a freer atmosphere. Gasser is said to have re-

marked to an intimate acquaintance that many of the staff had become too cloistered and would have gained by having to teach. His attitude resulted in a relaxation of intellectual restraints in various aspects of scientific community life. The weekly staff meeting, for example, became more of an open forum. Attendance was expected, as before, but whereas in Flexner's day junior staff members, overawed by the presence of distinguished superiors, seldom took part in discussions, they now spoke out. During the lunch-hour gatherings, there was greater freedom of association among the younger men; members of the hospital staff lunched with colleagues from the laboratories, with deepening acquaintance.

As the change of attitude and organization, reflected in casual daily contacts, permeated the Institute's general affairs, inevitably the director became more accessible to the younger men. He in turn was called upon to comprehend and sympathize with an ever-widening range of scientific ventures. For this, Gasser was admirably equipped. With his training as a physician and, in addition, his grasp of the mathematical and physical sciences, he was enabled to understand and share the intellectual interests of all ranks of the Institute's staff.

Older members of the staff felt the impact of their director's sound versatility when the time came to submit the annual report of each laboratory's work. Gasser took these documents very seriously. Men accustomed to having their reports accepted without technical questioning were surprised at first when Gasser subjected the drafts to close scrutiny and analysis. However exacting this attention might become, it conveyed to the investigators, more strongly than any direct commendation (of which Gasser was chary), a warm sense that their work was fully understood and soundly rated.

These changes in the character of the Institute were subtle and to an outside observer perhaps slight. Gasser had taken over a well-established organization, from a predecessor whose direction had won the admiration of both administrative boards and the founder's representatives. Innovations were not to be lightly undertaken, and, even if Gasser had wished to make radical changes, the financial situation of the Institute and of the business world during his administration would have denied him a free hand. Although the Institute's income had not suffered greatly from the financial crash of 1929–1930, it was fully committed to the support of the twenty-two Members and their associates in the laboratories and the hospital.

During Gasser's first years only one Member, Rufus Cole, director of the hospital, reached the age of retirement. The almost simultaneous retirement in 1939 and 1940 of six Members in the Department of the Laboratories — Carrel, Landsteiner, Levene, Michaelis, Osterhout, and Sabin — would ordinarily have freed considerable sums for new ventures; but just at this time the income from endowment had fallen sharply because of suspended interest payments on certain railroad bonds and reduced dividends on stocks. In 1939 the budget exceeded the available current income by 23 per cent; about $350,000 had to be withdrawn from the accumulated income fund to cover the operating deficit. The vacancies created by retirement could therefore not be filled by bringing in men with large new projects, although a limited number of promotions to membership from within the Institute made it possible to conserve talent that would otherwise have been called away to outside institutions. By 1940 the list of active Members in the Department of the Laboratories, which had numbered thirteen in 1935, now numbered nine, six having been lost by retirement and two gained by promotion. In 1941 the total of all ranks on the scientific staff of the Institute was 105 as against 134 in 1935–1936.

By that time, moreover, the Institute was heavily involved in the national defense effort, started as soon as World War II began in Europe and intensified after the entrance of the United States into the war. A few years after this emergency came the closing of the Princeton laboratories (to be narrated later) with the consequent necessity of accommodating in the New York buildings a considerable number of transferred workers. In 1948 the construction of new greenhouses on York Avenue to replace those abandoned in Princeton, and in 1949 the erection of an addition to the hospital, resulted in the expenditure of about a million dollars in excess of current income in each of those years. Although this deficit could be made up, as before, from income reserves of earlier years, the whole situation again tied the director's hands in regard to the Department of the Laboratories. The Institute's administrative traditions, still based upon considerations cogent when it was founded, reflected a fear of risking its independence by seeking outside support, and gave the director an implicit mandate to support the work entirely with its own resources.

Through circumstances beyond his control, Gasser had to conduct throughout his administration a "holding operation," which put him and his Boards to great effort to maintain the research standards and output of the Institute. The following chapters will show that the progress of research was by no means halted during this troubled time. Led by its second director, the Institute opened new pathways of discovery, and its increased attention to fundamental sciences presaged the step taken by President Detlev W. Bronk in 1953 when he began to make The Rockefeller Institute a graduate university.

WITH GASSER's advent, the Institute for the first time undertook to study the structure and function of the nervous system. The kind of work he and his associates did, and their findings, can only be understood against the background of a hundred years of previous effort in Europe and America to analyze the great network of nerve fibers and nerve cells which interconnects the tissues and organs of the body. By painstaking dissections and by microscopic study facilitated by ingenious methods of selectively staining nerve cells and fibers, anatomists had worked out the general plan of nervous connections within the brain and spinal cord and in the peripheral nerves and ganglia. They had achieved a great generalization, the neuron theory, which teaches that the whole nervous system is made up of individual cells (neurons), each consisting of a cell body with extensions in the form of fibers of varying lengths. Bundles of these fibers make up the nerves; other fibers constitute the intercommunicating pathways within the brain and spinal cord. The anatomical pattern was, however, by no means fully known, for these delicate strands could not be traced by visual means alone through the dense complexity of cells and fibers.

Something could be gained by experiments in which a nerve was cut or part of the central nervous system excised. Histologists had means of visually tracing nerve fibers which degenerated when cut away from their cell bodies; and the resultant loss of nerve function gave a physiological clue to the path of communications thus broken. Yet such experiments left many unsolved problems about the internal pathways of the brain, spinal cord, and ganglia. The rapidly developing techniques of electrophysiology, which Gasser had helped to create, made it possible to trace pathways in the intact nervous system, by stimulating a given region and then reading the transmitted signal as it reached its destined goal elsewhere in the body. A physician who elicits a knee jerk by striking the patellar tendon is in a crude way testing the condition of an already known nervous circuit. Utilizing refined electrical methods to trace unknown pathways, the experimenters needed to know as much as possible about the nature of the nerve impulse and the way it is conducted along a nerve. They knew, as already mentioned, that nerve impulses are akin to electrical currents, and that if any point on a nerve is stimulated by mechanical, thermal, or electrical irritation, an action current runs from that point along the nerve and shows itself on a recording device as a brief sharp elevation of electrical potential. This impulse gets its energy from the tissue over which it passes, much like a flash traveling along a train of gunpowder. In the living animal, impulses exactly like those produced experimentally in excised nerves are constantly being generated in the brain and spinal cord, sense organs, and visceral ganglia, serving to coordinate vital activities throughout the body.

From this sketch of the nature of the nervous system and the impulses it creates and conducts, it will be seen that countless details must be worked out to achieve full understanding of nervous activity. Investigators all over the scientific world have been working at them with increasing intensity for many decades. The newcomers to the Institute who began to cultivate some part of this immense field addressed themselves to two major questions which together cover much of the unknown territory. One of these concerns the nature of the nerve impulse itself: by what mechanisms is the chemical energy of living nerve tissue converted into a rapidly moving train of electrical impulses? The other question concerns the flow of the impulses along the nerves, following as closely as possible the chain of neurons by which a sensory or motor impulse makes its way from one end to the other of its traverse. What is the pathway, for example, over which a reflex like the knee jerk travels? Which of the several known sizes of nerve fibers carries the impulse from skin to spinal cord, and which from cord to leg muscles? How many neurons are linked in such a reflex arc? In more complicated reflexes and coordinated movements, where and how numerous are the relays of participating neurons?

Gasser and his associates in St. Louis and at Cornell Medical College had made a great contribution to the second of these questions by an ingenious use of the cathode-ray oscillograph to distinguish the impulses traveling over fibers in a mixed nerve carrying different types of signals, sensory, motor, and autonomic. These experiments had been done with excised frog nerves, because such tissues of cold-blooded animals readily withstand exposure and temperature changes during experiments. At The Rockefeller Institute, Gasser began to conduct similar studies on mammalian nerves. This of course required accessory apparatus for conducting the experiments at body temperature. Gasser and Harry Grundfest, who had come with him from Cornell Medical College, soon learned how to maintain mammalian nerves in their normal functional state, by adjusting not only the temperature and moisture but also the balance of oxygen and carbon dioxide in the environment of the excised fragment. For these experiments another associate, J. F. Toennies from the Berlin Technische Hochschule, constructed oscillographic amplifying instruments superior to those that Gasser had previously used.

Gasser and Grundfest's observations of the transmission of nerve impulses in mixed motor and sensory nerves showed that in the cat and other mammals, as in frogs, there are three chief kinds of nerve fibers, distinguishable by their respective diameters and by their rates of transmission, the rate depending upon the size. The largest, "A" fibers, carry sensory impulses from the skin and motor impulses to the skeletal muscles; those of intermediate size, "B" fibers, connect the central nervous system to outlying ganglia in the viscera. The fine "C" fibers, found in the autonomic nervous system, are not covered, as are the others, by myelin sheaths. Some of these "C" fibers convey sensory stimuli, especially pain, from the skin, while others supply the viscera, carrying incoming sensory stimuli and outgoing motor and secretory impulses. When a single impulse is initiated in a nerve by electrical stimulation at a given point, it travels at different rates according to the diameters of the different kinds of fibers, and therefore appears on the oscillographic record, taken at the other end of the nerve segment under study, as a series of waves arriving at different times. From a graphic record of such waves the presence of fibers of the various types can be detected. A visiting Fellow, J. B. Hursh, shared for a time in this work, which extended to mammals the information earlier obtained by Gasser and Erlanger from frog nerves, and greatly increased the precision of measurement of nerve conduction.

Gasser's highly sensitive oscillographic method of analyzing nerve impulses could of course be used also to investigate the first fundamental question mentioned above, how the living nerve fiber acquires and utilizes the electrical charges which exist along its surface and which when disturbed set up a wave — the nerve impulse — that traverses its length. It was known that a nerve fiber consists of a core of protoplasm, covered by a membrane so thin that it is invisible, which in turn holds to itself an outer layer of tissue fluid. The core has a high content of potassium ions, the outer fluid is rich in sodium ions. This arrangement forms a sort of tubular electrical condenser; when the nerve is at rest, there is a layer of positive ions on the outer surface of the membranes and a layer of negative ions on the inside. Stimulation or injury at any point increases the permeability of the membrane, allowing a shift of ions and making the surface layer at that point electronegative in relation to the neighboring areas. This sets up a flow of current along the nerve.

Behind this explanation of the nerve impulse lies a still more fundamental question: by what physical or chemical force is the living nerve placed and kept in the polarized condition, with balanced charges on the two sides of its surface membrane, ready to go into action when stimulated? In 1937 Gasser, with a volunteer assistant from Sweden, Jørgen Erik Lehmann, began investigating this question by studying the pattern of nerve impulses under the influence of conditions already known to affect nerve action, such as altered pH (acidity-alkalinity balance), altered potassium-sodium balance, and oxygen deprivation. Intensive work on this was taken over by one of Gasser's senior colleagues, Rafael Lorente de Nó, who joined The Rockefeller Institute as Associate in 1936 and was made a Member in 1941.

Lorente de Nó began his career at the Cajal Institute of Madrid, a leading center of anatomical studies on the nervous system, where he was assistant from 1921 to 1929, taking his M.D. at the University of Madrid in 1923. After two years as head of the department of ear and throat diseases at a hospital in Santander, he came to America as neuroanatomist at the well-known Central Institute for the Deaf in St. Louis. There he added to his thorough training in the anatomy of the nervous system a

long and varied experience in physiological experimentation on the pos-
tural reflexes associated with the internal ear, which finally led him to
study fundamental problems of nerve transmission. Aware of this, Gasser invited him to join The Rockefeller Institute.

For eight years Lorente de Nó worked on the nerve impulse, subjecting isolated nerves to a wide range of carefully planned and controlled
experiments, aimed at discovering to what extent the active state of the
nerve depends upon oxidation and other enzymatic processes within the
neuron. It is of course impossible to summarize such work briefly, but
the major conclusion can be stated in a few words: there is in the nerve
fiber a metabolic mechanism which converts chemical energy derived
from oxidative metabolism into electrical energy to be stored at the fiber
membrane. The production of a nerve impulse involves the release of a
small portion of this stored energy, which is restored after a brief refractory period.

Lorente de Nó also extended his studies from the nerve fiber, as an
isolated part of the cell, to the whole neuron. He found that the physico-
chemical factors operative in the fiber are also at work in the transmission of impulses over the cell body and into the shorter extensions (dendrites) by which the fiber makes contacts with endings of other nerve
fibers. In several other investigations he examined the activity of motor
neurons as they function in the ganglionic centers of the brain. In 1947–
1948 The Rockefeller Institute devoted two special volumes of its
Studies to a complete exposition of Lorente's findings, under the title "A
Study in Nerve Physiology." In a study of the transmission of nerve impulses through the outlying ganglia of the sympathetic system, he had
the assistance, from 1946 to 1951, of Yves Laporte (now at the University
of Toulouse), who worked also with David P. C. Lloyd before returning
to France. As the period covered by this history drew to a close, Lorente
de Nó resumed research on the basic electrochemical functions of the
nerve fiber, bringing in a wide range of physicochemical concepts.

Working under Gasser's general direction from 1938 to 1941, a
young investigator, Birdsey Renshaw, used the electronic recording
method to elucidate two moot questions about the interaction of neurons. One of these concerned the simplest type of spinal reflex, in which
a sensory stimulus traveling to the spinal cord elicits a motor impulse
from the cord to a muscle. Timing the speed of an impulse set up in such

a reflex circuit by electrical stimulation, Renshaw observed a very brief but significant delay of one-half to one millisecond between the initial stimulus and the resultant impulse toward the muscle. Stimulating the spinal cord directly and reading the outgoing signal, he noted delays of various durations, but never less than one-half millisecond. From this he deduced that the delay occurs at a synapse, *i.e.,* where one neuron ends in contact with another. Because the simplest reflex pathway involves the smallest unit of delay, there can presumably be only one synapse in its path; in other words, there is direct synaptic contact between the afferent and efferent fibers without the intermediation of other neurons. Renshaw's experiments constituted the first direct proof of this fact.

Neurologists knew that stimulation of a nerve may inhibit the activity of nerve cells in related parts of the brain and spinal cord. Such inhibition had been ascribed to some sort of blocking of transmission by interconnecting nerve fibers of the reflex path within the central nervous system, or to a subnormal state of such fibers. Renshaw in 1941 showed that an impulse set up in a motor neuron by electrical stimulation may traverse a collateral branch of the nerve fiber which runs back to other motor cells in the spinal cord, directly inhibiting for a brief period their ability to generate a stimulus to the muscle. This interpretation of nervous inhibition has since been broadened by similar observations on other parts of the nervous system and now appears to be very important in the theory of nervous action. Active nerve cells in long-range pathways (afferent and efferent projection systems), wherever tested, have been found to inhibit adjacent neurons. Work in progress at The Rockefeller Institute's laboratories of neurophysiology and of biophysics, and elsewhere, as this history is being written, suggests that inhibitory activity serves to stabilize the impulse-firing frequency of motor neurons, and to sharpen sensory impressions by cutting off impulses at the margin of a sensory field and so increasing the contrast of sensations.[5]

The third senior member of Gasser's group was David P. C. Lloyd, Oxford-trained physiologist who came to the Institute in 1939 as Assistant. Leaving in 1943 to serve as assistant professor of physiology at Yale, he returned in 1946 and was made a Member of The Rockefeller Institute in 1949. Lloyd has concerned himself with tracing the neuronal make-up of pathways of nerve action in the body, using electrophysiological methods to explore problems in which anatomical means of tracing nerve fibers had not been adequate. Beginning with experiments on the segmental activity of the spinal cord at its various levels, he went on to trace the course and exact mode of action of the long nerve bundles (pyramidal tracts) that run from the cerebral motor cortex down the spinal cord, stimulating muscular activity in the trunk and limbs.

In 1941 and 1946 Lloyd reported rigorous experiments on direct inhibition in the central nervous system, which demonstrated that impulses set up in a motor nerve cell, through its normal sensory connections, and destined to activate a muscle, act directly upon other motor neurons in its neighborhood, inhibiting some of them and facilitating action in others. The neurons supplying muscles antagonistic to the one originally stimulated are inhibited, while those supplying other parts of the stimulated muscle, or muscles working synergistically with it, are facilitated. The mutually dependent muscles acting about a given joint, together with the direct reflex paths that link them, form, Lloyd pointed out, a functional unit possessing within itself the elementary mechanism of reciprocal innervation, whereby purposeful simultaneous action of a group of muscles is integrated.

Another of Lloyd's investigations, which dealt with the familiar knee-jerk reflex, gave final proof of the fact, long suspected but not proved by anatomical methods, that the pathway for this reflex is made up of two neurons only, each consisting of a nerve cell with a fiber which, in an adult man, may be as long as three feet. The sensory component runs from the sensory endings in the thigh muscle to the spinal cord in the lumbar region and there ends in direct contact with the second component, which carries the motor stimulus to the thigh muscles.[6] C. C. Hunt (now professor of physiology at the University of Utah) did fundamental work in Lloyd's laboratory on the association of specific types of nerve fibers with the various kinds of nerve endings, sensory and motor, in voluntary muscle. Hunt also contributed to the work of Lloyd's group on reflexes involving only two neurons, by studying the conditions controlling excitation, inhibition, and transmission of nerve impulses over such simple reflex pathways. Most reflex pathways involve more complex chains of neurons, and are very difficult to trace. Later Lloyd and his colleagues worked on the physiological factors governing the participation of several or many neurons linked to form pathways for complicated reflex activities. A visitor from Australia, A. K. McIntyre (now professor of physiology at the University of Otago, New Zealand), took part in much of this research.

During these years (late 1940's and early 1950's) the neurophysiological laboratory gave much consideration to the fundamental properties of the nerve cell body, the dendrites, and the primary synaptic endings of nerve fibers upon nerve cells. Physiologists had been very successful in studying the conductive properties of the long principal fibers (axones) which make up the peripheral nerves and long tracts in the spinal cord. Lloyd and his colleagues realized, however, that the properties of the synapse, where an axone or dendrite of one neuron ends in contact with the cell body of another, will be determined by the conductive properties not of the axone, but of the dendrites and the cell-body substance. Pursuing this new concept, Lloyd's laboratory did pioneering research on the physiology of the synaptic endings of neurons.

As Gasser's wartime executive duties lightened, he returned to the study of conduction by nerve fibers of various types. His earlier work on this subject, for which in 1944 he won the Nobel Prize, had enabled him to classify nerve fibers according to their electrophysiological characteristics. Fibers of his class C, of very small diameter and having no myelin sheath, exist in nerves of two types very different in their anatomical distribution, one supplying the visceral organs and secretory glands, the other the skin. In 1938 Grundfest and Gasser had noted that the two types differ in details of their response to electrical stimulation. This finding led Gasser in 1946 to make a comprehensive study of the specific anatomical structure and physiological characteristics of the C fibers in nerves conveying sensory impulses from skin, which are now thought to mediate chiefly sensations of pain. The experimental procedure, in brief, was to place a piece of nerve in a moist chamber, stimulate it electrically, and record with an oscillograph the resultant impulses as they arrived at a point several centimeters from the site of stimulation. Calculations from the oscillographic tracings indicated the presence of fibers transmitting impulses at different rates, presumably because they were of different sizes.

Gasser and Erlanger had long ago observed the relation between size and rate of transmission in the relatively coarse fibers of motor nerves and those conveying sensations of touch, heat, and cold. Now Gasser was to see whether the same relation applied to the much finer C fibers.

Measuring their diameters as seen in enlarged photomicrographs of cross-sections of the nerve, he found a distribution of size apparently corresponding to the several rates of transmission. With the aid of Albert Claude (and of Keith Porter and George Palade in stages of the investigation beyond the period of this history), he used the immense resolving power of the electron microscope to secure even greater precision. The results showed that the velocities of conduction in non-myelinated nerves can be precisely accounted for by the relative diameters of the fibers. Numerous other findings of the investigation, too technical for discussion here, confirmed the existence of two types of C fibers, one carrying sympathetic impulses from the viscera, the other conveying stimuli from the skin to the spinal cord and brain. This laborious research added much to the total information still being accumulated by neurophysiologists about the pathways of the nervous system.

Research of this kind is technically very exacting. The class C fibers studied in Gasser's work are extremely fine, ranging from about half a micron to one and a quarter microns in diameter, the micron being one twenty-four-thousandth of an inch. The requirements for keeping nerve segments in good condition during an experiment, and for stimulating them precisely, are highly critical, as are also the optical and photographic requirements for accurate measurement in photographs which have to be enlarged to 12,000 diameters or more. Reading Gasser's papers and noting the variety of information in physiology, electronics, optics, photography, and applied mathematics which he utilized in his research, it is understandable that investigators who went to him for counsel always left impressed by the intellectual vigor and scientific knowledge he brought to their problems, no matter what their field of science.

IN 1939 AND 1940, as already stated, six Members of The Rockefeller Institute's Department of the Laboratories reached retirement age. Florence Sabin returned to her native Colorado to begin the notable new career sketched in Chapter 9. Landsteiner, Levene, Michaelis, and Osterhout all continued to work at the Institute, which provided laboratory facilities and secretarial and technical assistance adequate for their individual needs. Carrel did not request similar provision. He had become more a philosopher and mystic than a productive scientist. Flexner had been troubled by Carrel's failure to publish a report of the cancer research in the large mouse colony,[7] and, in view of growing demands upon a strained budget, the new director and the Board were doubtless relieved by his outright retirement. The situation distressed Carrel's friends, but as things turned out it was of little moment, for Carrel in his eagerness to make a bold stroke for his native country soon returned to France, ending his days there amid the confusion of World War II and its aftermath.[8]

PHOEBUS A. LEVENE, the Institute's first biochemist, continued until his death in 1940 the varied program described in Chapters 3, 5, and 7. Characteristically, the papers he wrote in his last years reported further progress in almost every one of the fields he had ever entered: proteins, amino acids, nucleoproteins and nucleic acids, lipoids, hexose sugars, glycoproteins and nitrogen-containing sugars, mucins and pectins. Although, like every ambitious scientific investigator, Levene sometimes attempted problems beyond the reach of current methods, it might almost be said of him, paraphrasing Oliver Goldsmith's epitaph, that he left scarcely any part of biochemistry untouched, and touched nothing that he did not clarify. During almost a half century of research in analytical biochemistry, he had filed in the scientific literature nearly seven hundred reports on the exact composition of substances known to exist in the animal body, ready to be consulted by medical biologists, zoologists, and geneticists, as progress in their fields more closely associated physiological function with chemical structure.

The calculated risk Flexner took when in 1905 he made the seemingly precarious appointment of Levene as a Member of the Institute had paid off outstandingly. Levene's research was intensely personal; for this reason his yield of scientific investigators is not distinguished. About forty men passed through his laboratories at the Institute, so many that only those whose names appeared significantly on research publications could be mentioned in these chapters. Many of them held assistantships for only two or three years. In view of Flexner's concern, expressed in 1919, that Levene's young men were not being systematically trained for independent work,[9] it is interesting to see what happened to them. Two, Jacobs and Van Slyke, became Members of The Rockefeller Institute, four or five others went on to professorships in important universities, and three or four to positions of comparable prestige in governmental and industrial laboratories. Nearly all the others have held responsible posts, most of them as chemists in industrial laboratories. This is a worthy record but scarcely comparable to that of several other Members of the Institute whose smaller output of men included a much higher proportion of research scientists. The verdict must be that Levene tended to choose young men primarily for their ability to handle advanced techniques, and by constant supervision qualified them to work in applied chemistry. The emergence of a half dozen of them as distinguished investigators shows that to work for a while under the close direction of a master, on his problems, need not sidetrack men bent on research careers. In his last years at the Institute, Levene had with him Gustave Meyer, who had joined him in 1908, Alexandre Rothen, who was to continue fruitfully their joint study of the optical properties of biochemical substances, and three assistants helping with the work on nucleic acids and carbohydrates that occupied him to the last.

Another biochemist, Max Bergmann, was at hand to fill the gap left by Levene and to represent the same brilliant tradition of German organic chemistry. Levene had been a pupil of Emil Fischer in that master's younger days; Bergmann, born in 1886, was a pupil of Fischer's later years, and his scientific executor. As director of the Kaiser Wilhelm Institute for Leather Research at Dresden, 1921–1934, Bergmann conducted research of great elegance on the chemistry of the amino acids, the nitrogen-containing substances of which proteins are composed. His crowning achievement while still in Germany was to develop a new and important method of synthetically combining amino acids into the larger peptide groups which, in turn, constitute the proteins. Emil Fischer had done this to a limited extent, forming a few simple peptides; Bergmann's methods enabled him to prepare almost any peptide. After Hitler came to power, Bergmann came to the United States. He did not need to look farther than New York for an appointment, for when Flexner learned he was available, The Rockefeller Institute at once made him an Associate Member, in charge of a subdivision of the chemical laboratory.

Here he began work in 1934 with a staff of three, two of whom had just taken their Ph.D. degrees, Joseph Fruton at Columbia and W. F. Ross at Harvard. The third was Leonidas Zervas, a brilliant chemist of Greek birth, who had worked with Bergmann at Berlin. Other recruits just out of graduate school—Otto K. Behrens, G. W. Irving, Stanford Moore, Carl G. Niemann, and W. H. Stein—joined him between 1935 and 1940. Ross and Behrens left after a year or two, for work which took them to high industrial scientific posts, one with the Shell Oil Company, the other with the pharmaceutical house of Eli Lilly and Company. Zervas returned to Athens, to become professor of biochemistry. After three years Irving left for an important career in the U.S. Department of Agriculture, and Niemann for the California Institute of Technology. Many other rising young investigators passed through Bergmann's laboratory, as Assistants or Fellows, on their way to academic, industrial, or governmental posts. Klaus Hofmann went to the University of Pittsburgh, and Emil L. Smith to the University of Utah. Calvin Golumbic is with the U.S. Department of Agriculture, Paul Zamecnik at the Huntington Memorial Hospital in Boston, Mark A. Stahmann at the University of Wisconsin, Max Brenner with the Ciba chemical industry in Basel, H. R. Ing at Oxford. Fruton remained at his chief's side during the remaining years of Bergmann's life, as did William Stein, who later succeeded to the leadership of the laboratory, jointly with Stanford Moore (on leave with the Office of Scientific Research and Development in Washington, 1942–1945).

Bergmann, modest, generous, and endowed with a sense of humor that made him an agreeable leader, took all these able, soundly trained young men into intimate collaboration in his program, forming a team so closely knit that it is often difficult to single out individual achievements from the record of their work together. Almost all the scientific papers published from Bergmann's laboratory were signed jointly by two, often three, or even four of the team. The inspiring quality of Bergmann's leadership is evidenced by three young men who began with him as laboratory technicians and went on to research positions: David G. Doherty at the Oak Ridge National Laboratories, Maurice M. Rapport at the Einstein Medical College of New York, and W. Parker Anslow at the University of Virginia.

In his lucid Harvey Lecture of 1935 Bergmann told just what he and his fellow workers were trying to do as they explored the structure of proteins.[10] These substances, which form a large part of living tissues and participate in every life activity, exist as very large molecules made up of amino acids, which are relatively small compounds of carbon, hydrogen, oxygen, and nitrogen. About two dozen amino acids are known to exist in various proteins. Insulin, for example, contains sixteen, repeated to make all together fifty-one amino acid units; other proteins contain different numbers and different selections of the available amino acids, in various orders of arrangement. Such complexity confers infinite variety upon the proteins, and explains how they can include such seemingly unlike products as casein, gelatin, silk; and how some of them act as hormones (*e.g.* insulin) or as enzymes (pepsin and trypsin) which digest other proteins, or in other specialized ways. This variety of structure also obviously accounts for the power of various proteins to elicit highly specific immunity reactions in the body, as seen in the blood groups and in protective inoculations against infectious organisms. It is therefore essential, as Bergmann said, to know the exact arrangement of the constituents of proteins in order to understand their roles in vital functions.

The problem was pointed up by the discoveries of Northrop and Kunitz, described in Chapter 7. They had isolated a number of crystalline proteins which are proteolytic enzymes. How is it, Bergmann asked, that one protein acts as a digestive enzyme while others composed of the same amino acids do not? Looking into the activity of some of the peptidases — enzymes which split the simplest peptide groups — Bergmann and Zervas developed a theory to explain the specificity of proteolytic enzymes — that is to say, the power of a particular enzyme to break up particular types of linkages in the peptide or protein chain — on the basis of the spatial arrangement of molecules in the attacking and the attacked substances.

Taking for study a group of such peptidases and proteinases, Bergmann and Fruton very ingeniously prepared a large number of artificial substrates, chemical compounds upon which the peptides could act. With these they could study the specificity of such enzymes in detail. The knowledge of protein-splitting and peptide-splitting enzymes acquired in this way enabled the investigators to break down proteins into their component parts with greater accuracy than previous workers had achieved. But now they faced another difficulty well known to protein chemists, that of separating out and identifying individual components of the complicated digestion mixtures in their flasks. As Bergmann remarked, such separations are constantly being performed in the metabolism of living animals and plants; chemists must learn to do the same thing and then to identify the products. By patient screening of likely chemical reagents, Bergmann found a large number of substances, chiefly organic acids, which would selectively precipitate specific peptides or amino acids from a nondescript mixture of protein split products. Combining these methods, by first splitting up the proteins and then identifying the products, Bergmann, Fruton, Moore, Stein, and Niemann determined the number of molecules of several of the amino acids in a molecule of a given protein.

As a contribution to national defense during World War II, Bergmann's group undertook an investigation of the chemical properties of the mustard gases, which will be reported in a later chapter. The conspicuous success of Bergmann's researches resulted in his promotion in 1937 to Member of The Rockefeller Institute. Seven years later, to the great loss of science and the Institute, he died of a malignant tumor at the age of fifty-eight. Fruton left at about this time to accept a post at Yale, where a few years later he became professor and chairman of the department of biochemistry. Since he was Bergmann's collaborator longer than anyone else, his name is generally bracketed with that of Bergmann as a pioneer in the development of knowledge of the specificity of proteolytic enzymes.

In 1945 Moore concluded his wartime service in Washington and returned to the Institute, where he and Stein, now jointly in charge of their section of the biochemistry laboratories, carried on the wartime work on mustard gas and, when that was finished, resumed their investigation of the constituents of proteins. During the 1940's a method of separating closely similar chemical substances, known as partition chromatography, had come to the front. In this method a solution of various substances to be separated is made to travel through a length of porous material — either a sheet of filter paper dipped by one edge into the solution, or a column of powdered starch or resin packed in a tube, into the top of which the mixed solution is poured. Percolating through such material, each individual component of the mixture migrates at its own rate, determined by its physical and chemical characteristics and those of the porous material, so that the components ultimately separate from one another, forming distinct zones in the paper or the column of wet powder. The method was named "chromatography" by Michael Tswett, a Russian botanist credited with its discovery in 1906, because he used it to separate plant pigments identifiable by their natural colors. When it is employed, as in most experiments nowadays, to distinguish colorless substances, these must be identified by chemical tests applied to the separate zones.

Chromatography was first utilized in 1941 as a practical method of separating amino acids by two English investigators, A. J. P. Martin and R. L. M. Synge. Stein and Moore began their work by improving upon a method, suggested by Synge, which employs a vertical tube packed with very fine grains of starch. When a solution made up to contain a dozen or more known amino acids in measured quantities was added at the top of such a column, the passage of the solvent caused the individual components to separate into zones along the column, each zone corresponding to one amino acid. The amount of each amino acid in the solvent emerging from the bottom was determined with the aid of a reagent (ninhydrin) which gives a blue color with amino acids, the effluent becoming now blue, now colorless, as each zone formed by a single concentrated amino acid emerged from the column. A graph of the result showed a characteristic peak for each of these substances. When an unknown mixture of amino acids resulting from digestion of a protein was tested in the same way, the peaks could be matched against the known standard curve already charted, and the material in each zone thus determined. The method could be applied to quite small amounts of material. Once standardized with all its possible irregularities and uncertainties under control, it was ideal for just such difficult substances as those with which Moore and Stein were concerned.

To its improvement the two collaborators devoted years of painstaking work. In 1951 they ingeniously adopted for use in the column, instead of starch, one of the new synthetic ion exchange resins, which they found to have higher resolving power and greater capacity. With this improvement they could obtain a graph of the effluent solution on which each of the seventeen most common amino acids appears as a separate peak. Even before the method had been developed to such precision they were able, in 1949, to put it to practical use in determining the amino acid content of the blood serum; and two years later they showed that it could be used to identify free amino acids in human urine, as found in health and in certain diseases. Both Moore and Stein were named Members of The Rockefeller Institute in 1952. As the period of this history closed a year later, they and their colleagues, C. H. W. Hirs and H. H. Tallan, were rapidly pushing forward the analysis of a large number of physiologically significant proteins. Among these was one of particular interest to other Rockefeller Institute workers, namely ribonuclease, an enzyme purified by René J. Dubos and R. H. S. Thompson in 1938 and isolated in crystalline form by Moses Kunitz in 1940. More recently, Hirs has gone far toward a complete structural analysis of ribonuclease, which he found to consist of a peptide chain of 124 amino acid residues of 17 different kinds.

In 1946 Gertrude E. Perlmann, a biochemist trained at Prague and at the Carlsberg Institute of Stockholm, went from the faculty of Harvard Medical School to Longsworth's physical chemistry laboratory at The Rockefeller Institute, where she took part in several joint investigations of the physical properties of proteins. After 1948 Perlmann developed an independent research program, utilizing the action of enzymes upon the protein molecule as a tool for elucidating protein structure. For her first area of attack she chose the structure of phosphoproteins. These substances are richly present in embryonic tissues and in milk and eggs, and presumably are important sources of phosphorus for the growing organism. They present many problems to the biochemist, first, because they are mixtures of individual proteins, difficult to separate and identify, and, second, because their internal structure — the way in which the phosphorus is bound to a protein molecule — is not fully understood.

Perlmann's attack on these problems began with an accidental discovery that certain enzymes (phosphoesterases) from plants and mammalian organs are able to remove phosphorus from ovalbumin, a protein in egg white. With this as a clue she used a number of such enzymes to break down and thus to elucidate the structure of a series of typical proteins, especially caseins, in which the phosphorus was suspected to be bound in different linkages. She also studied in this way the structure of pepsin, one of the most important phosphoproteins and itself an enzyme. Her work was greatly facilitated by the use of highly purified enzymes resulting from the work of Northrop and of Kunitz, described in Chapters 7 and 16. Perlmann's findings present the first experimental demonstration of the existence of certain specific types of linkage (diester and pyrophosphate bonds) in phosphoproteins. The evidence she gathered suggests that the phosphoproteins of the tissues serve as a reservoir for phosphorus, and that energy stored in the pyrophosphate is available for use in building phosphate-containing substances (*e.g.* adenosine triphosphate) which are essential fuels for many high-energy biochemical processes of cell life.

WALTER A. JACOBS, full Member since 1923 and head of the laboratory of chemical pharmacology since 1928, had years before taken the lead in developing Tryparsamide and in determining the structure of the cardiac glycosides, as told in Chapters 6 and 7. He began, about 1934, to investigate the plant alkaloids, another important group of substances which have an ancient place in the history of medicine and toxicology. To indicate their varied and in many instances powerful action as drugs or poisons, it is necessary only to mention morphine, strychnine, nicotine, quinine, and aconite. Chemists have long tried to work out the chemical constitution of these alkaloids and numerous others, discovered in a wide range of plant species, and the manufacture of alkaloidal drugs has grown into an important branch of the pharmaceutical industry.

The general name, alkaloid, means only that the substances so classified are of alkaline nature, and they can by a drastic simplification be considered derivatives of one of the commonest alkalis, ammonia; but the added molecular groups and side chains are so complex that to the layman the drug alkaloids do not in the least resemble ammonia nor any other familiar alkali. The basic problem in the study of such substances is of course to determine their chemical structure and to correlate it with their pharmacological action. Jacobs chose first to study the alkaloids derived from ergot. For centuries physicians have controlled hemorrhage after childbirth with this drug made from the little dark purple spurs of the ergot fungus, *Claviceps purpurea,* which grows on rye. Ergot can also be a poison; the consumption of grain heavily infested with it has sometimes caused epidemics of a curious disease known as ergotism, characterized by headaches and mental derangement and by cramps or even gangrene of the extremities, resulting from action of the ergot alkaloids upon the muscular walls of the arteries.

When Jacobs entered this field of research, eight or ten active alkaloids had been isolated in crystalline form. Beginning with the first of

these, ergotine (now more precisely called ergocristonine), discovered
by the French chemist Tanret in 1875, Jacobs tried various ways of
breaking down its chemical structure. In 1935 he and his associate Craig
found among the split products a previously unknown atypical nitrogen-
containing substance which they named lysergic acid. On further analysis by chemical degradation this turned out to be a unique amino acid
that occurs nowhere else but in ergot. The two investigators then found
that each of the ergot alkaloids consists of one lysergic acid group (or an
isomer, isolysergic acid) with other amino acids or their derivatives
joined together to form a cyclic peptide. Lysergic acid was the first substance of its peculiar class to be discovered. Suspecting that a similar
structure might be characteristic of those peptides which exhibit special
biological actions, Jacobs planned to study other poisonous fungi, but
the work was interrupted. In later years, investigators elsewhere have
found such distinctive cyclic peptides in mushrooms and in a number of
antibiotics, including the penicillin, gramicidin, and polymyxin groups.

The exact chemical configuration of lysergic acid posed a difficult
problem even after its general nature was known. The best way to confirm a supposed structural formula is to synthesize the substance from
known materials. Work on the synthesis of lysergic acid, begun by Jacobs about 1937 with Craig and R. G. Gould, yielded substances more
and more closely related to the one they aimed to create. After Gould
left in 1942, F. C. Uhle took his place and with Jacobs in 1945 achieved
the synthesis of an immediate derivative of lysergic acid, dihydrolysergic
acid, proving the correctness of the formula they had hypothetically
proposed. The importance of lysergic acid has since been greatly emphasized by the discovery, made in the Sandoz pharmaceutical laboratories
at Basel, that one of the salts (the diethylamide) is a powerful drug acting on the brain, one of a class of drugs which are introducing a new era
in the study of mental disease.

Jacobs and Craig, aided by Uhle, Y. Sato, G. I. Lavin, and others,
also studied the alkaloids of plants of the *Veratrum* group, the false
hellebores. The chemical structure of these alkaloids, they found, is
based not on an amino acid, but on a modification of the steroid structure
characteristic of a number of hormones and certain constituents of the
bile. Next they took up the aconite alkaloids, from plants of the monks-
hood and wolfsbane families. These include some of the most poisonous

substances known; aconite, the most familiar, was long used in medicine, though seldom prescribed today. Plants of a related family, the larkspurs, contain delphinine and other substances poisonous to grazing animals. Jacobs and Craig made a good deal of progress toward understanding their structure, which seems to be based on complex nitrogen-containing alcohols. Jacobs retired in 1949, but continued his researches at the Institute. As the period of this history closed, S. W. Pelletier, trained in organic chemistry at Cornell University, joined him, and the two have since achieved partial synthesis of some of the aconite derivatives and have ascertained the structure of atisin, one of the simpler of the group.

In 1949 Craig was made a Member of The Rockefeller Institute. During his long association with Jacobs in joint research, he had ingeniously designed new types of apparatus for dealing with the very small amounts of alkaloidal substances available in such work, by micro-distillation, sublimation, fractional crystallization, and hydrogenation. During World War II the introduction of complex drugs for preventing and treating malaria demanded exact determination of their chemical purity, a difficult task because of the large molecular size and poor stability of the compounds. In the course of research to resolve this difficulty, Craig developed a separation technique which he called "countercurrent distribution." This operates by placing the compound to be studied in an apparatus which repeatedly intermingles and then separates two immiscible solvent fluids, so that each carries along with it those substances in the mixture which are more highly soluble in one or the other fluid respectively.

In its latest and most highly developed form, this apparatus consists of an automatically operated battery of a thousand glass receptacles mounted along a single motor-driven rocking axle, in each of which a small quantity of the two immiscible solvents is first mechanically agitated, then allowed to separate, after which the lighter solvent is decanted into the next receptacle. This step is repeated a thousand times in a single run. Thus the separable constituents of the unknown drug, or other preparation being tested, are carried along the row of receptacles and, so to speak, sorted out. Any difference in solubility between the constituents of the preparation, however slight, is put to work a thousand times by the successive partial separations. The method has proved effective in many fields of chemistry and pharmacology, by demonstrating that preparations thought to be pure by all other known techniques were, in fact, mixtures. In the wartime work on antimalarials, for example, Craig was able to separate a standard sample of plasmoquin into a pure fraction forming nine tenths of its bulk and an isomer constituting the remainder.

One of the most important uses of countercurrent distribution in Craig's hands has been the separation of antibiotic polypeptides. Peptides are polymers of amino acids, often of large molecular size, some of which are known only as they turn up when a chemist splits a protein, as more or less accidental fragments of the total protein structure. Others — the natural peptides — exist as regularly occurring units of a protein, or as autonomous products of living tissues. One group of these — the ergot alkaloids — had been known for years through the work of Jacobs and Craig. Among others since identified are the pituitary hormones oxytocin and vasopressin, certain mushroom poisons, and a number of well-known antibiotics. The antibiotics are complex substances often of high molecular weight. Craig's attention was first called to them in 1939 –1940 when René S. Dubos and R. D. Hotchkiss discovered at The Rockefeller Institute two new antibiotics, tyrocidin and gramicidin (see Chapter 19). After the discoverers had carried the purification and analysis of these substances as far as possible by the methods of fractional crystallization and paper chromatography, Craig succeeded, by countercurrent distribution, in separating gramicidin into four closely related polypeptides. He and an assistant, T. P. King, carried the analysis of tyrocidin even further by separating it into three polypeptides, two of which they were able to split into their constituent amino acids, finally determining the exact sequence of these units in the ring of linked amino acids that constitutes the cyclic polypeptide.

With other colleagues — including G. T. Barry, A. R. Battersby, J. D. Gregory, Elizabeth J. Harfenist, Werner K. Hausmann, and James R. Weisiger — Craig accomplished similar separations and analyses of other antibiotic polypeptides, namely, polymyxins and bacitracins. In 1952 Craig and Harfenist succeeded in determining the correct molecular weight of insulin — 6,000, as against the earlier and erroneous figure of 12,000 — from specimens of the hormone especially purified by countercurrent distribution. As the epoch of this history closed, Craig was applying countercurrent distribution so effectively that a mixture of the slightly different insulins isolated from the pancreatic glands of cattle and hogs respectively could be separated and distinguished — an extraordinary feat in view of their closely similar physical and chemical properties.

The usefulness of Craig's pioneering work, spread far beyond The Rockefeller Institute, is shown by the fact that Vincent du Vigneaud of Cornell University Medical College employed countercurrent distribution in purification of the pituitary hormones pitressin and oxytocin, for which in 1955 he was awarded the Nobel Prize. Subsequently, C. U. Li of the University of California, Paul Bell of the American Cyanamid Company, and others have used Craig's method to separate other endocrine products of the pituitary gland, including the adrenocorticotrophic and lactogenic hormones.

CHAPTER FOURTEEN

Physical Chemistry, General Physiology, Nutrition

1935–1953

Oxidation-reduction reactions; iron-containing proteins, hemoglobin and porphyrins. Physical chemistry of proteins; physical constants. Physical chemistry of living plant cells. Chemistry of cell nuclei and of chromosomes. Osmotic pressure in cells. Nutritional factors in resistance to infection. Antimetabolites.

LEONOR MICHAELIS, The Rockefeller Institute's renowned physical chemist, was still an active Member when Gasser became Director in 1935. Retiring in 1940, he continued to work in his laboratory until shortly before his death in 1949. During these last years he worked on problems involving the interactions of colored molecules, including the structure of radicals in the crystalline state, the dimerization of radicals, and the interaction of quinhydrones and related colored crystalline compounds. One of these problems, of great importance in connection with the staining of tissues for microscopic study, was the nature of metachromasia, *i.e.*, the production of a new color when a basic dye interacts with acidic colloidal molecules. This had interested him since his earliest days with Ehrlich, and to it he returned in old age.

During these years, too, he capped a lifetime of work in oxidation-reduction reactions by brilliant experiments based on the concept, developed in his early work at the Institute, that oxidation and reduction reactions take place in two steps, with the temporary participation of free radicals. To his somewhat theoretical support of this hypothesis by electropotentiometric measurements, which, as we have seen, was unacceptable to many chemists, Michaelis in 1938 added incontrovertible proof by a very ingenious experiment. An atom bearing an unpaired electron, he reasoned, will exhibit the property of paramagnetism; that is, it behaves like a tiny magnet and can be detected by that property. If either an oxidation or a reduction reaction were conducted in a strong magnetic field, the transitory presence of free radicals ought to cause a measurable change of magnetic pull on the solution in which the reaction was progressing. Enlisting the aid of two physicists of the College of the City of New York, G. F. Boeker and R. K. Reber, and using special equipment placed at his disposal by Columbia University, Michaelis secured a triumphant confirmation of his hypothesis, and reconfirmed it in subsequent trials in which his associates M. P. Schubert and Sam Granick took part. His theory of the role of free radicals in oxidation-reductions and similar reactions has ever since been generally accepted.

Michaelis's chief associate during these later years was Sam Granick, who joined The Rockefeller Institute in 1938, immediately after taking his Ph.D. in plant physiology. For several years he worked with his chief on the semiquinone radicals, which Michaelis had found especially useful in the study of free radicals described in Chapter 7. Meanwhile the California chemist Linus Pauling discovered that hemoglobin (the iron-containing red pigment of blood) is paramagnetic, possessing unpaired electrons in the iron atom. Michaelis and Granick therefore began to apply their magnetometric method to the study of iron-containing proteins. This led them into a research in the properties of iron-protein compounds which, after 1945, Granick took over and made his own.

One of the compounds he studied was a recently discovered reddish substance called ferritin, found in many organs of the body, which contains 23 per cent iron. Preparing it in quantity from the spleens of horses, where it is especially abundant, Granick found it to be a protein combined with iron, having the remarkable property that when the iron was removed by chemical treatment the residual protein, which he named apoferritin, could be crystallized as before, but now in a colorless form. This would suggest that apoferritin is a sort of storage receptacle in the tissues, especially adapted to receive and hold iron. To study this idea Granick entered into collaboration with the departments of pathology and radiology at the University of Rochester, where, under the leadership of George H. Whipple, active research on iron metabolism was going on, and where the new method of tracing chemical substances by the use of radioactive isotopes was already in use. Later on, Geiger counters and other apparatus required for isotope study were installed at the Institute.

Granick, with Michaelis and their Rochester colleagues P. F. Hahn and W. F. Bale, worked out in considerable detail the pathway of metabolic iron. Iron in the ferrous state ingested in the food, they found, passes from the alimentary canal into the lining cells of the intestine and there, after being oxidized to ferric iron, combines with apoferritin in the cells, until the protein is saturated. The ferritin by this combination serves as a temporary storage form of iron. When the bone marrow needs more iron for the production of red blood cells, ferritin formed in the liver is broken down and the iron released becomes available to the marrow.

From these studies on the transport and storage of iron, it was a natural step for Granick to investigate the structure of hemoglobin. Hemoglobin belongs to the class of substances called *hemes,* in which a porphyrin—a complex chemical structure of linked hydrocarbon (pyrrole) rings — is combined with a central atom of iron. The rings bear a number of side chains which may be methyl or vinyl groups or propionic acid. Granick set himself the problem of studying the function of these side chains. The experiments, in which he was assisted by Helena Gilder, utilized cultures of a bacterium, *Hemophilus,* which can live only upon an iron-porphyrin compound; it cannot make its own heme for use in its respiratory processes. Bacteriologists grow it on media containing blood. About ten years earlier, A. Lwoff of the Pasteur Institute of Paris had studied the uptake of heme by a protozoan, *Strigomonas,* which also requires it for growth. Growing this organism on a medium low in heme, he found that the respiratory activity of his cultures rapidly increased when he added heme. This experiment showed that the protozoan cell is able to assimilate heme and attach it to the proper protein to form the protein heme enzyme which makes possible the utilization of oxygen.

Granick and Gilder studied the functions of the side chains of heme by supplying their cultures with synthetic porphyrins and iron porphyrins in which the side chains were variously modified. They found that porphyrins without iron and lacking vinyl side chains cannot support growth of the bacterium, whereas porphyrins containing iron but no vinyl groups can support growth. It appears, therefore, that the organism cannot of itself insert iron into porphyrins to create heme unless the vinyl side chains are present in the porphyrin molecule. By similar experiments, the investigators discovered that the propionic acid side chains are necessary for another purpose, serving to attach the heme (iron porphyrin) to a protein, for example to the globin of hemoglobin. This again was a step forward. European workers had found that free carboxyl (CO) groups are necessary in the heme molecule if it is to form a functional hemoglobin by uniting with a suitable protein. Granick and Gilder now showed that the ionized carboxyl groups of the propionic acid side chains are also required to support the growth of *Hemophilus*. By inference and deduction from these findings and from what is known of the structure of the globin of hemoglobin, Granick was able to suggest some properties of the sites of attachment of heme to the globin molecules, and to speculate about the course of synthesis of such a heme protein in an immature red blood cell as it develops in the bone marrow.

Going back to the porphyrin molecule, Granick undertook to discover how it is put together biologically. There are, he pointed out, two places in nature where porphyrin synthesis goes on at a rapid rate.[1] One is the bone marrow, the other is the chloroplasts of plant cells, where chlorophyll is synthesized. Because plant tissue is easier to get in quantity than bone marrow, he studied the chloroplasts, in the hope that some of the steps in the synthesis of chlorophyll might be related to those of heme synthesis. Choosing the single-celled green alga *Chlorella vulgaris,* he used X-ray treatment to damage genes and to interfere with certain enzymatic steps in the process of synthesis. When normal synthesis was stopped, the intermediate products accumulated and could be isolated. The upshot was the discovery of a pigment identical with the porphyrin of the heme of blood cells.

In 1953, Granick was still working on the biosynthesis of porphyrins. For about sixty years biochemists had been finding chemical similarities between the two vital pigmented substances, hemoglobin in animals and chlorophyll in plants. Granick's experiments, by showing that porphyrin is a normal precursor or intermediate stage in chlorophyll synthesis, confirmed the biochemical resemblance of hemoglobin and chlorophyll. Upon this find he built and expounded, in his Harvey Lecture of 1949, wide-ranging hypotheses concerning the evolutionary relation between biological oxidation in animals and photosynthesis in plants. Another inference from Granick's work is that anaerobic bacteria may not be, as some have supposed, an evolutionary step toward aerobes, but are, on the contrary, mutants that have lost part of the cytochrome mechanism of oxidation. Thus an investigation, at first focused upon a problem seemingly so recondite as that of free radicals in chemical reactions, finally threw light upon a phenomenon universal in living things.

WHEN THE laboratory of physical chemistry was first organized by Duncan MacInnes, its central aim, as we have seen in Chapter 7, was to obtain precise information about the physical forces involved in the chemical activities of living tissues. Continuing this task at the beginning of Gasser's directorship, MacInnes and his associates L. G. Longsworth and Theodore Shedlovsky were studying the properties of ionized salts and other charged particles, such as protein molecules, in solution. MacInnes's personal contributions and his influence as group leader were recognized by his promotion in 1940 to full Member of The Rockefeller Institute. As the experience of his associates increased, the program broadened into several lines of research, according to their respective interests and qualifications, but these lines were so closely interwoven and cooperation was so intimate that it is difficult to isolate their individual efforts for special comment. Their group experience with the theory of solutions prepared them to take a leading part in advancing a new technique for separation of mixed biological materials that came into use in 1937. In that year Arne Tiselius of Uppsala, Sweden, announced success in separating the protein constituents of blood serum and other biological fluids by means of their differences in electrical mobility. The method is essentially an adaptation of the moving boundary method introduced by R. D. Denison and B. D. Steele of Edinburgh in 1907. In 1939, MacInnes and Longsworth refined the method and utilized it, as mentioned in Chapter 7, in determining the "transference numbers" which express the relative current-carrying capacities of ions.

In this application of the method, which can be used with such complex solutions as blood serum or organic tissue extracts, a buffer solution containing proteins and a pure buffer solution are placed one above the other in a single column, with a sharply defined boundary between them.

When an electric current is passed through the column, charged particles of the proteins move into the pure buffer for varying distances, depending on their physical and electrical characteristics. The proteins now form a series of layers in the fluid, with boundaries which can be detected by appropriate optical inspection. After MacInnes and Longsworth set up a modified form of the Tiselius apparatus, Longsworth soon greatly improved it, by inventing an optical scanning system for automatically recording the differences of the refractive indexes of the successive layers. Data thus obtained enabled the observers not only to identify the individual proteins, but also to find the concentration of each protein in the mixture.

This method for studying proteins naturally appealed at once to other investigators dealing with all sorts of protein problems, and Longsworth found himself in great demand as counselor and collaborator. In reports, published in scientific journals from 1939 to 1942, on proteins in human body fluids in health and disease, his name is linked with those of Landsteiner, Van Slyke, and others at the Institute, and with those of workers at Columbia University, New York University, and Union Memorial Hospital of Baltimore. Theodore Shedlovsky, who had been working with MacInnes on solution theory, collaborated similarly with investigators within the Institute and outside it. One of the most striking of these joint efforts was that of Shedlovsky and Alexandre Rothen with R. O. Greep, H. Van Dyke, and B. F. Chow of the Squibb Institute in 1940–1942, which resulted in the isolation and identification, in highly purified form, of the so-called luteinizing and follicle-stimulating hormones of the pituitary gland.

Another collaborative investigation, in which Shedlovsky took part with Joseph E. Smadel of the Hospital of The Rockefeller Institute, yielded results of considerable value for immunochemical theory. T. M. Rivers and Smadel, endeavoring to develop an improved vaccine against smallpox, had prepared highly purified suspensions of the "elementary bodies" or virus particles of vaccinia (cowpox). This virus was known to be quite complex chemically, containing soluble substances of antigenic nature capable of eliciting at least five distinct antibodies in animals infected or immunized with cowpox virus. Two of the five immune reactions especially interested the hospital's workers, who called upon Shedlovsky, as an expert on electrophoretic analysis of proteins, to assist in isolating and identifying the antigenic materials.

One of the antibodies in question reacted with a heat-labile (L) substance in the virus, the other with a heat-stable (S) substance. In the light of the current concepts of antigenicity, this would mean that L and S were chemically distinct. Some investigators, however, finding that the two reactions sometimes worked simultaneously, sometimes separately, had ventured a guess that there is an L-S complex which may dissociate into separate L and S fractions. Through an intricate series of logical steps, Smadel and Shedlovsky confirmed by electrophoretic analysis the existence of such a dissociable substance and, what was much more important, demonstrated that L and S are parts of a single molecule, which they characterized with considerable precision as a protein of molecular weight about 240,000 and of elongated molecular form. This was the first actual proof of the existence of a single molecule capable of eliciting two different immune reactions. The results strengthened the general theory of protein antigenicity while extending the range of antigenic activity, and gave valuable support to concepts of immunochemistry and of virus structure that were in the making at the time.

Such collaboration, often occurring throughout the Institute's history, shows that its investigators were by no means as closely bound to their own immediate researches as is sometimes thought. MacInnes, Longsworth, and Shedlovsky did much to fulfill Osterhout's hope that the presence of experienced physical chemists among the physiologists and physicians would give the latter deeper insight into the physicochemical aspects of biology and medicine. When, after a few years, the ingenious technical devices of MacInnes's group, notably the glass electrode, mentioned in Chapter 7, and electrophoretic analysis, were widely established in other laboratories of the Institute, the physical chemists felt less pressure to spend time and energy in collaboration. Valuable as it can be, it is not the most important means by which independent investigators spread their influence across the boundaries between sciences. The situation is not like that of an industrial or military laboratory, where specialists expect to be assigned to teamwork on specific projects. Investigators in laboratories such as those of The Rockefeller Institute, on the contrary, propose to spend all or nearly all of their time following their own ideas wherever they may lead. Their contribution to the common enterprise is given largely through example, consultation, and advice, or more casually, but often no less effectively, in the give-and-take of staff scientific meetings and over the lunch table.

An incident narrated by MacInnes explains their reluctance to be diverted too far or too often, by showing how a specialist, attempting to help a colleague directly out of sheer good will or to demonstrate what his branch of science can do, may reach the point of diminishing returns. In response to an apparent need of bacteriologists at the Institute, MacInnes and Longsworth in 1936 devised an apparatus for cultivating acid-forming bacteria (such as the *Bacillus acidophilus* used to make acidophilus milk) in which the acid formed by the growing organisms was automatically neutralized and the culture kept at a constant pH value. This they accomplished by connecting MacInnes's precision glass electrode to a photo-cell system operating a pipette which automatically added alkali to the bacterial suspension as needed. Control of the pH resulted in a fourfold increase of the bacterial population and a ninefold increase of acid production. The method was necessarily too complicated to be taken over easily by technicians for continued use. When, because of this, the bacteriologists who had asked for it turned to a different line of attack on their problem, the apparatus was shelved, and the physical chemists felt that the time they had put into its design had been thrown away. Twenty years later, however, Walther G. Goebel of the biochemistry laboratories wanted to grow very large quantities of the colon bacillus (*Escherichia coli*) from which to extract antibacterial agents termed colicines. Having found that colicines develop in a culture only if the pH is closely controlled, Goebel revived and, with Shedlovsky's help, improved the MacInnes-Longsworth apparatus. He has used it to produce many hundreds of liters of *Escherichia* rich in antibacterial colicines.

Longsworth soon found that his electrophoresis method for the study of proteins was also well adapted for investigating the motion of simpler charged particles, namely the ions of salts in solution, during the passage of an electric current. Information thus gained could in turn explain the patterns shown by proteins under electrophoresis. The electrophoresis of simple salt solutions, however, demanded further knowledge of the refraction of light passing through them, since this was the means by which the electrophoretic readings were obtained. In this, as in some of the moving boundary experiments, Longsworth was assisted by Gertrude E. Perlmann.

The story of this episode in the work of the laboratory of physical chemistry is characteristic of its program in general. Needing to secure more accurate measurements of one or another vitally important phenomenon, the investigators began with a principle of physics applicable to the problem. Mastering the underlying mathematical theory, they systematically designed apparatus, refining it to eliminate, as far as possible, all sources of error, until they reached a degree of precision previously unattained. In this particular instance, Longsworth designed an improved optical method, based on diffraction patterns, for the readings. Returning, with its aid, to the study of proteins, he noted a certain possibility of error due to the presence of some of each of the components of a mixed solution in the "peaks" which were being taken as characteristic of a single protein. Vincent P. Dole, then a young assistant resident physician in The Rockefeller Institute Hospital, keenly interested in mathematics as an avocation, worked out a mathematical theory of the distribution of the constituents, which Longsworth confirmed in actual observations on salt solutions. Applying Dole's theory to electrophoretic patterns involving proteins, Longsworth obtained considerably greater accuracy than was previously possible.

In 1949 Longsworth was promoted to full membership in The Rockefeller Institute. In subsequent years he devoted himself to further refinements of electrophoretic analysis and especially to its application to particles smaller than those of proteins in solution.

Unabated interest in the physical chemistry of proteins led the Institute's physical chemists, about 1945, to explore the field further, and, in particular, to determine the molecular weights of certain proteins, with precision exceeding that heretofore achieved. To calculate these, the sedimentation rates of the proteins must be ascertained, and the group turned to the ultracentrifuge, which E. G. Pickels and Ralph W. G. Wyckoff had already introduced to the Institute and improved, as narrated in Chapter 7. Alexandre Rothen, formerly assistant to Levene, had experimented with an ultracentrifuge of the Beams-Pickels type, without attaining the full precision desirable for computing molecular weights. Rothen's first observations were made on several enzymes of protein nature, available in pure form through the work of Kunitz in Princeton. Because the resulting values checked only roughly with those obtained by other methods, he put much effort into improvements of the centrifuge mechanism, intended to regulate its speed and temperature. It was at the time the only instrument in the world equipped to operate at zero centigrade. With it Rothen measured the molecular weights of a number of biologically important proteins, notably the well-defined crystalline enzyme ribonuclease which he studied in 1940. At that time protein chemists accepted a hypothesis of T. Svedberg of Uppsala that the giant molecules of the heaviest proteins are made up of "building stones" of uniform molecular weight, at first assumed to be about 35,000, then 17,000. When Rothen found the molecular weight of ribonuclease to be about 13,000, a figure which did not fit the hypothesis, Svedberg's assumption was rendered improbable.

Summarizing in 1943 his results and those of others, Rothen remarked that although the ultracentrifuge had been of great value in establishing the fact that proteins and related substances have definite molecular weights, it still did not measure these weights to a higher accuracy than about 10 per cent. Wishing to check his own method on a stable, reproducible protein, he chose apoferritin (the iron-free fraction of heme discovered by Granick). His values of the molecular weights of apoferritin from man, horse, and dog agreed with each other within a range of possible error of little more than 1 per cent. The residual error appeared to result from variations or uncertain measurement of the temperature of the rotor, which at a speed of 60,000 or more revolutions per minute was difficult to control. Even this degree of precision, however, served an important purpose. In 1944 Rothen was asked to test a nucleic acid having a molecular weight of about 500,000, which, as Avery and his associates had discovered (Chapter 18), possessed the power of transforming one type of pneumococcus into another. Rothen found that the transforming property accompanied the nucleic acid as it was sedimented in the centrifuge; in other words, the nucleic acid was itself the active agent in bacterial transformation, not some hypothetical contaminant.

The sedimentation rate of a protein, for which still greater precision of the ultracentrifuge was urgently needed, is not the only quantitative measurement required for calculating molecular weight. Two other factors are involved—the specific volume of the protein and the diffusion constant. MacInnes and Longsworth undertook with success to increase the precision with which these two parameters could be measured. MacInnes developed the use of a magnetic float, with which he and an assistant, Margaret O. Dayhoff, could measure densities with an accuracy of one part in a million. The protein volumes thus determined now constitute the accepted standards in that field. Longsworth continued to develop his optical methods described above, and brought the measurement of the diffusion constant to a precision of 0.1 per cent, whereas up to 1944 a precision of 1 per cent was considered accurate.

The attempt to refine the measurement of sedimentation rates by improving the ultracentrifuge ran into serious engineering difficulties. In 1947–1948 an assistant, P. G. Ecker, and a visiting Fellow, C. W. Hiatt, built a new centrifuge equipped with a device, called a "thermistor," for continuous recording and adjustment of the rotor temperature, and other improvements. In 1951 Longsworth—then in charge of the physical chemistry laboratory, MacInnes having become Emeritus Member—reported that introduction of the temperature-sensitive device into the rotor had caused the reappearance of earlier idiosyncrasies of the air-driven machine, namely, vertical oscillation and swinging of the rotor, which greatly reduced its accuracy. Two other laboratories, one in a university and one industrial, had (as Longsworth knew) tried with similar lack of success to measure and control the rotor temperature. Meanwhile Pickels, the expert on the engineering aspects of ultracentrifuges, had left the International Health Division laboratories and had developed a motor-driven ultracentrifuge that was rendering the air drive obsolete. Recommending abandonment of this part of the triple program, Longsworth took comfort in the hope that the work of Ecker and Hiatt might ultimately contribute to the unsolved problem of precise temperature control in a mechanism spinning at 1,000 revolutions per second.

The incident has been narrated at some length because it illustrates a situation which those responsible for expenditures on scientific research, whether in public or private institutions, should fully understand. This is only one case, among many in the history of The Rockefeller Institute and of science at large, in which men, well informed as to theoretical principles, ingenious in invention, mechanically skilled, and supplied with adequate funds, have devoted their best efforts for years to an undertaking which continued to baffle them. The attainment of such exceedingly precise results as MacInnes had hoped for will probably have to await basic new developments in theory or materials. No immediate legislation or monetary subsidy can, in such a case, push the project further. In the face of demands for space ships or a cancer cure it is well for both the scientists and their sponsors to remember that success cannot always crown even the best-supported, most intelligent effort to solve an intricate problem.

About 1940 MacInnes began work on a new phase of the precise study of electrolytes which had underlain all his work. The problem was to obtain transference numbers, indicating the relative capacity of ions to carry electrical currents, when the ionizable substances are dissolved in non-aqueous solvents. In such solvents the usual method of applying an electrical potential and measuring the movement of the substances under its effects could not be used. MacInnes therefore adopted a method earlier used with aqueous solutions by Theodor Des Coudres of Leipzig and by Richard Tolman of Berkeley, California, in which the solution is spun in a centrifuge cell containing two electrodes, and the resulting electrical potential is recorded. Working for several years in association with B. Roger Ray, a visiting investigator, MacInnes developed the "electromotive force centrifuge"; as the period of this history ended, he and his assistants, Dayhoff and Robert L. Kay, were putting it effectively to use. Investigations made with it confirmed and extended, for aqueous solutions, the underlying thermodynamic theory. Interpretation of results obtained with non-aqueous solutions awaits further experimental work.

In the early 1950's MacInnes began an intensive effort to measure, with previously unattained precision, the value of the faraday, a physical unit expressing the number of coulombs of electricity necessary to produce one equivalent of electrochemical reaction at a metal-electrolyte boundary. It is one of the physical constants most used by physical chemists, being a factor in the computation of pH measurements, oxidation-reduction measurements, and other phenomena in this field. It is still more important to physicists in that it is related to the electronic charge, which enters into the interpretation of many physical measurements. This can be most accurately calculated by a formula in which one of the constants is the value of the faraday. This value must therefore be known as precisely as possible. The faraday is, however, the least accurately characterized of the fundamental constants, the chief researches on which its value was founded being more than forty years old. The method employed by MacInnes for obtaining the value of the faraday employs the iodine coulometer and involves the measurement to a few parts in a million of the electric current, the time, and the amount of iodine involved in the reaction. In thus passing beyond the bounds of physical chemistry to work on a problem of pure physics, MacInnes's work exemplifies the broadening scope of the Institute as it becomes a university faculty.

During World War II the laboratory of physical chemistry did experimental work of a character then secret, for the armed forces and other governmental agencies, which will be discussed in a later chapter. This sketch of its other work up to 1953 may appropriately end with an illustration of the way in which the imaginative physical chemist projects his thinking from pure theory toward the actual processes of living tissue. Theodore Shedlovsky, reflecting upon the electron exchanges that occur in oxidation-reduction reactions, said to himself that such exchanges probably cannot be directly responsible for bioelectrical phenomena, because in living tissues metallic conductors are not available for electron transport between the anodal and the cathodal sites. How then can electrical work be obtained from a chemical reaction without involving electrons? His hypothetical answer involves protons instead of electrons. The free energy of an acid-base reaction, he suggests, might be available as electrical work, if the site at which protons are released is separated from that at which they are accepted, and if protonic conductors exist. Aware that conductance by protons exists in certain glasses and some liquids, including water, Shedlovsky constructed a "protochemical" cell in which an electrical potential develops between two portions of a buffered solution of a salt, separated by a barrier of proton-conducting glass covered on one side by an insoluble fatty acid. This model may credibly represent in essentials the situation existing in living cells. Whatever the value of this particular concept may be to physiologists, the stimulus to thought, resulting from promulgation of such a hypothesis among biological workers, fulfills one of the aims of those who in 1926 brought physical chemistry as an independent discipline into The Rockefeller Institute.

About 1942 Alexandre Rothen, then working in collaboration with Landsteiner on monomolecular layers of proteins, observed a surprising phenomenon which has held his attention ever since. The molecules of many proteins are more or less spherical, with diameters of 25 to 100 Ångstrom units (one to four millionths of an inch), but when spread on water they form layers only 6 to 10 Ångstrom units in thickness. This is explained as the result of an unfolding of the complex molecular structure. Some active proteins, for example the oxytocic hormone of the posterior pituitary, lose their potency when thus unfolded; others, such as insulin, do not. Testing antigenic proteins spread out in such films, Rothen found that in no case do they fail to combine with the corresponding antibody. The most surprising find was that the combination of antigen with antibody occurred even if he placed between the two reacting substances a film or "blanket" of fatty material (stearic acid) several molecules deep, with a thickness up to 100 Ångstroms. On the other hand, a similar layer of stearic acid was sufficient to prevent insulin from reacting with protamine. This apparently indicated that there were no gaps in the stearic acid film, and forced Rothen to the paradoxical assumption that certain combinations of these very large molecules, for example antigen with antibody, can take place across a practically continuous barrier having at most only very minute intermolecular interstices. In later experiments he found biological reactions occurring across stearic acid layers, for example inactivation of a proteid enzyme by trypsin. Furthermore, he could substitute certain other barrier materials for the stearic acid; a plastic known as Formvar was utilized in many experiments. Careful analysis of this remarkable phenomenon, with systematic exclusion of all imaginable sources of error, has not shaken the original observations.

When Rothen first detected this phenomenon, he offered two possible explanations. Either the action takes place without intimate contact, or else, by a long-range interaction, the enzyme molecules are forced through the blanketing film. Recent experiments favor the second interpretation, showing that the process is not an ordinary diffusion, dependent only on a gradient of concentration. On the contrary, the molecular arrangement of materials located under the blanket, both the protein and an anchoring layer of fatty acid below it, takes part in determining whether or not the enzyme will diffuse. The interaction appears, therefore, to be a kind of forced diffusion through the barrier, influenced by the physical state and environment of the interacting substances. This phenomenon of action at a distance, though still enigmatic and controversial, may be of great importance in biological reactions.

Whatever the outcome as regards the principles involved, Rothen's arduous work has had a valuable practical result. Early in this investigation he needed to measure the thickness of the exceedingly thin layers of proteins and other substances used, with greater accuracy than could be attained with the currently used interference method of Langmuir and Blodgett. Utilizing known principles regarding elliptically polarized light, he developed an "ellipsometer" with which he could measure the thickness of a film with astounding accuracy, within two tenths of an Ångstrom unit. The instrument has been manufactured commercially for general use.

THE TERM "general physiology" signifies the study of physical and chemical activity of living matter at the level of the cells and the tissues, rather than of whole organs and systems. It was adopted by The Rockefeller Institute when Jacques Loeb became a Member, in order to avoid confusion with the simple appellation of "physiology" pertaining to Samuel J. Meltzer's laboratory. When Osterhout succeeded Loeb he continued the designation. Because of the current trend in biological science, exemplified and indeed largely influenced by Loeb and Osterhout, practically every research group in the whole Institute was ultimately concerned to some extent with general physiology, and several were deeply engaged in it; but only Osterhout's work at the New York laboratories and that of the Northrop-Kunitz group in Princeton were so classified.

Osterhout actively continued his researches in general physiology until he became Emeritus Member in 1939. A few months before his retirement, A. G. Jacques, his assistant for thirteen years, died by accidental drowning at the Bermuda Biological Station. His other assistants, S. E. Hill and J. W. Murray, left about this time for posts elsewhere. Osterhout, while retaining an office at the Institute, carried on his experiments mostly in the summers at Woods Hole, Massachusetts, with the aid of his wife (Marian Irwin). As shown by two summaries of his lifework, published when he was in advanced age,[2] he continued to supplement and extend the conclusions sketched in Chapter 7, by which through long years of assiduous work he had contributed much to our knowledge of the physical and chemical phenomena of living cells.

When in 1948 Alfred E. Mirsky was made a full Member of the Institute, he too elected to designate his investigations as general physiology. Since about 1936 he had been engaged in a far-reaching investigation of the chemistry of the cell nucleus and of the chromosomes. When in Chapter 10 we last reviewed his researches, he and Mortimer L. Anson were at work together on the problem of denaturation of proteins, in particular hemoglobin. Thinking about this phenomenon, in which a relatively small and reversible change of state of a protein makes a great difference in its physiological properties, Mirsky wondered whether denaturation could explain some of the more mysterious activities in which proteins participate. The contraction of muscle, for example, involves a great change in the viscosity of the contractile muscle protein, myosin. Denaturation of a protein is also accompanied by change of viscosity. May not contraction and relaxation of muscle be brought about by reversible denaturation of myosin in the muscle fibers?

Naturally, a first step in testing this bold conjecture was to prepare a quantity of pure myosin. When Mirsky had done this, he noticed certain physical and chemical peculiarities of the protein ascribable to the elongated, fiberlike character of its molecules. Learning that R. R. Bensley of Chicago had described another fibrous protein, "plasmosin," in the liver, which seemed to share some of these peculiarities, Mirsky undertook in 1942 to prepare and study that substance for comparison with his purified myosin. Improving upon Bensley's chemical methods, he found that plasmosin, unlike myosin, is a deoxynucleoprotein, one of a class of substances which biochemists knew existed in nuclei of animal cells. Realizing the importance of this clue, he put aside the question of muscle contractility and devoted his attention henceforth to the chemistry of nuclei.

Every nucleoprotein includes in its molecular structure a nucleic acid, made up of a nitrogenous base linked to a five-carbon sugar and to phosphoric acid. The sugar of plasmosin, Mirsky found, is deoxyribose, and the specific nucleic acid is, therefore, deoxyribonucleic acid, or DNA. This was a significant new appearance of the substance identified years before by Levene and Jacobs, but only recently found, as we have seen, to be a vitally important constituent of viruses. Mirsky now associated himself with A. W. Pollister of the Columbia University zoology department, an experienced cytologist, and the two proceeded to demonstrate that the deoxyribose-containing nucleoprotein Mirsky had extracted from liver cells indeed came from the chromosomes of those cells. This they did by use of a test for DNA, known as Feulgen's reaction, which normally stains the chromosomes. When they extracted sections of fresh liver with substances known to dissolve DNA, the Feulgen reaction no longer appeared.

Mirsky's laboratory was in 1945 transferred from the hospital to Gasser's physiology group, where Hans Ris, a recent graduate of the Columbia zoology department, joined him in continued investigation of the chemistry and staining reactions of DNA. For several years Mirsky and Ris, with G. J. Gasic and other visiting investigators and Fellows, were busy improving and refining their microscopic and chemical methods, and applying these to the detailed analysis of chromosomes — exacting, patient, often tedious work of a kind that cannot be adequately described by a few paragraphs like these. Developing methods suggested by previous workers, they learned how to isolate relatively large quantities of nuclear and even of chromosomal material free from other cell constituents, and to measure the amount of chromosomal DNA in cells of various tissues. By determining the total amount in a suspension of nuclei, and then counting the number of nuclei in a measured aliquot, they calculated the amount of DNA per nucleus in sixty different species of animals. The result strongly supported the supposition that DNA is the active material of the genes. Within an experimental error of about 10 per cent, all somatic nuclei of a given species, whatever organ they come from, contain the same amount of DNA. The amount differs from species to species. Examining many animals arranged in order of evolutionary development, from sponges to mammals, Mirsky and Ris found that the DNA content of their cell nuclei increases systematically from lower to higher forms. It is difficult to avoid the conclusion that this increase of DNA provides material for a larger number of genes in the more complex organisms.

The nuclei of the germ cells, spermatozoa and ova, Mirsky and Ris found, have only half as much DNA as the somatic cells. When spermatozoon and egg unite to form a new individual, the full amount of DNA is restored, exactly as would be expected from microscopic observations which show that each of these cells possesses one half the number of so-matic chromosomes, and presumably carries half the genes.[3] Thus only about seventy years after Gregor Mendel's experiments in his monastery garden at Brünn, biochemists in New York were able to isolate and pre-cisely identify the material which carries Mendelian inheritance factors.

Turning his attention to the proteins with which the nucleic acid is linked to form nucleoproteins, Mirsky found that in the somatic cells of practically all mammals and in some plants these proteins belong to the class called histones, discovered in 1884 by Albrecht Kossel of Berlin, but not known to be widely distributed in nature. In spermatozoa, how-ever, the proteins of the nucleoprotein complex belong to another class of simple proteins, the protamines.

In 1949, the year after Mirsky became a Member of the Institute, Ris was called to the University of Wisconsin, shortly to become a full profes-sor of zoology. With Vincent Allfrey, Marie Daly, and Herbert Stern, who came to him in 1948–1949, and several visiting investigators and Fel-lows, Mirsky next turned his attention to the general chemistry of the nucleus, seeking to learn something about the way in which this domi-nant organ of the cell presides over the vital activities of the whole cell substance. Methods already existed for isolating nuclei in bulk for chemical study, but these involved the use of aqueous solutions, which inevitably caused the loss of many important substances by extracting them from the nuclei. Mirsky took up and improved a method recently introduced in Europe, employing only non-aqueous solvents, and was able, with his colleagues, to preserve and identify a number of enzymes in the nuclei. Stern studied the carbohydrate metabolism of isolated nu-clei. With Allfrey and Daly, Mirsky investigated interactions between the nucleus and the rest of the cell (the cytoplasm), aiming to relate detectable changes in the nucleus and its constituents to physiological events in the cytoplasm over which it presides. They found, besides histones and pro-tamines, more complex proteins combined with DNA in the chromo-somes. Enzymes, moreover, were discovered in the nuclei of different tissues, in such variety that the chemical activities of nuclei may be said to be differentiated just as the cytoplasmic parts of cells of various organs and tissues are differentiated to perform their specific functions.

By the early 1950's, Mirsky and Allfrey were opening a new chapter of their work, based on a demonstration that synthesis of proteins in the nucleus depends on DNA. In all probability, the possession of a material so favorable for metabolic studies as living isolated nuclei will provide Mirsky and his associates with a long-continuing opportunity for new discoveries as striking as those they have made during the past two decades.

EUGENE L. OPIE, who joined the original staff of the Institute in 1904 but left in 1910, at last returned in 1941. During the thirty-two-year interim he had been professor of pathology at Washington University, St. Louis, at the University of Pennsylvania, and at Cornell University Medical College. Between the last two professorships, he had been director of the laboratories of the Henry Phipps Institute for the study of tuberculosis. In these posts he carried on distinguished research on the pathology of inflammation, on chemical and bacterial damage to the liver and kidneys, on trench fever and pneumonia in wartime, and on the pathology, epidemiology, and control of tuberculosis.[4]

When Opie reached retirement age at Cornell Medical College, The Rockefeller Institute welcomed him back as Guest Investigator. That title, proffered in admiration and respect, grew oddly inappropriate as Opie's stay continued much longer than his original term, and he was subsequently styled Affiliate of The Rockefeller Institute. With characteristic mental resilience and versatility, he has in recent years devoted his research to the osmotic properties of living cells, a field of inquiry new to him and indeed little explored by anyone. Summing up his work in a Harvey Society Lecture,[5] Opie pointed out that although all the functions of the body are dependent on the movement of water, not much has been known about the conditions that determine the exchange of water between the cells and the fluid surrounding them. Osmotic activity of cells is doubtless one of the chief factors controlling this exchange.[6] In plants, with their rigid cell walls, osmotic pressures of many atmospheres may be attained, sufficient, for example, to raise sap to the top of a tall tree. Animal cells, with their more yielding structure, do not attain pressures of any such magnitude, and the osmotic forces are difficult to measure.

Adapting a procedure used by others at the Institute for a different purpose, Opie measured by changes in specific gravity the loss and gain of water by tissues immersed in salt solutions of varying concentration.

Later he measured water directly by changes in wet and dry weight of tissues. Doing this in rapidly conducted experiments with tissues removed from freshly killed animals, he could obtain readings that reflected the physical properties of living tissues. The unexpected outcome was that the osmotic pressure within the cells of the organs studied — liver, kidney, adrenal cortex, pancreas, and salivary glands — is considerably higher than that in the intercellular spaces. Asking himself why, during life, water does not rush into these cells and cause catastrophic swelling, Opie was compelled to assume that the surface membrane of the cell, whose properties are as yet imperfectly understood, is able to control the entrance and exit of certain dissolved substances and to maintain the relatively high osmotic pressure he had observed.

Experiments on tissues in various pathological states, for example, tumor cells and organs damaged by poisonous substances, revealed a low level of osmotic activity; that is to say, the cell walls are abnormally permeable. As the cells recover from damage, the activity regains its original level. During fetal and early postnatal life, the osmotic pressure of cells in the liver and kidney, lower even than that of the maternal blood, gradually rises to equal that of cells of adult organs. Opie's general conclusion is that energy supplied by metabolism builds up the molecular concentration of dissolved substances within the cells, raising the osmotic pressure well above that of the blood plasma, lymph, and intercellular fluid. The high osmotic pressure thus accumulated presumably provides energy, in turn, for secretion and other vital functions of the cell. The whole process, operating on a microscopic and submicroscopic scale, is comparable to nature's grandest hydraulic cycle, in which the sun's energy raises water to high levels from which it runs down again, supplying power used by man to turn mill wheels and drive hydraulic rams.

DURING THE last years of Leslie Webster's career, he was pursuing with his principal assistants, as narrated in Chapter 8, two lines of research that grew out of the study of experimental epidemics on which Flexner had started him. One of these, an investigation of virus diseases affecting the central nervous system, done with Jordi Casals-Ariet, will be mentioned later. The other, done with his colleague Howard Schneider, began with a question that students of infectious diseases had often asked as they observed the progress of a disease through a human or animal population: Can the diet of the host affect the outcome of an infectious disease? This is at first glance a simple question, subject to direct experimental study; but as Webster and Schneider experimented together for a few years, and as Schneider continued the work after his chief's death in 1943, the question became year by year less simple. The story of the effort to answer it illustrates the complex nature of the interaction between organisms — in this case so complex that the unraveling of one difficulty seemed only to disclose another.

The two investigators began with the inbred strains of mice Webster had developed, which differed in their susceptibility to a species of *Salmonella*, the germ of mouse typhoid. It was soon found that the difference in susceptibility had been so firmly established by genetic selection that no experimental difference in diet could override it. Schneider learned that he must turn to the study of random outbred populations of mice, in which, as in the human population, individuals have not been selectively bred to resist germs. Next he discovered that a similar difficulty appertained to the infectious organism; he could not use a genetically uniform strain of *Salmonella* so highly pathogenic that it would kill his mice regardless of their nutritional state. To detect dietary effects on the disease, Schneider had to use heterogeneous, and therefore less fatal, *Salmonella* cultures, as well as heterogeneous mice. The difficulty about the mice he overcame by raising a colony of house mice, deliberately and randomly outbred. The need for genetically heterogeneous *Salmonellae*, neither too virulent nor insufficiently virulent, he met by an ingenious "double strain" test, in which the mice were inoculated first with a strain of weak virulence and then with a strong one. At best, the work is tedious; to test a given diet requires, when everything goes well, forty mice and eight weeks' time.

The laborious efforts by which Schneider arrived at a controllable experimental method took seven years and more. With it he was able to work out experimental diets on which the mortality rates of infected mice differed by as much as 48 per cent. As the work progressed, he was forced to ascribe the effects of various diets on susceptibility to *Salmonellae* to one or more unknown vitaminlike substances present in foodstuffs in very small quantities, of the order of one part in a million. Efforts to extract and isolate the unknown substances yielded at best a few milligrams. As the period of this history ended, the next step, no less difficult than the early ones, was to learn the chemical nature of these accessory factors in dietary resistance to infection.

Such is the trail, beset by many obstacles, along which Schneider traveled in his search for an answer to an apparently simple question. When invited to the rostrum of the New York Academy of Sciences, as a recognized leader of research in the field, to summarize a series of papers delivered in a symposium on nutrition in infections, Schneider was compelled to say that this discussion of recent research by many workers had brought out no clear and simple connection between nutrition and resistance to infection. Their relationship, as he had shown, involves an integrative process wherein populations, both of hosts and pathogens, have properties not possessed by individual hosts and individual pathogens. Schneider had accumulated a great body of experience on nutritional problems in general, and philosophic insight into the nature of infections and infectious organisms. He had developed research techniques and set an example of critical analysis useful to other workers. With good reason he entitled an article reviewing some of his experience "Nutrition, a Problem in Enquiry." The history of experimental science is full of instances like this, of questions vitally important to theory or for the practical needs of mankind, but so complex, so fraught with unknown factors, that years of preliminary study are required to clear away initial ignorance and confusion and to open a path for future research by working out new techniques.

THE VERSATILE scientist Dilworth Wayne Woolley has been successively classified by The Rockefeller Institute as bacteriologist, physiologist, and biochemist. When he first came to New York as a Fellow of the Institute in 1939, a man of twenty-five, he was assigned to the hospital to take part in a program of research in nutrition which the director, Rivers, was hoping to start. For this he was exceptionally qualified by previous studies of the chemical structure of accessory dietary factors. He had contributed much to the general concept, then in the making, of vitamins as a class of chemically specific substances essential for nutrition. Working with a group in the nutrition laboratory of C. A. Elvehjem, while a graduate student in agricultural chemistry at the University of Wisconsin, Woolley made brilliant contributions leading to the isolation and identification of niacin (nicotinic acid), one of the vitamin B group.[7]

Demonstration by the Wisconsin workers that this substance cures black tongue in dogs suggested that it would also cure pellagra. This hope was quickly confirmed by physicians treating human patients. Shortly thereafter, Woolley achieved the purification and synthesis of a substance having many of the properties of pantothenic acid, another member of the vitamin B group, shown by R. J. Williams of the University of Texas and others to be essential for the growth of yeast. When, later, pure pantothenic acid was tested on both chicks and yeast, its demonstrated role in the nutrition of creatures so different helped establish the concept that the B vitamins are biocatalysts used by many forms of life.

Soon after beginning work at the Hospital of The Rockefeller Institute, where he introduced the use of mice for chemical studies of nutrition, Woolley discovered an unknown food factor, lack of which caused the animals to lose their hair. Within a year or two he identified this factor as inositol, a carbohydrate which had previously been shown, by E. V. Eastcott of the University of Toronto, to be required by yeast. Thus inositol came to be recognized as a B vitamin. Continuing work begun at Wisconsin on the nutritional requirements of hemolytic streptococci, Woolley was on the trail of another vitaminlike factor which he called strepogenin. In 1940 Gasser recognized that a man of such wide-ranging originality, with a mind always reaching beyond the borders of the known, would be more at home in a research laboratory of his own than in the more specifically channeled work of the hospital. Therefore he transferred Woolley to the physiological group working in the Department of the Laboratories, where the young biochemist continued his observations on the effects of B-deficient diets.

Woolley next became interested in a group of peculiar proteins which had been found by nutrition workers to react with and destroy certain vitamins. Among the two or three such substances then known was one found in raw white of egg, which when fed to animals produced a deficiency of biotin, a B-complex vitamin. Systematically extracting egg white, Woolley obtained a minute amount of a specific substance which he and Longsworth of the physical chemistry laboratory purified and identified as a protein with a molecular weight of 70,000. This substance combines molecule for molecule with biotin and thus inactivates it. These results confirmed an earlier discovery by E. E. Snell, R. E. Eakin, and R. J. Williams of the University of Texas, whose name for the biotin antagonist, avidin, is now generally used. Woolley and his assistant L. O. Krampitz (later professor of microbiology at Western Reserve University) soon identified another antivitamin. Workers at the University of Minnesota had observed that a severe disease of foxes and minks in captivity is caused by feeding them raw fish, and can be cured with a B-complex vitamin, thiamine. Woolley and Krampitz showed that what causes the disease is a specific protein enzyme in the fish diet, which splits the thiamine molecule in such a way as to destroy it.

In 1938, while testing the potency of various derivatives of nicotinic acid, Woolley had noticed that two of them, chemically quite similar to the original substance, could not substitute for it in relieving the symptoms of black tongue, and in fact intensified the deficiency. Pondering over this observation, which seemed very strange at the time, he learned that an English biochemist, D. D. Woods, working with bacteria, in 1940, had discovered a similar antagonism between the sulphanilamide drugs and the vitamin paraaminobenzoic acid, which resemble one another in chemical structure. With this second case of antagonism as a clue, Woolley's imaginative mind immediately conceived the idea that one of such a pair of substances acts as an antimetabolite with respect to the other — that is to say, its similarity of structure allows it to compete for a place in the chemical reactions and combinations through which the substance it antagonizes takes part in the physiological activities of the body. Some such idea had already occurred to others without leading to effective research; Woolley made it his own and started a series of investigations aimed at establishing general concepts upon which to base the pharmacological use of the antimetabolites. Among a great many chemical analogues of active substances which he procured or synthesized for tests, a considerable number proved to act as antimetabolites.

In his first experiments he found that merely replacing the sulphur atom of thiamine by two carbon atoms converts the vitamin into a highly active drug, which produces in animals the characteristic signs of thiamine deficiency. This was the first demonstration of antimetabolic action in any living creature higher than the bacteria. Making slight changes in the structure of riboflavin, Woolley obtained an agent which causes signs of deficiency of that vitamin. By similar procedures during a decade he found antimetabolic analogues for several other vitamins, including ascorbic, folic, nicotinic, and pantothenic acids, and vitamins

E and K; and also for some of the biologically active purines and hormones. These experiments, and the subsequent work of other investigators, have demonstrated that a specific deficiency of almost any physiologically active substance can be established by forcing it to compete in the body with a compound differing slightly from it in chemical structure. Woolley was even able to predict, in certain cases, specific changes in structure that would create an antimetabolite against a physiologically useful compound. He made a strikingly correct prediction, for example, that tocopherol quinone, an analogue of vitamin E which he made synthetically, would cause resorption of the embryos of pregnant mice by interfering with the normal protective action of that vitamin. In another *tour de force* of the same kind, he deliberately planned and produced an antimalarial drug which is an analogue of pantothenic acid. As will be recounted in Chapter 16, William Trager of the Princeton laboratories had found that pantothenic acid is necessary for multiplication of the malarial parasites in cultures, and had suggested that the parasites might be able to accept the analogue but not to utilize it. This conjecture Woolley proved correct by direct experiment.

Such competitive effects can occur, Woolley and his associates showed, in all sorts of living creatures, including viruses, bacteria, fungi, plants, birds, and mammals. Different organisms, however, differ in their susceptibility to various antimetabolites, because of specific nutritional requirements or other physiological variables. Woolley pointed out that this sort of chemical competition may explain certain disease processes, as demonstrated by investigations on pellagra. That disease was known, partly through his own work, to result basically from a deficiency of nicotinic acid in the diet, but its symptoms appear to be induced or exacerbated by something introduced by eating Indian corn. Woolley looked for and found a toxic substance in corn which acts as an antimetabolite for nicotinic acid. Known antagonisms between certain hormones, and various phenomena of drug action, may depend also upon antimetabolites. The subject, with its fascinating opportunities for conjecture, prediction, logical analysis, and experimental test, remains open to further investigation. As a pioneer and recognized leader in the field, Woolley published in 1952 a book covering the history of this research and expounding a general theory of the nature and action of antimetabolites.[8]

Woolley was made a Member of The Rockefeller Institute in 1948. Since that time, with Robert B. Merrifield, Elliott N. Shaw, and other associates, he has chiefly been studying the applications of antimetabolites to the chemotherapy of various diseases. He is also investigating a general problem of great importance growing out of his work on antimetabolites and on growth-promoting factors — the relation of chemical structure to specific activities of protein constituents, especially peptides. His results in this field belong, however, to the next epoch of the Institute's history.

Research of the sort Woolley has done calls for varied talents, including first of all the ability to form and retain mental images of complex chemical formulas, so as to recognize resemblances of structure and to detect likely sites for modification of the molecular pattern. The investigator in this field must be a skilled synthetic chemist, able to make the substances he wants to test, for they are not always available through the chemical industry. He must be able also to plan animal experiments of a highly diversified character. The story of Woolley's career would be incomplete if it did not record that his achievement — made possible by keen chemical insight, vivid imagination, and a powerful memory — is that of a man working without the aid of vision during practically the whole period of his connection with The Rockefeller Institute. Keeping up his reading with the help of friends and especially of his devoted wife, he plans and conducts experiments, and prepares scientific reports as do his seeing colleagues. His 1952 volume on antimetabolites, mentioned above, makes use of facts reported in some five hundred articles in the scientific literature, all of which he recalled from memory when dictating the book. In the laboratory he depends, of course, on his helpers to report on visible chemical reactions and to read measuring instruments, but by no means to execute ordinary laboratory procedures for him. Fellow workers who watch him manipulating chemical apparatus, or weighing out foodstuffs for his experimental animals, regard his daily performance as a triumph of scientific intelligence matching the ingenuity and persistence of his researches.

CHAPTER FIFTEEN

Immunology, Microbiology, Pathology, Cytology, 1935–1953

The nature of allergy and other immune reactions. Neurotropic viruses; arthropod-borne viruses. Physiology of lymph flow. Virus tumors. Elementary structure of cells; electron microscopy.

KARL LANDSTEINER's term as Member of The Rockefeller Institute and leader of research on immunology ended in 1939, four years after Herbert S. Gasser became Director. Until his sudden death in 1943, he continued active work in the laboratory, studying the relation between the chemical structure of antibodies and their specific affinities. To this period belongs an important investigation of the serological reactions of protein derivatives (peptides) from silk, and the contributions to the work on the Rh factor, described in Chapter 8.

Meanwhile his long-time associate Merrill W. Chase continued and gradually took over a line of research which Landsteiner had opened up many years earlier. As described in Chapter 8, Landsteiner had discovered that a simple chemical compound, not capable of acting as an antigen in immunity reactions, may become antigenic by attaching itself to a natural protein of the animal body. The simpler element (hapten) provides the specificity, so that, when again exposed to the simple substance, the animal responds by an immune reaction to that substance alone. This phenomenon is all too well known to sufferers, more and more numerous in our population, who have thus acquired allergic sensitivity to chemical substances.

Landsteiner's and Chase's investigations threw new light upon a highly varied array of bodily reactions included under the general term "allergy." Among them are serum sickness following transfusion with incompatible blood, anaphylactic shock, food allergies, many cases of asthma, dermatitis from poison ivy and from certain drugs, atopic eczema, and tuberculin sensitivity. In each of these conditions there is an altered capacity to react to certain specific substances taken into or applied to the body, generally reflecting prior contact with the same substance. This altered reaction may variously involve, according to the specific circumstances, prostration and shock, fever, respiratory spasm, an attack of hives, a digestive upset, or some symptom of local tissue damage or functional disturbance. Such reactions generally begin immediately after exposure to the antigen; another type of response (delayed reaction) is characterized by a skin eruption that appears only after some hours or days. The allergic reaction may affect the whole body, or may produce only local disturbance, such as the "reaction of immunity" experienced by almost everyone who is revaccinated against smallpox. All these various reactions seem to depend upon one chemical mechanism that can lead to a production of antibodies, though not every instance of allergy is as yet fully explainable on that basis. It was long thought that certain allergic phenomena, for example delayed sensitivity of the skin to non-protein drugs and to ivy poisoning, could not be explained by antibody formation, because the irritating agent was not a protein and was therefore presumably not able to elicit an antibody reaction. This question The Rockefeller Institute workers attacked in the light of Landsteiner's discovery that non-protein substances could form antigenic complexes by binding themselves to non-antigenic proteins.

The earliest of Landsteiner's studies of sensitization of the skin by simple chemical compounds, done with John L. Jacobs in 1935 and 1936, dealt exclusively with the type of allergy in which the skin becomes sensitive and reddens or blisters under a second exposure to the inciting substance. In 1936 Chase joined Landsteiner in observations which confirmed the hypothetical explanation by reversing the experimental steps. They first injected guinea pigs with a compound containing a simple chemical substance, for example picryl chloride or dinitrofluorobenzene, firmly bound to a non-antigenic protein from guinea pigs' blood. After this preparatory treatment, they found, the skin became sensitive to the simple substance alone.[1] Other types of allergic reaction also could be caused by sensitization to simple compounds; for example, by injecting picryl chloride or dinitrofluorobenzene into guinea pigs already sensitized to those substances, they produced true anaphylaxis of the extreme type that occurs in that species, ending with spasm of the bronchial muscles and fatal shock. This anaphylactic response was quite independent of delayed sensitivity to the same chemical when applied to the surface of the skin. In 1939, Chase and Landsteiner carried out a long series of ingenious experiments on ivy poisoning in guinea pigs, confirming and extending work done shortly before by F. A. Simon and associates in Boston, which brought this kind of skin irritation clearly within the class of allergic reactions.

Such is the background against which, after Landsteiner's retirement and death, Chase continued the work on immunology with ever-broadening comprehension of allergic reactions. The line of research he has followed ever since, in its various ramifications, began with a hypothesis he and Landsteiner tested. They reasoned that if the sensitization they produced with simple incitants is indeed a form of immune reaction to a hapten-protein conjugate, it should reside in the tissues of the sensitized animal, like immunity against bacterial products. It should, moreover, be transferable from the sensitized animal to a normal one by inoculation with tissues or cells, just as passive immunity to diphtheria, for example, is conferred by antitoxin from an immunized animal. Testing this supposition, they sensitized guinea pigs to picryl chloride and then injected into the peritoneal cavity an irritant which produced an exudate full of cells drawn from the tissues and the blood. Removing the exudate with a syringe, and injecting it into a normal animal, they found that the latter's skin became sensitive to the simple incitant through this passive transfer of sensitivity or immunity. Washed cells from the exudate had the same effect. Among the cellular constituents of such a peritoneal exudate, white blood cells of the lymphocyte type are always very common.

Aware that Philip D. McMaster of The Rockefeller Institute and, later, others elsewhere had shown that the lymph nodes, where similar cells abound, are prolific sites of antibody formation against bacterial toxins, Chase asked whether the lymphocytes of sensitized animals would also be able to induce the production of antibodies. Testing this question, he noted that the intensity of transfer of passive immunity by an exudate was proportional to the content of lymphocytes. Finally, using refined techniques and a very sensitive test object, the uterus of the anaphylactic guinea pig, Chase found that washed cells from the spleen, lymph nodes, and the "buffy coat" of centrifuged blood, rich in lymphocytes, were effective in transferring sensitization. Using minute amounts of serum by special methods, he could study the origin and course of antibody production in a single guinea pig. Still more refined studies on the origin of antitoxin production in single rabbits showed that the antibody appearing in the new animal was not present in the transferred cells, but represented a new production. The way was then open for another series of studies on the timing and measurement of antibody formation under controlled experimental conditions.

Three years after the first transfer of skin sensitivity to simple chemicals, Chase in 1945 similarly transferred cutaneous hypersensitivity to tuberculin from one guinea pig to another by injecting sensitized lymphocytes. This was the first evidence of a common mechanism operating in ostensibly different types of allergy, namely, bacterial allergy and contact dermatitis. Numerous investigations in other laboratories have confirmed all these findings made at The Rockefeller Institute and have begun to extend to problems of human allergic disease.

Chase studied another aspect of allergic sensitivity of great practical as well as theoretical importance. Certain forms of human allergy (hay fever, asthma) often recur in successive generations of a family, a fact which has been ascribed, with little evidence from genetic studies, to the influence of hereditary constitution. Noting that individual guinea pigs sensitized to simple substances conspicuously differ from one another in the degree of their response to the inciting drug, even under uniform conditions of housing and diet, Chase undertook to discover whether in this case hereditary constitution has a significant role. Selectively breeding from a common stock to obtain two strains of animals differing in skin sensitivity of the contact type, in four generations he obtained two lines, in one of which the majority responded intensely, in the other but slightly. Similar results were obtained by selective breeding for sensitivity to ivy poisoning, to tuberculin, and to still another antigenic combination utilizing a different mycobacterium. The importance of heredity in predisposing to human allergic disease remains an unsolved question. Chase's animal experiments, still in progress in 1953, place the issue squarely before students of human genetics.

In further studies with chemical allergens, Chase found that if he administered such substances to guinea pigs by certain special routes, for example by feeding, he could induce a condition of "non-responsiveness," showing itself when he tried to sensitize the pigs to the same chemical this time applied to the skin. The persistence of this unresponsiveness, which lasts for much more than a year, shows that the experimenter may set an artificial ceiling upon the animal's capacity to respond to a given allergen or antigen. This observation may provide a clue to differences in human sensitivity to such agents, well illustrated by the diverse susceptibility of individuals to poison ivy.

By the labors of many years briefly recounted in the foregoing pages, Chase has greatly clarified the nature of allergic sensitivity of the skin, and has shown that this type of specific irritation is closely related to allergies of other kinds — a conclusion which becomes ever more important to human medical practice as new drugs and reagents are introduced by the chemical and pharmaceutical industries. By piecing together the manifold puzzle presented by allergy, he and fellow workers in other laboratories have opened new fields in dermatology and other branches of clinical medicine, and are gradually achieving a general understanding of the body's reactions to foreign proteins and other allergenic substances.

IN THE first quarter of this century medical science was confronted with two epidemic diseases affecting the central nervous system and known to be caused by filtrable viruses: poliomyelitis and the less clearly definable Australian "X" encephalitis. About 1930 many more virus infections of the brain and spinal cord, previously unrecognized or ill defined, rather suddenly began to be reported from various parts of the world, some occurring sporadically, others as epidemics. Among the latter were the Western and Eastern equine encephalomyelitis, St. Louis encephalomyelitis, and Russian tick-borne encephalitis. How many of them were really new is an unanswered question. Similar diseases appear more or less recognizably in the medical literature of earlier periods; perhaps, growing knowledge of virus diseases and particularly of poliomyelitis had merely alerted twentieth-century investigators and given them methods by which to identify and compare diseases previously indistinguishable. At any rate, the apparently sudden emergence of these infections of the brain, with devastating effects in many cases, alarmed public health officers in many countries, and drew the attention of numerous laboratories to the problems of cause, pathology, and diagnosis presented by the various types of encephalitis.

Peter K. Olitsky and his associates at The Rockefeller Institute were well prepared to take part in this intricate study, for Olitsky had already investigated the transmission and immunological reactions of other viruses of the neurotropic type, capable of infecting the nervous system, namely, that of herpes (shingles) and the "neurovaccine virus" which sometimes contaminates smallpox vaccine. As early as 1928, Olitsky began studying vesicular stomatitis virus, which is neurotropic in laboratory mice, but causes lesions of the skin, hoof, and mouth in horses and of the udder in cattle. Using a technique introduced by H. B. Andervont of the U.S. Public Health Service, and Max Theiler of The Rockefeller Foundation, for producing encephalitis in mice with the viruses of herpes and yellow fever, respectively, Olitsky with H. R. Cox and J. T. Syverton produced infections of the central nervous system by injecting the stomatitis and equine encephalomyelitis viruses into the brain and by instilling them into the nasal passages.

Well established by 1933 in the field of neurotropic viruses, Olitsky and his group went on to study the properties of the viruses of Eastern and Western equine encephalomyelitis, avian encephalomyelitis, vesicular stomatitis, mouse encephalomyelitis (as a model for poliomyelitis), and poliomyelitis itself. They opened many lines of research on routes of invasion, on immunization and other forms of protection of animals, and on the influence of host factors — for example, age — on resistance to infection. Heretofore, poliomyelitis had been experimentally transmitted only to monkeys, except for a successful attempt in 1939 by Charles Armstrong of the U.S. Public Health Service to transfer the "Lansing" strain to mice. In 1943 Olitsky, Morgan, and Schlesinger got another strain to grow in mice and isolated the MEF1 strain, now a component of the Salk vaccine. All of Olitsky's senior colleagues from 1933 to his retirement in 1952 — Casals, Cox, Harford, I. M. Morgan, A. B. Sabin, Schlesinger — and visiting investigators Leonora Brown, O. Lahelle, L. C. Murphy, R. O. Anslow, Golda Selzer, and R. H. Yager took part in these experiments. Many other guest investigators from abroad, and short-term assistants too numerous to be listed here, benefited by Olitsky's experience and ability to encourage and instruct his juniors.

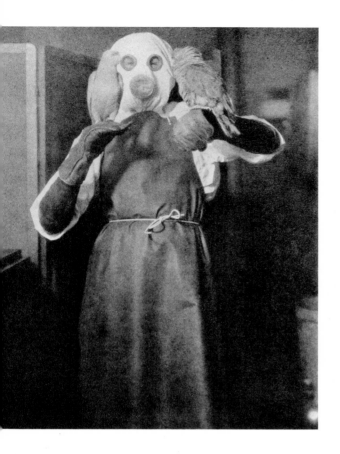

Protective clothing worn by workers investigating psittacosis (parrot fever). The masked figure is George P. Berry, now Dean of Harvard Medical School.

Noguchi landing at Accra in 1927

OSWALD T. AVERY

KARL LANDSTEINER

FLORENCE R. SABIN

LEONOR MICHAELIS

Among the more striking and novel results of the studies on poliomyelitis led by Sabin and Olitsky was their cultivation of the causative virus on human embryonic brain tissue, through several successive transfers. This feat, performed in 1936, challenged the view, then prevalent, that the virus would not grow outside of the bodies of human subjects, apes, and monkeys. It was followed up, thirteen years later, by J. F. Enders, T. H. Weller, and F. C. Robbins at Harvard, who found that monkey tissues could be used in the culture medium and opened the way for Jonas Salk's development of an effective vaccine for the prevention of the disease.

Simon Flexner had supposed (as mentioned in Chapter 3) that poliomyelitis virus enters the human body by way of the nasal passages and the olfactory nerves — an idea of great importance for the epidemiology of this disease. In experiments on monkeys, Sabin and Olitsky found that the virus produces characteristic lesions in the olfactory bulbs of the brain when administered intranasally, but not when given by other routes. The animals could be rendered resistant to inoculation by the nasal route by a preliminary treatment of the nasal membranes with astringent solutions of alum or tannic acid. This method, however, proved ineffective with human subjects when tested by Canadian workers during epidemics. Sabin, while with Olitsky from 1935 to 1939, looked in vain for lesions of the olfactory bulbs in human patients who had died in the early stages of poliomyelitis, and his later work at Cincinnati confirmed the conclusion that the virus does not usually invade the human body by the nasal route. Another observation made by Sabin and Olitsky — that in monkeys experimentally infected with poliomyelitis, tonsillectomy increases the danger of bulbar paralysis, the most serious form of the disease — led to the present-day rule of physicians to avoid, as far as possible, operations on the mouth and throat during seasons when poliomyelitis is prevalent.

Adapting the MEF1 strain of poliomyelitis virus, mentioned above, to the brain of the newborn mouse, J. Casals, of Webster's laboratory, and Olitsky devised a practical complement-fixation test for diagnosis of the disease, and with Sabin defined its use in clinical practice. Tests of this sort are used to detect the presence in the blood serum of an animal of an antibody against a given infectious agent. If the antibody is there, the serum binds complement, a substance in the blood which completes the combination of antibody with the antigen of the infectious agent. Working at a time when investigation of poliomyelitis was going slowly, largely for lack of ability to cultivate the virus freely, Olitsky and his group used the equine neurotropic viruses as models for working out methods of poliomyelitis research, in experiments aimed at developing means of prevention and of specific treatment by immune serum. These experiments revealed differences between the routes of invasion of viruses that are strictly neurotropic, traveling only along nerve tracts, and others which can travel by way of the blood stream. Studying the influence of age on susceptibility to infection with the equine viruses and on the formation of antibodies against them, Olitsky, Sabin, Cox, and Morgan observed instructive and useful differences which enabled Olitsky and Harford to devise an improved virus-neutralization test depending upon the difference in susceptibility of young and old animals. This has since become a routine laboratory technique.

Olitsky, Cox, Morgan, and Schlesinger successfully vaccinated guinea pigs and mice with wholly inactivated Western equine encephalomyelitis vaccine, even against a thousand times the lethal dose of the virus given directly into the brain. Later Olitsky and Casals found that the Russian tick-borne virus, also in the form of an inactivated virus vaccine, could induce immunity lasting almost throughout the animal's life. These results did not accord with the idea prevailing at the time, that only "living" or active virus immunized to such a degree. Morgan and Olitsky also proved that when antibody against the virus falls to a low point, as happens several months after vaccination with the Eastern virus vaccine, a booster injection of vaccine induces a greater response of antibody than the same dose did at the initial vaccination. Hence when the practical value of Salk's vaccine as a preventive of poliomyelitis became evident, Olitsky and his group were not surprised. They discovered, moreover, that when neurotropic viruses invade the body via the blood stream, as, for example, after mosquito bites, resistance to infection depends upon the level of neutralizing antibody in the blood serum; the availability of antibody to the tissues of the nervous system is the important factor in protecting them.

An incidental outcome of this work was the recognition of a serious, though fortunately not very common, disease previously unknown in America. In 1935, while tracing the spread of a neurotropic virus in guinea pigs, Sabin and Olitsky found that they had somehow also introduced into their animals a protozoan parasite which itself produced severe encephalitis, and which they identified as a species of *Toxoplasma*. Although the organism had been known for some time in Europe and Africa, this was the first evidence of its existence on the North American continent. When a few months later Abner Wolf and David Cowan of the Neurological Institute of New York described a peculiar case of fatal encephalitis in a child, obviously caused by protozoan infection, Olitsky and Sabin suggested that the invader was *Toxoplasma,* and advised the physicians how to identify it by animal inoculation should other cases occur. In 1938 Wolf, Cowan, and Beryl H. Page, encountering another case, carried out the necessary animal passage in mice and proved for the first time that *Toxoplasma* can cause disease in man. Later Sabin developed a diagnostic test for toxoplasma infection, showing that it is more common than physicians had supposed, especially in children, in whom infection from the mother may begin *in utero.*

In 1943 Jordi Casals joined Olitsky's group after the death of Leslie Webster. From Webster's laboratory of experimental epidemiology, Casals brought with him an improved complement-fixation test for several neurotropic viruses, devised by himself and R. Palacios, a guest investigator from Chile. The test could be employed not only for diagnosis of an infection or for identification of a virus, but also for grouping viruses according to the similarities of their antibody reactions. In addition to the antibodies which fix complement, another type, which neutralizes virus, was studied by Olitsky, Casals, and Morgan; and in 1949 a third, designated as "HI," which shows itself by inhibiting the agglutination of avian red blood cells when virus is added to them, was investigated by Olitsky, Yager, and Casals, using a series of neurotropic viruses. By testing with these three antibodies, a virus can be precisely identified, and, especially by the HI test, reliable information obtained as to the relation of one virus to another.

When Olitsky retired, Casals joined the Rockefeller Foundation Virus Laboratories, under the direction of Max Theiler, and continued, with his colleague Delphine H. Clarke, to improve the accuracy of HI reactions. At this time, field workers of The Rockefeller Foundation and others engaged in the study of virus diseases were constantly sending to the Foundation's laboratory specimens presumed to contain viruses, from North, Central, and South Africa; from Asia, especially India; from the Amazon Valley, Trinidad, California, and elsewhere. More than fifty "new" viruses (*i.e.*, not theretofore identified) were disclosed within a few years — and still they come. Most of these can infect man, as shown by development of specific antibodies in the blood, with or without overt symptoms. Some are known to cause definite diseases, sometimes serious and even fatal. Not all of these viruses came from human patients or associated mammals; many are found in ticks and, especially, in mosquitoes.

Casals and his colleagues — Leonora Brown, Clarke, J. S. Porterfield, and Theiler — were able to classify most of these neurotropic viruses, which Casals now named "arbor" (arthropod-borne) viruses, into three groups, according to their HI reactions. They discerned unsuspected relations of certain virus diseases of man to others causing encephalitis in man or animals only under special conditions; ordinarily, the infection does not show itself in man by neurological symptoms. Others, such as yellow fever and dengue, cause encephalitis in laboratory animals, but do not ordinarily act upon the human nervous system. The first indications of interrelationship among viruses of Western, St. Louis, and Japanese encephalitis and those of Russian tick-borne encephalitis and louping ill, in the early 1940's, led Olitsky and Casals and others to postulate that all these diseases may have had a common ancestor, but, as they spread over the world, developed differences in immunological and serological reactions by which they are now distinguishable.

A serious disease, often fatal, known as disseminated demyelinating encephalomyelitis, occurs in human patients now and again, following or during the late stages of certain virus infections, and sometimes after use of vaccines, such as that used against rabies, which contain brain tissue. The lesions in the nervous system resemble those seen in spontaneous human diseases, such as multiple sclerosis, diffuse sclerosis, and a score of others, all showing under the microscope essentially similar changes in the brain and spinal cord.

The possibility that diseases of this kind could be studied experimentally in animals was realized in 1933–1935 by Thomas M. Rivers, Douglas A. Sprunt, George P. Berry, and Francis M. Schwentker of The Rockefeller Institute Hospital, who attempted to produce similar lesions in monkeys by injecting emulsions of brain tissue carrying various viruses. The results exculpated the viruses as the cause of disseminated encephalomyelitis, and suggested that the brain tissue was itself the noxious agent. The investigators were even able to produce the condition in monkeys by repeated injections of brain tissue alone, and suspected that experimental disseminated encephalomyelitis is an allergic reaction. Other workers promptly confirmed the findings in rabbits and guinea pigs, but the outcome of individual experiments was unpredictable; lesions occurred in only half or less of the trials, and the conditions for success were difficult to define. One effective aid to production of lesions was, however, disclosed by these efforts, namely, that of adding to the brain tissue "Freund's adjuvant," certain oily substances mixed with suspensions of inactivated tubercle bacilli.

At this stage of the investigations, in 1948, Olitsky and a visiting investigator already mentioned, Lieutenant Colonel R. H. Yager of the U.S. Army Veterinary Corps, entered the field with a successful effort to produce acute disseminated encephalomyelitis in genetically selected mice, using lines obtained by brother-sister mating of the Rockefeller Institute strain of mice developed first by Webster and continued by H. A. Schneider. These mice proved to be highly responsive to injections of brain tissue mixed with suitable adjuvants. From such experiments Olitsky and colleagues concluded that the mechanism underlying the reaction could indeed be allergic hypersensitivity to some component of brain tissue. After many vain attempts to produce it with various tissue ingredients, Olitsky and another visiting investigator, Chloe Tal (now at the Hebrew University, Jerusalem), in 1952 succeeded in doing so with proteolipides, a new group of lipoproteins recently isolated at Harvard University by Jordi Folch-Pi, a former Associate in Van Slyke's laboratory at The Rockefeller Institute Hospital, and his colleague M. Lees.

Olitsky's retirement in 1952 as Member of The Rockefeller Institute did not interrupt the course of his research. As the period of this narrative closed, and thereafter, he was at work with Johanna M. Lee and Howard A. Schneider on several further lines of attack on disseminated encephalomyelitis. A study, pursued with Norton D. Zinder, of hereditary differences in susceptibility of four of the inbred strains of mice begun by Webster and maintained by Schneider, as already described, points in relatively simple Mendelian fashion to hereditary factors controlling the incidence of the disease. Schneider, Lee, and Olitsky also found that diet can influence susceptibility. If mice of a strain 100 per cent susceptible are fed on a synthetic instead of a natural diet, susceptibility is reduced to 15 per cent; if biotin, folic acid, and B_{12} vitamins are added to the synthetic diet, susceptibility increases to 70 per cent. Further work on the ecologic factors influencing susceptibility or resistance is still in progress under Schneider. Specialists in diseases of the nervous system are closely watching the experiments of Olitsky and his colleagues for clues to the cause of multiple sclerosis and other imperfectly understood human diseases of similar pathological nature.

FLEXNER'S RETIREMENT in 1935 left Peyton Rous as senior worker in the laboratories of pathology. A year or two earlier Rous, returning to the field of experimental tumors, had left to his colleagues the work described in Chapter 8 on the chemical reactions of elementary tissues and on the associated problems of blood and lymph flow, which had occupied him and his group for about eight years. We shall return later to his own new program. Meanwhile, his recent associates had attained academic posts: Frederick Smith became professor of bacteriology and dean of the medical school of McGill University; Stephen S. Hudack, in a career in surgical teaching, went to Western Reserve University; and Douglas R. Drury went to the University of Southern California as professor of physiology.

Philip D. McMaster, remaining at the Institute as an Associate Member and conducting independent investigations, continued the line of study he and Hudack had begun, on the formation of lymph, the pattern of the lymphatic vessels as disclosed by means of vital stains, and the drainage of the interstitial fluid of the tissues. The two workers had already emphasized the wealth of lymphatic vessels in the skin and had shown that the walls of these delicate vessels are semipermeable membranes, permitting the entrance and exit of fluids and of very finely divided particles, such as the colloidal dyestuffs which they used as test materials. Slight injury of the skin produced by a scratch, exposure to heat, or mild chemical irritation increases the permeability of the walls of the lymphatic vessels, permitting them to admit into the lymph stream molecules of blood pigment (hemoglobin) and other large protein particles deposited by the injury in the interstitial spaces of the skin. Experimenting on human volunteers, including themselves, by injecting colored solutions into the skin of the arm, they observed rapid streaming of fluid in lymph vessels toward the lymph nodes at the elbow or shoulder. With Robert J. Parsons, his assistant from 1935 to 1938, McMaster proceeded to study the forces that drive the lymph flow, even in the motionless limb, without assistance from muscular movement, which normally speeds the flow of lymph. Experiments on the rabbit's ear, where lymphatic vessels are readily observed, showed that pulsation of the blood vessels assists in pumping fluid along the neighboring lymphatics. In patients with heart failure and reduced blood pressure, the lymphatics fail in their function of fluid transport, adding to the edema so commonly present in that condition.

A natural further step in analyzing the mechanism of lymph production was to study the conditions of pressure and flow of the interstitial fluid of the skin, which is brought there by the blood stream and removed partly by the lymphatics, partly by the veins. For this study, the ears of small animals, especially mice, offered ideal material, for they are thin enough to transmit light, clearly revealing the smallest vessels under the microscope. Working with anesthetized animals, McMaster was able to introduce exceedingly fine hollow needles into the skin, without opening either blood or lymph vessels, and to measure the pressure upon tiny droplets of fluid placed in the tissue spaces. Under normal conditions, this pressure is very small, he found, but if the veins are obstructed or the tissue injured in any way, the pressure of the tissue fluid rises sufficiently to hinder the filtration of fluid outward from the blood capillaries. In such circumstances, there is a gradient of pressure from the tissue spaces to the lymphatics, which causes the tissue fluid to drain at an increased rate into the lymphatic system.

Since it was known that the lymph nodes act as filters for bacteria in the lymph stream passing through them, McMaster conceived the idea that the nodes may also be sites of antibody formation against invading microorganisms. In a variety of experiments done with Hudack, he found that if they injected pathogenic bacteria into the skin, antibodies appeared in the nearest lymph nodes, along the line of lymphatic drainage from the site of the injection, as soon as they did in the blood, and in much higher concentration. McMaster and J. G. Kidd found later that substances which neutralize viruses are also formed in the lymph nodes. These results obviously accorded with the findings of Merrill

Chase, described earlier in this chapter, which in a different way implicated the lymphocytes, the most numerous cells in the lymph nodes, as
agents in antibody formation.

The studies of McMaster, Hudack, Parsons, and Kidd, taken in their
entirety, show that the lymphatic system of the skin, far from being a
mere network of passive collecting vessels, is anatomically more extensive and functionally more active than had been generally supposed. The
lymphatics are so abundant that the skin can nowhere be penetrated
without opening them. The flow of lymph transports foreign material
rapidly toward the lymph nodes. The walls of the lymph capillaries respond to various stimuli by marked increase of permeability. Around
burns, for example, they pour out quantities of lymph and accept debris
in the form of protein aggregates for removal. This concept of the lymphatic system, developed by The Rockefeller Institute's pathologists,
fitted closely with the findings of contemporary investigators using other
approaches — among them those of Florence Sabin, who had studied the
embryology of the lymphatic system at the Johns Hopkins University, and
of the physiologist Cecil K. Drinker and his colleagues at Harvard Medical School. To the greatly improved understanding of the lymphatic system being achieved at this time by anatomists, physiologists, and pathologists, McMaster had made a notable contribution.

For his experiments on the pattern and function of fine blood and
lymph vessels in the skin, McMaster needed a colored injection fluid of
protein nature, which would enable him to see the vessels under functional conditions. Such a substance was obviously to be found in a compound of a protein with a dye such that, once injected, the dye would
not split off from the protein, to confuse the picture by circulating alone
in the vessels or diffusing through their walls. A compound of this sort
had been prepared for another purpose at Columbia University, about
1939, by Michael Heidelberger, formerly of Jacobs's laboratory at The
Rockefeller Institute, and a colleague, F. E. Kendall; but their red-
tinged soluble protein was not strongly enough colored to serve Mc-
Master's purposes. He turned, therefore, to the azoproteins. With a technician chemist, Heinz Kruse, in 1940, he tried a number of brilliantly
blue dyes of the "azo" type and found two which could be firmly coupled
with serum protein as a whole or with serum albumin. The very strongly
colored compounds thus formed served excellently to visualize fine vas-

cular channels under the microscope. Better still, McMaster saw that because of their protein content they could be used as tracer antigens, making visible the distribution of foreign protein introduced into the body, and marking the sites at which it is stored and where, presumably, the first stimuli to antibody formation arise. Landsteiner had shown in 1922 that azoproteins are antigenic, and F. R. Sabin had in 1939 used the red Heidelberger-Kendall compound with some success as a tracer antigen.

McMaster's new blue compounds, however, were even better adapted to physiological experimentation. They behaved in the bodies of mice much like other proteins and were so strongly antigenic that they could be used to produce anaphylactic shock. When injected into the blood stream they were taken up, all over the body, by the reticulo-endothelial cells, which were already known from classical immunological studies to be active in removing bacteria and antigenic protein particles from the blood and body fluids. With their new and superior colored antigen, McMaster and his associates could now study many unsolved problems concerning the interactions of antigen and antibody at the actual sites of immune reactions in the living tissues. As 1953 approached, McMaster, with Kruse, E. Sturm, and J. L. Edwards, seeking to determine how long antigens can remain in the body and retain their power to elicit antibodies, found that after injection of the color-tagged protein, colored material remains in the livers of mice and rabbits for many weeks, where, if not degraded, it can continue to stimulate the production of antibodies. This would explain the prolonged antibody formation observed in certain experiments by various workers with foreign proteins, bacteria, and viruses, but not understood. McMaster, who became a full Member of The Rockefeller Institute in 1951, continued the attack on this and many similar problems, in years beyond the range of this history.

CANCER PROBLEMS continued to occupy workers in the laboratories of pathology, following the lead set by Peyton Rous and, later, by James B. Murphy, who succeeded him as formal head of cancer research. As already reported in Chapter 9, Rous returned to this field in 1934 to work with a virus that R. E. Shope had discovered to be the cause of papillomas, singular growths often found on the skin of wild cottontail rabbits. Shope generously offered the virus to Rous with all the opportunities it offered for profitable research, which kept him and his associates busy for more than two decades of experiment and reflection. These rabbit growths had all the attributes of atypical benign tumors, and yet very malignant cancers frequently originated from them. With his associates Rous conducted a widely ranging investigation of the reactions of the host animal to the tumors produced by the papilloma virus, and to the virus itself as manifested by the production of antibodies. Their findings emphasized the specific role of the virus in changing normal cells into tumor cells of a special sort and maintaining them in this condition. The many other agents of various kinds with which tumors can be induced experimentally act by bringing about a cell change with which they have nothing further to do. How it comes about and why it persists, causing tumor formation, is still unknown. The viruses which produce tumors, on the other hand, not only make normal cells become tumor cells, but maintain them in this condition, as Rous and his group proved.

As Rous summarized the findings in a Harvey Lecture in 1941, such viruses accompany the cells which they have rendered neoplastic as these multiply into tumors, increase in amount in association with them, go along with the tumor cells when they are transplanted into new hosts, and can often be recovered in a state enabling them to produce tumors of precisely the same kind when introduced into still other hosts. Even when, as sometimes happens, a virus can no longer be recovered from a tumor it has elicited in an animal by inoculation, it is present in a hidden form, and can be detected obliquely — for example, by tests revealing an antibody against the virus in the blood of the animal and even in the tumor itself. Such findings, added to information at hand from the Rous chicken sarcoma and from various other virus-produced tumors he had found, and from a few others discovered elsewhere, made it impossible to disregard the hypothesis that malignant tumors in general are virus-produced, and that experimental causes, such as radiation or carcinogens like tar and the more lately discovered polycyclic hydrocarbons, only bring latent viruses into action.

Several young men who worked in Rous's laboratory at this period, with him or separately, thus began careers in research and teaching. Joseph W. Beard, Associate in pathology, who participated in the earlier stages of the investigation, went to Duke University in 1937 to lead work in experimental surgery. John G. Kidd joined the group in 1934, and, rising to the rank of Associate Member of the Institute, was called to Cornell University Medical College in 1944 as professor of pathology and pathologist in chief to the New York Hospital. William F. Friedewald, Assistant (1938–1942), became professor of bacteriology at Emory University.

Rous and his associates were especially concerned to know whether present knowledge of viruses can suffice to account for tumor formation in general. With William E. Smith, who joined him as assistant in 1943, Rous opened up an ingenious new method of testing potentialities of tissues to respond to carcinogenic agents. Transplanting bits of various epithelial organs from mouse embryos to suitable sites in the bodies of adult mice, the investigators subjected the transplanted material to the action of a powerful chemical carcinogen, methylcholanthrene, under circumstances which prevented the drug from acting upon the adjacent connective tissue to cause the destructive sarcomas which had balked previous investigators attempting to induce epithelial tumors (carcinomas). Carcinomas of extraordinary variety and number resulted from this exposure of rapidly growing and differentiating cells to the cancer-inducing stimulus. In 1948–1949, Rous, Smith, and another assistant, E. S. Rogers (now at the University of Tennessee), produced lung tumors in newborn mice by injecting their mothers during pregnancy with urethane, a simple chemical substance previously known to cause lung tumors only in aging adult mice. In 1949, Rous and Rogers found that the simultaneous application of a chemical carcinogen and Shope virus to normal epidermis resulted in papillomas which became malignant much sooner than would otherwise have happened. Previous experiments, in which Kidd participated, had shown that infection of benign tar-induced tumors with the Shope virus, by way of the blood stream, would cause them to become cancerous at once. In this way, Rous and his co-workers went on accumulating a great mass of evidence for the participation of viruses in the causation of tumors and in the transformation of benign tumors into carcinomas.

At an earlier period, Rous, Kidd, and Ian Mackenzie had shown that painting the skin of rabbits with a tar that induces tumors changes many more cells into tumor cells than can ever give rise to visible growths, the great majority lying latent through life. Yet anything which will stimulate normal cells of the same kind to multiply (for example, turpentine, which induces scurf on the skin) may cause some of these potentially neoplastic cells to form tumors at once. Many of them, however, require long urging. The substances that do the urging are now known as *promoting agents*. Their action is quite different from that of the agents that change normal cells into tumor cells, in a way not yet understood. These are *initiative agents*. The distinction was first demonstrated experimentally by Friedewald and Rous. Like the recognition of latent tumor cells, it has theoretical importance and has become part of the useful new knowledge of tumors.

Rous's retirement in 1945 as Member of The Rockefeller Institute seems in retrospect a mere incident in a career of research that still goes on productively fifty years after its brilliant start. After the last assistants of his official term, W. E. Smith and Rogers, left the Institute for research and teaching posts elsewhere, other young men continued to come to the laboratory as Fellows, new recruits enlisting with the veteran leader of an unceasing campaign.

The laboratory of cancer research, led by James B. Murphy, began during the early years of Gasser's directorship to move away from the specific study of malignant disease into the more general field of cytology. Cancer research had proved a baffling task for Murphy, as for many others, but the breadth and variety of the work in his laboratory saved his colleagues in the end from the sterility that might have overtaken them had they clung to the forlorn hope of a direct attack on the cancer problem by conventional methods. Murphy's pages in the annual confidential reports of the Institute's chief investigators to the Director — which reveal their tentative projects and their perplexities far more frankly than do published articles — narrate a long series of far-ranging, but mostly inconclusive, experiments on the physiology of cancer growth. With the aid of his assistant Sturm, he investigated substances associated with transplantable fowl and mouse tumors, which seemingly inhibited their growth. Turning their attention to mouse leukemia, the two experimented with various chemical and physical agents, in the hope of finding something that might stimulate or inhibit the malignant overgrowth of white blood cells characteristic of that disease in mouse and man. One phase of this search yielded a practical find: Murphy and Sturm discovered that they could slow down the growth of lymphatic leukemia cells in experimental animals by administering adrenal cortical extracts or pituitary extracts which stimulate the adrenal. Removal of the adrenal gland, on the other hand, enhanced susceptibility to transplanted leukemia tissue. Following these clues, physicians tried similar hormone preparations on human leukemia patients and found that, in some cases, they can be used to palliate, though not to cure, the disease.

Although the genetic approach to the cancer problem was not a major objective of Murphy's group, Clara Lynch accumulated additional data during this period on the relation between heredity and environment in the development of lung tumors in mice. She could make a finer analysis not only by noting the percentage of mice with tumors but also by counting the number of tumor nodules in each individual. These criteria, applied to data for both spontaneous and tar-induced lung tumors, showed that the degree of susceptibility not only is affected by environment, but also is under genetic control, although it is not a single genetic entity. These conclusions were confirmed by an experiment with the carcinogen 1:2:5:6-dibenzanthracene. The time at which induced tumors appeared as well as tumor incidence and the number of nodules per individual were compared with similar data for spontaneous lung tumors in each of three strains. At least three genes and probably more appeared to be involved.

Contemporary papers by H. B. Andervont and M. B. Shimkin emphasized that the degree of susceptibility was inherited. And the contributions especially of W. E. Heston supported the general conclusions reached at this time and carried the analysis further by extensive studies of the degree of susceptibility occurring in strains of mice and crosses between them.

The view developed in the early work that multiple factors were concerned in the inheritance of lung tumors has been substantiated by experiments begun in 1941 by Heston and continued up to the present time with the occasional assistance of colleagues at the National Cancer Institute. By means of linkage tests, an association has been demonstrated between known genes in the mouse and both spontaneous and induced lung tumors.

Clara Lynch retired in 1947 but continued to work along various lines at the Institute. Turning her attention to leukemia, she obtained valuable information from about forty generations of the Rockefeller substrain AKR that she developed from Furth's well-known leukemic AK strain. AKR mice appear to lack a mammary tumor agent, but are susceptible to one carried by another strain. She reported other details of importance to investigators using such means for cancer and leukemia research.

A new leukemic strain of mice produced by inbreeding and selection from a random-bred Princeton stock is serving as material for her present work on leukemia and viruses.

Murphy encouraged his senior associate, Albert Claude, to begin a project that at first seemed to yield nothing of importance, but in the end resulted in new techniques and major discoveries, not about cancer, but about the structure of normal cells and the chemical activities of submicroscopic organs within them. One of the major aims of Murphy's group, and of Claude in particular, was to isolate the agent causing Rous's Chicken Sarcoma I. Repeated attempts to achieve this by various means, including adsorption, precipitation, or dialysis of the suspected submicroscopic particles had failed. In 1935 two English workers, J. C. G. Ledingham of the Lister Institute and W. E. Gye of the National Institute for Medical Research, separated a tumor-producing agent from Rous tumor material in partially purified state, by high speed centrifugation of pulped tumor material.

Claude hoped that with careful control of the speed of the centrifuge and other factors in preparing the tumor tissue he might more perfectly isolate material responsible for malignant growth, that is to say, virus particles or something of less definable nature. Trying it with the Rous chicken sarcoma in 1939 and in 1940, he did in fact spin out several kinds of granules, including very small ones which carried with them the tumor-producing activity. He soon found, however, that normal tissues yielded closely similar bodies which he could not distinguish physically or chemically from those coming from tumor cells, even though they did not carry the tumor-producing potency. Layers of varied appearance and consistency, formed by centrifugation, proved to be made up of identifiable cell elements of different specific gravity — for example, nuclei, lipid globules, secretion granules, the tiny but numerous mitochondria whose function had long been a puzzle to microscopists, and still smaller, almost submicroscopic, granules which he called microsomes. By decanting and recentrifuging the separate layers, Claude could obtain for study practically pure suspensions of each of these elements. The obvious importance of this means of studying the constitution of cells drew Claude's attention away from the search for components of cancer cells toward investigations in normal cytology.

The Chicago anatomist R. R. Bensley and his student Normand B. Hoerr had since 1934 been using a similar method of analyzing the formed elements in cells, and had made rough chemical tests which showed, for example, that the mitochondrial granules contain proteins and lipids. At first there was some discrepancy between the cell elements identified respectively by the University of Chicago and The Rockefeller Institute investigators, chiefly because of differences in methods of preparation; but in 1946 three workers in Murphy's laboratory, G. H. Hogeboom, W. C. Schneider, and George Palade, found that homogenization and centrifugation in a sugar solution preserved the form of the mitochondria so well that their identification was certain. Even before this stage was reached, however, Claude began to study the chemical nature of the various cell elements obtained by centrifugation. In 1943 he and J. S. Potter of the Carnegie Institution's Department of Genetics at Cold Spring Harbor, Long Island, were the first to obtain from interphase (non-dividing) nuclei threads of chromatin, previously known to microscopists only in the chromosomes of dividing cells. A few years later, as mentioned in Chapter 14, Alfred E. Mirsky and A. W. Pollister, working with more favorable material from tissues of fishes and birds, and from mammalian thymus glands, similarly extracted chromatin from cell nuclei and proved its association with the chromosomes. The protein ingredient of such protoplasmic particles as mitochondria and the microsomes, Claude found, is combined with ribonucleic acid, one of the two kinds of nucleic acid first identified at The Rockefeller Institute years earlier by Phoebus Levene, and now known to participate in many important life processes.

Claude and his co-workers greatly advanced the quantitative precision with which the all-important nucleoproteins and enzymes could be located in the various granules and organelles of the cell. This they did by carrying out a systematic and complete "fractionation" of the cell substance into portions that are separable by centrifugation. By analyzing each of these portions for its content of physiologically important materials, they were able to work out a balance sheet giving the amounts of nucleoproteins and enzymes in each kind of cell element, expressed as a proportion of the corresponding values for the whole of the tissue sample. In this way, Claude not only isolated the microsomes and proved their distinctive identity, but also showed that they contain about half of the ribonucleic acid of the cell.

This increased precision of technique and analysis considerably increased biochemical understanding of the mitochondria also. As early as 1912, the anatomist B. F. Kingsbury of Cornell University had suggested that these minute rod-shaped or granular bodies, found in all cells, may be centers for the utilization of oxygen. Sometime before 1943, Arnold Lazarow of Bensley's Chicago laboratory and workers elsewhere found that two important oxidative enzymes, succinoxidase and cytochrome oxidase, could be identified qualitatively in mitochondria-containing material prepared by Bensley's method. In 1943 Hogeboom of Murphy's group and Rollin D. Hotchkiss (then with Avery's group in The Rockefeller Institute Hospital) began, at Claude's suggestion, a precise study of the enzyme content of the particles isolated from cells. These investigators, working with rat's liver, first homogenized and then fractionated by controlled centrifugation, showed conclusively that cytochrome oxidase and succinoxidase are indeed associated with the mitochondria. When Hogeboom, Schneider, and Palade introduced the sugar-containing suspension medium mentioned above, giving them superior preparations of intact mitochondria in large amounts, they were able to measure the amount of these enzymes in the mitochondria, and to prove that they contain all the succinoxidase and much of the cytochrome oxidase in the cells. Thus these remarkable cell elements, hardly more than objects of curiosity to microscopists when first observed forty years earlier, were shown to be vitally important organs of tissue respiration.

Hogeboom left the Institute in 1948 to take an important post in the National Cancer Institute at Bethesda, Maryland. He and Schneider, who accompanied him there, continued to study the chemical nature of cell organelles; they and their fellow workers in many other laboratories proceeded to locate additional enzymes in the mitochondria, which are now looked upon as veritable packets of chemically active substances taking part in cellular metabolism.

Keith R. Porter, who was to lead the study of cell structures at The Rockefeller Institute after Claude's return to Belgium, joined the lab-

Pioneer oxygen chamber, devised by William C. Stadie

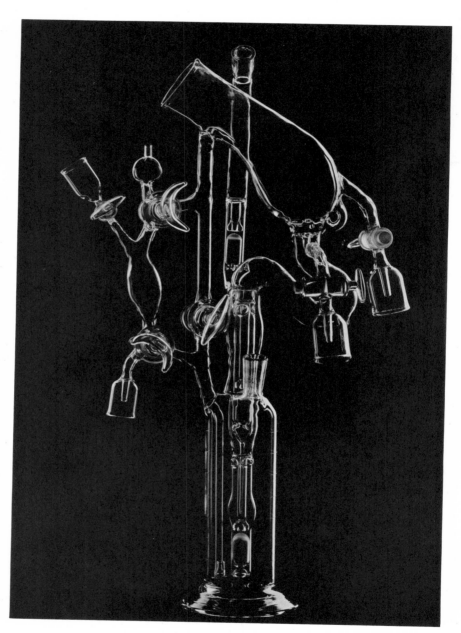

The Carrel-Lindbergh pump

oratories in 1939 at Murphy's invitation, a year after taking his doctor's degree in zoology at Harvard. Murphy, always reaching out for clues to the problems of cancer and of normal growth as well, conjectured that the microsomes Claude had extracted from both normal and sarcomatous cells might carry the power to cause differentiation of tissues or to induce tumor formation. One way to test this hypothesis was to implant the particles on chick embryonic membranes. He chose Porter as an experimental embryologist qualified to make the experiment. Soon finding the project fruitless, Porter resumed an investigation of broad biological interest which he had begun as a graduate student and carried on at Princeton during a fellowship year. Working with frogs' eggs, by deft manipulation he was able to remove the egg nucleus immediately after fertilization, forcing the embryo to develop with the male parental chromosomes only. The experimental pattern could be varied, for example, by fertilizing eggs of a southern race of frogs with sperm of a northern race having slightly different traits, and vice versa. By comparing the resulting embryos, Porter made the beginnings of an analysis of the relative roles of the nucleus and the cytoplasm in determining the characteristics of the embryo. Further variations and extensions of this method of research are still in use by zoologists. At The Rockefeller Institute, where no other work in experimental embryology was then under way, Porter felt himself isolated from fellow workers in this field and he left it when the advent of the electron microscope provided a new outlet for his talents.

During the years 1940 to 1945, when Claude was trying to identify the various elements he had isolated from cells, and to compare them with similar elements found by Bensley and others, he was stretching to the limit the powers of the ordinary optical microscope to see these tiny objects. Just at that time the electron microscope, in process of experimental development for about fifteen years, reached a state at which biologists could use it and gain the benefits of its immense resolving power, about a hundred times greater than that of the optical microscope. One of the first practical users of such an instrument in New York was the industrial research laboratory of the Interchemical Corporation. E. F. Fullam of its staff, learning of Claude's difficulties, suggested a trial of the new instrument, and in the autumn of 1944 the two men made the first electron photographs of mitochondria, at primary magnifications of 4,000 to 5,000 diameters. Crude as their pictures were, they revealed structural details of these minute objects beyond the reach of the optical microscope. Claude and Fullam had to work with isolated mitochondria, because even the thinnest tissue sections cut with an ordinary microtome, one or two microns thick, were too thick to be resolved by the electron microscope.

Porter, at the time working for another purpose with tissue cultures of chick embryo tissue, noticed that some of the cells spread themselves extremely thin on the cover slip. With the same manipulative skill he had shown in his work with frogs' eggs, he succeeded in transferring such cells to the specimen grid of the electron microscope. Excellent micrographs of cells made by this method, at magnifications of 4,500 diameters or more, displayed the smallest previously known cell elements with exceptional clarity and, in addition, revealed new structural details. Notable among these was a netlike pattern of extremely fine canals or chains of vesicles in the extranuclear substance of cells (later named "endoplasmic reticulum"), that was to occupy Porter and his associates for a long time to come. Claude and Porter were thus the first investigators to use the electron microscope for the study of whole cells and their components, and with this achievement the laboratory became an internationally recognized center of research in cytology, although it was not so designated by name until 1950.

For a year or two Claude busied himself chiefly with efforts to cut and handle sections of tissues sufficiently thin to be effectively penetrated by the electron beam, that is to say, of the order of 0.1 micron as against a thickness of one or two microns attainable at best by conventional microtomes. Working at first with an instrument developed by Fullam at the Interchemical laboratories, and later with a better machine built in The Rockefeller Institute shops, he achieved some degree of success. At the time, however, extreme thinness was not the only new requirement for adequate study with the electron microscope. Suitable methods for fixing and dehydrating tissues had also to be developed. Porter, therefore, applied himself to perfecting methods of fixing whole cells for use with the electron microscope, as well as to observations on various types of cells and tissues. With several associates, notably Edward G. Pickels of The Rockefeller Foundation and two visiting Fellows, Clinton V. Hawn

and Parker Vanamee, he studied the structure of cancer cells, the formation of fibrin clots, the development of connective tissue (collagen), and
the behavior of collagen when rendered soluble by acids or alkalis.

Electron microscopy of whole cells from tissue cultures also aided
two striking achievements in the visualization of virus particles. The first
of these was a step toward Claude's long-set goal of isolating the virus of
the Rous chicken sarcoma. With ordinary microscopes, no one had ever
seen inclusion bodies or other abnormal elements that might represent
the filtrable agent in the tumor cells; nor had Murphy and his colleagues
succeeded in isolating as an agent either a chemical substance or a living
organism. In 1947 Claude, Porter, and Pickels grew Rous sarcoma cells
in tissue culture and photographed them with the electron microscope
with a final magnification of 5,900 to 15,800. In contrast with normal
connective-tissue cells, the sarcoma cells contained large numbers of
round bodies about 70 to 85 millimicrons (approximately 1/300,000
inch) in diameter, singly, paired, or in rows. This dimension agreed with
values, previously obtained indirectly by filtration and centrifugation, of
virus suspensions, and there is no doubt that they are actually particles
of the virus which causes the Rous tumor.

The next year Porter and Helen P. Thompson, a visiting Fellow,
used the same method to visualize another much-discussed virus, that
causing mammary carcinoma of mice. In 1933 J. J. Bittner of the Jackson Memorial Laboratories at Bar Harbor, Maine, reported the astonishing fact that the disease, previously thought to be an inherited liability,
is due to something transmitted to young animals in their mother's milk.
Later several investigators showed that the unknown agent had many of
the characteristics of a virus. Workers in two cancer laboratories examined extracts and centrifugates of cancer tissue under high magnification and believed they saw minute particles of a special sort, but such
observations are liable to error, because of the presence of particulate
elements normally existing in cells. Porter and Thompson, going further, grew mammary-gland cells of the cancer-bearing mice in tissue culture, and studied them directly with the electron microscope. Their
micrographs revealed the presence of numerous minute particulate
bodies of a peculiar kind, spherical in form, with a dense inner zone and
clear outer layer. Subsequent work at The Rockefeller Institute and else-

where has amply confirmed the nature and significance of these virus particles, the first to be detected that were beyond doubt related to any form of carcinoma.

From 1944 to 1947, Claude and Porter, lacking an electron microscope of their own, made use of one owned by the laboratories of The Rockefeller Foundation at The Rockefeller Institute. The Institute had installed one of these instruments at the Department of Animal and Plant Pathology in Princeton in 1944. It was operated by Julian A. Carlile, the department's photographer, and used by Louis O. Kunkel, John H. Northrop, and Wendell M. Stanley for photographing plant viruses. The research laboratories of the Radio Corporation of America in Princeton, where this instrument was designed, and its service department in Camden, were close at hand to keep the apparatus in working order. In New York, however, the Director, Gasser, watching with concern the shifting programs of the cancer research laboratories, and aware of the difficulties involved in applying the electron microscope to complex animal tissues, bided his time before authorizing the purchase of a second instrument. Expensive in first cost, requiring skilled technical assistance to keep it in operation, and incessantly consuming photographic supplies, it might prove to be only a formidable scientific toy. Executive caution disappeared, however, before the flood of astonishing pictures and new interpretations of cell structure coming from Claude's group, and in 1948 Claude and Porter got their own RCA instrument.

James B. Murphy reached the age of retirement in 1950. He did not live to witness the continuing development of electron microscopy in the laboratories he had so long directed, for his death within the year brought to an end his career of devotion to cancer research.[2] In reorganizing Murphy's group, the Institute recognized the new trends in the investigation of cell structure. Claude had been called back a year before to Belgium, as professor of cytology and experimental cancer study and director of the Jules Bordet Institute at the University of Brussels. Gasser placed Porter in charge of a laboratory of cytology not limited to cancer research, and recommended his promotion to Associate Member. He had an able co-worker, George E. Palade, an M.D. of the University of Bucharest, who had joined Claude's laboratory in 1946. After working with Hogeboom and Schneider on the biochemistry of mitochondria, as already mentioned, Palade dealt successfully with an important problem in cell chemistry, concerning the location, in the cells of various organs, of acid phosphatase, an enzyme participating in fundamental biochemical reactions. In collaboration with Claude, he studied a puzzling object occurring near the nucleus in practically all cells and known by the name of its discoverer as the "Golgi apparatus." Palade rose rapidly from Assistant to Associate Member in 1953.

In the laboratory of cytology from 1950 to 1953 the investigators aimed chiefly at the improvement of techniques. Porter devoted himself to experimentation on the mechanics of cutting the extremely thin sections required for electron microscopy, and, in collaboration with J. Blum, head of the Institute's machine shop, designed and built an efficient microtome. Palade, who undertook to find better methods of fixation, introduced a fixing fluid so satisfactory that it is now widely used. The next phase was a systematic exploration of animal tissues for structural patterns of general significance. In 1952 and 1953 Palade studied the structure of mitochondria in many kinds of cells. Porter, with Don W. Fawcett, examined the structure of ciliated epithelial cells, concentrating on the very minute cilia which create currents on the surface of many animal membranes, for example, those lining the trachea and the oviduct. With H. Stanley Bennett of the University of Washington he continued a study of the contractile myofibrils of muscle which he began in 1951 with a group of Chicago investigators. With Maria A. Rudzinska of The Rockefeller Institute he explored the structure of a large protozoan, *Tokophrya,* especially interesting because of its possession, within a single cell, of highly differentiated organs, specialized for feeding and reproduction. Following up what is probably the most important general discovery of the laboratory of cytology, that of the endoplasmic reticulum mentioned above, Porter and Palade, joined for a time by Sanford L. Palay (now at the National Institutes of Health, Bethesda, Maryland), worked together upon the elucidation of this network of minute spaces and the related substrate of basophilic material in the cytoplasm of all cells.

The foregoing three chapters do not include the story of research carried on by investigators of two groups that were transferred to the Department of Laboratories during Gasser's directorship. In 1944, after the retirement of Oswald T. Avery, leader of research in immunochemistry in The Rockefeller Institute Hospital, his principal associates —

René J. Dubos,[3] W. F. Goebel, and R. D. Hotchkiss — moved to the Department of the Laboratories, where they continued independent lines of investigation begun in the hospital. When the Department of Animal and Plant Pathology in Princeton was discontinued, six of its senior workers — A. C. Braun, F. O. Holmes, Moses Kunitz, L. O. Kunkel, N. R. Stoll, and William Trager — joined the laboratories in New York, beginning work there in 1949–1950. R. E. Shope rejoined them in 1952. For the sake of continuity in narration, the investigations of all these men, before and after their change of affiliation within the Institute, will be described in the following chapter.

CHAPTER SIXTEEN

Princeton: Animal Pathology

1935–1953

Virus diseases of domestic animals; pleuropneumonia-like organisms; bovine mastitis; parasites of sheep; insect viruses; nutritional needs of insect larvae; axenic cultivation of parasitic worms; cultivation of malarial parasites. Constitution and disease. Purification of enzymes and of antitoxins. Chemistry of bacteriophages.

ALTHOUGH OUR account of the Department of Animal and Plant Pathology in Chapter 12 left off when Herbert S. Gasser succeeded Simon Flexner as director of The Rockefeller Institute, there were no administrative changes at that time to alter or redirect the research program in Princeton. The work of the several groups of investigators can therefore be resumed as of 1935.

In that year Carl TenBroeck, director of the department, was bringing to a close the investigation of equine encephalitis, described in Chapter 12, which had occupied him and several associates since 1933, when he and Malcolm Merrill first described the Eastern form of the disease and distinguished it from the Western. By this time TenBroeck and Merrill, and other investigators, had found six or seven species of the *Aedes* mosquito that conveyed encephalitis. Having found immune bodies in the blood of chickens and turkeys, TenBroeck ended these studies still convinced that birds of some local species must serve as a year-round reservoir of infection. As yet, however, no such host has been positively identified.

Lester S. King (now professor at the University of Illinois), during his stay at TenBroeck's laboratories from 1937 to 1940, carried on several lines of research growing out of his chief's work on equine encephalitis. He studied the pathology of the disease in small laboratory animals, and investigated various other forms of encephalitis, in dogs, goats, and moose. Upon this broad experience he based thoughtful discussions of the mechanisms which normally protect the brain from invasion by way of the blood stream, and of the spread of neurotropic viruses from the point of entry to the tissues of the central nervous system where they set up their specific lesions.

TenBroeck's next contribution dealt with the virus of hog cholera, which many years before he had transmitted for the first time to a small animal, the white rat, in which he could maintain it for a week. In 1932 Friedrich Hecke of the Insel Reims Research Station in Germany reported the cultivation of hog cholera virus in tissue culture, but his work went unconfirmed because of the expense involved in using swine as test animals, and also because of the risk of working with a virus so likely to spread. TenBroeck in 1940 repeated and improved the method of its cultivation by adding minced hog testicle tissue to the culture medium in flasks, or by grafting bits of it onto chick embryonic membranes. Carrying the virus through twenty-six successive transfers on media thus enriched, he produced typical hog cholera by inoculating swine with the culture. Shortly before World War II, TenBroeck and his colleague Roger M. Herriott of the plant pathology laboratories attempted to improve the technique of preparing vaccines from cultivated viruses. They sought chemical agents which would destroy the disease-producing potency of a virus as formaldehyde does, while preserving its power to elicit antibodies. The search, interrupted by the war, was resumed in 1946, when they found a substance with the desired characteristics, namely, the irritant mustard gas used in chemical warfare. Scientists who studied mustard gas during the war found that it acted as a poison of certain enzymes, and that it inactivated tobacco mosaic virus. TenBroeck and Herriott now found that it could inactivate also a number of other viruses, including that of rabies, in such a way that the viruses retained much of their specific immunizing power and hence were useful as vaccines. With it they produced a vaccine against rabies.

In 1935 an epidemic of meningitis of a special type (acute lymphocytic choriomeningitis) broke out in the mouse colony in Princeton. Erich Traub recovered a virus to which he gave several years of intensive study before he left the Institute in 1938. As already mentioned in Chapter 10, one of the Princeton staff contracted this disease during the mouse epidemic and was studied at The Rockefeller Institute Hospital by T. M. Rivers and T. F. M. Scott, who isolated from him a filtrable agent identical with Traub's. Traub's observations show that the mouse is the natural host of this potentially serious infection, which, fortunately, only occasionally causes illness in human beings. The virus, kept alive in mice by healthy carriers, is acquired by infant mice from their mother while still *in utero* or shortly after birth. Usually remaining latent, like many other viruses it is occasionally awakened to virulence by some accidental circumstance, causing a disease which spreads with epidemic rapidity.

James A. Baker, who came to Princeton from Cornell University in 1940 and remained until called back to a professorship there in 1947, added to the department's record of virus discoveries by isolating a filtrable agent causing infectious diarrhea in calves, and another responsible for a form of pneumonia in cats. In 1946 he achieved serial passage of hog cholera virus in rabbits. Björn Sigurdsson, a visiting Fellow from Iceland (now at the Institute for Experimental Pathology at Reykjavik), worked with TenBroeck in 1941–1943 on the cultivation of rabies, vesicular stomatitis, and influenza viruses in chick embryos.

In 1935 Richard E. Shope published the results of his continuing study of a cattle disease, pseudorabies or "mad itch," which he had first observed in 1930. Although not contagious in cattle, it quickly kills most of these animals that contract it. How it spreads in epidemic form was therefore an enigma. Shope first demonstrated that the same infection causes a relatively mild, but highly contagious, illness in swine. Next he showed that the virus exists in the nasal drippings of infected swine; he could transmit the virus to rabbits by injecting nasal washings from infected swine, or by rubbing a sick hog's nose against a patch of abraded skin on the rabbit's abdomen. This he took to mean that swine can directly infect cattle by nosing them near a scratch or abrasion. Inquiring about conditions on several farms where epidemics of pseudorabies had occurred, he learned that in every instance swine had been allowed to run with the cattle. In another phase of the research, he found that wild brown rats develop a fatal infection following ingestion of pseudorabies virus in cattle droppings, and, in turn, swine which eat the rat carcasses become infected. Rats therefore carry the virus from one farm to another. These discoveries gave cattle breeders obvious clues to the control of pseudorabies.

During these years Shope was also occupied with the closing stage of his investigation of the rabbit fibroma and myxoma viruses, described in Chapter 11; and he continued the study of swine influenza which had held his attention for many years. Readers will recall that Shope had shown that swine influenza is caused by a virus, which brings the hog down with a severe attack only when associated with a harmless bacillus, *Hemophilus influenzae suis*. About 1939 he made the surprising discovery that a parasitic nematode worm, the swine lungworm, may harbor and transmit the swine influenza virus. Eggs laid by lungworms in the hog's bronchial vessels are coughed up and swallowed by the hog, emerging in its feces. Ingested by an earthworm, they pass through the larval stages in the worm; when the earthworm is eaten by a hog, they develop to the adult stage, and in doing so reach the hog's lungs. This whole cycle may be completed in a month or may take several years. Lungworm eggs shed while the host hog is suffering with influenza carry the virus in a latent form. Swine that swallow the larvae remain well unless some temporary disturbance of health awakens the virus, which then provokes a severe and sometimes even fatal attack. Although Shope could draw no immediate conclusions regarding the spread of human influenza from this complicated process, his work opened a new vista into the theory of epidemics. The swine influenza story suggests, for instance, that even though no similar parasitic transmission occurs in human influenza, there may be some sort of pre-epidemic seeding of its causative virus, like that which exists in herds of swine carrying a latent virus, which would account for the explosive spread of human epidemics.

Shope was made a full Member of The Rockefeller Institute in 1940, but resigned his post in 1949 when the Princeton department closed, and went to the Merck Institute for Therapeutic Research, as assistant director. In 1952 he returned to The Rockefeller Institute. It is a sign of his characteristic unwillingness to drop any problem not completely solved that, in 1953, he was again working on swine diseases, trying to identify the factors which precipitate an attack of swine influenza in animals carrying latent virus, and factors responsible for a similar consequence in hog cholera. Another quality of this wide-ranging biologist —

his alertness to opportunities for research presented by fortuitous events — was illustrated when, in war service in the South Pacific, Shope collected and brought home living molds of many species, thinking to find some which might produce new antibiotics. One of these, obtained in Guam from a moldy patch on the isinglass cover of a photograph of his wife, when tested at the Merck Institute yielded a substance able to destroy various viruses in experimentally infected mice. Its potential value has led to intensive studies, still in progress, in more than one pharmaceutical research laboratory.

Margaret H. D. Smith (now professor of microbiology at New York University), working with Shope in 1946–1948, cultivated the rabbit fibroma virus, which had defied efforts to grow it in tissue culture. By using chick embryos as hosts for the virus, as had Rous and Murphy years before with the Rous sarcoma virus, she found that she could transfer it through eighteen successive passages without loss of virulence.

Frederik B. Bang came to Princeton in 1941, after several years with the U.S. Public Health Service.[1] Earlier, during a fellowship year at Vanderbilt University, he had worked with E. W. Goodpasture, cultivating viruses in chick embryos and studying their host-parasite relationships. At The Rockefeller Institute Bang employed this experience in experimental studies on several viruses in which other workers at the Institute were deeply interested. In 1941–1942 he cultivated the virus of pseudorabies on which Shope had done pioneer work in 1930. He found that in chick embryos this virus behaves in an unusual way, not only causing a reaction in the embryonic membranes, as do many viruses, but spreading through and damaging all the tissues of the central nervous system, as does the mad itch infection in cattle.

Bang's next study also followed up one of Shope's discoveries. Shope had found, as already mentioned, that swine influenza is caused by the concerted action of a virus and a bacterium, but had been unable to produce this complex kind of infection experimentally in other species. In chick embryos, however, Bang was able to produce a synergistic action of the two agents (swine influenza virus and *Hemophilus influenzae*), resulting in a mortality several times greater than that caused by either one alone. This confirmation of Shope's findings not only is of practical importance as regards swine influenza, but is theoretically suggestive, in connection with human influenza, for a similar synergism between a virus and one or another bacterial organism (*Bacillus influenzae, Dialister pneumosintes,* etc.) had been suspected of causing the severe epidemic forms of that disease. In 1942–1943 Bang joined forces with Herriott in partially purifying the equine encephalitis virus.

After World War II, during which Bang was diverted from virus research, he took up the study of Newcastle disease, a fatal virus infection of chickens, which sometimes causes a relatively mild disease of poultry handlers. Purifying the virus by ultracentrifugation, using the equipment Stanley's group had introduced for work on tobacco mosaic virus, Bang made the first electron micrographs of the virus particles of Newcastle disease. In 1947 this energetic, highly cooperative investigator was called to the Johns Hopkins Medical School. The department which he heads there, formerly designated as parasitology, has been renamed pathobiology in accord with Theobald Smith's concepts of the biology of disease.

John B. Nelson's experience with fowl coryza, narrated in Chapter 11, prepared him for rapid success, in 1937, in analyzing an outbreak of infectious catarrh in the Princeton colony of white mice. In the nasal discharges of infected animals Nelson found small round (coccobacilliform) bodies much like those he had discovered in the fowl disease. Cultivating these organisms in the laboratory, he produced the catarrhal disease by inoculating healthy mice. In 1940 he found similar organisms in rats ill with a catarrhal discharge, and in subsequent experiments showed the identity of the rat and mouse strains of coccobacilliform bodies, by reciprocal transmission of the disease from mice to rats and vice versa, through direct contact and also by nasal instillation of infective exudates and of cultures containing the coccobacilliform bodies.

These organisms, like those Nelson had found responsible for fowl coryza, belong to the group of pleuropneumonia-like organisms, which, under the abbreviated title PPLO, have begun to attract considerable interest as possibly pathogenic for man. There is a growing suspicion that organisms of this type are responsible for certain infections of the human urinary and genital tracts. Observations made by Nelson in 1953 may be significant in this connection. Injecting a strain of PPLO responsible for catarrhal disease in mice into female mice by way of the abdominal cavity, Nelson found that the organisms caused an acute infection of the ovaries and oviducts (fallopian tubes), and for several weeks thereafter could be recovered from the vagina.

One of Nelson's investigations, conducted in 1938–1943, seems to have settled a very old problem. Ever since Edward Jenner in 1798 introduced vaccination with cowpox as a preventive of smallpox, bacteriologists and laymen alike had been puzzled by the relation of the two diseases, so close biologically that one confers immunity against the other. Once it was known that both variola (smallpox) and vaccinia (cowpox) are caused by viruses, the question became, more specifically, whether smallpox virus can transform itself into cowpox virus. Some evidence of such a change, occurring during multiple passages through laboratory animals, had been adduced, but chiefly from laboratories where both viruses were under study, so that contamination of one by the other could not be fully ruled out. Nelson, having developed two bacteria-free strains of variola virus which he kept going for years in embryonated hens' eggs, observed no transformation in two hundred transfers of one strain, forty-four of the other. Successfully establishing one of the strains in the rabbit's testis, he again observed no transformation in ten transfers. From those findings he deduced that smallpox virus remains biologically stable, maintaining its own specific characteristics even under drastic experimental conditions. Although variola and vaccinia viruses presumably had a common origin, they now evidently constitute two distinct species.

When Nelson returned to Princeton after World War II, he began investigating endemic pneumonia of rats, a disease long familiar and vexatious to breeders of rats for laboratory use. Nelson found that he could transmit it to mice by inoculating them with lung exudates or suspensions of lung tissue from infected rats. The disease appears to be identical in the two species. Excluding bacteria and pleuropneumonia-like organisms, he found the causal factor to be a large-particle virus carried by adult animals, often without harm to them, and transmitted by mother rats to their young at birth. In 1948 Nelson resumed an effort, begun with J. W. Gowen in 1931, to develop a rat colony free from the two chief respiratory infections of this species, otitis media and endemic pneumonia. In the earlier attempt he and Gowen had eliminated otitis but not pneumonia. This time Nelson began with animals acquired from the well-known colony then conducted by Father J. A. Reynier, Notre Dame University's specialist in axenic (germ-free) culture. These rats, though not themselves germ-free, had been taken from their mothers at birth and, therefore, had not acquired the pneumonia virus. With the fresh start, and with experience gained from years of work with small-animal infections, Nelson succeeded in building up a rat colony free from both endemic viral pneumonia and otitis media.

His latest research during the period ending in 1953 dealt with a form of hepatitis which appeared in a group of mice among which mouse leukemia was occurring. Another type of virus-induced hepatitis was reported about this time by Christopher Andrewes and J. W. Gledhill of the National Institute for Medical Research in London. Nelson found the hepatitis in his mice was also caused by a virus which he was able to separate from the leukemia cells. He found that in any mouse colony many mice may be carrying the hepatitis virus in latent form. When such mice are used for serial transmission of the leukemia tumor, after a certain number of passages the added burden causes the latent virus to become active and set up hepatitis. Working, subsequently, with another transplantable malignant disease, resembling the well-known Ehrlich ascites tumor, Nelson found that it too can trigger the hepatitis virus into activity. In this case something more happens; the presence of hepatitis is accompanied by a slow regression of the tumor, sometimes even its complete disappearance. Nelson is actively continuing his study of the intricate problems raised by this apparent interplay of a virus and a tumor.

The practical benefits accruing from Nelson's long study of the bacteriology and virology of laboratory animals were publicly recognized later when the Animal Care Panel, an organization devoted to the improvement of animal care in laboratories, gave him its Charles A. Griffin Award, noting that his research on endemic pneumonia of rats had led not only to control of this respiratory infection, but also to elimination of many other diseases in animal colonies.

As mentioned in Chapter 11, Frederick S. Jones began to study bovine mastitis (infection of the cow's udder) in 1916, as soon as the Princeton laboratories were opened, and did much to incriminate hemolytic streptococci as its chief cause. When he died in 1934, Ralph B. Little, a capable investigator long associated with Jones, carried on this work. He extended Jones's bacteriological findings, producing mastitis experimentally by inoculating cows' milk ducts with hemolytic streptococci of both bovine and human strains. Little also showed that mastitis caused by *Streptococcus agalactiae* can be controlled by systematic bacteriological tests of the milk of individual cows, with prompt elimination of infected animals from the herd. By this means two herds were kept free of the disease for three and four years respectively.

This method of control was, however, very expensive for dairymen, because in some herds a third or even a half of the cows were infected. In 1940 Little joined forces with René J. Dubos and R. D. Hotchkiss, of the Institute's New York laboratories, who had discovered, by ingenious experiments to be described in Chapter 19, an antibiotic they called gramicidin which is effective against streptococci. This drug, the three workers found, destroys the invading organisms in 60 per cent or more of cases, and thus greatly reduces the number of cows to be eliminated from the herd. Following up these pioneering experiments, investigators elsewhere found other antibiotics also effective against mastitis. As a result, this disease, when caused by *Streptococcus agalactiae,* is now fairly well under control, but unfortunately the udder of the dairy cow, developed through long ages for high milk production, remains an all-too-favorable culture site for disease germs. Other organisms besides the streptococcus may cause mastitis, and the disease remains a serious problem for dairy farmers.[2]

C. V. Seastone (now professor of microbiology at the University of Wisconsin) had a share in this study of antibiotic treatments, by testing a sulfa derivative which proved effective. Interest in the general problems of streptococcal disease led him to study in 1939 a peculiar chronic lymph-gland infection of guinea pigs caused by a hemolytic streptococcus, which at the instance of Theobald Smith had been kept going in a small group of animals ever since its discovery in Princeton in 1931. During Seastone's observations of the infected colony, he had an opportunity, as Theobald Smith had some years before with a similar disease, to witness a striking occurrence with far-reaching implications for the study of epidemics. Apparently because of a sudden variation of the infecting streptococcus, an acute and fatal illness broke out in the little colony of guinea pigs, killing half of them, and then subsided, leaving the chronic infection to go on as before.

In the later years of Little's research he investigated with James A. Baker a quite different infection of the udder, caused by an organism of the *Leptospira* type, which he showed to be responsible for epidemics of an acute febrile illness of cattle, occurring in New Jersey, Pennsylvania, and Illinois, and characterized by secretion of abnormal or bloody milk. After the Princeton laboratories closed, he still needed facilities for research with large animals, and in 1950 he transferred his work to the experimental farm of the University of Pennsylvania's School of Veterinary Medicine. There he studied infectious and nutritional diseases of horses, cattle, and goats. His retirement concluded forty-one years of continuous service on the staff of The Rockefeller Institute.

IN 1934 Rudolph Glaser's attack on the Japanese beetle, by using the nematode worm *Neoaplectana* to parasitize the beetle grubs, was in full swing, as told in Chapter 12. Using his culture methods, the U.S. Bureau of Entomology was growing the nematodes by tens of millions. The New Jersey Department of Agriculture took part in the program, by developing methods of introducing the nematode larvae into soils infested with beetle grubs, and by testing the results in the field. With three of its workers, C. C. Farrell, E. E. McCoy, and H. B. Girth, Glaser demonstrated that the worms could be established in the soils and could effectively reduce the beetle population.

While these studies were in progress, the Bureau of Entomology found that another natural enemy of the Japanese beetle, a spore-bearing bacterium causing "milky disease" of the grubs in the soil, offered an easier method of attacking the beetle. The artificial introduction of *Neoaplectana* into the soil was therefore discontinued, but Glaser's experience with it was not wasted, for he returned later to nematode worms in research on axenic culture.

Glaser was one of the pioneer workers in the field of bacteria-free cultivation of invertebrate animals. As we shall see, many biological problems can be solved only by keeping the animals under study free from microbial contaminants. The effort to do this created a special field of research led by Reynier of Notre Dame, who worked largely with small mammals. The word "axenic" was introduced by two of Glaser's associates, Baker and Malcolm S. Ferguson, with advice from the Princeton University Department of Classics, because they needed a more precise term than "sterile," which has the additional implication of reproductive sterility. Earlier, Glaser had cultivated *Paramecium* and other protozoa freed from living contaminants. William Trager's axenic cultivation of mosquito larvae, to be discussed later in this chapter, was directly stimulated by Glaser's work. Norman R. Stoll and his colleagues also entered the field, making the parasitology laboratories in Princeton a center of such research.

Glaser's return, about 1937, to work of this kind, to which he was to devote his chief attention until his untimely death in 1947, began with the development of a method for the sterile cultivation of houseflies.[3] His chief effort, however, grew out of Stoll's investigation of *Haemonchus* (parasitic wireworm of sheep) and the latter's attempt to find a method of making sheep resistant to it. Stoll foresaw that to develop a vaccine against *Haemonchus* he must somehow obtain quantities of the uncontaminated worm larvae. For this purpose, and also for controlled studies on the life history and behavior of the parasite, Glaser and Stoll made an immensely difficult effort to cultivate the larvae axenically.

Haemonchus has a life cycle similar to that of the hookworm; the first two larval stages live free in the soil, but the last two larval and the adult stages are obligate parasites. As the second-stage larva completes its development, the cuticle of the worm separates from its body, forming a sheath, the presence of which indicates that the third-stage larva within can now infect sheep. This protective cuticular sheath is normally lost after the larva is ingested by the sheep host. Glaser and Stoll were able to sterilize *Haemonchus* eggs and to rear the free third and fourth stages, using some of the larvae successfully to infect a susceptible lamb.

The free-living larvae did not, however, grow axenically in the large numbers required to initiate *in vitro* development of the parasitic stages. The two investigators met the difficulty by growing infective larvae in sheep dung under normal non-axenic conditions, then chemically removing the sheath and sterilizing the larvae. These they reared *in vitro*, bacteria-free, through the third and fourth larval stages, and sometimes even to the first adult stage. In this way they had carried *Haemonchus* larvae *in vitro* well beyond the point at which they would have died except in the body of a sheep. This was a very significant advance; eighteen years elapsed before P. P. Weinstein and M. Jones of the U.S. National Institutes of Health succeeded in developing a parasitic nematode of a mammal axenically *in vitro,* farther than Stoll and Glaser had carried *Haemonchus.* When the latter found themselves in 1938 unable to carry *Haemonchus* as far in culture as they desired, Glaser turned again to *Neoaplectana.*

Stoll, however, continued to study *Haemonchus,* with particular attention to breaking the block at the end of the free-living stage, and thus to initiate development into the fourth stage. The chief requirement, he found, was to keep the larvae at the temperature of the sheep host, under reduced oxygen tension. The transition from the infective third-stage larva to the beginning of the fourth stage was accelerated by the addition of commercial heat-stable liver extract and balanced dilute salt solution.

Aiming to cultivate the parasite *Neoaplectana* axenically, Glaser succeeded in growing the worms in test tubes on pieces of fresh sterile rabbit kidney on sterilized dextrose agar. This was the first time any investigator ever grew generation after generation of a parasitic worm *in vitro,* through its complete life cycle, without a return to the host. After this success with *Neoaplectana glaseri* he achieved a similar result, in collaboration with E. E. McCoy and H. B. Girth of the New Jersey Department of Agriculture, with a related species, *Neoaplectana chresima.* The program was interrupted by World War II, when Glaser worked on urgent problems of malaria. At the time of his death at the age of fifty-nine, he held the rank of Associate Member of The Rockefeller Institute.

Stoll, by 1942, commanded a method of obtaining large quantities of germ-free infective *Haemonchus* larvae, which gave him unique material for immunological work. Using thousands of these exsheathed larvae in a single dose, he could inject them as a vaccine, subcutaneously or intraperitoneally, into his lambs. Unlike many other parasitic nematodes, Stoll found, *Haemonchus* larvae do not wander through the body of the host. Those he injected remained where they were placed by the needle, forming a pool of antigenic material capable of eliciting antibodies against themselves. Out of ten sheep treated, nine showed evidence of protection, six of them to a high degree, when tested by feeding them by mouth a huge dose of the larvae.

These promising pioneering attempts to vaccinate sheep against parasitic worms were interrupted in 1943 by Stoll's call to wartime service with the Navy in the South Pacific. Returning to his laboratory in Princeton, shortly after Glaser's death, he began attempts to cultivate the beetle parasite *Neoaplectana glaseri* in fluid media, in the hope of making the cultures more convenient for experimental use. By adding a filtered extract of raw liver to the veal infusion broth used by bacteriologists, he created a favorable medium. About three years of experimentation with technical details of the cultivation method brought success. He was finally able, starting with worms grown axenically on kidney tissue, to carry the worms in fluid cultures for about three generations, long enough to provide convenient material for experiment. Keeping the stock cultures in kidney tissue going all this time, he reported in 1953 that he had carried them for seven years, during which they had passed through more than one hundred and eighty generations *in vitro*, and that after this long period they were still capable of parasitizing their natural host, the Japanese beetle. Stoll has followed up this achievement in later work, beyond the scope of our history, upon the axenic culture of other parasitic animals, notably an entameba closely related to that responsible for amebic dysentery in man.

Malcolm Ferguson took part in the axenic culture work of Glaser's group from 1938 until he joined the U.S. Public Health Service in 1947. He began with a trematode worm, the fluke *Posthodiplostomum minimum*, which in its adult stage is hermaphroditic and lives in the intestine of the wild duck. It passes through an intermediate, or metacercarial, stage in which it is encysted in the muscles of fish. Ferguson was able to free metacercariae from the cysts and grow them axenically in test tubes until they produced eggs — the first successful accomplishment of this kind in the axenic culture of trematodes. Later, working with another fluke, *Diplostomum flexicaudum*, he cultivated an earlier stage, carrying the larvae *in vitro* to the metacercarial stage. In 1942 he and Baker extended the use of axenic culture by adapting it to the little Mexican viviparous fish, *Platypoecilus maculatus*. Utilizing the special opportunity provided by the development of the fry in a sac in the mother fish's ovary, they were able to deliver the young by a kind of miniature caesarian section and to start them off in life in a bacteria-free state.

William Trager in 1933 joined The Rockefeller Institute's Princeton group of parasitologists, directly from his graduate studies at Harvard. For a year he was a guest worker, as a National Research Council

Fellow, and for another year was assistant in Glaser's laboratory, but he was soon working independently. His first publication from the Institute dealt with a disease of larval silkworms, known as *grasserie* and also as "polyhedral disease" because it was characterized by polyhedral cell inclusions in certain of the larval tissues. Glaser and others had shown that this condition is caused by a virus, and supposed the polyhedral bodies to be analogous to the rounded or granular cell inclusions commonly seen in virus diseases of animals and plants. The cultivation of viruses outside of their hosts had been progressing rapidly, following Carrel's demonstration in 1910 that the virus of the Rous chicken sarcoma could be propagated in tissue cultures of susceptible cells. Carrel, Rivers, Olitsky, Traub, Long, and others, at The Rockefeller Institute and elsewhere, had propagated viruses from vertebrate animals in this way, and White had accomplished the same feat at the Princeton laboratories with two plant viruses. Trager then tried to find out whether a virus from an insect host could be similarly propagated and whether it would behave, in tissue culture, like those viruses which are associated with diseases of vertebrates.

Previous attempts to cultivate insect tissues *in vitro* had met with little success, but Trager finally got silkworm ovaries to grow on culture slides. Inoculating these cultures with blood from caterpillars infected with grasserie, he readily grew the virus, and transferred the disease to fresh caterpillars. In tissue culture the virus behaved much like those associated with vertebrate animals, multiplying only in the presence of living cells, in which it formed the polyhedral inclusion bodies characteristic of grasserie.

Another of Trager's early investigations at the Institute dealt with a biological theorem, known as Przibram's rule, from the European zoologist who formulated it in 1912. This is a mathematical formula expressing the rate of growth of an insect, from which Przibram and others in turn drew certain conclusions as to the rate of cell division in the growing organism, on the assumption that the cells of the insect or its larva remain the same size throughout the period under study. Noting that no one had tested these conclusions by direct measurement, Trager went to the great labor of measuring under the microscope a statistically adequate number of cells of larvae of the silkworm and of a species of greenbottle fly, sectioned for the purpose. His finding — that the entire growth of the fly larva results from increase in size, not in number, of the cells composing the larval tissue — surprised biologists, and forced them to reconsider previous assumptions about the rate of cell division. In the silkworm larva, Trager found, some tissues grow by increase of cell size only, others by cell division as well. These facts have found their way into current biological treatises.

In 1935 Trager began to study mosquito larvae, especially those of the yellow fever vector *Aedes aegypti,* to discover the dietary requirements for their growth. He faced at once the peculiar difficulty that the water in which these larvae ordinarily grow contains bacteria, upon which they feed. Any dietary experiments done with larvae under such conditions would fail to disclose the essential requirements of the larvae as distinguished from those of the bacteria. Up to that time, however, all efforts to grow mosquito larvae in bacteria-free media had met with almost total failure. Drawing on the experience of Glaser's laboratory with axenic culture techniques, Trager was able to adapt to his own purposes a method used by Glaser and Nicholas Coria, a year or two before, to cultivate the familiar protozoan *Paramecium* in a salt solution enriched with various organic products.

Provided with a supply of bacteria-free *Aedes* larvae, he proceeded to test their nutritional requirements by varying the constituents of the culture fluid. In this way he found two factors, or rather groups of factors, without which the larvae could not grow, one of which can be supplied by a yeast extract, the other by a liver extract. Pursuing research with axenic larvae until about 1948, Trager identified, one by one, the specific essential substances in the two extracts, which included riboflavin, nicotinic acid, thiamin, pantothenic acid, and biotin, all well known to nutrition workers in other fields. His findings greatly helped to establish the general principle that insects require the same growth factors of the vitamin B complex as do vertebrates.

In 1938, while conducting experiments on guinea pigs with the American dog tick, *Dermacentor variabilis,* Trager observed that if he permitted successive batches of tick larvae to engorge themselves upon a single guinea pig during the course of weeks, the first batch yielded a large number of engorged larvae, but later batches yielded few or none. This form of acquired resistance, which Trager was the first to discover, persists for months. He went on to test several related species of ticks on rabbits and deer mice, and observed the development of cross-immunity; that is, animals infested with larvae of one species of tick became resistant to related species as well. In subsequent experiments Trager immunized guinea pigs to dog-tick larvae by inoculating them intracutaneously with an extract of larval ticks; furthermore, he was able to transfer such immunity passively, by inoculating the animals with serum from other guinea pigs made resistant by repeated infestations. Resistance of this kind helps greatly to explain the survival of wild mammals in regions heavily infested with blood-sucking ticks.

Having succeeded in cultivating the yellow fever mosquito, Trager next attempted the far more difficult cultivation *in vitro* of a mosquito-borne parasite that causes malaria. For this he chose to use, not the agent of human malaria, but the species *Plasmodium lophurae,* originally found in an Oriental pheasant, which can be transmitted experimentally to ducks and chickens. Working with such an avian parasite, he would always have readily available test animals (chicks) with which to determine the infectivity of his cultures.

Malaria parasites grow only within the red blood cells of infected animals. At first, therefore, Trager used fluids designed to preserve red blood cells. He tried a modification of the Rous-Turner preservative solution used in blood banks, but had better success with a salt solution to which he added chick embryo extract, liver extract, yeast, and other organic materials. By 1943 he had succeeded in keeping the parasites alive for as long as sixteen days, with a small increase in number. His best result was obtained after he added pantothenic acid to his culture medium, and he reasoned from this that an analogue of pantothenic acid, which would compete with it for a place in the metabolic processes of a parasite, might serve as an antimalarial drug. This idea, mentioned already in Chapter 14 in connection with the work of D. W. Woolley, proved correct, and was confirmed elsewhere, although the discovery has not been put to use.

These studies on the nutritional requirements of the malaria parasite led Trager to consider also the nutritional state of the host in relation to susceptibility. It was known that individual animals and men differ in susceptibility to malaria, but no one had demonstrated a direct relation between any particular factor and the degree of susceptibility. Poor nutrition had been suggested as one such factor, but without experimental evidence. In 1942 Trager attacked this problem by subjecting chickens and ducks to a deficiency of biotin, one of the essential dietary factors. Such a deficiency is easily produced by feeding an excessive amount of egg white, which contains an anti-biotin substance. The experimental result, that the biotin-deficient hosts developed much more severe infections with the *Plasmodium lophurae* than did non-deficient controls, was the first direct evidence of a nutritional factor in susceptibility to malaria.

Returning to Princeton in 1945, after a wartime assignment to study human malaria in the Pacific area, Trager resumed his cultivation of *Plasmodium lophurae*. Thus far he had utilized methods which kept alive the red blood cells in which the parasites ordinarily grow. Now he attempted to cultivate *Plasmodium* freed from red blood cells. It was obvious, of course, that obligatory intracellular parasites of this kind, dependent for support upon the metabolism of the cells in which they grow, must have lost some, perhaps many, of the chemical potencies by which free-living cells independently utilize nutritive substances. Trager's experiments, therefore, were of the trial-and-error method, involving the addition to his cultures of substances which the parasite needed but could not synthesize for itself. Among the first were those which furnish energy by metabolizing carbohydrates; the addition of adenosine triphosphate and pyruvic acid immediately increased the life span of parasites living free in the culture medium. Pursuing this line of research as lately as 1952, Trager improved the solution by adding certain other substances, notably malic acid and the oxygen-mobilizing coenzyme A, which are of prime importance in biosynthetic reactions. By this painstaking gradual development of the artificial culture medium, he succeeded in cultivating parasites freed from red blood cells, for periods as long as five days. Those which were about to divide when first released from the duck's red blood cells into the culture medium completed their division and proceeded to the mature state in which they normally exist in the blood cells. The difficulties Trager had to overcome in reaching this success show how far the malarial parasite has gone along the road of parasitic degeneration.

R. Barclay McGhee (now professor of biology at the University of Georgia) assisted Trager from 1948 in the investigation of malarial parasites of birds, studying particularly the natural resistance of the red blood cells to invasion by the parasites, which, he found, increases with maturity of the red blood cells. This led McGhee in 1949 to study the course of infection with *Plasmodium lophurae* in chick embryos, which he found to possess no natural resistance to malarial infection. Following this up, the next year McGhee accomplished the remarkable feat of establishing a malaria parasite of birds (again the useful *Plasmodium lophurae*) in a mammal, the mouse. Heretofore such experimental cross-infections had succeeded only within the same biological class, *e.g.*, bird to bird, man to monkey. McGhee's success was achieved by an ingenious, though very tedious, procedure. First growing his parasites in the non-resistant chick embryo, he transferred them to infant mice by inoculating the embryo's blood. Although the resistance even of very young mice was sufficient to kill off all but a few of the injected parasites, those which survived in the mouse's blood constituted a relatively vigorous strain. McGhee then gave this strain a chance to increase in numbers and vigor by transferring it back to chick embryos. After several such passages the parasites were able to maintain themselves in the mouse and could be kept going by transfers directly from mouse to mouse every seven days.

When the Princeton laboratories were closed Trager moved to the New York laboratories and has continued to work in the field of nutrition of insects and their parasites.

When the research group of Wade Hampton Brown, Louise Pearce, Harry S. N. Greene, and their associates was in 1935 transferred from the New York laboratories to those in Princeton, Brown had been at work for six years in a valiant attempt to study the relation of bodily constitution to disease. His interest in this subject stemmed directly from his previous studies on experimental trypanosomiasis and syphilis, and on the rabbit tumor which he and Louise Pearce had succeeded in transplanting. The studies had shown him the importance of the host's constitution in reaction to these diseases. In this conclusion he was not alone. Whereas for many decades pathologists and bacteriologists had emphasized the external causes of disease, certain medical thinkers were now beginning to consider the importance of the patient's constitution, with its innate tendencies toward abnormality and disease, and its varying inherent ability to resist such external enemies as bacteria and viruses.[4] This trend was greatly influenced by two newly developing sciences, anthropology and genetics. At this period a school of medical men, led by George Draper (once a member of the staff of The Rockefeller Institute's hospital), was expounding the so-called "constitutional medicine," in an attempt to define anthropological types susceptible to particular diseases; and exponents of genetics and its quasi-scientific sister, eugenics, were emphasizing heredity as the underlying cause of constitutional similarities and differences between individuals.

Wade Brown devoted the last twenty years of his life to applying both these disciplines in working out the relation of constitution to disease in an experimental animal colony. He had, to begin with, a great mass of data, accumulated during years of research on syphilis and malignant tumors in rabbits, conducted with Louise Pearce and their associates (Chapter 9). From these records he drew for his Harvey Lecture, given in 1929,[4] an analysis of constitutional status, as measured by variations of organ weights, and of the chemical constituents of the blood, and to these variations he related the incidence of disease in his rabbit colony. In rabbits, he concluded, as presumably in human beings, bodily constitution is an essential factor in liability to disease. Observations on seasonal variations in susceptibility of rabbits to disease suggested that the physical environment — sunlight, temperature, diet — is one of two major determinants of constitutional status, the other being heredity. He planned, therefore, to work with animals of known genetic constitution, in order to link together these two important factors in susceptibility and resistance to disease.

In the years that followed, Brown and his collaborators watched their rabbit colony closely for animals presenting signs of skeletal and endocrine disorders, inherent nutritional defects, and spontaneous tumors. Such animals were bred and their progeny followed. By 1933 the group had isolated for study several such conditions that had a hereditary basis; at least, they could be produced regularly, by mating selected animals of the affected family line, and could be transmitted to an unrelated line by hybrid mating.

Because Brown was primarily interested in disease patterns, not in the isolated single characters and simple combinations which non-medical geneticists were using to trace Mendelian heredity, he chose to study a group of diseases involving widespread anatomical, physiological, and biochemical disturbances, for example, avitaminosis, cretinoid-acromegalic affections, ricketslike diseases, toxemia of pregnancy, and tumors of several kinds. By their very nature, these diseases defied simple methods of genetic analysis and called for an extensive breeding program to overcome the variability of the inherited disease complexes. Yet Brown's comments at the time show a good deal of insight into the nature of hereditary functional disorders. He realized that these are inherited (as he put it) in a conditional way, the hereditary influence often producing a potential rather than an actual anomaly or disorder, the expression of which is elicited by environmental factors. This conclusion has stood the test of time and is an integral principle of modern medical genetics.

Brown knew that his program would have to go on for a long time to realize its full possibilities. He did not grudge the cost to himself, in time and labor, of keeping up the immense rabbit colony, nor of the necessarily extensive microscopic and chemical studies entailed by the investigations. His working day often did not end until midnight. Soon, however, the demand for space in which to house animals exceeded the facilities of the New York laboratories. Three harassing epidemics of a hitherto unknown virus disease, resembling smallpox in man, devastated the colony in 1932, 1933, and 1935, setting the work back and necessitating deficiency appropriations for extra supplies and expenses. Flexner, foreseeing increasing difficulty in housing this large and troublesome enterprise in New York, recommended its transfer to Princeton in 1935.[5]

Shortly after the move, a human disaster struck the work; Brown suffered a painful and incapacitating illness (duodenal ulcer) that for several years kept him from directing the work and from which, indeed, he never fully recovered. To his senior colleagues Louise Pearce and Harry Greene fell the task of carrying on and ultimately terminating the program. Pearce had contributed much to Brown's massive information on environmental conditions, through work done with him and an assistant, C. M. Van Allen, on the effects of light upon bodily status, and on organ weights of rabbits and their susceptibility to experimental syphilis, trypanosomiasis, and cancer. In 1930–1931 she and A. E. Casey (now pathologist at the University of Alabama) made a thorough study of the blood cells of rabbits, both healthy and ill with experimental syphilis and cancer. When the epidemics of rabbit pox struck the colony, Pearce, aided by Paul D. Rosahn (now pathologist to the New Britain,

Connecticut, Memorial Hospital) and C. K. Hu, a visitor from Peiping, isolated the virus and carried out an elaborate study of immune reactions, the susceptibility of rabbits under various conditions, and the epidemiology of the disease. Meanwhile Greene carefully described the clinical manifestations and pathology of rabbit pox and studied the relation of constitutional factors (age and state of health) to susceptibility. Thus the calamitous effects of the rabbit pox epidemic upon the programed study were to some extent offset by the acquisition of extensive information about the nature and transmission of a remarkable virus disease.

Greene had joined the New York laboratories in 1931 as an Assistant with Brown, and was promoted to Associate about the time of the move to Princeton. He was studying one of the hereditary conditions in which Brown was interested (oxycephaly, an anomaly of the skull), when the outbreak of rabbit pox diverted him to its investigation. When the emergency was over, he studied in detail a form of toxemia of pregnancy in the rabbit which, he found, was determined by heredity but precipitated by conditions of stress occasioned by other constitutional factors which became decisive during pregnancy. Aided in part by an assistant, John A. Saxton, Jr., Greene also investigated the pathology and hereditary transmission of a number of different tumors that occurred spontaneously in the colony. Although the rabbit had been considered relatively free from spontaneous tumors, the continuous, intensive study of every animal used in all phases of the program yielded six or eight varieties of cancer of the mammary gland, uterus, kidney, and skin. Earlier experimenters had found that the anterior chamber of the eye is a favorable place for the growth of transplanted tissue, which in that location is relatively sheltered from the body's mechanisms of defense against foreign tissues. Using his collection of various tumors, Greene made many experiments on the transplantation of tumor tissue to alien species, successfully transplanting several rabbit tumors to the eyes of guinea pigs, swine, goats, and sheep, and several types of human malignant tumors, similarly, to rabbits and guinea pigs. In 1942 he reported having grown a human fibrosarcoma more than two years in the eye through fourteen successive transplantations from one rabbit to another.

The administration of The Rockefeller Institute, concerned about the magnitude of Brown's enterprise, in view of his precarious health, informed him in 1940 that the Executive Committee had voted not to carry his experiments beyond his expected date of retirement (1943), although it would review the evidence in favor of continuing the work after he had written up the results for publication. Brown began, nevertheless, to reduce the list of diseases and abnormalities under study. When Greene left in 1941 to join the Yale department of pathology, which he headed a few years later, he took with him the research on tumors, and, later, the tumor-bearing stocks of rabbits were transferred to his laboratory in New Haven. After Brown's sudden death in 1942, before he could begin to write up the work, Pearce attempted to salvage as much as possible. Advised by a committee of eminent pathologists and geneticists (Eugene L. Opie, Sewall Wright, Leslie C. Dunn, and Clarence C. Little), she considerably reduced the colony, continuing active breeding of one disease condition only, a form of premature senescence; and began to prepare for publication the accumulated data on achondroplasia, osteopetrosis, an eye defect including cataract and glaucoma, cystic disease of the kidney, and a complex condition combining hydrocephalus and several other abnormal conditions.

To complete the breeding experiments, close down the colony, and prepare reports from Brown's records, not all of which were available, was a task sufficiently heavy to occupy Louise Pearce for years to come. Before she retired in 1950 she published several papers describing the character and inheritance of achondroplasia and osteopetrosis. Since then, in spite of many other duties in the field of medical education, including the presidency for several years of the Woman's Medical College in Philadelphia, she continued until her death to analyze the records and to describe some of the other hereditary conditions that were studied from 1929 to 1950.

Looking back on the story of this ambitious project, dogged by so much ill fortune, it is difficult to conjecture what would have come of it if Brown had lived. It is easy to say in retrospect that it was too elaborately planned, that Brown collected types of disease and anomalies in such numbers that they could never have been worked up, and that he was too much concerned with complex patterns of disease that defied genetic analysis. It must be remembered, however, that when he conceived the program the medical profession was far less aware of hereditary and constitutional factors than it is today. Greene, looking at the state of medical knowledge at the time of Brown's death, wrote in an obituary notice that from the point of view of human constitution and the inheritance of disease, the implications of Brown's work were revolutionary, demanding a reconsideration of fundamental concepts in pathology and genetics. Even though the work was not completed and remains to a large extent unpublished, its progress was currently known to fellow scientists in the field. Through papers published by the Princeton group, through personal presentation of results at scientific meetings, and through reports by visitors to the laboratories, this intensive effort presumably had its share in the formation of a balanced view of hereditary and constitutional factors in disease.

JOHN H. NORTHROP's laboratory of general physiology, housed in Princeton, though not formally part of the Department of Animal and Plant Pathology, was in 1935 continuing to study the chemistry, physical properties, and activities of enzymes. As recorded in Chapter 7, the notable achievements of Northrop and Moses Kunitz had included the isolation of the two major digestive enzymes, pepsin and trypsin, in crystalline form. Now they succeeded in crystallizing a second protein-splitting enzyme of the pancreas, chymotrypsin. They also isolated and crystallized trypsinogen and chymotrypsinogen, the precursory forms of trypsin and of chymotrypsin, which had until then been more or less hypothetical. Roger M. Herriott, in the group since 1932, in 1938 similarly purified and crystallized pepsinogen.

Just why these powerful enzymes of the stomach and pancreas do not digest the living tissues in which they are formed had long been a physiological mystery. Northrop and Kunitz found at least a partial answer in 1935 by isolating from the pancreas in pure form a trypsin-inhibiting protein. A decade later, when workers elsewhere reported the presence of a similar trypsin inhibitor in soybeans, Kunitz isolated that substance also. Herriott in 1941 obtained a pepsin inhibitor from stomach tissues. Following this up, he made detailed studies of the chemical and physical properties of pepsin itself. Mortimer L. Anson, another member of Northrop's group (now retired after leading research in the laboratories of Lever Brothers Company), in 1935 shared in this remarkable burst of discovery about enzymes, by isolating in crystalline form carboxypeptidase, a pancreatic enzyme which splits certain amino acid compounds formed by the primary action of trypsin upon proteins. This enzyme is now very useful for the elucidation of protein structure. Later Anson studied two other protein-splitting enzymes, papain, from papaya fruit, and cathepsin, representative of a group occurring in many animal tissues. From this experience he worked out exact methods for estimation of pepsin, trypsin, papain, and cathepsin in solutions. Others of the group who contributed briefly to various phases of the enzyme work were J. A. V. Butler (now professor of chemistry at the University of London's Institute of Cancer Research), Victor Desreux (now professor of chemistry at the University of Liége), J. H. Milstone (now at the New Haven Hospital), and Maurice Welsch (now director of the Institute of General and Medical Microbiology of the University of Liége).

Kunitz, acquiring ever greater mastery of techniques for purifying and crystallizing enzymes, kept adding to the list of his achievements. In 1939 he crystallized ribonuclease and in 1948 deoxyribonuclease, enzymes of vast importance in virus activity, genic inheritance, and every life process depending on the nucleoproteins. As part of a war project, he and Margaret R. McDonald crystallized hexokinase, an enzyme participating in sugar metabolism, and also ricin, a toxic protein found in castor oil. In 1951 Kunitz added pyrophosphatase, activator of another step in the utilization of carbohydrate, to his unparalleled list of crystalline enzymes. During a lecture Kunitz remarked that for success in research of this kind "All you need is a barrel of ammonium sulphate and a drum of concentrated sulphuric acid." In the discussion that followed, Northrop retorted that Kunitz was overmodest. "One also needs," he said, "a barrel of patience." Those who have tried similiar work can best understand how greatly Kunitz's success depended also upon imagination, experience, and indefinable scientific artistry.

Northrop, Kunitz, and their associates were by no means occupied solely with *tours de force* of preparatory biochemistry. Their aim in purifying enzymes was to use them to study with precision the kinetics of enzyme activity in building and digesting proteins and in transferring energy in living tissues. For every paper describing the crystallization of an enzyme, they published a dozen dealing with the kinetics and the chemistry of enzyme action. This work, the bulk of the laboratory's output, constitutes a significant portion of the world's stock of knowledge on this subject. Too technical for description here, it is clearly detailed by Northrop, Kunitz, and Herriott in their book *Crystalline Enzymes.*[6]

In 1936 Northrop, leaving the study of enzymes largely to his associates, resumed the investigation of the chemical nature of bacteriophages which he began in 1930. At that time his associate A. P. Krueger worked out methods for estimating the number of bacteria in suspensions and the amount of bacteriophage in cultures. These methods were sufficiently accurate to permit Northrop and Krueger to study the kinetics of the reaction between a bacterium and its phage. They concluded that the major events in the complete process of bacteriophagy (dissolution of bacteria by phage) are mathematically predictable. This result, which strongly suggested that the process is a chemical reaction, determined the course of Northrop's subsequent research. In 1936 he was able to announce the isolation from *Staphylococcus aureus* cultures of a highly purified nucleoprotein which, in spite of all the chemical manipulations necessary to purify it, retained the characteristics of a bacteriophage. When introduced into a culture of staphylococci it invaded the bacteria, grew in amount, and ultimately destroyed the culture. Shortly after this initial discovery Northrop found that his phage material was actually a nucleoprotein containing ribonucleic acid. The analogy with Stanley's tobacco mosaic virus was complete, and microbiologists have ever since classified bacteriophages as viruses. Subsequent research in many laboratories has confirmed the finding that bacteriophages are essentially aggregates of nucleoproteins which are somehow able to replicate their substance by drawing upon the host bacteria for the necessary chemical ingredients. Bacteriophages are thus brought together with the viruses of plants and animals, and with the genic material of the chromosomes, into a class of biologically and chemically related agents which determine the genetic behavior of living cells.

Northrop never put aside altogether the study of bacteriophages and after World War II made it his chief interest. Meanwhile he turned in 1941 to the study of another, quite different, biologically active substance, namely, diphtheria antitoxin. Various investigators at The Rockefeller Institute, beginning with O. T. Avery in 1915, and in other laboratories had shown that antibodies and antitoxins are proteins closely related to those of normal blood serum. W. F. Goebel and B. F. Chow at the Institute, and a former Institute worker, M. Heidelberger, at Columbia University had obtained practically pure pneumococcus antibodies; and M. L. Petermann of the University of Wisconsin and A. M. Pappenheimer, Jr., of the University of Pennsylvania had jointly isolated partially purified diphtheria antitoxin.

Northrop attacked the problem of further purification by an ingenious method. Starting with blood plasma from horses immunized against diphtheria, in which the antitoxin was but one among many proteins, and in small quantity at that, he separated the antitoxin from the other proteins by precipitating it with diphtheria toxin from cultures of the bacilli. Trypsin, he knew, would digest and destroy the toxin but not the antitoxin. With the pure trypsin he and Kunitz had prepared, he digested the precipitated toxin-antitoxin compound and recovered the antitoxin thus freed in a state pure enough, after some final steps, to permit crystallization. The crystals possessed full antitoxic power and constituted the first antitoxin ever brought to crystalline purity. This triumph of skill and precision might have been followed at once by others of the same sort, had not the exigencies of World War II diverted Northrop and his entire group to other work. After the war Northrop and W. F. Goebel resumed the purification of pneumococcus antibody from the serum of immunized horses, at the stage where Goebel had left it in 1935. Together they carried the procedure far enough to obtain this antibody also in crystalline form. In 1946, as mentioned in Chapter 7, Northrop somewhat tardily received the Nobel Prize, jointly with F. B. Sumner of Cornell University and W. M. Stanley.

The men who took part in all this work are now widely scattered. Anson left in 1942 for an important industrial research post. In 1948 Herriott accepted a call to the chair of biochemistry at the Johns Hopkins University School of Hygiene. When in 1949–1951 the Princeton department was discontinued, Kunitz elected to move to the New York laboratories. Made a full Member of The Rockefeller Institute in 1949, he has continued his work, as Emeritus Member, since 1953.

Northrop had no mind to return to life in New York City, from which he had happily escaped by moving to Princeton almost a quarter century before. Given his choice of location, he elected to work on the

University of California campus in Berkeley. Consequently, The Rocke-feller Institute acquired a laboratory three thousand miles from Man-hattan. Northrop took with him Winston H. Price, who had joined the Princeton group in 1946, and the two continued to investigate the origin and properties of bacterial viruses.

Price left Berkeley in 1951 to join the staff of his former colleague Herriott at the Johns Hopkins School of Hygiene, and was succeeded for a few years by James S. Murphy (son of James B. Murphy [1884–1950], Member of The Rockefeller Institute). With these colleagues, Northrop carried on a great deal of exploratory work, aiming to explain the way in which the bacteriophage virus is formed in the bacterial cell. The grow-ing assurance of microbiologists, based in part upon Northrop's discov-ery of 1936–1938 that the phages are nucleoproteins like certain viruses of higher organisms, had given great philosophical as well as practical importance to the question of their chemical nature and origin. Bacterial viruses, moreover, seemed to offer the investigator a special opportunity to study the chemistry of viruses in hosts (bacteria) which are more rapidly growing, more easily controlled, and less complex than animals and higher plants.

These preliminary experiments of Northrop and his two co-workers impressed him with the resemblance of virus production to the appear-ance of genetic mutations. Bacteria, for example, may undergo muta-tions which cause a given strain to alter its biological properties. In 1944 Oswald T. Avery, Colin M. MacLeod, and Maclyn McCarty of The Rockefeller Institute Hospital, in a brilliant investigation which will be discussed in a later chapter, analyzed a case of this sort. They showed that the transformation of a harmless strain of pneumococci into one causing fatal pneumonia is induced by one of the nucleic acids. Molecules of a particular form of deoxyribonucleic acid are somehow able to transfer genetic information from one kind of bacterial cell to another and cause the change to be inherited indefinitely. The production of a new nucleo-protein which acts as a phage rather than a virus, Northrop conjectured, may also result from a mutational change in the intimate structure of a nucleic acid molecule in the bacterial cell, by which the nucleic acid be-comes a genetic determinant of virus production.

To test this hypothesis, Northrop availed himself of a large bacillus,

B. megatherium, which European workers had already been studying, because in cultures it constantly produces bacteriophage markedly "lysogenic" for other organisms, without apparent harm to the culture. For several years, Northrop conducted exhaustive experiments with a variety of chemical and physical agents known to produce mutations in lower organisms, including bacteria and yeast. He also varied the conditions under which the bacterium was grown, in order to stimulate changes in the rate of lysogeny or other modifications in the production of phage virus. From the results of these experiments, mathematically analyzed and compared with known mutational changes, Northrop concluded that a virus is a special transforming principle, produced by the cell, which has the power to transfer genetic information from one cell to another.[7]

CHAPTER SEVENTEEN

Plant Pathology, 1935–1953

Plant viruses; transmission of aster yellows virus by leaf hoppers; susceptibility and immunity to viruses; distribution and nomenclature; plant tissue culture; crown gall. Nature of crystallizable viruses. Closing of the Princeton laboratories.

By 1935 THE LABORATORIES of plant pathology in Princeton had achieved brilliant success in the investigations of virus diseases of plants, begun in 1931 under Louis O. Kunkel's direction. Kunkel always gave his juniors as free a hand as possible, generously declining to associate his own name with their publications even when he had helped to start their investigations and had given them his experienced guidance. Many of them became independent investigators, and in 1935 three of the men he had brought to the Institute, Francis O. Holmes, Philip R. White, and Wendell M. Stanley, were conducting well-established research programs in special areas of the field.

Kunkel himself, with the assistance of several young newcomers to his laboratories, continued to investigate the cause, transmission, pathology, treatment, and prevention of a number of plant virus diseases. Foremost among these was the "yellows" disease of asters, which, as mentioned in Chapter 12, he had first begun to study almost a decade before he joined The Rockefeller Institute.

The story of Kunkel's interest in aster yellows begins in 1923, when he joined the Boyce Thompson Institute of Plant Research at Yonkers, New York, founded by Colonel W. B. Thompson, a wealthy New York banker whose hobby of growing prize asters led him to establish laboratories for the study of plant pathology. Working there, Kunkel recalled his discovery, made while he was in Hawaii, of a disease of maize, transmitted by an insect. With this clue he soon proved that aster yellows is caused by a virus similarly transmitted, in this case by a small insect, the leaf hopper, *Macrosteles fascifrons*. The spread of yellows could not be controlled, as one might hope, by insecticides, because a single surviving leaf hopper can distribute the virus widely through the greenhouses and outdoor plantings. Screening is more successful and, in view of Kunkel's discoveries, has been adopted by commercial growers. Noting that the disease dies down in the summer months, Kunkel demonstrated experimentally that the virus is sensitive to high temperatures, and introduced heat treatment of diseased plants as a curative measure for this disease and others caused by heat-sensitive viruses, for example, peach yellows and peach rosette disease.

Kunkel also found that the virus is sensitive to high temperatures while in the body of the insect carrier. Experimenting with heat-treated insects, he discovered that after he partly destroyed the virus in a batch of leaf hoppers, they regained infectivity at an increasing rate during the next week or two. The obvious deduction was that the virus is able to multiply in the leaf hopper. Kunkel suggested this hypothesis in 1926. It was first supported by experimental evidence in 1935 by a Japanese worker, Fukushi, working with rice stunt virus, and was definitely proved by direct experiments conducted by Lindsay M. Black, one of Kunkel's young colleagues, who joined the Institute in 1937 after training in plant pathology at Cornell. Using a technique originally devised by H. H. Storey, an English investigator working in Africa, Black injected virus-free leaf hoppers with fluid from ground-up infected insects. He learned that the concentration of the transferred virus depended upon the length of time it had been incubating in the insects from which he prepared the fluid, proving that the virus multiplies while in the insect.[1]

This important finding, announced in 1940–1941, has been followed up in various directions by Black himself and others. Karl Maramorosch, who joined Kunkel's group in 1949, strikingly confirmed the multiplication of the virus in the insect carrier by passing it through ten successive batches of leaf hoppers; each time he diluted the infectious juice a thousand times with salt solution, yet the insects of the tenth batch were as infectious as those of the first. More recently Maramorosch has confirmed the multiplication of several plant-disease viruses in other insects.

Yellows virus can be transmitted directly from plant to plant by the slow method of grafting infected tissue on a healthy plant; it would be quicker to inject it with a needle, but this has never yet succeeded. The needle, however fine and delicately handled, injures the plant tissues, and, in any case, cannot transmit enough virus to insure infection. Nature, however, has developed a method which the Princeton pathologists adapted to their own purposes. There is a well-known parasitic vine of the genus *Cuscuta,* commonly known as dodder, which attaches itself to other plants by fine processes which penetrate the plant tissues. Through its coiling stems, twined from plant to plant, this parasite provides a bridge of living tissue over which viruses can readily travel. Such transmission of a plant virus disease is said to have been first detected by botanists in India, studying the parasitic sandalwood.

When in 1940 C. W. Bennett of the U.S. Department of Agriculture reported in a brief note that he had observed the transmission of sugarbeet curly-top disease and cucumber mosaic from infected to healthy plants by way of the parasitic strands of dodder, Kunkel and Folke Johnson, a Fellow in his laboratories, grasped the potentialities of this kind of transmission for experimental work. Within a year or two, Johnson, having the Institute's rich stock of plant viruses at his command, used dodder to transmit a half dozen of them, including those of aster yellows and tobacco mosaic. This ingenious trick considerably widened the range of experimental research on aster yellows, by facilitating the use of plants which the leaf hoppers would not attack. It could be used, for example, to infect a convenient host for storing the virus. A plant of the periwinkle family from Madagascar proved especially suitable for this purpose. The method also provided another way of infecting new host plants which do not contract the disease under natural conditions. When a virus is thus transferred to a species to which it has not been previously adapted, it may behave in a more controllable way for experimental study, or show unexpected peculiarities helpful in isolating it from contaminating viruses.

An entry in the Institute's Confidential Reports for 1947 rather surprisingly describes the introduction of mechanization into the study of dodder transmission, which would seem to be as unmechanical as any field of research could be. A young assistant, George W. Cochran (now research professor of plant pathology at the Utah State Agricultural College), devised an automatic machine for winding dodder stems around cylinders covered with alternating leaves of diseased and healthy plants.

Thus tightly wound, dodder puts out large numbers of processes which penetrate the leaves, creating a very short and direct pathway between them. The machine could also be used to wind the vine around artificial stems soaked with juice from diseased plants, in order to get the parasitic tissue to take up the virus. Ingenuities of this sort can relieve the often monotonous routine of laboratory investigation.

Kunkel brought his ever-broadening experience with plant virus diseases, and the technical improvements which he and his staff created, to bear on a number of diseases of great economic importance. In addition to the yellows of peaches and other virus infections of fruit trees, these include "false blossom" of cranberries, "witch's broom" of potatoes, corn stunt and other diseases of maize, and the bolting disease of carrots. Significant for the future of research in this field are his numerous studies and reviews of the general biology of plant viruses — the pathology of the diseases they cause, their genetics and mutations, and the dynamics of virus growth.

W. C. Price, who came from the Boyce Thompson Institute with Kunkel in 1932, contributed to the general experience of the group by wide-ranging studies on various phenomena associated with virus disease in plants. His description and analysis, in 1935–1936, of the recovery of tobacco plants from ring-spot disease, with subsequent immunity against reinoculation with the same virus but with persistence of latent virus in the leaves, presents a good example of the hidden presence and attenuation of an infectious agent. Such a state of affairs, in which the host and the infecting organism have, so to speak, made a truce and live together without harm to either, has been studied intensively in both plants and animals by many investigators at The Rockefeller Institute. Latency and attenuation are now regarded as significant features of the natural history of disease. In 1945 Price succeeded in crystallizing the virus of the Southern bean mosaic disease, adding it to the small list of viruses, beginning with tobacco mosaic virus, which had been prepared in crystalline form up to that time. Price left the Institute in 1945 to join the University of Pittsburgh as research professor of botany; in 1954 he was appointed virologist at the Lake Alfred Citrus Experiment Station in Florida.

Ernest L. Spencer, a plant physiologist with special interest in the chemistry of plant nutrition, worked at the Princeton laboratories from

1932 to 1941, studying chiefly the relation between the mineral nutrition of plants and their susceptibility to viruses. He clearly showed that an ample supply of nitrogen, provided by heavy fertilization of the soil, enhances the biological activity of viruses. Spencer went from the Institute to an academic post in plant pathology at Rutgers University, and has subsequently led soil chemistry investigation at Florida State agricultural stations.

K. Starr Chester, Fellow and Assistant from 1933 to 1937, studied plant viruses from the standpoint of immunology. Helen Purdy Beale of the Boyce Thompson Institute had opened the field by her finding, published in 1929–1931, that if rabbits are injected with material containing tobacco mosaic virus, precipitins are formed in their blood, which will neutralize the virus by precipitating it from solution. Following up this clue, Chester, in 1934, first confirmed Beale's observations, and then supplemented them by precise experiments that for the first time demonstrated specific, quantitative neutralization of a plant virus by an immune substance. Immune reactions of this kind, long known to investigators of bacterial infections in animals, were beginning to be recognized in virus infections, and Chester had now extended their range to plant viruses. He was able, moreover, to answer a major question concerning this kind of immunity, by showing that the virus itself, and not an accompanying protein, is the antigen which provokes the rabbit to build an antibody against injected virus-containing material. This phenomenon provides a highly selective way of distinguishing viruses apparently similar in their distribution or in their effects on host plants. Chester applied it at once to a group causing mosaic and similar diseases of tobacco, potatoes, and peas, then under study in Princeton and thought possibly to be interrelated. These were clearly distinguishable by his serological tests, whereas several virus strains known to have been derived from tobacco mosaic virus were serologically alike. Later, by a modification of the test, he could even distinguish some of these from each other.

When in 1935 Stanley's crystalline tobacco mosaic virus became available for serological study, Chester's experience equipped him to test its purity not only with the precipitin test but by two other methods utilizing the antigenic properties of proteins, namely, complement fixation and the anaphylactic reaction. The pure virus, he found, induced the formation of precipitins and elicited complement fixation as did crude virus extracts from plant tissue. Anaphylactic reactions, on the other hand, were readily induced by ordinary plant proteins which are virtually indistinguishable, within any one family of plants, by the precipitin test. In 1937 Chester went to the Oklahoma Agricultural and Mechanical College as professor of botany and plant pathology, later joining the Battelle Memorial Institute of Columbus, Ohio.

Arnold J. Ullstrup, plant pathologist specializing in fungus diseases, was a Fellow in Princeton from 1935 to 1937, studying two unusual pathogenic fungi, one a rare variety of *Fusarium* from Japan, not previously observed in the United States, the other a parasite of the potato and sugar beet, which he found unexpectedly causing a leaf blight of China asters. After his fellowship, Ullstrup went to the U.S. Bureau of Plant Industry as plant pathologist.

Lindsay M. Black followed up his find on the virus of aster yellows by wide-ranging investigations of insect-borne plant virus diseases. He found, for example, additional instances of viruses that multiply in their insect vectors, and new viruses carried by leaf hoppers. One of these has the striking property of causing tumors to grow on the roots or stems and leaves of plants infected with it, wherever the tissues chance to be wounded. After leaving Princeton in 1946, Black was for a time at the Brooklyn Botanical Gardens. Since his appointment in 1952 to a professorship of botany at the University of Illinois, he has created there an important center of research on the virus diseases of plants.

FRANCIS O. HOLMES, it will be recalled, came to The Rockefeller Institute as a protozoologist, when Louis Kunkel was first building a staff qualified to open a wide range of inquiry into the causes of plant diseases. As it became clear that viruses were of major importance, while protozoan infections were rare in plants, Holmes capably turned to the pathology of virus diseases. At first he studied the local lesions caused by the infecting organisms and the spread of the infection through the plant. His invention of a method for quantitative estimation of the infectivity of a virus has been mentioned in Chapter 12. Holmes soon found himself interested in the genetic aspects of plant virus diseases. In 1936 he demonstrated inherited differences in invasiveness of different strains of tobacco mosaic virus. These, he supposed, reflect unit differ-

ences in the structure of the virus, of the same sort as single-gene differences in higher organisms.

Holmes devoted his chief attention, however, to the genetics of the
plant itself, as regards heritable susceptibility to infection. In an early
paper (1934) he described a genetic factor in a mutant strain of tobacco
mosaic virus which limits it to the region where it first enters the infected plant, so that it produces local necrosis instead of the usual widespread mottling of the leaves. This factor he found by experiment to be
a single dominant Mendelian gene. By hybridizing various species of
Nicotiana he was able to transfer the localizing factor from one species
to another. Further work with varieties of the garden pepper, *Capsicum
frutescens,* revealed several additional hereditary types of response to infection with tobacco mosaic virus. Thinking to utilize such differences
to test the relationship between kinds of plants, Holmes, with great industry and persistence, collected and grew seventy-three species, of
twenty-three families, of herbaceous dicotyledons. Inoculating them
with tobacco mosaic virus, he found that two thirds were susceptible,
and observed that the susceptibility of any given species is rather closely
associated with its position on the evolutionary family tree of such
plants, as worked out by taxonomists.

In all this work the practical aim of developing virus-resistant strains
of commercial plants was intermingled with the search for basic principles. In 1938, for example, by ingenious and elaborate genetic procedures, Holmes transferred the localizing (necrotizing) gene from non-
commercial species of *Nicotiana* into the common tobacco plant (*N.
tabacum*), in the hope of incorporating it in commercially useful tobac-
cos, where it might cut down the spread of infection within the plants
and ultimately eliminate the virus through failure of contagion. He
found also that South American relatives of the cultivated tomato plant,
Lycopersicum esculentum, possess hereditary resistance to tobacco mosaic virus, and he succeeded in transferring this resistance to hybrids between *L. esculentum* and the resistant *L. chilense.* Similarly, he found
and crossbred South American tomatoes that were resistant to the virus
causing "spotted wilt" of garden tomatoes. In 1947–1948, in conjunction with scientists in Hawaii, Holmes observed and characterized a new
virus disease of the papaya plant, occurring in that region.

A casual observation made in 1941, that rib grass and related weeds of the plantain family in the Princeton countryside suffer from infection with a distinctive strain of tobacco mosaic virus, led to a discovery of practical value. New Jersey tomato growers were plagued, about 1948–1949, with a damaging disease characterized by internal browning of the fruit. Testing the characteristics of the virus causing this disease, Holmes found it to be a derivative of the strain of tobacco mosaic virus he had noted in plantains. On one New Jersey farm he achieved practical control of the infection by locating tomato fields at a safe distance from all plantains.

Holmes's ever-increasing acquaintance with plant virus diseases was now leading him to broad hypotheses and observations concerning their evolution, distribution, and classification. In the late 1940's he studied the distribution of two tobacco viruses, those causing tobacco etch and tobacco mosaic disease. Subjecting no less than 310 plant species to inoculation with these viruses, he found that they, though different in immunological reactions and in such physiological characteristics as resistance to heating, can infect related plants in a predictable way. Although the mosaic virus infected 116 species that were naturally immune to etch, all 83 species that were susceptible to etch virus proved susceptible to both. The two viruses must, therefore, require certain similar environmental and nutritional conditions which are found in those plants which the etch virus can infect, and are no doubt related by descent from a common ancestor.

Information collected through these explorations of the host-virus relation gave Holmes a clue to the probable geographical origin of tobacco mosaic virus. This disease is now world-wide, occurring wherever tobacco is grown; but, as Holmes pointed out, its three chief hosts, tobacco, tomato, and garden pepper, are all New World species. Resistant strains of these plants and related species, no doubt produced by genetic mutations, are more common in the New World than the Old. The virus is probably, therefore, of New World origin.

Taking advantage of the fact that mutations are constantly occurring in small numbers in any given species, Holmes has sought new virus-resistant strains of tobacco by growing seedlings in huge numbers, testing them for spontaneous resistance, and breeding from promising individuals. Concurrently, he has since the 1930's been crossbreeding strains found by other observers to be resistant in some degree. He has recently (since 1953) succeeded in combining several resistance-conferring genes in one hybrid strain, less susceptible to infection by the tobacco mosaic virus than any previously known.

The classification and nomenclature of viruses still poses a serious problem. Few laboratory workers gain experience with a sufficient number of different viruses to qualify themselves as taxonomists. They tend, moreover, to designate those they deal with by names miscellaneously derived from the hosts they infect, the lesions they cause, the place where they were discovered, or some other non-systematic feature, *e.g.*, tobacco mosaic, pea wilt, polio, Newcastle disease. More than two centuries ago Linnaeus brought order out of confusion in botanical classification by publishing his *Systema Naturae,* in which he introduced a systematic method of classification, and rigorously adhered to a binomial nomenclature by genus and species. In 1939 Holmes, with enterprise and scholarship, compiled a *Handbook of Phytopathogenic Viruses,* describing all known viruses of plant diseases, with a nomenclature in the standard binomial form. Most of the Latin names he either invented or adapted from the vernacular terms found in the literature. In 1948 he was invited to provide a classification and nomenclature of all known viruses, including bacteriophages, to be published in the sixth edition of Bergey's *Handbook of Determinative Bacteriology,* a collaborative work in standard use.

These attempts to do for viruses what Linnaeus did for plants were, of course, fraught with great difficulty, because of the diversity of available information and of the rapid progress being made in the field, with constant addition of new viruses and revision of current ideas about their relationships. Holmes's nomenclature naturally excited a good deal of controversy, yet he is the recognized pioneer in a task that will finally be carried out when sufficient information is available. In 1953 Holmes was variously occupied with further efforts to breed and propagate virus-resistant plants, to find other methods of combating virus diseases, and to achieve an orderly classification of the viruses.

THE STUDY AND USE of plant tissue cultures at The Rockefeller Institute was initiated in 1932 by Philip R. White. A brief review of his earlier work, described in Chapter 12, will help to explain his progress in this later period. While White was a graduate student of botany at the Johns

Hopkins University, his professor, stimulated by certain ideas presented by Erwin F. Smith of Washington, D.C. (whose name we shall encounter again in connection with plant tumors), suggested that White look into the possibility of culturing plant tissues *in vitro,* and sent him to consult Warren H. Lewis and Margaret Reed Lewis at the Baltimore embryological laboratory of the Carnegie Institution of Washington. These investigators were achieving brilliant results with animal tissue cultures, using somewhat simpler, and from the chemical standpoint better-defined, culture media than the blood plasma mixtures introduced by Carrel and Burrows at the Institute.

After a year at the University of Missouri, White undertook in earnest to develop methods for the cultivation of plant tissues, first at the Boyce Thompson Institute, and later at the Berlin Institute for Plant Physiology. Continuing this effort after joining The Rockefeller Institute, he was able to report by 1934 that he had grown excised tomato root tips for more than a year, through fifty-two passages, in a simple liquid medium made up of inorganic and organic chemical ingredients. From a single fragment 10 millimeters long he had produced approximately 35,000 sprouting stems and more than 400,000 millimeters of root tissue. An arithmetical calculation showed that the materials of the original fragment must have been diluted below the limits of molecular size. In other words, the entire substance of the ultimate tissue had been derived from the nutrient, which, accordingly, proved to be adequate for all growth requirements of the tissue.

Later in 1934 White reported having grown root tissue of tomato plants infected with the tobacco mosaic and aucuba mosaic viruses respectively. In this tissue the viruses actively multiplied as long as he followed them, up to twenty-five weeks or more, and, presumably, could have been maintained indefinitely. In 1934 a French botanist, R. Gautheret, achieved partial success in the culture of cambium, the formative tissue that gives rise to wood and bark. His cultures were perhaps the first true plant tissue cultures, in the strictest technical sense, in that they consisted of undifferentiated cells rather than mixtures of partly differentiated cell types which might influence each other by vital characteristics acquired before the initial fragment was excised from the plant. White's root cultures had already satisfied the other requirement of a "true" tissue culture, namely, the power of unlimited growth, but the root tissue he started with was partly differentiated.

Better evidence even than Gautheret's was, nevertheless, still required to prove unlimited growth of undifferentiated tissue. This White produced in 1939 by growing procambial tissue of a hybrid variety of tobacco which possessed unusual capacity for proliferation, forming calluses wherever the stems or leaves were abraded. With this callus tissue, which he cultivated through forty passages of one week each, White secured unlimited growth of undifferentiated cells. This was a tissue culture no less "true" than Carrel's famous culture of chicken heart fibroblasts (Chapter 5). If all the new growth could have been kept, the increments of growth would have reached the unimaginable figure of ten billion billions to one. About the same time, Gautheret and another French worker, P. Nobecourt, achieved similar results.[2] Such undifferentiated cells, White found, could be induced to differentiate, forming leafy branches, simply by transferring them from a semisolid to a liquid nutrient. The actual stimulating factor seemed to be a reduction in oxygen supply.

White's first successful culture medium had consisted of water, inorganic salts, and organic chemicals, all of known constitution except one item, a small amount of yeast extract, forming about 1/10,000 of the mass of the nutrient. Because this one unknown might include unidentified essential substances potent in minute quantities, White undertook to eliminate it. Analysis of the yeast extract proved that the effective material could be divided into two fractions, respectively soluble and insoluble in 100 per cent alcohol. The nature of the former fraction was solved in 1937, when James Bonner of the California Institute of Technology, and W. J. Robbins and M. A. Bartley at the University of Missouri, about the same time proved it to be thiamine (vitamin B_1). The alcohol-insoluble fraction, White found, contained chiefly amino acids. Successively eliminating one after another of each of these from his culture medium, he cut down the number of essential amino acids to nine, and in 1939 to one, glycine. Now White possessed a completely known and relatively simple nutrient fluid, containing only water, sugar (sucrose), and ten inorganic compounds supplying minerals, chlorine, and nitrogen, with glycine and thiamine as the only organic ingredients. This solution supports continuous unlimited growth of tomato roots. Later, the research groups of Robbins and Bonner demonstrated that two other organic substances, pyroxidine (vitamin B_6) and nicotinic acid (vitamin B_{12}) improve the growth of tissues, of some plants at least, in cultures. White confirmed their experiments, and added the vitamins to his nutrient medium.

White's experiments with cultures of callus tissue induced him to think about the forces which carry nutrients and oxygen into the interior of such tissues. He observed, for instance, that if a fragment of callus tissue is left growing in a culture tube, beyond the time at which he would ordinarily divide and transplant it to keep the undifferentiated cells going, it undergoes a certain degree of differentiation, giving rise to elementary leaves and other differentiated structures. Because his earlier experiments had shown that such differentiation results from a change in oxygen supply, White supposed that some force, hitherto scarcely envisioned, is exerted by the cells of such tissues to drive water, and with it oxygen and nutrients, into the interior of the mass of growing tissue.

White's curiosity about fluid movements in the simpler tissues of plants, greatly aroused by this observation, was reinforced by a query from his chief. Louis Kunkel, interested in sap movements as a possible explanation of the travel of viruses through plants, asked White whether he could devise methods of studying the movement of water in his root cultures. Experimental study of the question went back to Stephen Hales, an eighteenth-century English clergyman, who applied a simple pressure gauge to a grapevine stock, and was astonished to find that it could raise water to a height of forty feet. Ingeniously adapting the same method to his tiny root filaments, White attached very small manometer tubes to growing root tips in culture, and was equally astonished when he found that his tomato roots developed pressures of two or three, sometimes even six, atmospheres, or ninety pounds to the square inch, a sufficient force to raise water about two hundred feet. The pumping mechanism for the development of this great force resided in single excised roots of the tomato, less than a millimeter in diameter and only a few centimeters long. As White pointed out, this root pressure can operate when other forces due to evaporation at leaf surfaces are not in action, for example, when the plant lacks leaves, or when evaporation ceases in moisture-saturated air. This mechanism is important because it is capable of moving small masses of water under great pressure. White was unable to state the nature of the pumping force, beyond the probability that it depends on the biochemical activity of living cells.

As his next investigation, White, whose interest in plant tissue culture had its origin in the early crown-gall studies of Erwin Smith, collaborated in the earlier phases of the research of Armin Braun on crown-gall tumor, and later followed up certain questions about the crown gall in which he was especially interested. This part of his research program will be dealt with in following pages dealing with Braun's studies.

In 1943 and 1944 White turned his attention to animal tissue cultures, with the hope of doing in that field what he had done with plant tissue culture — that is, develop a culture medium containing only substances of known chemical nature. All successful tissue culturists working with animal tissues had found it necessary to enrich the media with organic materials of unknown constitution. Ross Harrison, the pioneer, had used frog's lymph. Carrel and Burrows substituted blood plasma enriched with extracts of embryonic tissue. Subsequent workers, led by Warren H. Lewis and Margaret R. Lewis, succeeded in getting animal tissues to grow without plasma, but they still required embryo juice or some other complex, empirically chosen organic enrichment. Many workers attempted to find out what were the essential ingredients of embryo juice, one of the more nearly successful among them being Albert Fischer, director of the Biological Institute of the Carlsberg Foundation in Copenhagen, Carrel's assistant in the early days of tissue culture at the Institute. Taking advantage of all that had been discovered by Fischer and other workers plus his own experience with plant tissue culture media, White produced in 1946 a fluid medium consisting entirely of materials of known composition, including a considerable array of vitamins and amino acids, thus making possible experiments on the metabolism and nutritional requirements of tissues, without residual error due to unknown ingredients. On this synthetic mixture, White kept chick connective tissue cells (fibroblasts) in good condition for fifty-eight days, and heart muscle beating for forty-four days.

White and others have since pushed this method, of building up a medium directly from known ingredients, to still further success. Raymond Parker, long an associate of Carrel at The Rockefeller Institute, later published, with some of his colleagues at Toronto, a culture medium containing sixty chemical ingredients, and yet found that embryo extract, added to this complex solution, improved the growth of cells. In 1945 White left Princeton for a post at the Lankenau Hospital Institute for Cancer Research in Philadelphia, and six years later joined the Jackson Memorial Laboratories at Bar Harbor, Maine. Charity Weymouth, who worked with him there, later published a stable, completely defined nutrient solution of forty ingredients which supports growth of certain mammalian cells at rates equal to those obtained in the older organic complexes. The goal set by White in 1943 was for these cell types at last attained.

Armin C. Braun, a graduate of the University of Wisconsin, continued his studies in bacteriology and plant pathology at the Pasteur Institute of Paris and the Biologische Reichsanstalt of Berlin, then spent a year with the U.S. Department of Agriculture, and came to The Rockefeller Institute in 1938. About 1940 he began to study crown-gall tumors, which grow on many species of plants. As he points out in an interesting review,[3] these crown-gall tumors had attracted wide interest ever since 1907 when Erwin F. Smith and C. O. Townsend of the Department of Agriculture isolated a bacterium, now called *Agrobacterium tumefaciens,* from crown galls and showed that it can produce tumors of this sort in healthy plants. At that time no animal tumor had as yet been produced experimentally; Peyton Rous's work on virus tumors of chickens was two years in the future. Smith showed that crown gall is in many ways similar to malignant animal tumors; for example, infection at a given point is often followed by the development of secondary tumors at distant points, resembling the metastases of a carcinoma or sarcoma in this respect, but with the important difference that they do not arise from transported tumor cells. There was a further apparent difference: unlike animal cancer, crown-gall tumors were thought to grow only under continuing stimulation by bacteria, and, therefore, not to be truly independent.

In 1941 Braun published his first observations on crown gall. Studying such tumors produced on sunflower plants by inoculation with *Agrobacterium tumefaciens,* he found that many of the secondary tumors developing at a distance from the site of primary infection were free of bacteria. With this observation in mind, he called upon his colleague Philip White to contribute his experience in plant tissue culture to a

HERBERT S. GASSER

THOMAS M. RIVERS

joint attack on the problems of crown gall. Braun's experiments provided bacteria-free tumor tissue, which White could grow under controlled conditions. Their first cultures, reported in 1941 and 1942, showed conclusively that the bacteria-free crown-gall cells could reproduce themselves independently, like cancer cells. Fragments planted on the culture medium grew profusely in an uncoordinated manner, whereas normal sunflower tissues grew poorly on the same medium. Small pieces of this cultured, germ-free tumor tissue implanted into a healthy sunflower plant formed crown-gall tumors. The cells making up the crown gall had, in fact, undergone a permanent change, no longer needing bacterial stimulation to make them form tumors. Braun later obtained bacteria-free crown galls of another plant, the periwinkle *Vinca rosea,* by eliminating the bacteria by heat treatment. Shortly afterward, White isolated bacteria-free cultures from similar tumors as well as from tumors of *Nicotiana* that were of genetic, not bacterial, origin. The two workers had, in short, discovered and placed under experimental control plant tumor tissue of several types, characterized like animal cancer by a change from normal regulated growth to independent and unregulated proliferation.

Having thus established that the cells were permanently changed, Braun next attempted to discover the nature of the change and how the bacterium produces it. With Thomas Laskaris he inoculated tomato plants with a culture of *Agrobacterium* so attenuated that it did not produce tumors. The cells around the point of inoculation were, however, in some way altered, for if the plants were treated with growth-stimulating chemicals they produced large tumors whose cells could be perpetuated by grafting to healthy plants. Evidently, the disorderly growth of the tumor is dependent upon an initial change in the nature of the constituent cells.

Two hypotheses regarding the origin of tumor cells are current. One suggests that the transformation from the normal state results from a genetic mutation of somatic cells, the other that it is effected by an agent which, like the genes, is self-perpetuating, but which comes from outside the organism, for example, a virus or a chemical substance produced by the cell. Braun found an ingenious way to decide between these two possibilities in the case of crown gall. Certain tumors, induced by crown-gall bacteria under special circumstances, contain tissues which go on indefinitely forming distorted buds and leaves. Braun removed and grafted such diseased shoots onto healthy plants, and, when they had grown out to considerable length, again removed the tips of the shoots and grafted them onto fresh host plants. Eventually, their tissues, because of their rapid growth and the resulting successive dilution of the crown-gall factor, got rid of the tumor-inducing agent altogether and grew normally. Altered genes in the nuclei of the cells would have persisted; the disappearance of the crown-gall factor meant that it must have resided in the non-genetic part of the cell.

Was it then a virus, or an altered component of the cell itself? This question was answered by utilizing experience Louis Kunkel had gained some years before when he used heat treatment to eradicate the virus of peach yellows. Braun inoculated plants with crown-gall bacteria and then destroyed the bacteria by heat, after varying lengths of time. He found that the bacteria needed about four days to establish the tumor process fully; in less time, they produced only small, slow-growing tumors. The important point was that the alteration, whether of the full four-day type or the lesser one reached in two and a half or three days, persisted without change in degree when the treated tissue was grafted or tissue-cultured. If a virus had been involved it would have set its own rate of growth and development. The tumor agent must, therefore, be closely bound to the chemical structure of the plant cells. Further experiments, in which the heat treatment was closely controlled, showed that elevated temperatures, not high enough to kill the *Agrobacterium,* are able to inhibit the tumor-inducing factor. Another key observation was that the wounding of the plant occasioned by inoculating it with crown-gall bacteria is a necessary condition for the initiation of tumors. A wound-healing factor in the juice of the injured cells seems necessary to make plant cells susceptible to the tumor agent.[4]

George L. McNew, Fellow, 1935–1939, devoted practically his entire stay at the Institute to a thorough study of *Phytomonas stewarti,* a microorganism that causes bacterial wilt of Indian corn. Working partly alone and partly in collaboration with E. L. Spencer, McNew studied variant strains of the organism, examining the effect of mineral nutrition and nitrogen supply upon its virulence, and the factors influencing its ability to invade plants of various ages. With Braun, he applied agglutination tests to the identification of different strains of *Phytomonas*. Since leaving the Institute, McNew has had a varied career as a plant pathologist and is now managing director of the Boyce Thompson Institute.

Ralph P. Elrod, also trained as a bacteriologist and immunologist, was a Fellow and later Assistant in Braun's group from 1941 to 1947. His first investigation dealt with the relationship of two very similar bacterial genera, one of which (*Erwinia*) includes species causing "soft rot" of vegetable tissues; the other, the group of coliform organisms, is typified by the well-known *Bacillus* (now *Escherichia*) *coli,* common in the environment of animals and men. In 1942 Braun and Elrod reported an even closer relation between bacteria infecting plants and animals, by identifying an organism having the remarkable property of thriving equally well on either plant or animal tissue. This bacterium had been known by one name (*Pseudomonas polycolor*) as the cause of wilt disease in tobacco and other plants, and by another name (*Bacillus pyocyaneus,* later changed to *Pseudomonas aeruginosa*) as a common bacterial invader of animal tissues, which occasionally causes serious purulent infections in human beings. Study of the biological characteristics and immunological relations of these organisms convinced Braun and Elrod that they are identical. The two investigators made also a thorough study of the genus *Xanthomonas,* a puzzling group of plant pathogens which they were able to systematize and classify by immunological methods.

While studying the life history of the crown-gall bacterium, Elrod and Braun in 1946 were among the first to use the electron microscope on plant materials for observing the exceedingly slender filaments (flagella) possessed by *Agrobacterium tumefaciens* and many other bacteria, and for investigating the possibility of sexual phenomena among the bacteria. In 1947 Elrod was called to the University of South Dakota as professor of microbiology and public health.

OUR NARRATIVE of Wendell M. Stanley's work on the virus of tobacco mosaic was interrupted, at the end of Chapter 12, as of the year 1935, when he had just achieved its crystallization. This startling discovery of particles having the self-reproducing property of living things, and yet composed of atoms rigidly arranged in crystalline form, opened many pathways for future research. Stanley now corroborated and extended the findings, improving the method of isolation, crystallizing yet another plant virus (aucuba mosaic), and confirming the identity of the crystals and the virus by showing that they possessed the same infective power. H. S. Loring, Fellow and Assistant, 1935–1939 (later professor of biochemistry at Stanford University), joined Stanley in isolating and comparing special strains of the virus. With R. W. G. Wyckoff, whose method of high-speed centrifugation (developed at The Rockefeller Institute, as narrated in Chapter 7) greatly facilitated the earlier stages of the investigation, Stanley isolated still other plant viruses, including that causing "ring spot" in tobacco. Wyckoff's young colleague Jonathan Biscoe (later professor of physics at the University of Maine) joined his two seniors in analyzing, with the ultracentrifuge, crystalline viruses from different strains of tobacco mosaic. Procedures utilizing centrifugation for the purification of viruses are now in use throughout the world.

George I. Lavin, a chemist who had contributed to research in several of the Institute's laboratories, in New York and in Princeton, by his skill in ultraviolet spectroscopy, was called in to study with Stanley the absorption spectrum of the crystalline tobacco mosaic virus. A. F. Ross (later professor of plant pathology at Cornell University) studied the reaction of the virus with formaldehyde and proved that he could reverse the inactivation, rendering the virus infective once more. This gave powerful support to Stanley's contention that the virus activity is a specific property of the crystallizable protein. In 1939 Loring—following up the demonstration by F. C. Bowden and N. W. Pirie of Rothampstead, England, that the tobacco mosaic virus belongs to the class of nucleoproteins—prepared the enormous quantity of five hundred grams of the virus, and, subjecting it to analysis, split off the nucleic acid, in which he identified the sugar and the four constituent purines and pyrimidines.

Within three years after the first isolation of the crystalline nucleoprotein by Stanley, its identity with the infective tobacco mosaic virus had been fully proved. By the efforts of Stanley's group and others in several parts of the world, more than a dozen specific and highly characteristic nucleoproteins, possessing the properties of known viruses, had been isolated. The next stage of Stanley's program called for study of virus particles by the methods of physical chemistry, to ascertain their molecular weight, dimensions, and forms. His chief collaborator in this phase was Max A. Lauffer, Jr., who came directly from graduate studies to undertake investigations on the optical properties, viscosity, sedimentation rate, and other physical characteristics of the virus particles in solution. In 1944 Lauffer went to the University of Pittsburgh, where he later became head of the department of biophysics, and dean of the division of natural sciences. While studying the characteristics of the tobacco mosaic virus, Stanley also pushed ahead the detailed examination of its chemistry, again in collaboration with able young associates. Claude A. Knight, Jr., devoted himself chiefly to the identification of amino acids, and Gail L. Miller to the reactions of various organic compounds with the virus.

This systematic exploration of the nature of crystallizable viruses would doubtless have progressed rapidly to additional new discoveries and important generalizations had not World War II diverted Stanley and his group to an intensive study of the influenza virus, at the request of the Office of Scientific Research and Development, and to the development of anti-influenza vaccine for the Armed Forces. The year after the war ended (1946) came the award of the Nobel Prize to Stanley. He hardly had time, however, to get back to his prewar program, with Knight and two or three younger associates, when he accepted in 1948 an invitation to become professor of chemistry and to organize a large virus laboratory at the University of California in Berkeley; and Knight accompanied him.

There, a decade later, again under Stanley's leadership, notable progress was made by men who based their work on the painstaking analysis of the characteristics of viruses, carried out in Princeton and elsewhere since the original discovery. Heinz Fraenkel-Conrat and Robley Williams of the Berkeley virus laboratory, for example, succeeded in separating the nucleic acids from the protein components of certain viruses, and then recombining them to form intact infectious viruses. Fraenkel-Conrat later demonstrated that the separated nucleic acid possessed virus activity. Just twenty years after Stanley's crystallization of tobacco mosaic virus, two of his collaborators, F. L. Schaffer and C. E. Schwerdt, succeeded in crystallizing poliomyelitis virus, the first virus affecting man or animals to be crystallized. These feats must have been heartwarming to the leader who in 1935–1938 had striven against widespread skepticism to prove that an infectious agent with the power of self-reproduction could exist in crystalline form.

IN 1947 IT WOULD have been difficult to find anywhere in the United States a group of scientists, in a single institution, reaching so high a general level of distinction and official recognition as that of the Department of Animal and Plant Pathology of The Rockefeller Institute in Princeton and in the associated laboratories of general physiology. Director TenBroeck's senior associates — Kunkel, Northrop, Shope, and Stanley — had been elected to the National Academy of Sciences, and were members of the American Philosophical Society. Two, Stanley and Northrop, had received the Nobel Prize. The six Associate Members — Glaser, Holmes, Kunitz, Nelson, Pearce, and Stoll — were internationally recognized in their fields. Among the thirteen Associates and Assistants, six would hold full professorships in universities, and several others would attain equivalent rank in other research capacities. Any university would have been proud to claim so brilliant a group of investigators.

Yet at this time the Board of Trustees of The Rockefeller Institute faced a momentous decision concerning the Department of Animal and Plant Pathology. For the past year or two, the Trustees had been asking themselves whether it was wise any longer to maintain extensive laboratories in Princeton as well as in New York. Their reasons for raising this question were entirely financial and administrative, and they were looking ahead rather than at the immediate situation. A memorandum introduced for the Board's consideration in May 1947, by its president, John D. Rockefeller, Jr., began by remarking that far-reaching economic changes had taken place in the United States, as a result of the depression of 1929 and World War II. The rate of income on invested funds was falling, while the budget of the Institute for salaries and material continued to increase. Plans for modernization and rearrangement of the hospital would necessitate a further increase of fixed charges. Duplication of facilities in New York and Princeton was costing about $150,000 per year. If the Institute were in the future to attract the best men by offering them appropriate salaries and adequate conditions for their work, its current income would have to be conserved and carefully allocated.[5]

Rockefeller was concerned also about other problems, not mentioned in the memorandum he laid before the Trustees. The physical separation of the two parts of the Institute tended to establish in the minds of the public, and of scientists as well, an impression that they were distinct organizations. Even staff members spoke of "the Princeton Institute" and "the New York Institute." The distance of fifty miles was enough to create local problems and conflicts of interest. Consolidation of the laboratories at one place would avoid such difficulties, as well as save money.

Rockefeller's memorandum proposed that the bulk of the research carried on in Princeton be transferred to New York, the remainder to be discontinued or carried on elsewhere through subsidies.[5] This proposal had already been made known informally by the Director to the Board of Scientific Directors in January 1947, when Gasser, acting upon a request from Rockefeller, Jr., as president of the Board of Trustees, asked them to consider it in the light of the unpromising budgetary prospects of the next few years. On reflection, the Scientific Directors unanimously declared themselves in favor of consolidating the Institute, but by no means all of them were ready to abandon Princeton, at least without thorough study of the alternative possibility of moving the whole Institute there. The Director reported that the president of the Board of Trustees had agreed to make a survey of the merits of this proposal.[6]

Shortly afterward, a Trustee, Lindsley F. Kimball, visited Princeton for this purpose, at Rockefeller's behest. Although no report of his survey is recorded, the arguments for and against each of the alternatives are fresh in the minds of those who took part in the discussions of both boards.[7] To clear the ground for their presentation, it should be added that still another possible course of action was suggested by one or more of the Scientific Directors, but not seriously considered. This was to affiliate The Rockefeller Institute with a university in some other city; Harvard, Yale, and the University of Rochester were named. This idea seems to have resulted from doubts about the continuing necessity of a research institute without university status and a teaching program, such as ultimately resulted in a radical modification of The Rockefeller Institute's aims six years later, under the presidency of Detlev W. Bronk.

Rockefeller, Jr., having presented the idea of consolidation to the two boards, left them free to discuss it from every angle. The Rockefeller family, represented on the Board of Trustees at that time by Rockefeller, Jr., and his sons John D. Rockefeller, 3rd, and David, preferred to keep the Institute in New York City, but, in accord with their fixed policy regarding institutions they supported, would have respected any decision the Institute's two boards might have taken.

Those members of the Board of Scientific Directors who favored closing the Department of Animal and Plant Pathology were swayed by another consideration beside the need to conserve expenditures and consolidate the administration. However important and successful the research in progress in Princeton, its character, they felt, had changed. Investigation of the diseases of large domestic animals, which had been Theobald Smith's chief interest, had largely given place to more general and basic research utilizing small animals. Diseases of horses, cattle, sheep, and swine were now being studied widely in schools of veterinary medicine and in state agricultural experiment stations. Only Shope, working chiefly with swine diseases, and Stoll, studying parasites of sheep, had active programs under way for which large animals would be required for a long time to come. The plant pathologists, likewise, not now working to any great extent with field crops, were giving their attention chiefly to experiments on greenhouse plants and to the biochemistry and biophysics of viruses. Room could be found in the New York laboratories for the greater part of the research in animal pathology, parasitology, and biochemistry, and new greenhouses could be built for the plant pathologists.

A few of the Scientific Directors, on the other hand, proposed abandoning the New York laboratories and uniting the whole Institute in Princeton, where the staff could be housed in pleasant semi-rural surroundings, with lower living costs and with good schooling and playgrounds for their children. Princeton University had always been hospitable to the Institute's Princeton staff. It possessed library facilities in general science rivaling those in New York, and provided readier access to consultants in the basic sciences than was available in the metropolis. Two considerations prevailed against this radical proposal. One was the great cost of abandoning the excellent buildings on the York Avenue site and rebuilding in Princeton. The other concerned the hospital, which depended upon the vast population of the metropolitan area to supply it with the specially selected clinical material needed for its researches. Patients suitable for study might be reluctant to stay in a hospital fifty miles from home and family.

These were the considerations upon which the Trustees, looking to the future of the Institute as well as to the immediate circumstances, tentatively voted in May 1947 that the Princeton department should be closed. In June, after long and detailed discussion of the Trustees' resolution, the Board of Scientific Directors voted that, in order to strengthen all phases of activity in the Institute, it would be wise to integrate the Department of Animal and Plant Pathology with the Department of the Laboratories in New York, and that the integration could appropriately be completed in July 1951. A few days later the Trustees definitively adopted this plan.[8]

The administration of the Institute had not discussed the impending step with senior members of the Princeton scientific staff, to whom the decision was a great shock. Naturally, they were deeply concerned not only about the fate of their work, but also about leaving the countryside where they wished to live and rear their children. A period of considerable uncertainty and — for many of those involved — distress followed the announcement that the Department would be closed. During the ensuing year a dozen members of the research staff, of whom at least five were scientists of outstanding achievement or promise, left the Institute.

The Princeton laboratories were closed in September 1950. By that time all employees of the administrative, research, and technical staffs who had not resigned were relocated without financial hardship, either at the New York laboratories or in positions outside The Rockefeller Institute. Only about half of the research staff elected to reassemble in New York. Of the full Members, TenBroeck chose not to move, remaining in Princeton until he reached retirement age in 1951. Kunkel, who became Emeritus Member in 1949, moved his laboratory to New York and continued his work there. Shope, swayed by love of his country home, resigned in 1949 to become (as already mentioned) assistant director of the Merck Institute for Therapeutic Research in Rahway, New Jersey; but in 1952 he rejoined The Rockefeller Institute in New York. Northrop (as already mentioned) chose to continue his research at the

University of California where Stanley had already gone in 1948. Kunitz, made a full Member in 1949, returned to New York, whence he had come some years before.

Five Associate Members and Associates — Braun, Holmes, Nelson, Stoll, and Trager — transferred their work with the Institute to New York. Louise Pearce chose to reside near Princeton in order to continue working up the records of the investigation of constitutional disease begun by the late Wade Hampton Brown. Glaser died in the autumn of 1947. Ralph B. Little joined the research staff of the University of Pennsylvania's School of Veterinary Medicine. Ernest W. Smillie, superintendent of the Department of Animal and Plant Pathology, carried well the executive burden of liquidating the Princeton laboratories, and when that task was completed joined the New York staff as assistant to the business manager, in charge of the animal quarters.

Many friends of The Rockefeller Institute in America and abroad, unaware of all the considerations which had impelled the Trustees to discontinue the Princeton laboratories, viewed the step with dismay. An eloquent expression of their concern, which is at the same time a tribute to the accomplishments of the staff at Princeton, appeared in 1948 in the English scientific journal *Nature,* from the pen of J. A. V. Butler, a distinguished physical chemist who, as a Fellow of The Rockefeller Foundation, had worked in Princeton with Northrop in 1939–1941.

Scientific workers in England, Butler wrote, heard with regret, and almost with incredulity, that the Princeton laboratories were to be closed. Although it would be impertinent to question the reasons for this decision, friends of the institution, and especially those who had received its hospitality, were distressed that its discontinuance was thought necessary. The founding of the Princeton laboratories was a logical consequence of the Institute's policy to provide facilities for the study of disease in all its manifestations, in animals and plants as well as in human beings. This policy had been magnificently justified by the results, too numerous to mention in the space at Butler's disposal. Citing a few notable achievements, he declared that the work of Northrop and his colleagues had done more than that of any other group to open up the chemistry of enzymes. Stanley's work had decisively initiated the modern study of virus particles. Shope's study of the rabbit papilloma was only one of the many important discoveries in animal pathology. The scientific establishment now being dispersed, Butler wrote, had made uniquely important contributions to biological and medical research.[9] Looking back more than a decade later upon this difficult and painful time, his verdict still holds good; but the lasting admiration of colleagues everywhere assuages the heartache of those who loved their scientific home in Princeton and made their careers there. The New York laboratories, strengthened by the able men who came from Princeton, carry forward under unified leadership a program of research that is basic to the study of disease in animals as well as in man.

CHAPTER EIGHTEEN

The Hospital, 1935–1953

Bacterial transformations; virus diseases; virus pneumonias; biology of viruses. Rheumatic fever; the anemias; muscular dystrophy; cirrhosis of the liver. Nephrosis and nephritis; fat metabolism; endocrine diseases. Trend toward basic investigations.

Rufus Cole was still head of the Hospital of The Rockefeller Institute during the first two years of Gasser's directorship. When in 1937 Cole retired to a quiet life of scholarship in his country home, Thomas M. Rivers succeeded him as director of the hospital, retaining also the leadership of his own laboratory of virus research.[1] The next few years were to see major shifts in the personnel and interests of the hospital staff, as older members retired and their successors brought in new programs or new methods of attacking old problems. Cole's retirement, for example, was roughly coincident with a radical change in the Institute's study of acute respiratory diseases. Lobar pneumonia, to which he had devoted his own research career since the hospital opened in 1910, was waning in frequency and importance as a clinical problem. Oswald T. Avery still was leading the investigation of the chemistry of the pneumococcus, which he had begun long ago at Cole's suggestion; but he and his colleagues, studying the capsular polysaccharides, had gone far beyond the practical aim of finding means to control this one organism, and had built up a great structure of fundamental immunochemistry.

Among the incidental results of their comprehensive work was a discovery of considerable diagnostic value, concerning a peculiar protein that appears in the blood during the acute phase of certain infectious diseases. In 1930 W. S. Tillett and Thomas Francis, Jr., Cole's senior clinical associate on the hospital staff, observed that blood serum from a patient suffering with lobar pneumonia in the acute stage contains a substance which forms a precipitate with a dilute solution of one of the complex sugars, designated C-polysaccharide, found by Avery and his co-workers in the cell body of the pneumococcus. A few years later, Avery and T. J. Abernethy found the unknown substance to be a protein. With Colin M. MacLeod of the hospital's resident staff, Avery then isolated it in a relatively pure state, so that its immunological properties could be studied. In 1947 Maclyn McCarty, National Research Council Fellow (later a Member of The Rockefeller Institute), succeeded in crystallizing the C-reactive protein; and in 1954 H. F. Wood, McCarty, and R. J. Slater published evidence that it may be a β-globulin. The C-reactive protein has been found useful as an index of the progress of certain acute bacterial infections, especially rheumatic fever and tuberculosis; in tuberculosis its disappearance from the blood is a good indication that the infection has become inactive.

Avery retired in 1943, ceasing to work in the laboratory three or four years later.[2] His last years of service were marked by a great discovery that was to link together some of the basic phenomena of immunity and heredity. The story of the transforming factor begins in 1928, when a British pathologist, Fred Griffith, reported that when he inoculated mice with a mixture of a harmless strain of living pneumococci and the dead remains of a virulent strain, the mice, to his astonishment, died from infection with live organisms of the virulent type. Since he could not believe that the killed bacteria had come to life, he had to assume that something in their dead bodies had transformed the living harmless strain into the virulent one. This discovery naturally excited Avery's interest, because he and an assistant, Martin H. Dawson, had observed similar changes from non-virulence to virulence in a strain of pneumococci, induced by passage through animals or by growth on certain culture media. He therefore asked Dawson to look into Griffith's transformation. Dawson confirmed the finding; and in 1931, working at Columbia University, he and a visitor from Peking Union Medical College, Richard H. P. Sia, succeeded in causing dead pneumococci to transform living organisms, as in Griffith's experiment, but in laboratory glassware instead of in a mouse. In 1932 J. L. Alloway of Avery's group carried the feat a step further by using as transforming agent, not whole dead cells, but a cell-free extract made from them. Evidently the transforming agent was a chemical substance.

Avery himself now entered the investigation, working with MacLeod and, later, with McCarty. Growing large amounts of the virulent Type III pneumococcus, the investigators extracted and systematically broke apart the chemical constituents of the organisms, testing the transforming power of each fraction, until in 1944 they arrived at a practically pure substance possessing the transforming power in very high concentration. This proved, surprisingly, to be a nucleic acid of a type which Levene and Jacobs had first identified years before at The Rockefeller Institute. It was deoxyribonucleic acid (DNA).

Because this substance was obtained by conventional methods of chemical analysis, Avery and McCarty could not exclude the possibility that its transforming action might be due to a small amount of protein contaminant. They knew that an enzyme, DNase, would destroy the DNA without affecting the proteins, and McCarty, venturing into the difficult field of enzyme chemistry, succeeded in preparing from beef pancreas a quantity of DNase good enough for preliminary experiments. Treated with this, the substance lost its transforming power. To clinch the matter, the Institute's great expert on the purification of enzymes, Kunitz, in 1950 prepared a highly purified crystalline DNase which confirmed McCarty's earlier results. The demonstration that a nucleic acid was the effective agent in inducing a heritable change in a living organism was unexpected, since nucleic acids had generally been thought to be chemically undifferentiated and rather inert, biologically; the general traditions of physiological chemistry, moreover, suggested that any such effect could be exerted only by proteins. Since that time, however, many investigators (among them Alfred E. Mirsky, whose work has been discussed in Chapter 14) have shown that DNA exists in chromosomes of higher animals and is a constant and characteristic ingredient of the genes. Thus the work of Avery's group on bacterial transformation points to a striking similarity of the chemical mechanism of heredity throughout the biological scale from bacteria to mammals.[3]

The more clinical and practical part of Cole's program, including the study of lobar pneumonia at the bedside, the investigation of immunity to the various types of pneumococci, and the effort to improve the antisera against them, was in the hands of a group of young men, including Thomas Francis, Jr. (later professor at the University of Michigan and a leader in poliomyelitis control), Kenneth Goodner (now professor at Jefferson Medical College), Theodore J. Abernethy of Washington, D.C., Frank L. Horsfall, Jr., and Colin MacLeod, now professor of medicine at New York University. But after Francis departed in 1935, and Cole retired in 1937, there was little left for these men to do, except what the military call a "mopping-up" campaign. Lobar pneumonia was for various reasons becoming less common, and the use of antibiotic drugs, beginning about 1938 with the sulfonamides, was to reduce its toll of death. Among the first to use sulfa drugs against lobar pneumonia was MacLeod, with George S. Mirick and E. C. Curnen, of the resident staff of The Rockefeller Institute Hospital. The diffuse bronchopneumonias, which as we now know are mostly caused by viruses, took the place of lobar pneumonia as the chief object of the Institute's research on acute respiratory diseases. The continuation of this program, under the leadership of Frank L. Horsfall, Jr., will be narrated later in this chapter.

After Thomas M. Rivers in 1937 became director of the hospital, his virus research group continued intensive study of several major problems. These stemmed from work begun by Rivers and were, under his direction, in part taken over for further development by his juniors, each member of the closely knit team contributing his special talents and experience. With Ralph S. Muckenfuss (now director of the Naval Biological Laboratory in Oakland, California) and Eugen Haagen, a guest worker from Germany, Rivers had grown the viruses of vaccinia and herpes simplex (cold sore) in bits of cornea from rabbits' eyes cultivated in clots of rabbits' plasma. Under these conditions, the virus was found not only to multiply, but to produce characteristic lesions in the excised corneal tissue. This was, so far as can be ascertained, the first production of a characteristic viral lesion in tissue cultures.

In Chapter 10 we mentioned the work on vaccinia (cowpox) virus in tissue culture, by which Rivers and his associates had developed a vaccine which conferred a degree of protection against smallpox, but became too much attenuated (because of the inadequate culture method then available) to give complete protection. This partial success paved the way for a notable accomplishment in the fight against another dreaded disease, yellow fever. While working with vaccine virus, Rivers had many talks with Wilbur A. Sawyer of The Rockefeller Foundation's International Health Division, and Max Theiler of its yellow fever laboratories, located in The Rockefeller Institute. These men perceived that a similar attenuation of yellow fever virus might afford a strain incapable of causing the disease, yet able to confer immunity against the potent natural virus. Stimulated by the experience of Rivers, Theiler and his group eventually developed an attenuated yellow fever virus suitable for use as a preventive vaccine, an achievement of enormous importance for which Max Theiler in 1951 received the Nobel Prize for Medicine.

Continuing study of the virus of vaccinia by Rivers and his fellow workers made that organism one of the best understood of all animal viruses. Bacteriologists had long observed in vaccine lymph certain minute objects called "elementary bodies," which in the light of growing knowledge of viruses in general were now supposed to be living virus particles. In 1935, J. Craigie of the Connaught Laboratories, Toronto, developed a method of isolating virus in quantity from the skin of vaccine-infected rabbits. Rivers and his colleague Robert F. Parker (now professor of microbiology at Western Reserve University), utilizing this method, compared the number of elementary bodies in a given suspension with its relative infectivity, and soon proved that the elementary bodies are indeed virus organisms. By progressively diluting his suspensions, Parker proceeded to show that a drop containing a single particle can set up a vaccinia lesion when injected into a rabbit's skin. Craigie's method of concentrating the virus yielded a quantity sufficient for Parker and T. P. Hughes (now of the World Health Organization) to ascertain the relative amounts of the chief constituents of protoplasm — fats, carbohydrates, and protein — present in the virus.

In 1938 Joseph E. Smadel, who had been working with Homer Swift on rheumatic fever, joined Rivers. The two, collaborating with the ultracentrifuge specialist E. G. Pickels and with Theodore Shedlovsky, an expert on electrophoresis, from the Institute's physical chemistry laboratory, determined the size and density of the virus particles. Charles L. Hoagland of the hospital staff, an outstanding biochemist, joined the team and, with Rivers, Smadel, and their assistants, in 1940–1942 studied the more abstruse chemical composition of the virus, with particular regard to the nucleoproteins, which were, by this time, known to be essential constituents of living tissues and organisms. The information about vaccinia virus gained in this way constituted the first adequate description of the chemical content of an animal virus. It showed that organisms of this sort possess a considerable degree of biochemical elab-

Headquarters Building, U.S. Naval Medical Research Unit No. 2

Group at U.S. Naval Medical Research Unit No. 2, Guam, in 1946
Left to right: Richard E. Shope, Admiral Chester W. Nimitz, Thomas M. Rivers

JOHN D. ROCKEFELLER 3RD

oration, differing greatly in this respect from plant viruses of the tobacco mosaic type.

In 1942 Smadel, Hoagland, and Shedlovsky studied the antigenic proteins of vaccinia virus, arriving at the remarkable discovery, discussed in Chapter 14, of a protein molecule capable of eliciting simultaneously two different immune reactions. When the electron microscope became available for biological research, R. H. Green of the hospital staff, Smadel, and T. F. Anderson obtained excellent photographs of the virus particles. By a curious reversal of the usual order of discovery, the exact form of the organism was observed only after its chemical content was fairly well known.

Meanwhile Smadel also began to study the virus of choriomeningitis, a disease primarily of mice, which Rivers and T. F. McNair Scott in 1935 found and identified in human patients (Chapter 10). With R. D. Baird of the hospital staff and Margaret J. Wall, Smadel in 1940 concentrated the virus from the spleens of experimentally infected guinea pigs, and from this material prepared a soluble antigen which could be used in diagnostic tests by the complement-fixation method. Rivers, Smadel, and S. M. Ward, in similar fashion, concentrated the virus of infectious myxoma of rabbits, and prepared soluble antigens for use in immunological studies of this disease.

During World War II these investigators were nearly all called into the armed services. When Rivers returned from his work with the Navy, he found himself heavily involved in the administration of the hospital. Smadel remained with the government, becoming, in time, director of the division of communicable diseases at the Walter Reed Army Medical Center and, later, associate director of the National Institutes of Health. Hoagland's biochemical interests led him into general problems of metabolism and into a study of diseases of the muscular system, to be mentioned later. In 1946 Rivers dissolved the laboratory of virus research, continuing, however, to serve as informal adviser to other workers in the hospital and the laboratories. It had been characteristic of his group that, although they necessarily studied a limited number of viruses, they did not lose sight of the general phenomena of virus biology. Through numerous reviews, monographs, lectures, chapters in handbooks, and service as consultant, Rivers and Smadel spread the influence of their laboratory widely.

As the study of lobar pneumonia diminished, influenza took first place in the hospital's investigation of acute respiratory disease. In 1934 Francis was already at work with the influenza virus, learning to cultivate it and to study the development of immunity to it in experimental animals and human patients. That year Horsfall, who later succeeded Francis as clinical chief for acute respiratory disease, came from McGill University. While a member of the resident staff of The Rockefeller Institute Hospital, he took part in the immunochemical work of Avery's group, working chiefly with Kenneth Goodner. Together they studied the role of lipids in immune reactions. In 1936–1938 Horsfall, Goodner, MacLeod, A. H. Harris, 2nd, and René Dubos developed anti-pneumococcus sera from rabbits, which rivaled the standard horse sera in curative power and caused much less severe allergic reactions. Further work along this promising line was rendered unnecessary by the advent of antibiotic drugs.

AFTER COMPLETING his residency in the hospital, Frank Horsfall joined the International Health Division of The Rockefeller Foundation. Stationed for four years in its laboratories, he led an elaborate study of influenza in its various aspects, including the epidemiology of the disease and the immune reactions of animals and human beings to the influenza viruses. Through this work Horsfall became an authority on influenza.

In 1941 he was appointed a Member of The Rockefeller Institute, as chief of the group studying acute respiratory diseases, under Avery's nominal leadership. Horsfall's first major effort in his new post was an investigation of "primary atypical pneumonia." This name designates a common form of pneumonia, first clearly recognized about 1930, which differs in many respects from lung diseases caused by bacteria. It began to be encountered, or at least recognized, more and more frequently, and during World War II it was more common than all other forms of pneumonia combined. It did not respond to antibiotics and often ran a long course, but fortunately was rarely fatal. The disease was difficult to distinguish from various types of bronchopneumonia associated with psittacosis, epidemic influenza, and other virus diseases.

Horsfall's chief associates in this investigation were E. C. Curnen (now professor at the University of North Carolina), G. S. Mirick (now scientific director of the New York City Health Research Council),

Lewis Thomas (now professor in New York University), and J. E. Ziegler (also of New York University). Because primary atypical pneumonia had the appearance of a virus disease, Horsfall's team looked for a virus and found one, but, like several previous investigators who had inculpated other viruses, they could not prove its causal relation to the disease. In 1943 Thomas found that in the course of an attack of primary atypical pneumonia, the patient may develop in his blood specific antibodies against a particular type of non-hemolytic streptococcus, designated as "MG." Summarizing the results of several years of work, Horsfall suggested that the disease may result from a double infection with this streptococcus and some other agent, possibly a virus. Here the problem of the cause of this baffling disease rested for several years; subsequently, it was found that some — perhaps a fourth — of the illnesses classified as primary atypical pneumonia are caused by members of the newly isolated "adenovirus" group. There still remains a large number of cases for which no virus is as yet certainly known.

Although The Rockefeller Institute's study of acute respiratory infections was for some years focused upon primary atypical pneumonia, all types of diffuse pneumonias were treated in the hospital, including that associated with influenza. Horsfall's group carried on a more or less continuous investigation of the influenza virus, both in the laboratory and at the bedside, studying in particular the immunological characteristics of the various strains recovered from endemic cases and local epidemics. Having always in mind the search for methods of combating virus infections of the respiratory tract, Horsfall found his immunological studies rather discouraging, because the multiplicity of viral strains with differing immunological characteristics that turned up in his laboratory seemed to diminish the hope of controlling influenza by vaccines.

Another, more promising, area of attack, Horsfall thought, was the biological cycle of virus multiplication, which runs through four phases in fixed sequence. First, the cells of the infected animal adsorb the virus particles. Next, there is a latent period during which the virus is not observable but is adapting itself to the cells and beginning to multiply within them. In the third phase, new virus material becomes apparent and continues to increase. In the fourth, the newly formed particles are released from the infected cells. Two ways were known, and partially understood, by which the multiplication cycle of an animal virus might be blocked. One of these was the "interference phenomenon": host tissues infected by a given virus may not be subsequently infectible by another. The second way of blocking the virus multiplication, by chemical substances, had been illustrated by recent investigations in which certain dyestuffs were found to inhibit the multiplication of a virus. These blockages evidently result from interruption of biochemical synthesis of virus materials in host cells. Their study demanded precise enumeration of cells and virus particles, and observation of the time relations of normal and blocked multiplication cycles. New quantitative techniques were necessary, to which Horsfall contributed a photometric method of counting virus particles.

In a long series of papers, Horsfall and his collaborators C. O. Forssman, G. I. Lavin, H. S. Ginsberg, and J. E. Ziegler reported quantitative studies of interference between influenza viruses of different strains inoculated into chick embryonic membranes. They found that all, or nearly all, the cells of the host tissue must be blocked by the first infective virus before the tissue becomes insusceptible to the second, or challenging, virus. A remarkable fact is that virus particles rendered inactive by heat or by ultraviolet radiation, though themselves no longer able to multiply, can inhibit reproduction of the challenging viruses. It appears that the first virus particles to reach the cells initiate chemical changes there, which interfere with multiplication of the second virus. Similar phenomena occur in the living mammal as well as in the chick embryo; for example, Ginsberg, G. K. Hirst, and Horsfall observed that inoculation with influenza virus, which does not normally reproduce itself in the mouse brain, blocks a subsequent infection of the brain by Western equine virus; and that mumps virus, which does not establish itself in the mouse lung, blocks the reproduction of a pneumonia-producing virus.

Several of the young men who worked with Horsfall for two or three years on viruses and related problems have done distinguished work in virology since leaving The Rockefeller Institute: G. K. Hirst, now at the New York City Public Health Research Institute; F. M. Davenport, who has done much valuable work on influenza at the University of Michigan; D. A. J. Tyrrell, now with the National Institute for Medical Research at Mill Hill, London, whose work recently culminated in the cultivation of a virus of the common cold; and E. D. Kilbourne of Cornell

University Medical College, investigator of the influenza viruses and virus interference.

Study by Horsfall's group of the second kind of interference, that induced by chemical agents, goes back to 1940, when Horsfall was with The Rockefeller Foundation. He and a colleague, R. C. Hahn, had discovered in the lungs of healthy mice a virus which, after serial passage through several mice, became virulent, causing fatal pneumonia. Horsfall and Curnen began in 1943 a quantitative study of the immunological reactions and infectivity of this new pneumonia virus of mice, called PVM. They found that it unites with special substances in the lung tissue, causing local damage, and Horsfall and M. Volkert found that these virus-binding substances, presumably proteins, may play a decisive role in starting an infection. Horsfall and Ginsberg also showed that there is a direct relation between the concentration of virus in the lung and the severity of the pneumonic disease. It follows, therefore, that any treatment which can retard the multiplication of the virus may have a beneficial or even curative effect upon the illness.

An unexpected observation corroborated this idea and started Horsfall's group on a further series of experiments. In 1947 Horsfall and McCarty tried injecting mice with PVM together with the MG streptococcus, mentioned above as possibly combining with some unknown virus to produce primary atypical pneumonia. When given with PVM, however, the streptococcus lessened the severity of the virus infection, apparently by inhibiting the multiplication of PVM in the tissues. Testing substances extracted from cultures of the streptococcus, Horsfall and McCarty found that the inhibitory substance was a polysaccharide. Ginsberg and Horsfall, aided by Walther Goebel's expert knowledge of the chemistry of polysaccharides, tried the new substance on mumps virus cultivated in chick embryos and found that it inhibited this virus also. In 1951 Ginsberg and Horsfall used a polysaccharide of bacterial origin to cure virus pneumonia of mice, caused by PVM, which in untreated animals was invariably fatal. The next year, in similar experiments, Igor Tamm of the hospital staff, Karl Folkers of Merck and Company, and Horsfall discovered that chemical substances of quite another class, benzimidazoles, likewise inhibit the multiplication of several viruses. This promising line of research was still engaging Horsfall's group in 1953.

Any account, such as this, of the research of medical scientists following obscure leads in a difficult and complex field risks losing sight of their concurrent service to the community. It must not be forgotten that the men who conducted this intensive laboratory work under Horsfall's direction were also responsible for the care of patients suffering from all forms of pneumonia, to whom they brought the benefit of the best current knowledge of diagnosis and treatment, in accord with the established aim of the Hospital of The Rockefeller Institute. The chief of such a group, moreover, gaining experience and knowledge, acquires a position of leadership in his professional field. He serves the public through his writings and participation in national and international councils, and spreads his influence through the young men he trains.[4]

RHEUMATIC FEVER continued to be a major subject of study in the hospital under the leadership of Homer Swift and his successor, Maclyn McCarty. Investigators of this baffling disease had become more and more convinced that it results, directly or indirectly, from infection with hemolytic streptococci of group A in Rebecca Lancefield's classification. Yet the nature of the disease remained obscure, and conjecture persisted that it might be caused by something else, perhaps a virus or one of the pleuropneumonia-like organisms. In 1938–1939 Swift, with his assistant T. M. Brown, made a final and unsuccessful effort to find some such organism in the inflamed joints, even though he had already practically accepted the hemolytic streptococcus as the cause.

Rheumatic fever is characterized by general, diffuse symptoms, including fever, with painful swelling of the joints, and often damage of the heart valves and heart muscle. Since the organisms are not seen invading the tissues of the patient, how they cause damage is by no means clear. For this reason, the investigators have not been able to attack the problem by studying the immediate relations between the organism and its human host, as, for example, students of tuberculosis could by observing the tubercle bacillus attacking the tissues of the lung. Instead, they have had to divide their approach into more or less distinct but convergent lines, studying on one hand the biology of the streptococcus, including its biochemistry and immunochemistry, and, on the other hand, the reactions of patients and of experimental animals to the insidious invader.

Lancefield, as in earlier years, followed the first of these lines, devoting her attention henceforth largely to immunochemistry. Because of the growing suspicion that the hemolytic streptococcus sets up rheumatic fever through some kind of immune reaction, all sorts of substances that can be isolated from the bacteria, or from a culture medium in which they have been grown, have been studied for antigenic properties. Among these substances, certain proteins especially interested the Rockefeller Institute group. Lancefield had discovered that group A hemolytic streptococci, when treated with dilute acids, yield a substance of protein nature, designated as the "M" protein, which is type-specific; that is to say, through minor differences in its structure it serves to separate group A streptococci into a variety of types which can be distinguished by serological methods. Working with Swift, Hirst, W. A. Stewart, R. F. Watson, and A. T. Wilson, Lancefield demonstrated that this substance is closely associated with the virulence of A-group streptococci and with their ability to elicit protective immune reactions. Thus in streptococci protein antigens play the same role as do polysaccharides in pneumococci. For that reason Lancefield studied the chemical nature of M protein intensively, working alone and later with Gertrude A. Perlmann, and after many years of work isolated the protein of Type I in highly purified form. With the above-named associates and with Vincent P. Dole, she has also studied other antigenic proteins of hemolytic streptococci.

Much of what we know about the epidemiology of streptococcus infections is based upon the identification of the types of the organism involved in specific diseases. Lancefield has continued to apply her vast experience in typing a wide range of organisms and in correlating their biological and chemical characteristics with their degrees of virulence. An example of the usefulness of such work is the recent finding of a Cleveland investigator, Charles H. Rammelkamp, that one form of Bright's disease, acute hemorrhagic glomerulitis, is usually caused by hemolytic streptococci of one particular type, Lancefield's type 12.

Swift continued to lead the investigation of streptococcal infections, joining with his associates in studying the patterns of disease caused by streptococci, the development of immune states, and treatment. In view of the hypothesis that rheumatic fever is an allergic reaction to infection or reinfection with hemolytic streptococci, he and J. K. Moen, and, later, he and Smadel, experimented with other allergic conditions of possibly similar nature, including bacterial hypersensitivity and allergic nephritis. When the antibiotic drugs became available, he promptly tried them, studying sulfanilamide with Smadel in 1938–1939 and penicillin with R. F. Watson and Sidney Rothbard in 1944. These workers were among the first to find that certain antibiotics were capable of destroying hemolytic streptococci in infected tissues and body cavities.

After 1946, when Swift retired from active direction of the group, until his death in 1953, he and G. E. Murphy attempted to produce rheumatic fever in animals. They came nearer, perhaps, to this goal than previous experimenters had come. By repeatedly inoculating the skin of rabbits with hemolytic streptococci, they produced localized heart lesions that resembled the "Aschoff bodies" characteristically found in the heart muscle of patients who die of heart failure following rheumatic fever.

Maclyn McCarty, who succeeded Swift as leader of the investigation, had come to the hospital staff in 1941, a few years after taking his medical degree at Johns Hopkins. As a member, at first, of Avery's group, he had taken part in the investigations, described earlier in this chapter, on the "transforming factor" of the pneumococcus, and on the "C-reactive protein." Later, with H. C. Anderson and H. F. Wood, he showed that the appearance of C-reactive protein in acute rheumatic fever can be used as a measure of the activity of the disease process. Anderson and McCarty, moreover, using a special form of C-polysaccharide from pneumococci as a test reagent, found that rabbits inoculated with an acute infectious disease, or with active bacterial products, such as typhoid vaccine, develop in their serum an acute-phase protein completely analogous to the C-reactive protein in man. This observation provides a laboratory model of the phenomenon, laying the groundwork for subsequent investigations. McCarty and his associates also investigated numerous other biological and immunochemical products of streptococci, trying to discover substances that might help to explain the disease picture in rheumatic fever or to suggest methods of treatment and prevention. S. D. Elliott of London, following up experiments begun while a visiting Fellow at The Rockefeller Institute, succeeded in purifying both a protein-splitting enzyme and its inactive precursor, the first crystalline products to be obtained from hemolytic streptococci; and he investigated in detail the chemical, enzymatic, and serological properties of these two closely related proteins.

Anderson, Henry Kunkel, and McCarty studied the significance for rheumatic fever of a find made in 1933 by W. S. Tillett (a former Rockefeller Institute physician) and R. L. Garner, that certain hemolytic streptococci grown in human fibrin clots are able to liquefy the fibrin, but not similar clots of the blood of other species. The action is due to a substance, streptokinase, which brings about the activation of a proteolytic enzyme precursor, normally present in blood plasma. This specificity for human zymogen of an organism which produces rheumatic fever, a disease peculiar to man, seemed worth looking into. Accordingly, the three investigators assayed the antibody against streptokinase in the blood of a large number of patients with scarlet fever, some of whom would be expected to develop rheumatic fever as a sequel of the acute infection. This study grew out of the Institute's Navy program in World War II, and the blood sera tested came from patients at the Great Lakes Naval Training Station. The result showed that those scarlet fever patients who later developed rheumatic fever had a higher antibody response to streptokinase than those who recovered without such a sequel. This, however, is not a unique attribute of streptokinase; Anderson, Kunkel, and McCarty's study, together with the work of others, indicates that the average antibody response to a variety of streptococcal antigens is enhanced in rheumatic fever. Rothbard, Watson, Swift, and A. T. Wilson had published in 1949 evidence of the same kind obtained in their study of patients in The Rockefeller Institute Hospital. This instance illustrates the importance of studying the enzymes which a pathogenic organism releases into its environment, for they may play a role in the virulence and invasiveness of the bacteria as well as in specific injury of the tissues.

In 1948 McCarty discovered that cultures of group A hemolytic streptococci contain deoxyribonuclease, the enzyme which breaks down deoxyribonucleic acid. Patients who have had streptococcal infections may develop an antibody against the deoxyribonuclease. McCarty found that this antibody, and also an antiserum against streptococci prepared experimentally in rabbits, will inhibit the activity of streptococcus deoxyribonuclease, but not that of the similar enzyme prepared from pancreatic tissue. These facts show that the streptococcal enzyme is a specific product of the bacteria, and strengthen the suspicion that it may take part in producing the lesions of streptococcal disease.

An individual may suffer several different group A streptococcal infections within a single year. This raises the question whether the recurrent infections are due to immunologically distinct types within the single group of organisms. In 1946 Watson, Rothbard, and Swift, still working in the Navy's wartime research program, attacked this problem by infecting rhesus monkeys with various types of group A streptococci, and found that successful inoculation with any one type was followed by resistance to the same type for several months or longer, but not to other types. This resistance, they found, was related to the antibodies against Lancefield's specific M antigen. Some years earlier, Rothbard had elaborated a method of testing human blood serum for type-specific antibodies against streptococci, by observing its power to inhibit bacterial growth. Using this bacteriostatic test, Rothbard and Watson in 1948 reported that, as a human streptococcal infection proceeds, streptococci isolated at successive periods may or may not have lost the power of forming the M substance; if they have lost it, they no longer resist the protective bacteriostatic powers of the patient's antibodies. If they go on making M substance, however, they remain potentially pathogenic, and a patient who harbors them is presumably liable to become a dangerous carrier of infection.

Ever looking for clues to the mechanism of tissue damage in rheumatic fever, and still suspecting an allergic reaction of some sort, two members of McCarty's group, C. A. Stetson, Jr., and R. A. Good, in 1950–1952 turned their attention to an allergic reaction discovered in 1928 by Gregory Shwartzmann of New York. If a rabbit receives an intradermal injection of bacteria or bacterial toxin, and twenty-four hours later is given the same bacterial product by intravenous injection, a severe hemorrhagic reaction develops at the site of the first injection. If the first injection is given intravenously instead of intradermally, many tissues are sensitized simultaneously and the second injection sets up a general Shwartzmann reaction throughout the body. Stetson and Good closely examined the cellular basis of the reaction. They found that it depends upon the presence of leucocytes that accumulate in the tissues under the stimulus of the first or preparatory injection. When they prevented the accumulation of leucocytes by treatment with benzol or other substances toxic to such cells, the second injection did not elicit a Shwartzmann reaction.

After studying rheumatic fever continuously for almost four decades, the Rockefeller Institute investigators had gained hints as to the cause of this perplexing disease, and had worked on its treatment and prevention with antibiotics. By more general studies, they had greatly advanced knowledge of the classification, biology, and biochemistry of the hemolytic streptococcus, and of the epidemiology of the diseases it causes. Moreover, about one thousand patients suffering with rheumatic fever, admitted to the hospital beginning in 1919, have received skilled diagnosis and the best treatment currently known. Men who have gone to other institutions after taking part in this work now form a corps of experts on rheumatic fever and other streptococcal diseases; at The Rockefeller Institute the attack on these maladies continues under the leadership of McCarty and Lancefield.

By THE MIDDLE 1930's Alfred E. Cohn, head of the hospital's cardiology group, was no longer active in research. He came to the Institute daily, however, to confer with his juniors, and sat in the dining room after lunch until three o'clock every day, fascinating his companions by urbane and wide-ranging conversation. At his apartment in New York, he and Mrs. Cohn held a weekly dinner, quite sumptuous and rather formal, to which he usually invited some of the Institute's workers, conversing with them on literary and other cultural topics until the small hours of the morning.

In the hospital wards and in Cohn's laboratory, his associates kept up the program of research on heart disease and on aging. J. Murray Steele (now professor at New York University) was completing the latter project by studying changes imposed by age on the structure and function of the dog's heart; A. G. Macleod (now of the Upjohn Company) was helping to wind up another project, the analysis of electrocardiograms from patients with heart disease. About 1939 Cohn, Steele, and H. A. Schroeder (later of Washington University) began an intensive study of diseases characterized by high blood pressure, first classifying these conditions according to known or presumed causes, and then choosing one type, arterial hypertension, for special investigation.

It was characteristic of Cohn's breadth of interest that, as a part of the investigation of arterial hypertension, he organized a psychiatric study, the only extensive one ever made at The Rockefeller Institute. The subjects were twenty-four patients undergoing clinical study and treatment by Cohn, Steele, and Schroeder, in collaboration with two psychiatrists, N. W. Ackerman of New York and Carl A. L. Binger, then of Cornell Medical College and a former member of Cole's staff. Their investigation brought out definite evidence of a characteristic personality type associated with a tendency to arterial hypertension. For five years also beginning in 1939 Cohn, G. E. Burch, Jr. (now professor of internal medicine at Tulane University), and Charles Neumann (later of New York University) studied the normal status and disturbances of the smaller blood vessels, especially those of the extremities.

In 1944 Alfred Cohn retired and the group of cardiologists he had trained so well was dispersed. After retiring, Cohn found ample occupation in service on a score of institutional boards and committees in various fields of science, philanthropy, and art. In 1950, with Claire Lingg, formerly of the New York Heart Association, he published a thoughtful report on the social burden of disease in the United States. He went on writing lectures and essays; the charming book *No Retreat From Reason* well illustrates his talents as medical philosopher and raconteur.[5]

CORNELIUS P. RHOADS, leader of the group working on diseases of the blood, retained for some years his interest in the anemias. Intrigued by the idea that the destruction of blood in pernicious anemia may be caused by some toxic substance in the circulating blood, he put much effort into the biochemical and biophysical study of the blood and its chemical derivatives. Konrad Dobriner, a German-born physician, joined him in 1936 in what was to be a long association; and the two were aided by The Rockefeller Institute's spectroscopist, G. I. Lavin, and a succession of Fellows and junior physicians of the hospital. Although their findings did not reveal the cause of blood destruction in the anemias, Rhoads and Dobriner afterward used the spectroscopic methods they and Lavin had developed in extensive research at the Memorial Hospital of New York on carcinogenic substances.

Rhoads's last major work at The Rockefeller Institute Hospital was a thorough study, in association with W. Halsey Barker and R. R. Bomford of the hospital staff, of a class of diseases which the two investigators termed "refractory anemias," because they are not benefited by any known treatment except blood transfusions. The description of the pathology, clinical course, causes, and treatment of the refractory and aplastic anemias, by Bomford and Rhoads, published in 1941, has become a classic in the literature of these perplexing diseases.

Rhoads necessarily devoted a great deal of time to the care of his patients, and his skill and kindness as a physician were much appreciated. After twelve years in The Rockefeller Institute, he became director of Memorial Hospital for Cancer and Allied Diseases, and in 1945 director also of the Sloan-Kettering Institute. His associate, David K. Miller, went to the University of Buffalo, as professor of medicine.

THE STORY OF Charles Lee Hoagland's career runs a full gamut of human interest from an orphan boy's rise, in typical Horatio Alger fashion, to a tragically early end. Hoagland was a foundling, born in Nebraska in (he variously stated) 1907 or 1908. He did not know who his parents were, but believed that his mother was French. In 1927, while working as a bus boy in a hotel in Springfield, Missouri, he volunteered to do some typing after hours for a guest, Senator A. L. McCawley of the Missouri legislature, a substantial lawyer. The young man's service was so competent and his personality so winning that the Senator at once offered him permanent employment. The McCawleys made him a member of their family, treated him with full affection as a son, and, after a few years, formally adopted him. These generous foster parents managed, in spite of financial reverses in the depression of 1929, to put him through college and enable him to study medicine at Washington University, St. Louis, where he was graduated in 1935.[6] His brilliant record as a student and hospital physician brought him in 1937 an invitation to work at the Hospital of The Rockefeller Institute.

Hoagland was assigned at first to Cole's and Avery's group, and for a couple of years assisted MacLeod and Goebel in immunochemical work on the pneumococcus. In 1940 he was transferred to the laboratory of Rivers, where for three years he took part, with Rivers and Smadel, in the pioneering study of the chemical structure of vaccinia virus. One of Hoagland's contributions, his demonstration of the presence of the vitamin riboflavin in the virus, was regarded by his fellow workers as a triumph of ingenuity and chemical insight. In addition, Hoagland and Sylvia M. Ward (Mrs. J. Murray Steele) investigated certain fundamental enzyme reactions involved in the nutrition of a bacterial organism, *Hemophilus influenzae*.

By this time Hoagland had established himself as an all-round biochemist and a competent physician as well. He was rapidly promoted, rising in five years from Assistant to Associate Member. To Rivers, as director of the hospital, Hoagland about 1941 proposed a bold venture in clinical research. He believed that he could profitably use his experience in metabolic chemistry to study a class of diseases in which vitamin deficiencies and failures of enzyme action result in grave disturbances of metabolism. When Rivers agreed, Hoagland chose to begin with one of the most serious and least understood of these diseases, progressive muscular dystrophy. In this study he was joined by Helena Gilder and Robert E. Shank (now professor of preventive medicine at Washington University, St. Louis). Forty patients, mostly children, suffering with this heritable degenerative affection of the muscles, were subjected to thorough clinical and metabolic study. The only clue to the nature of the physiological disturbance had been discovered three decades earlier by The Rockefeller Institute's first biochemist, Phoebus Levene, working with L. Cristeller at the Montefiore Home in New York. They found that persons suffering with muscular dystrophy excrete in their urine excessive quantities of creatin, a nitrogenous substance found in muscle, where it, or rather one of its derivatives, takes part in the reactions by which stored energy is made available for muscular work. Seizing upon this functional abnormality as a point of attack, Hoagland, Shank, and Gilder made a thorough study of creatin metabolism in their patients, and began searching for presumptive disturbances of hormone action, vitamin lack, or enzyme failure that might drain substance and energy from muscle. Time was not granted them to pursue this quest, for fate intervened, first through the nation's entrance into World War II, and then through Hoagland's disastrous illness.

Late in 1941, when Rivers was organizing a research unit for the Navy, in which Hoagland was to be enrolled, the medical examiners refused the young man an assignment to active duty, because of abnormally high blood pressure. He must already have been suffering much discomfort, but never complained and carried on his work at high speed.

He was instead appointed civilian consultant to the Navy Medical Department, and with Shank, who was commissioned as lieutenant commander, altered his research program at the Institute to fit the Navy's needs. As in other wars in which United States forces have been involved, infectious hepatitis was a serious problem. The Army had over 175,000 cases, the Navy thousands more. Research on the causative virus was in progress elsewhere, but Hoagland's group was particularly fitted to study the biochemical and physiological aspects of the malady. In July 1944, the Navy began sending to the Hospital of The Rockefeller Institute all hepatitis patients from the First, Third, Fourth, and Fifth Naval Districts, about 400 in two years. Hoagland's rapid rise in The Rockefeller Institute secured him ample facilities with which to handle this great load of clinical and laboratory work; in 1945 he was made a full Member and given a laboratory of his own. Among those who worked with him in 1944–1946, besides Shank and Gilder, were O. F. Binkley, E. C. Curnen, Kendall Emerson, Jr., Henry G. Kunkel, D. H. Labby, George S. Mirick, and J. E. Ziegler (all of whom now occupy professorial positions in medical institutions).

Hoagland and his group aimed to work out biochemical tests with which physicians could ascertain the extent of liver damage, to observe the extent and rate of repair of the liver during recovery, and to try out various methods of treatment. Their most important contribution was to the dietary regime. It had been thought that patients with damaged livers could not tolerate fats, because they produced insufficient bile to emulsify fats in the intestine. Hoagland, Labby, H. G. Kunkel, and Shank proved that their patients could digest a relatively high proportion of fat, and did better on such a diet. On the other hand, their tests of drugs and dietary adjuvants revealed nothing useful, and their experience led them to treat hepatitis by rest and a well-balanced diet alone. This treatment, now generally adopted by physicians, has made thousands of patients more comfortable and hastens the slow course of liver regeneration. During this period Hoagland also studied a number of cases of cirrhosis of the liver, testing a liver extract developed at the Institute, which at first seemed helpful, but has since dropped out of use.

This intensive program called for a good deal of organization, which Hoagland handled well. As his reputation spread outside the Institute, he was offered professorships of medicine, physiology, and biochemistry in leading medical schools. In lay circles also he was winning personal regard and social position, which meant much to him, and which, indeed, he sought, urged, no doubt, by need of the standing he had lacked in his rootless childhood. There is no telling how far he might have gone, in research and possibly in the administration of medical investigation, if his health had not given way. Always tense and restless, he gave himself no rest under wartime pressure. In June 1946 severe symptoms of malignant hypertension forced him to quit work, and he became a patient in the hospital where he had himself cared for so many other young men. One of the most poignant documents in The Rockefeller Institute's files is the clinical history in which the resident physician, Sidney Rothbard, for two months sadly recorded the painful, agitated progress toward death of his colleague, stricken by a malady for which medical science had found no cure.[7]

Hoagland's illness and death left his juniors in charge of his hospital service and a large program of laboratory work. Shank had left The Rockefeller Institute earlier in the year for a post in public health research. The others, three young men between thirty and thirty-two years of age, efficiently assumed their unexpected burden, under the temporary general supervision of Rivers and Van Slyke, the hospital's chief chemist. Labby devoted himself chiefly to completing for publication the researches on which Hoagland had been engaged; in 1947 he accepted a post at the University of Oregon. Kunkel, aided by E. H. Ahrens, Jr., who had joined the staff only a month before Hoagland's death, carried on the main lines of Hoagland's program. An unfinished investigation, in which the whole group had taken part, dealt with the use of human serum albumin by injection into the blood stream in cases of cirrhosis with severe ascites (dropsy). The treatment proved helpful in some cases and was used for a time in other disorders. W. J. Eisenmenger, with Ahrens, Kunkel, S. H. Blondheim, and A. M. Bongiovanni of the hospital staff, studied the relation of sodium and other electrolytes in the blood to retention of water in cirrhotic ascites.

Another investigation which Kunkel, aided by Labby, carried on largely as his own project, even before Hoagland's death, concerned the chronic liver disease which sometimes follows an attack of infectious hepatitis. For this long and arduous task Kunkel had unusual facilities, available nowhere else. The records of Hoagland's wartime study of hepatitis kept him in touch with hundreds of men whose initial attacks had been studied and documented, and who, being service men registered with the Veterans Administration, could be followed through their post-convalescent years far more thoroughly than could the general run of patients. Keeping some of these ex-patients under observation for as long as ten years, Kunkel and Labby described a variety of complications that occurred during convalescence and later. A few of these men had suffered so much liver damage from the virus that they developed cirrhosis, the most serious sequel of hepatitis; in these patients Kunkel and his associates were able to observe its progress from incipiency to full development. Much of what is said on this subject in current textbooks stems from their observations.

The occurrence of such complications after an acute disease calls upon the physician-scientist to devise diagnostic tests that will give warning when convalescence does not proceed favorably, and thus guide further treatment. As Kunkel's program developed, he sought to meet this need, dealing largely at first with the exact determination of the levels of lipids and proteins in the blood. In 1944 a British physician, N. F. Maclagan, hit by accident upon the fact that if blood serum from a patient with liver disease is mixed with a buffered salt solution containing a bit of thymol, the mixture becomes turbid. He conjectured that the turbidity results from precipitation of one of the serum proteins, gamma globulin, known to be present in excessive amounts in cirrhosis and hepatitis. Hoagland and Kunkel immediately sought to explain in more exact terms the chemical basis of this reaction, and found that it works not only with gamma globulin but also with certain lipid-protein complexes. Using the test to follow the course of hepatitis in seventy-six patients, Kunkel found it a very sensitive indicator of liver disturbance and a reliable sign of impending relapse in hepatitis. Because it is a test for two different substances, which vary independently in the course of the illness, he developed separate methods for testing gamma globulin and total lipids in blood serum.

Kunkel arrived at his new test for gamma globulin by a remarkable combination of chance and chemical insight. Happening one day to use tap water instead of distilled water to dilute a serum sample, because of a breakdown in the distillation system, he observed marked turbidity of the serum. When he found that only one of his laboratory taps — one which was not often used — yielded water with this peculiar property, he guessed that some metallic substance in the relatively stagnant water of that particular pipe was combining with the globulin. Chemical analysis promptly pointed to copper. With this clue and by substituting (for technical reasons) zinc sulphate for the copper salt, Kunkel created a test for gamma globulin which is now in standard use.

Through intensive study of patients with every type of liver disease, and through experience gained from exact measurement of proteins, fats, and electrolytes in these cases, Kunkel and Ahrens became expert in the classification and differential diagnosis of the various types of cirrhosis. Ahrens took special responsibility for the study of lipid metabolism. One of his procedures was quantitative estimation of the three major classes of lipids found in the blood, triglycerides, cholesterol, and phospholipids. The first two, being insoluble in watery fluids, are present as very small particles or molecular aggregates, and can be estimated very crudely by the degree of turbidity of the serum. Ahrens noticed that in certain conditions in which the serum lipids were known to be high, for example, obstructive jaundice, the serum is characteristically clear, whereas in nephrosis a similarly high lipid content produces turbidity. He discovered that this striking difference results from the fact that phospholipids, which are water-soluble, emulsify and disperse the particles of the other lipids.

This finding led to deeper interest in a disease of the liver which had previously been poorly understood and inadequately described. Among their jaundiced patients, Ahrens and Kunkel noticed a number of women, about twenty in all, whose illness was characterized by a high level of total blood lipids, with a clear serum resulting from an excessively high proportion of phospholipids. They named this disease primary biliary cirrhosis, because it begins spontaneously, or at least without any obvious cause, unlike other forms of cirrhosis which result from alcohol toxicity or vitamin deficiency or acute hepatitis. The study of primary biliary cirrhosis led Ahrens to think about another serious and perplexing condition, arteriosclerosis. In view of the growing belief that this is in some way related to faults of lipid metabolism, among which excess of cholesterol has been most commonly incriminated, Ahrens suggested that the deposition of lipids in the arterial walls may depend upon the ratio of phospholipids to the other lipid constituents of the blood, rather than upon the absolute level of any one of the three classes. This suggestion has been widely used by investigators of arteriosclerosis, as a guide to further research.

To prepare himself for further investigations in this field, Ahrens in 1949–1951 joined the laboratory of Lyman Craig and with him worked out methods of using Craig's countercurrent distribution apparatus for the separation of the various lipids and their derivatives, including fatty acids and bile acids. During the following year he was chief resident in pediatrics at the Babies' Hospital, Columbia University Medical Center, but returned in 1952 to The Rockefeller Institute, where for a time he was associated with Vincent Dole's laboratory. He directed his own researches independently, assisted by D. H. Blankenhorn, William Insull, Jr., and T. T. Tsaltas of the hospital staff.

Meanwhile, Henry Kunkel, who continued to lead the investigation of liver diseases, was promoted in 1949 to the rank of Associate Member and Physician to the Hospital. In 1950–1951 he spent a year in Stockholm with the celebrated physical chemist Arne Tiselius, learning the recently perfected techniques of electrophoresis. After his return, aided in part by R. J. Slater of the hospital staff, he worked on electrophoretic identification and measurement of proteins in blood and other body fluids. In 1952 Kunkel was appointed a full Member of The Rockefeller Institute. When in 1951 Alexander G. Bearn, a young physician from Guy's Hospital, London, joined the staff, Kunkel and he began to study Wilson's disease, a disturbance of amino acid metabolism in which degenerative changes in the liver are associated with neurological lesions and alterations in the body's utilization of copper. By 1953 Bearn had assembled what was probably the largest group of patients with Wilson's disease ever gathered in one hospital, and was well launched upon his research into the metabolic and genetic problems of this peculiar malady.

THE HOSPITAL's study of diseases of the kidney was continued, as it had begun two decades earlier, on two main lines. As might be expected from the association of its leader, the biochemist Van Slyke, with a staff of physicians responsible for the care of patients, the group investigated both specific diseases of the kidney and the underlying physiology of the organs and systems involved.

In 1935 Van Slyke's collaborator Irvine H. Page, who had been engaged in various chemical and physiological investigations of the group since 1931, began an intensive study of arterial hypertension. Little was known about the cause of this common feature of renal disease. Page aimed primarily to test a widely held conjecture that the nervous connections of the kidney participate in the production of high blood pressure by transmitting noxious stimuli from the damaged kidney to the circulatory system. With the cooperation of surgeons — among them J. E. Sweet of Cornell Medical College, who in 1904 had been the first Resident Fellow of The Rockefeller Institute — he observed the results of various operations in which the nervous connections between the kidney and the rest of the body were cut off, both in dogs with induced hypertension and in patients suffering from essential hypertension whose renal arteries had been denervated or splanchnic nerves resected in the hope of relieving the high pressure. The results, on the whole, failed to implicate the nerves of the kidney in the production of hypertension. Page therefore shifted his attention to other possible explanations, and, after he left the Institute in 1937 to direct the Eli Lilly Clinic of Indianapolis, he began to search for a chemical substance that might raise the blood pressure in nephritic patients. This led to his discovery (more or less simultaneously with E. Braun-Menendez of Buenos Aires) of hypertensin or angiotonin, a pressor compound formed by the action of an enzyme of the kidney, to which hypertension of renal origin is now generally ascribed.

After Page's departure the special investigation of hypertension was dropped, but Van Slyke's clinical colleagues continued the study of Bright's disease in general, and, in particular, the condition known as nephrosis. Nephrosis is a symptom complex which, in some cases, is associated with obvious tissue damage in the kidneys; in other cases, especially in children, relatively little kidney damage is seen, nor, indeed, any obvious cause of the illness. The disease is characterized by loss of proteins from the blood into the urine — producing albuminuria with a low level of albumin in the blood — by a high level of fats and other lipids in the blood, and by retention of fluid in the tissues (edema). During 1935–1950 more than a dozen young physicians of the hospital staff studied the disease in patients and in the laboratory. Among them were Lee E. Farr (now at the Brookhaven National Laboratories), who led the clinical studies until 1940; D. A. MacFadyen (now professor of biochemistry at the University of Illinois), W. W. Beckman, G. C. Cotzias, Kendall Emerson, Jr., and Palmer H. Futcher (all of whom went on to responsible posts in other institutions); and R. M. Archibald and Vincent P. Dole (now Members of The Rockefeller Institute). After World War II, Francis P. Chinard, Howard A. Eder, and Henry D. Lauson resumed the study until Van Slyke's retirement.

These competent physicians, working with Van Slyke's guidance in chemical matters, by no means mastered the problem of the nature and cause of nephrosis. A recent textbook calls that disease "one of the most complex and most fascinating mysteries of medicine." Their long and patient investigations, however, and their experience with hundreds of cases of nephrosis, contributed greatly to the clinical picture of the disease. They observed the effects of various diets upon the levels of albumin and lipids in the blood, and studied the metabolism of proteins, amino acids, and fats, the balance of salts in the body and its effects upon edema, and a dozen other phases of the pathological physiology of diseased kidneys. The results of this work are gathered, mostly anonymously, in textbooks and reference works, for the instruction of medical students and physicians. Only those who took part in the work can appreciate the endless laboratory tests and the often poignant hours of attendance upon the sufferers whose presence in the hospital made possible a better understanding of the natural history of another baffling disease.

While these studies on patients were in progress, the group was constantly at work on physiological and biochemical problems of renal function. Van Slyke, for example, undertook to discover the source of the ammonia of the urine, the simplest chemical form in which nitrogen is excreted. Unsatisfied by the then current view that the ammonia is largely derived from urea, Van Slyke, with Archibald, Futcher, P. B. Hamilton, Alma Hiller, and R. A. Phillips made experiments of a new type, utilizing an operation devised earlier at The Rockefeller Institute by C. P. Rhoads and improved by Phillips. In this a dog's kidney is displaced from its normal site and brought near the surface, so that blood samples can be obtained directly from the renal artery and vein. By analyzing the blood, as it entered and left the kidney under various conditions, the experimenters traced the ammonia chiefly to an amino acid derivative, glutamine. Archibald's part in this work led him into an exhaustive study of the chemical characteristics and physiological role of glutamine and of an enzyme of the kidney, glutaminase, which breaks it down to ammonia.

Another noteworthy achievement was the discovery and identification of a previously unknown amino acid, the twenty-second, until now the last discovered of those known to form part of the chemical structure of mammalian proteins. In 1921 Van Slyke and Hiller detected an unknown substance among the basic amino acids yielded by the hydrolysis of gelatin. Fifteen years later these investigators, with D. A. MacFadyen and R. T. Dillon, crystallized the unidentified substance and found that it was hydroxylysine, an amino acid closely related to lysine, which was long known as a protein constituent and one of the "essential" food amino acids. Hydroxylysine has been found in significant amounts in no other protein than collagen, the structural supporting-tissue protein from which gelatin is made. The hydroxylysine presumably is responsible for some of the unique properties of collagen. Working at the Brookhaven National Laboratory in the 1950's with lysine and hydroxylysine labeled with radioactive carbon, Van Slyke and F. M. Sinex have found that in rats all the hydroxylysine of the collagen is formed from lysine, by addition of an oxygen atom when collagen is synthesized in the animal body.

Especially during the first two decades of work in the Hospital of The Rockefeller Institute, Van Slyke and his collaborators often found themselves lacking analytical methods for special and chemical problems, and were forced to devise them. Van Slyke's manometric method for measuring blood gases, developed in 1921 and now universally used, was mentioned in an earlier chapter. It was applied in his laboratory also to other microanalyses in which gases evolved by various reactions can be measured. Examples are the determination of organic carbon by measurement of carbon dioxide evolved by combustion, and of free amino acids by measuring the carbon dioxide evolved from their reaction with ninhydrin.

By other techniques, gravimetric, titrimetric, and photometric, various other analytical procedures were developed, including those for determination of the "ketone bodies" of diabetic acidosis, for blood sugar, urea, ammonia, chlorides, lipids, and proteins, and for measuring the specific gravity, osmotic pressure, and pH of blood plasma. In these developments practically all members of the group participated, including, besides those already named, A. B. Hastings, J. Sendroy, Jacques Bourdillon, Roger L. Greif, B. F. Miller, J. R. Weisiger, and others who were on the hospital staff for a year or two only. R. M. Archibald took a leading part in the determination of enzymes in blood and urine; Vincent P. Dole applied the new electrophoretic technique to the identification of proteins in the urine, and used his mathematical talent in the precise formulation of many pertinent problems. A simple way of measuring the specific gravity of blood and plasma, by letting drops of these fluids fall into copper sulphate solutions of standardized specific gravities, was developed by Van Slyke and Phillips, during World War II, for use of the armed forces. This method indicated plasma protein and blood hemoglobin concentrations as accurately as most of the current chemical methods, and was quickly adopted by the American and British forces, proving so practical that it has become a routine procedure in many civilian hospitals.

When Van Slyke was investigating the lipids of the blood, with particular reference to their variations in renal disease, he was assisted from 1937 to 1940 by Jordi Folch-Pi, who came to The Rockefeller Institute after completing his hospital service in Barcelona. As an outcome of his experience with Van Slyke, Folch-Pi interested himself in the lipids of the brain, and, especially, in the phosphatides (lipids containing phosphorus) which occur plentifully in that organ. Earlier work had indicated that the brain phosphatides consist of lecithin containing ethanol amine as the nitrogenous base. Analyses of purified "cephalin" had consistently given low results for carbon, which no one could explain. Folch-Pi and H. A. Schneider, using the gasometric methods previously evolved in the laboratory, found that a large part of the brain cephalin contains as nitrogenous base, not ethanol amine, but the amino acid serine. This discovery that cephalin is not a unit, but consists of two phosphatides, was a milestone in lipid chemistry. Working with Wayne Woolley, Folch-Pi showed, furthermore, that brain tissue contains a fourth type of phosphatide, in which one of the constituents is the cyclic carbohydrate inositol. Inositol phosphatides had previously been found in tubercle bacilli, but not in animal tissues. In 1946 Folch-Pi left The Rockefeller Institute to direct biochemical research at a well-known psychiatric institution, the McLean Hospital, in Waverly, Massachusetts.

Van Slyke's retirement in 1948 did not interrupt his research, for he went at once to the Brookhaven National Laboratories, as biochemist and assistant director. Most of his senior associates had been invited to other institutions; Dole and Archibald were conducting laboratories of their own at The Rockefeller Institute. More recent recruits engaged in the renal disease program finished their terms of hospital residence and scattered to positions elsewhere. Van Slyke had maintained his extraordinary record of preparing men for research careers. Of fifteen young men who came under his influence during the years 1935 to 1948, either on his laboratory staff or doing renal disease research at the hospital, five were in 1959 full professors in various universities, two were Members of The Rockefeller Institute, and all the others (except two who had died) were occupying responsible posts in teaching and research institutions.

VINCENT P. DOLE, who took an active part in the study of renal diseases while on the resident staff from 1941 to 1946, spent the year 1946–1947 at the arthritis clinic of the Massachusetts General Hospital, and the following year visited European centers of research on diseases of the kidney. Returning to The Rockefeller Institute in 1948, he was placed in charge of a laboratory for the study of hypertensive diseases, with G. C. Cotzias and Lewis K. Dahl of the resident staff as his colleagues. In 1951 he was promoted to be a Member of The Rockefeller Institute.

Dole based his program on the assumption that abnormal levels of blood pressure are in some way associated with disturbances of intermediary metabolism, and that tests could ultimately be devised to reveal biochemical aberrations in hypertensive patients. This called for a good deal of preliminary exploration; meanwhile Dole and his assistants had the practical problem of treating their patients. At the time, medical practice was favoring diets low in salt and, in particular, one recently introduced which consisted chiefly of rice and fruit. This diet was also low in protein; both low-salt and low-protein diets had often been recommended in nephritis with somewhat vague aims of reducing the work load of the kidney, or of avoiding irritations supposed to be caused by salts or by proteins, particularly in red meats. A number of workers were checking these ideas by thorough biochemical and metabolic studies; Dole, with the resources of The Rockefeller Institute's hospital at his command, was in a position to do this with selected hypertensive patients, closely following their metabolic state by all relevant tests. He, Cotzias, and Dahl soon confirmed the value of the low-salt diet for reducing the blood pressure. Their studies supported the long-discussed view that it is the sodium ion of common salt, not the chloride ion, which somehow contributes to the elevation of blood pressure in hypertensive patients. By adding known amounts of protein to the rice-fruit diet, they learned that a relatively high protein intake does not significantly raise the blood pressure.

Physicians had observed that low-salt diets usually cause loss of weight, even if the total calorific value of the food is not restricted. Looking into this, Dole and his associates found that it is the low protein, not the low salt content, that diminishes appetite, resulting in loss of weight. Seeing in this discovery a possible method for treating obesity, Dole, Irving L. Schwartz, and their group put 42 obese patients, in the hospital wards and in the outpatient service, on a diet containing only about 35 grams of protein daily, but with fats, carbohydrates, and salts unrestricted. Thirty-two of these people lost 100 or more grams daily (more than 1½ pounds per week) during many consecutive weeks, without complaining of hunger or weakness. Analyzing the basic physiology of this remarkable result, Dole observed that in adults the requirements for protein and non-protein calories are interrelated. On a diet lower in protein than that to which the patient has been accustomed, a mechanism comes into play which tends to lower the fat content of the body, proportionately. This regulation of the composition of the tissues in turn affects the patient's appetite for non-protein calories, and results in loss of weight on a low-protein diet without a consequent imbalance of the chemical constitution of the body. One hardly knows whether to admire more the persistence of the investigators in carrying out the enormous number of chemical analyses required by this kind of research, or the willingness of obese women to live for months upon diets chosen for their specific content, with palatability a secondary consideration.

The specific diets used at The Rockefeller Institute Hospital during the course of these experimental studies were placed at the disposal of physicians and dieticians qualified to test them further, by publication in a professional journal. They were not recommended to the public for self-directed use.

Reviewing his studies in this field, Dole pointed out that the discussion of obesity in medical textbooks, and the remedies proposed, have rested more on assumptions than on understanding of the metabolic problem. The fat individual is assumed to be a physically normal person who eats too much or, in any event, someone who would become normal if he ate less. Not enough attention has been given to the possibility that obesity may be merely a symptom of underlying metabolic disturbance.

If the theory that obesity results solely from overnourishment is correct, it should meet two tests: fat people, studied under conditions that permit close observation of their food intake, should prove to be consistent overeaters; and after their weight is brought to normal by suitable reduction diets, they should show a normal metabolism and stay reduced on normal diets. Dole's results indicate quite clearly that obesity involves more than this theory of mere overeating. Markedly obese persons do not necessarily overeat as compared with normal persons of the same age, sex, and height, living under comparable conditions; nor do they become metabolically normal on reduction. Indeed, as they lose weight, their energy consumption often falls to a markedly subnormal level, and some patients become lethargic and emotionally depressed; to stay at normal weight, many of them must continue to limit their diet to subnormal quantities of food.

According to the overnourishment theory, the subnormal metabolism of patients during weight reduction and immediately afterward could be attributed to temporary disturbances of energy storage and utilization. In time, the metabolism of reduced patients should become normal at the lower level attained by the new dietary regime. In Dole's experience this has not occurred. After weight reduction which cost the patients much time and self-denial, all of them left the hospital determined to stay thin. Instead, they almost invariably regained weight, many of them to the figure recorded on their first visit. Only those who continued to diet succeeded in staying below their original weight. None of the grossly obese patients became a truly normal thin person able to eat ordinary meals.

These results have been clarified by recent laboratory studies of adipose tissue. The overnourishment theory of obesity assumes that body fat is simply a reservoir to hold excess calories. Actually, as has been shown by work in Dole's laboratory and elsewhere, adipose tissue is one of the most active structural materials in the body. It synthesizes fat from sugar, influences energy metabolism by a controlled release of fatty acids, and responds to various hormones. Quite possibly it is the central tissue affected in diabetes; the obesity and impaired sugar metabolism in that disease appear to be symptoms of some more fundamental disorder. The same may be true of other kinds of obesity. Dole's studies thus provide a new basis for evaluation of the obese patient.

A casual observation made while Dole was studying the low-salt diet led him into a new field of inquiry. Reduction of salt in the diet, he noticed, diminished the concentration of sodium in the sweat. Consulting scientific literature for an explanation of this effect, he found that the formation of sweat had never been worked out, and, with his colleague Schwartz, investigated it. Their first step was to invent a method for obtaining and quantitatively analyzing small amounts of sweat. This they accomplished with a small collecting chamber applied over an area of skin which they stimulated to excrete sweat by a painless intradermal injection of a cholinergic drug. A droplet of sweat, one thousandth to one tenth of a cubic centimeter, was absorbed onto a preweighed disc of filter paper in the chamber and was subjected to microanalysis for sodium, urea, and other significant constituents. To this technique they added an ingenious method of locating and counting the sweat glands, by applying to the skin a piece of paper chemically sensitized to change color wherever it absorbed a droplet of moisture. With these research tools, Dole and Schwartz studied the excretion of water, salt, and urea. By 1953 they were beginning to formulate a physiological theory of sweat-gland function.

REGINALD M. ARCHIBALD's program of research on diseases of the endocrine system grew out of his association with Van Slyke's group in studies of kidney function. As already mentioned, after joining The Rockefeller Institute Hospital in 1940, Archibald took part in investigating the formation of ammonia in the kidney, contributing an intensive study of glutamine, the amino acid from which most of the urea is derived, and of glutaminase, an enzyme which controls its breakdown to ammonia. He also studied another enzyme, arginase, which breaks down the amino acid arginine to urea. This enzyme is useful not only in the bodily economy, but also as a tool for biochemical analysis. By virtue of its selective action upon arginine alone, it can be used to measure the amount of that particular substance in blood samples or tissue extracts containing other amino acids. Archibald rapidly worked out methods of purifying arginase, activating and inactivating it, and using it in assaying arginine.

These laboratory studies led him to think about other functions of the kidney to which little attention had been given. Van Slyke's group had studied chiefly the excretory functions by which the kidney rids the blood stream of urea, ammonia, and other soluble nitrogenous wastes, excess salts and water, and many other urinary constituents. Archibald now became interested also in the metabolic functions of the kidney, by which certain substances brought to it by the blood are broken down to excretable form, whereas others are converted by synthetic processes to utilizable or non-toxic states and returned to the blood stream. These functions are carried on by enzymes of the kidney cells which, presumably, are subject in part to endocrine controls. Archibald therefore saw a fertile research field in the study of hormones acting on metabolic enzyme systems in the kidney and elsewhere. Clinical studies on the subject were, however, put aside for a time when he was appointed to the chair of biochemistry at the Johns Hopkins University School of Hygiene.

In 1948 Archibald returned to The Rockefeller Institute as a full Member, and was given a service in the hospital for the study of endocrine disturbances, with a newly fitted-out laboratory. His first associates were two biochemists, Dominic D. Dziewiatkowski and Herbert Jaffe, and two young hospital physicians, Jacques Genest and Roger L. Greif. Bernard Camber of London joined him from 1949 to 1951, and Clayton Rich in 1951. During his stay in Baltimore, association with two well-known clinical endocrinologists, Lawson Wilkins and John Eager Howard, had fostered and broadened his interest in diseases due to disturbances of the thyroid hormone and of the steroid hormones of the testis, ovary, and adrenal cortex. He realized that in order to understand the mechanisms by which hormones exert their effect upon enzymes in the tissues, it would be necessary to devise better methods than were available for the separation and quantitative determination of the hormones and the relevant enzymes. With this aim, he and his colleagues spent the next few years largely in quantitative biochemical investigations. While still in Baltimore, with the aid of Evelyn Stroh (now Mrs. Archibald), he had been the first to apply the newly developed countercurrent distribution method of Lyman Craig (described in Chapter 13) to the fractionation of urinary steroids.

Back at The Rockefeller Institute, Archibald, with Genest, Camber, and Greif, studied the steroid hormones of adrenal origin in blood and urine. Jaffe investigated the chemistry of certain color reactions which are useful in detecting and assaying steroid hormones. Dziewiatkowski gave special attention to the growth of cartilage and, in particular, to disturbances of sulphur metabolism of cartilage, associated with deficiency of the thyroid hormone. Greif worked on methods for measuring the activity of hyaluronidase, an enzyme involved in the metabolism of cartilage and connective tissue. Concurrently with these technical developments in the chemical laboratory, Archibald and his clinical associates admitted to their service in the hospital chiefly patients suffering with abnormalities of skeletal growth.

As the work progressed, the need for further knowledge of the chemical and physical properties of the cells and tissues involved in these diseases became ever more clear. As Archibald continued to receive and care for patients, and to learn from his efforts on their behalf where the significant problems lay, the record of his group reveals a steady shift toward fundamental research on the metabolism of bone and cartilage, and on the chemistry of the hormones and enzymes that participate in the growth and function of these tissues.

THE TREND DESCRIBED in the preceding paragraph reflects again a recurrent experience in the research programs of the Hospital of The Rockefeller Institute, which led to an inevitable broadening of the founders' intentions. As seen by Gates and Rockefeller, Jr., as well as by Herter and the other early Scientific Directors, the hospital's specific aim was to investigate selected diseases, in the light of the most recent scientific knowledge, with the hope of discovering means of direct cure and prevention. General investigations in the medical sciences were left to the earlier-established Department of the Laboratories, but the hospital physicians were also provided with laboratories, close to their wards, in which to pursue the immediate study of disease processes.

Such a close union of medical science with the physician's art was unique in the world when instituted in 1910, and to this day is nowhere excelled in its concentration of skills upon specific diseases. Yet the kind of success it has achieved is quite different from what the founders hoped to see; discoveries of specific cures for individual diseases and of specific means of preventing these diseases have been relatively few at the Hospital of The Rockefeller Institute. The pneumonia serums developed in the early decades were apparently curative in suitable cases; intraspinal syphilis therapy helped many tabetics; a dietary treatment of diabetes, born of desperation before the advent of insulin, prolonged life for numerous sufferers; in recent years, obesity has been relieved by a scientific regime. On the other hand, the two greatest achievements in medical practice made at The Rockefeller Institute — those at least which have directly relieved the suffering and saved the lives of the greatest number of people — were the discovery of a method of preserving blood for transfusion by Rous, Turner, and Robertson, and the development of a curative drug for African sleeping sickness by Jacobs, Heidelberger, Brown, and Pearce. Both of these came directly from the general laboratories without any influence from the hospital side.

To laymen this outcome may seem paradoxical, but to physicians, realizing how obscure and complex are the human ailments chosen for study, it is understandable that spectacular discoveries about specific diseases are not made to order; they can see that the clinical work of The Rockefeller Institute Hospital has made its contribution in other and broader ways. Its physicians have improved many diagnostic methods and invented new ones. They have worked out the pattern and course of many obscure diseases. Basing their treatment of the sick upon constant physiological and chemical research, they have found new ways to assist the *vis medicatrix naturae* by improving the comfort and nutrition of their patients. Above all, the hospital has influenced the university medical clinics of the whole country — by its example of medical research conducted by physicians responsible for patients — and has provided scores of expertly trained medical scientists to man key posts in teaching and research.

Meanwhile the scientific investigations paralleling and supporting this remarkable clinical program have undergone a steady shift of emphasis, in almost every one of the separate programs, away from the specific disease toward underlying problems of physiology and biochemistry. Rufus Cole's efforts to develop antipneumococcal serums led, in Avery's hands, to major developments in immunochemistry. The investigation of rheumatic fever contributed immensely to the biology of streptococcal organisms. The study of virus diseases accumulated basic knowledge of the viruses and their relations with their animal hosts. The attack on nephritis resulted in fundamental contributions to the physical chemistry of the blood and of the kidneys. The study of muscular dystrophy was shifting to general metabolic biochemistry even before its leader's untimely death, and his successors have gone still further into fundamental research in that field. The erstwhile student of a single heritable disease now explores a wide range of human genetics; men investigating diseases of endocrine origin increasingly devote themselves to the chemical interreactions of enzymes and hormones.

The physicians of The Rockefeller Institute Hospital, working in a research environment, did not limit their attack, with precarious hopes of success, to particular illnesses; instead, the contemplation of disease as a general biological problem led them to look ever more deeply into organic structure and function, and to build a body of knowledge upon which the scientific medicine of the future can be firmly based.

CHAPTER NINETEEN

The Chemistry of Heredity, Virulence, and Immunity; Antibiotics

Outcome of Avery's study of the pneumococcus; the polysaccharide antigens of pneumonia and dysentery organisms; antibiotics from soil bacilli; induced enzymes; experimental tuberculosis, improved culture methods; chemistry of bacterial transformation, relation of transforming factors to genes. Administrative personnel of the Institute; growth of the staff. Increasing endowment.

RUFUS COLE built better than he knew when in 1910 he began the study of immunity in lobar pneumonia. Few investigations undertaken at The Rockefeller Institute have been pursued continuously for so long a time, or with such fruitful results. We have seen how the effort to produce serums against pneumonia led to intensive investigation of the chemistry of the pneumococcus by Avery and his associates. This in turn opened up unforeseen lines of research in the chemistry of immunity and of heredity, which a half century later are still being followed at the Institute. Our narrative of the hospital's scientific achievements, therefore, comes to a most fitting conclusion with the work of Goebel, Dubos, and Hotchkiss, begun in association with Avery and carried on independently after his retirement.

Walther F. Goebel, who took his Ph.D. degree in chemistry at the University of Illinois in 1923, came to The Rockefeller Institute the next year as an assistant in Avery's laboratory. Joining Avery and Heidelberger in their study of the specific antigens in the capsular polysaccharides of the pneumococcus, Goebel shared in the discovery (discussed in Chapter 10) that these are complex sugarlike substances, which in their native state are probably combined with the proteins of the bacterial cell. Later he carried the analysis further by splitting the huge polysaccharide molecule into its component simpler sugars and identifying them. Subsequently, he found that simple sugars could be experimentally linked with proteins to form antigenic compounds; that is, an animal injected with such a compound would develop antibodies against it. This led to the establishment of an important principle: the immunological specificity of a carbohydrate depends upon its precise molecular structure. Following this up, Avery and Goebel were able, by combining ordinary albumin with the specific polysaccharide extracted from the pneumococcus, to create an artificial antigen that would elicit antibodies not only against itself, but also against virulent pneumococci.

This is the stage the investigation had reached in 1929. Obviously, the next step in the effort to understand nature's chemical processes by imitating them in the laboratory was to replace the specific polysaccharides of the pneumococcus by counterparts synthetically produced. Goebel therefore began a thorough study of the type-specific capsular carbohydrates of the pneumococcus and also of another well-known organism, the Friedländer bacillus. He found that several of these substances contain glucuronic acid, and suspected that this sugar may be important in determining their immunological specificity.

In this study he had Avery's cooperation in immunological matters, and the assistance, from 1929 to 1935, of Frank H. Babers, a biochemist. When Babers left for a post elsewhere, Rollin D. Hotchkiss joined the group, synthesizing various new compounds for use in the experiments. By 1935 Goebel had acquired a masterly command of the chemistry of these substances, and was ready to prepare artificial antigens containing a wide range of sugars of advancing complexity. Within a year the search was getting warmer; an artificial antigen containing a glucoside of glucuronic acid, prepared in the laboratory, reacted with the serum of horses immunized against virulent pneumococci. With one more step — the introduction of a more complex carbohydrate, cellobiuronic acid — the goal was achieved; Goebel had created, with a synthetic sugar derivative, an artificial antigen so close to that formed by living pneumococci that when injected into rabbits it protected them against infection with the highly virulent Type III organisms.

This triumph of immunochemical skill and insight gave final proof of the concept, developed by The Rockefeller Institute's workers during the course of twenty years, that the antigenic specificity of the pneumo-coccus resides in the polysaccharides of the bacterial capsule — a concept since found true of a number of other organisms. This is one of the foundation stones of immunochemistry. It might have had immediate practical as well as theoretical consequences, for example, in the produc-tion of synthetic vaccines and curative drugs potent against the pneumo-coccus, had not the introduction of sulfonamides and antibiotic drugs changed the whole course of pneumonia therapy.

In 1938 and 1939 Goebel began a pioneer investigation of the chem-ical nature of the substances responsible for the human blood groups. The A, B, and O substances are present in the blood in such minute quantities and in such a complex environment that they had defied isolation from that source. Small amounts of the A substance had, how-ever, been recovered from other body fluids, and partially analyzed. A group of biochemists in Berlin led by F. Schiff fortunately discovered in 1933 that commercial pepsin contains the A substance in relatively large amounts. Going on from there, Landsteiner and Chase at The Rocke-feller Institute in 1936 identified some of its constituents, finding among them an unexpected carbohydrate derivative, acetyl glucosamine. Two years later Goebel, while preparing for his own use large quantities of the specific polysaccharides of Type III pneumococcus, obtained as a by-product another polysaccharide not involved in immunity to the pneu-mococcus. When he found this to be rich in glucosamine, he suspected that it might be the same substance that Schiff and Landsteiner and Chase had found in pepsin. Serological tests and further chemical analy-ses proved this to be the case.

In the same year, at Harvard Medical School, Maxwell Finland and E. C. Curnen (later of Cole's staff at The Rockefeller Institute Hospital) reported that the serum of horses immunized against Type XIV pneu-mococcus sometimes produced severe reactions when administered ther-apeutically to pneumonia patients. Goebel, alerted by his previous work, took this hint. With the assistance of Paul B. Beeson (now professor of medicine at Yale) and Charles L. Hoagland of the hospital staff, he isolated the capsular polysaccharide of the Type XIV pneumococcus and by chemical and serological tests found it to be closely related to the A blood-group substance. Subsequent investigators have found that all blood-group substances react with Type XIV antisera. Goebel's demonstration that one of them, the A substance, is a polysaccharide had brought together two hitherto seemingly unrelated fields of immunochemistry, and had opened the way for great advances in our knowledge of the chemistry of the blood-group substances.

After Avery's retirement in 1943, his senior associates carried on their work independently. Goebel was in 1944 made a full Member of The Rockefeller Institute, with a laboratory in the pathology and bacteriology section of the Department of the Laboratories.

During World War II Goebel was called upon by the Office of Scientific Research and Development to use his experience with the chemistry of antigens in studying bacillary dysentery, a disease often disastrous to troops in camp and in the field. Assisted by O. F. Binkley (now professor of biochemistry at Emory University) and Ely Perlman, he developed methods for extracting the specific antigens from the Flexner dysentery organism, *Shigella paradysenteriae.* Working out the physical, chemical, and immunological properties of these complex substances, Goebel found that they are made up of proteins, lipids, and carbohydrates. He and Perlman showed that, as with the pneumococcus, the ability of the *Shigella* antigens to elicit antibodies against only those organisms which themselves produce the antigens in question depends upon the carbohydrate portion of the antigenic substance. In 1952 Goebel and his associate Margeris A. Jesaitis confirmed these results with a much more highly purified antigen. Their findings, if made a decade or two earlier, would, no doubt, have been used to develop a vaccine against bacillary dysentery. This, however, had been made unnecessary by the advent of sulfa drugs effective against intestinal organisms.

What actually came of this wartime project was a further important advance in general immunochemistry — another illustration of the tendency, discussed at the end of the last chapter, away from *ad hoc* studies of individual diseases toward investigation of the underlying general biology. Goebel's demonstration of a common chemical basis of specific antigenicity, in organisms as different as pneumococci and dysentery bacilli, drew his attention to another and especially puzzling type-specific relation between a parasite and its host, namely, that of the bacteriophages and the bacteria they invade and destroy.

Bacteriologists already suspected that the sensitivity of certain bacteria to particular phages is somehow connected with the specific antigens produced by the invaded bacteria. In 1949 Goebel and a technician, Elizabeth M. Miller, took up this question. They found that the susceptibility of a given type of *Shigella* to its phage is indeed related to the type-specific antigen; this substance, by which the bacterium elicits an immune reaction in an animal it infects, also provides sites of chemical union and subsequent entry of the phage.

Phages cause lysis of their bacterial hosts; that is, they cause them to dissolve, and when this happens in a test tube murky with living bacteria the culture fluid becomes clear. When Goebel extracted the antigen from dysentery bacilli and added it to the phage, the phage was destroyed and could no longer clear a culture of *Shigella*. At first sight it seems paradoxical that one and the same substance when free in a culture destroys the phage, yet while in the bacterium attracts the phage and attaches it to the host. In the latter case, however, Jesaitis and Goebel found, the antigen also destroys the phage after attaching it, thereby setting free the inner substance of the virus particle and permitting it to enter the bacterial cell. There it induces the formation of additional virus particles which make their exit from the ultimately destroyed cell to begin a new viral cycle. In 1948 Goebel collaborated with Ginsberg and Horsfall in a study, mentioned in the previous chapter, of antigenic polysaccharides from streptococci, which were found to inhibit the virus of mumps in embryo cultures.

At various times Goebel turned from the study of antigens to that of the antibodies they elicit in the host animal. In 1935 B. F. Chow and he prepared almost pure antipneumococcus antibody by a method of their own, superior to that of previous workers. After the successful effort of Northrop, Kunitz, and Goebel in 1942 to crystallize diphtheria antitoxin, Northrop and Goebel attempted to carry the purification of the antipneumococcus antibody still farther by crystallizing it. In this they succeeded, but so great is the complexity of the protein constituents of the antibody that even crystallization did not yield a molecularly homogeneous substance.

In the early 1950's Jesaitis, studying the nucleic acids of certain bacteriophages (the "T-even phages"), found them to contain glucose, a simple 6-carbon sugar, in addition to deoxyribose, as an integral part of the molecule. This was the first discovery of a saccharide other than deoxyribose in a deoxyribonucleic acid. The significance of the unexpected finding, the latest in a series of discoveries concerning nucleic acids begun almost sixty years ago at The Rockefeller Institute by Phoebus Levene, is yet to be elucidated.

In 1953 Goebel, with Guy T. Barry, was opening up a new line of research, studying mysterious substances, known as colicines, which are produced by colon bacilli (*Escherichia coli*) of various strains. They have the remarkable property of selectively killing various intestinal bacteria, and in this respect resemble bacteriophages, but unlike phage they cannot be propagated by serial passage. Yet some microorganisms develop colicine-resistant strains as they do against phages, and chemical agents which release phages from bacteria will likewise release colicines. Because of these resemblances some investigators suspected colicines to be precursors of phages. The colicines had never been isolated in pure form, and their chemical nature, therefore, was obscure. By skillful procedures, Goebel and his associates obtained one of these substances (colicine K) in a highly purified state and found it to be a protein-carbohydrate-lipid complex in which the protein possesses the antibacterial property.

During the preparation of colicine K, Goebel encountered several previously unknown substances with unusual properties, which appear to be involved in the chemical processes of infection and immunity. The outcome of these discoveries, which he continues to follow up, must be left to a later historian.

RENÉ J. DUBOS, born in France in 1901, came to the United States after finishing his studies at the Institut National Agronomique, and took his Ph.D. degree in 1927 at Rutgers University under Selman A. Waksman, the distinguished specialist in agricultural bacteriology. Immediately after leaving Rutgers, Dubos joined The Rockefeller Institute as a Fellow in Avery's laboratory, beginning a career which has taken him through all the successive ranks to full membership. His first major assignment, mentioned in Chapter 10, warrants fuller discussion here, because it pointed Dubos's way to a later achievement.

Avery was not content with his own proof that the type-specific antigens of the pneumococcus capsule are polysaccharides, because this result had been reached by a relatively drastic inactivation of the polysaccharides by acid hydrolysis, which might possibly have wrought other, unrecognized chemical changes. He wanted to do the same thing by the far gentler method of enzymatic digestion. This was his reason for taking on his staff a man trained in soil bacteriology; an enzyme with the required action was likely to be found in bacteria engaged in the destruction of vegetable organic matter decaying in the woods and fields. The most promising of all places in which to find a bacterium capable of digesting polysaccharides, Dubos thought, was a cranberry bog, for he had read that polysaccharides disappear rapidly from decaying cranberries. With such bogs close by in New Jersey, it was not long before he found an organism of the desired type—a hitherto unknown species. When he cultivated it on a medium in which the only source of carbon was a small amount of Type III polysaccharide, the organism, starved, so to speak, into accepting this carbohydrate as food, acquired the power of digesting the polysaccharide-containing capsules of Type III pneumococci. Extracting the digestive enzyme from his cultures, Dubos provided Avery with the means of finally proving the serologic activity and type specificity of the bacterial polysaccharides. Next Avery, Dubos, Francis, Goodner, and E. E. Terrell found that the new enzyme would protect mice against experimental Type III pneumonia, would clear up severe experimental skin infections of rabbits caused by the Type III bacillus, and would cure experimental pneumococcus pneumonia in Java monkeys. In all probability, an attack on human lobar pneumonia would have developed along this line after 1935, if the sulfonamides had not revolutionized the treatment of pneumonia.

Cultivating this useful soil bacterium on various media, Dubos made the momentous discovery that it would produce the anti-Type III enzyme only when compelled to use the Type III polysaccharide as food. On media not containing the polysaccharide, it grew abundantly but would not produce the enzyme. This was the first instance to be revealed of an "adaptive enzyme," as Dubos called it, or, in current terminology, "induced enzyme." Later, he found another instance, this time a bacterium producing an enzyme able to oxidize a nitrogenous waste product of muscle metabolism, creatinine, when grown on media containing creatinine. These observations taught him that the bacterial cell has multiple biochemical potentialities, but those which it actually brings to realization depend upon the available nutritive substances which it must metabolize. Although he was unable at the time to exploit these findings,

Dubos perceived that he had come upon a fundamental concept of biology, significant not only for future research in bacteriology, but as a general principle of life processes, characteristic even of human effort and adaptability. In this lesson, learned from a lowly soil bacterium, he found the greatest intellectual satisfaction of his research career.

Along with this work, and for a few years after 1935, Dubos, with wide-ranging curiosity, studied numerous other enzymes produced by bacteria. Meanwhile the enzyme he had found to have the power of oxidizing creatinine was put to work in a clinical test devised by him and B. F. Miller (now director of the May Institute for Medical Research, Cincinnati) for the estimation of creatinine in blood and urine. In another enzyme study, Dubos and a visiting Fellow, R. H. S. Thompson (now professor of biochemistry at Guy's Hospital Medical School, London) were in 1938 the first to prepare from the pancreas and other tissues a purified enzyme capable of selectively breaking down the nucleic acid of yeast cells. Later, they showed that it could also decompose a similar substance formed by pneumococci; it proved to be a ribonuclease acting upon ribonucleic acids in general and, as such, became a valuable tool in the numerous investigations of such substances that have figured so largely in The Rockefeller Institute's studies of the chemical basis of immunity and genetics.

The next phase of Dubos's research arose from the need for agents that would destroy microorganisms of the Gram-positive class, which includes streptococci and staphylococci as well as pneumococci. He reflected that, in view of the great variety of biochemical reactions performed by microorganisms, there might well exist in nature bacteria capable of attacking the cell walls of other bacterial species. Proceeding on the assumption that all organic matter added to the soil eventually undergoes decomposition through the agency of microorganisms, he undertook to promote the development of organisms having the desired potencies. This he did with great ingenuity, by seeding pans of soil in the laboratory with living cultures of various pathogenic Gram-positive bacteria. In 1939, after repeating this procedure for two years, the bacterial flora of his soil sample at last included a Gram-positive bacillus, at first unidentified, which would disintegrate heavy suspensions of staphylococci and many other Gram-positive organisms. From cultures of this organism (finally identified as a known species, *Bacillus brevis*), he obtained a cell-free extract, which not only killed the susceptible kinds of organisms in culture tubes, but also protected mice against infection with virulent pneumococci. With Carlo Cattaneo, a visiting Fellow from Rome, he prepared a protein-free substance one hundred times more potent than the original extract.

In 1940 Hotchkiss joined Dubos in further chemical exploration of these finds. Search of the literature revealed various hints of similar properties in other microorganisms; following these clues the two investigators gathered a dozen or more species of bacilli from soil, manure, sewage, and cheese, which produced bactericidal substances similar to that of *B. brevis*. Cultures of all these, subjected to chemical partition, yielded an alcohol-soluble, water-insoluble bactericidal fraction which Dubos named tyrothricin. From this, he and Hotchkiss obtained two different crystalline bactericidal substances, tyrocidin and gramicidin, which effectively attacked Gram-positive organisms. Joining forces with the chemist Fritz Lipmann (then at Cornell Medical College), they found that gramicidin is a polypeptide containing a peculiar array of amino acids. The use of gramicidin and tyrocidin in 1940 by R. B. Little, Dubos, and Hotchkiss to treat mastitis in cows has been mentioned in Chapter 16. This appears to be the earliest systematic and effective use of an antibiotic of biological origin in the treatment of actual disease. Although both these compounds proved too toxic for internal use in human patients, they are still used for local therapy by external application.

Before Dubos and his co-workers announced their findings, there had been only a few reports of such substances, none of which had gone beyond the stage of laboratory investigation. One of them, penicillin, had been discovered by Sir Alexander Fleming in 1929, but in 1938 this now famous antibiotic was merely one of a number being screened for possible investigation by Sir Howard Florey and E. B. Chain in a survey they had undertaken at Oxford. Dubos, by publishing in 1939 his conclusions on the first stage of his highly original, logically developed, and decisive work with tyrocidin and gramicidin, gave great impetus to the heretofore slowly developing search for antibacterial agents, and stimulated widespread efforts that soon resulted in the discovery of many valuable antibiotics now in clinical use. It is pleasant to record that Selman Waksman, Dubos's teacher, among the investigators following this lead, isolated several new antibiotics, including one of the most useful, streptomycin.

Dubos was promoted in 1941 to the rank of Member of The Rockefeller Institute. The next year he accepted the Harvard professorship of comparative pathology and tropical medicine (once held by Theobald Smith), but he returned in 1944 to the Institute. Since his return Dubos has been leading an investigation of the tubercle bacillus, *Mycobacterium tuberculosis,* in which he and his associates have attacked two major problems: the chemical nature of the virulence of the organism, and the factors in the host which react with the bacillus and contribute to resistance to infection.

It was first necessary to improve the cultivation of the organism. *Mycobacterium tuberculosis* grows slowly, and, when cultivated by conventional methods, refuses to grow, as do most bacteria, throughout a liquid medium. On the contrary, it forms dry pellicles or large clumps on the surface of the nutrient fluid, within which myriad bacterial cells exist in every state from full vitality to starvation, asphyxia, and death, according to the accessibility of air, moisture, and nutritives. This peculiar growth habit, obviously caused by the water-repellent lipid coating possessed by mycobacteria, prevents use of the bacteriologist's standard methods of estimating the numbers and rate of growth of bacteria in culture, of isolating individual strains and separating virulent from non-virulent types, and of collecting metabolic products, antigens, and toxins from the culture fluid. Typhoid bacilli or streptococci, for instance, which grow throughout a fluid medium, can be estimated by the turbidity they produce, or, more exactly, by a direct count of a sample droplet. They can be uniformly diluted; separate strains can be bred from a mixed culture, and a new colony started from a single cell by "plating out" the culture on agar; they can be precipitated uniformly by antibodies; their chemical products can be filtered off for study. On the other hand, tubercle bacilli, concentrated in surface colonies, cannot readily be subjected to any of these procedures.

It was known that rapid and submerged growth of tubercle bacilli will take place in water-diluted egg yolk, and it had been suggested that this was due to the water-soluble phospholipids of the yolk. Pursuing this line of thought, Dubos tried a series of lipids from plant and animal tissues, and found them favorable to submerged growth, though (like egg yolk) for various reasons inconvenient or impractical for this use. On the assumption that these phospholipids were acting as wetting agents, he next turned to certain synthetic water-soluble detergents consisting of esters of long-chain fatty acids. Testing a dozen of these he found one, an ester of oleic acid, known to the detergent trade as "Tween 80," whose physical qualities exactly served the purpose. Standard culture fluids containing a little of this wetting agent supported active submerged growth of all mycobacteria tried by Dubos, including two human strains of *M. tuberculosis.*

With Bernard D. Davis (now professor of bacteriology at Harvard University Medical School), Dubos began in 1945 to study the effects of various wetting agents and their contaminants on the growth of small masses of inoculated organisms, and on the state of dispersion attained in the culture medium. The aim was to find the best way to grow new cultures from very few cells, if possible from a single cell, in order to isolate pure strains from a mixed culture. Tween 80, Dubos and Davis found, contains small residual amounts of the unesterified long-chain fatty acids from which it is prepared, which are toxic to the bacilli. To counteract these, they added serum albumin, which previous investigators had found to facilitate submerged growth. Combining with the fatty acids, the albumin prevented their inhibiting action. The combination was highly successful; such synthetic liquid culture media supported submerged growth at a previously unheard-of rate. From very minute inocula, masses of bacilli no larger than one hundred-millionth of a milligram, visible growth developed in less than two weeks; and the organisms developing diffusely in the fluid medium maintained the individual form and staining properties characteristic of the classical culture methods.

Dubos was now able to obtain homogeneous cultures, in suspension, of vigorous, relatively fast-growing tubercle bacilli, instead of the tough, intractable masses of compacted bacteria. He could, moreover, grow cultures from very small masses of bacteria, even from a clump of only three or four cells, and could separate strains for study of their special characteristics. Working with associates Gardner Middlebrook (now director of research at the Jewish Hospital, Denver) and Cynthia Pierce in 1946–1947, he used the new cultures to compare the growth pattern of virulent and non-virulent strains of tubercle bacilli. The virulent strains, they found, form a pattern of serpentine cords (whereas the non-virulent organisms gather in irregular clumps); apparently, some substance in the surface layers of individual bacilli, associated with their virulence, causes them to adhere end-to-end and so grow in strands. Dubos, always interested in the history of his science, looked into the early literature and found that Robert Koch, discoverer of the tubercle bacillus, had noticed this pattern of growth without recognizing its biological significance.

Other signs of inherent physical and chemical differences became apparent to Dubos's group. In 1949, for example, working with Middlebrook and, later, with Emanuel Suter (now professor of bacteriology at the University of Florida), Dubos found that only the virulent bacilli have the ability to bind to themselves the dye neutral red in its brilliant red form. Meanwhile, a Swiss visiting Fellow, Hubert Bloch (now professor at the University of Pittsburgh), began, under Dubos's direction, a study of the phagocytic white blood cells which ingest bacilli. His experiments, continued elsewhere but since confirmed and extended at The Rockefeller Institute by Cynthia Pierce and a visiting Fellow, S. P. Martin (now professor of medicine at the University of Florida), showed that phagocytes which take up virulent tubercle bacilli immediately become motionless, whereas those which ingest the non-virulent bacilli continue normal activity. Thus evidence gradually accumulated that virulence is related to the physical and chemical structure of the bacilli.

Since Koch's day the guinea pig had been the animal generally used for studies on experimental tuberculosis, because it appeared much more susceptible to infection than the other laboratory animals. In the 1940's, however, several investigators found mice more susceptible than had formerly been supposed. Confirming this, Pierce, Dubos, and Middlebrook in 1947 not only were able to infect mice with their vigorous bacilli grown in liquid culture, but could also control the course of the disease, modifying almost at will its rate of progression and outcome. This they did by choosing bacterial strains of differing virulence, and by varying the site and method of inoculating the animals. According to the mode of infection, they produced tuberculosis of the lungs, brain, or peritoneal cavity. Different strains of mice, they found, show hereditary differences in susceptibility. In a preliminary investigation that was followed up intensively after 1953, Dubos and Pierce found that the survival time of mice infected with virulent tubercle bacilli could be markedly affected by the kind of diet fed to the mice. With another associate, J. G. Hirsch, Dubos began about 1950 to study a series of natural organic compounds, including spermine, which they found to have strong antimycotic action. In short, the technical improvement which Dubos had made in methods of cultivation of the tubercle bacillus enabled him to subject that organism to a whole range of procedures with which bacteriologists study the biology of pathogenic organisms.

In another study Dubos, Pierce, and F. J. Fenner, a visiting Fellow from Australia (now professor of bacteriology at Canberra), cultivated the bacillus of Calmette and Guérin in the new liquid medium. This is a well-known type of *Mycobacterium tuberculosis* which is relatively nonvirulent but retains the property of eliciting a certain degree of immunity in animals and human beings infected with it. Because of this characteristic it has been widely used, under the designation of BCG, as a preventive inoculation against tuberculosis. Dubos and his associates, now readily able to isolate and grow destructive strains, examined BCG for the traits they had found different in virulent and non-virulent tubercle bacilli, and found, as Calmette and Guérin had done years earlier in tests on animals, that it is intermediate between the harmless and the definitely pathogenic strains. Now enabled by their culture methods to select distinctive strains of BCG and grow them rapidly, they compared their biological and immunological properties, with a view to choosing the best strains for the preparation of preventive vaccines. This work prepared the way for an extensive program after 1953.

In 1951 the American Tuberculosis Association presented Dubos with the Trudeau Medal, an award for distinguished contributions to the knowledge of tuberculosis. In her presentation address, Florence R. Sabin, Emeritus Member of The Rockefeller Institute, called attention not only to the contributions that have been outlined here, but also to another kind of service rendered by Dubos, that of interpreting to the public the nature of scientific investigation and the contributions of great scientists, as exemplified by his notable biography of Louis Pasteur, published in 1950.[1] In addition, he edited a widely used *Handbook of the Bacterial and Mycotic Infections of Man,* now in its third edition. In several other books, and in numerous reviews, lectures, and semipopular articles, Dubos has been a lucid expositor of modern bacteriology and a critical judge of its influence upon the public health.

Rollin D. Hotchkiss came to The Rockefeller Institute as a Fellow in Avery's group, immediately after taking his Ph.D. degree in chemistry at Yale. Like Avery's two other chief associates in his later years, Hotchkiss was to go on through all ranks of the Institute. In 1935–1936 he worked with Goebel, taking an active part in the program of synthesizing saccharides in order to create artificial antigens akin to the natural polysaccharides responsible for type specificity of the various strains of the pneumococcus. He and Goebel achieved the synthesis of several key derivatives of glucuronic acid, especially aldobionic acid, one of the disaccharide carbohydrates formed by the virulent Type III pneumococcus. In 1937–1938 Hotchkiss went to the Carlsberg Laboratory in Copenhagen to investigate with K. U. Linderstrøm-Lang the hydrolysis of peptide bonds in proteins.

Returning to The Rockefeller Institute, he joined Dubos, who in 1938 was beginning his search for antibacterial biological agents. The part Hotchkiss took in this influential investigation, by applying his biochemical experience and skill to the extraction and purification of tyrothricin, tyrocidin, and gramicidin, has already been recounted. Some years later, Hotchkiss also collaborated with Albert Claude, of J. B. Murphy's cancer research laboratory, in the investigation, described in Chapter 15, by which the mitochondrial granules present in all cells were proved to contain important oxidative enzymes. G. H. Hogeboom, whose cooperation Hotchkiss soon enlisted, carried on these studies to most fruitful conclusions.

In Chapter 18 we recounted the story — now a classic of genetic biochemistry — of Avery and McCarty's discovery of the transforming factor, which has the power when taken up by pneumococci of various types to convert them into the virulent Type III. Following this pioneer work, other investigators elsewhere looked for additional capsular transforming agents, and within a decade two dozen or more transformations of antigenic and other biological characteristics of bacteria were discovered. In each case the transforming agent was identified as deoxyribonucleic acid (DNA). The molecular structure of this substance, as we now know, is so complex that it can exist in an enormous number of forms, differing from one another only in the position of a few atoms or side chains; but such a difference is sufficient to confer the power to alter specifically some one characteristic of the organism into which the individual DNA is introduced.

In 1948, four years after the original discovery, Hotchkiss, with Avery's encouragement, began to study the nature of the transformation phenomenon, which had excited general interest because of its resemblance to some features of gene-determined inheritance and of the propagation of viruses. The principal difficulty in research upon the type of transformation thus far studied, Hotchkiss perceived, is that the newly modified cells are not clearly distinguishable, as living individuals, from the parent untransformed ones in the culture, and can only be separated from them by tedious procedures. He therefore devised a way to secure cultures in which the altered cells constitute a large proportion of the population. Into a culture of pneumococci, he introduced a quantity of penicillin, which killed all the bacterial cells except those rare individuals, perhaps one in ten million, which by mutation had acquired resistance to the antibiotic drug. Cultivating these surviving mutants, he propagated a resistant strain which could be kept pure (as regards penicillin resistance) by killing off with the drug any strays that mutated back to the original state of non-resistance. From these cultures he extracted a DNA which proved able to confer penicillin resistance upon non-resistant strains of pneumococci. It was an exciting experience, he wrote,

> to select a penicillin-resistant pneumococcal strain and having subcultured it for a number of months without ever letting it meet penicillin again, to make from it a purified DNA preparation which, stored indefinitely in the refrigerator, can be used at any time to induce penicillin resistance in a cell strain, which so far as one knows, had never previously encountered this antibiotic.[2]

In a similar way Hotchkiss transferred resistance to several other antibiotic drugs, including streptomycin, from one strain of bacteria to another. Audrey Evans, supervisor of media preparation for the Institute's bacteriological laboratories, becoming interested in the problem, joined Hotchkiss in a similar experiment with sulfanilamide resistance. Each of these transfers was accomplished, they found, by its own specific DNA. Another, somewhat different, sort of biological character available for such experimentation is the ability to utilize, as food, substances not normally available to the bacteria and to which they are quite unaccustomed. Hotchkiss, with a visiting Fellow, Julius Marmur, investigated one instance of this, the ability to grow on mannitol, a sugar alcohol, and found that this ability could be similarly transferred by a DNA extracted from cultures of a strain able to use mannitol, whether or not it was actually doing so at the time. In other words, it was the potentiality to develop a chemical system for utilizing mannitol that was transposed, rather than a system already existing for this purpose.

This was the stage Hotchkiss had reached in 1953. Since that time he and his associates have continued their investigations and have greatly amplified their evidence that the action of bacterial transforming agents closely parallels that of the classical genetic units (genes) of higher organisms.

Thus the continuous investigation of the pneumococcus, begun in the first years of The Rockefeller Institute's hospital by Cole and Dochez, with the hope of combating one specific disease, lobar pneumonia, was carried on for a half century by Avery, MacLeod, McCarty, Goebel, Dubos, and Hotchkiss, with ever-deepening insight into fundamental biological processes. The men who promoted and led the work at its start — Flexner and Cole — could not have foreseen any such outcome; not even Frederick T. Gates — the enthusiast whose dream of great achievements by American medical science led to the foundation of The Rockefeller Institute — could have imagined that the search for a cure or preventive of pneumonia would lead to fuller understanding of the continuous and specifically patterned reproduction of the fundamental units of living matter.[3]

Besides the work described above, in 1945 Hotchkiss developed, in answer to a colleague's query, a new method of demonstrating polysaccharides in tissues, now widely used in histological laboratories and dermatological clinics. George K. Hirst, then of The Rockefeller Foundation's International Health Division Laboratory at the Institute, had observed a new immune reaction, involving the clumping of red blood cells by influenza viruses, which he thought might depend upon the presence of polysaccharides on the cell surfaces. Hotchkiss suggested that he could test this supposition by treating the red blood cells with periodic acid, which destroys polysaccharides by converting them to new compounds (aldehydes). The idea proved correct; the treated cells would no longer agglutinate. Hotchkiss, aware that aldehydes form colored compounds with the well-known Schiff's reagent, next suggested that a staining method to reveal the presence of polysaccharides could be based on this sequence of reactions. For some reason, the procedure did not succeed with red blood cells, but when tried on other tissues, with precautions Hotchkiss worked out on strict chemical principles, it proved to stain a wide variety of natural polysaccharides, leaving other tissue ingredients untinged, in all sorts of cells other (oddly enough) than the one for which it was devised. An English investigator, J. F. McManus, in 1946 proposed an almost identical reaction for staining one particular kind of polysaccharide, namely, mucus. The method is, therefore, often designated as the Hotchkiss-McManus stain. Even before Hotchkiss published his account of it in 1948, Walther Goebel used it successfully to demonstrate the oxidation of polysaccharides in dysentery bacilli. Since then it has been put to work in many biological investigations. Dermatologists have found that it sharply reveals the presence of fungi infecting the human skin, and the Hotchkiss stain is now in standard use for a practical purpose quite unforeseen by its inventor.

IN THIS AND SIXTEEN preceding chapters we have followed the scientific investigations of the research staff of The Rockefeller Institute from their beginnings in 1904 to 1953, when the period of our narrative ends. This corps of pathologists, clinicians, biologists, chemists, physicists, and other scientists numbered 12 when the laboratories were first opened, and 125 in 1953, the fiftieth year. Closely at work with the investigators were the technicians and secretaries of the several laboratories; the librarians and the staffs of the departments of illustration and photography, publications, pharmacy, media preparation; the workers in the instrument shop, the animal house, the multifarious services of supply, housekeeping, and maintenance of buildings and grounds; and the nursing staff and X-ray service of the hospital. Behind all these and coordinating their work were the business manager, the assistant business manager, and, in the later years, personnel and social service officers. Flexner's budget for the first year of laboratory operation, 1904–1905, called for seven persons — a stenographer, a clerk, a laboratory helper, and four janitors — to assist the twelve investigators. Some of these must have served in double capacities, for Eugene Opie recalls that as Flexner's senior associate he had a man helping him with experiments, and that someone was at hand to prepare microscopic sections; but in those days scientists did a good deal of routine laboratory work and even dishwashing with their own hands, and the juniors — the Assistants and Fellows — had to be their own technicians. As more investigators joined the Institute, the supporting staff rapidly increased, its growth speeded also by the advent of the hospital. In 1953, including administrative officers, it was more than fifty times the original force of seven; and against the original proportion of less than one aide to each scientist there were now more than three to one.

Only the scientists can know how much the work of a research institution depends upon an intelligent and loyal operating staff led by competent executive officers. The Rockefeller Institute was fortunate in its succession of business managers, men whose high character and abilities were recognized outside as well as within the Institute. The services of the first two, Jerome D. Greene and Henry James, have been recounted. The third, Frank A. Dickey, died after less than a year in office.

Dickey's successor, Edric B. Smith, trained as an engineer at Harvard, had already demonstrated quiet efficiency and reliability as acting business manager when James was away in the army during most of World War I. He was placed in full charge of the business office in 1920. Greene had been designated general manager, James simply manager, with the implication in both cases that the post was almost equivalent in rank to that of the director of the laboratories. With growing experience, and perhaps in reaction to James's somewhat rigid conduct of his duties, the administration defined Dickey's and Smith's post more narrowly as that of business manager. Greene and James were making their way toward careers in high business and institutional circles; Smith made a career of his job at the Institute, which for thirty-five years he served with wisdom and unobtrusive kindliness. His training in engineering made him valuable in the planning and supervision of construction of Welch Hall in 1927–1928, and of the North Laboratory (now Theobald Smith Hall) in 1928–1930; the conversion of the original isolation pavilion to a residence for nurses, in 1950; and in the partial rebuilding and enlargement of the hospital in 1951–1952. Under the By-laws of the Institute, Smith served also as secretary of the Corporation from 1937.

Another man whose skill and competence helped to set the high standards of the Institute's business operations was the bursar, A. D. Robertson. A dignified, precise man, who had learned bookkeeping with a large manufacturing concern, he seemed to his assistants a disciplinarian; but the tradition of orderly accounting he set them is remembered to this day in the administrative offices. When Robertson retired in 1946, his successor was Charles Petrzelka, who began his career with the Institute in 1917 as an office boy. Encouraged by Flexner and by a friendly immediate superior, he studied accounting in evening classes, and was transferred to the Bursar's office, which he now heads, handling with ease and understanding all the new complications that have grown up in scientific institutions through social security, income taxation, and government-grants accounting.

Simon Flexner's generous interest in everyone who worked at the Institute paid valuable dividends through his recognition of dependability and talent in several other young men who began at the bottom of the ladder and rose, with his encouragement, to responsible administrative posts. When Welch Hall was erected, growth of the buildings required a superintendent of maintenance. To this new post Flexner appointed a young man, Bernard Lupinek, whose abilities he had detected soon after giving him a job as office boy in 1911. Happening to see the lad sketching floor plans, Flexner had him take a course in architectural drawing, from time to time told him what he should study next, and saw to it that the talents he revealed were fully utilized in the Institute. Lupinek has handled many important practical problems in equipping the buildings put up since 1927.[4]

About 1915 the business of purchasing and distributing equipment and supplies for the laboratories and the hospital grew heavy enough to require a purchasing agent instead of a mere storekeeper. By that time also the hospital's needs for prescriptions and medical supplies, theretofore met by an outside pharmacy, had increased sufficiently to suggest employing a pharmacist. Flexner had the happy idea of combining the two duties in one post; the arrangement worked so well that it has been continued throughout the Institute's history. Soon after Anthony J. Campo, the present incumbent, came to the Institute in 1917 as a clerk, Flexner encouraged him to study pharmacy. Thus qualified for a place in the purchasing agent's department, Campo was made its head in 1938, and in that capacity supervises, with constant efficiency and with helpfulness to the scientific staff, a service of great complexity. The immense quantities of apparatus of all kinds, chemicals, and various other supplies required by the laboratories and hospital now reach a value of $1,500,000 annually.

Nancy P. Ellicott, first superintendent of the Hospital of The Rockefeller Institute, whose independent character and forceful administration of the nursing service were mentioned in Chapter 4, retired in 1938 and was succeeded by Alice N. Lockie, a graduate of the school of nursing of the General Hospital, Hamilton, Ontario. Miss Lockie and her assistant superintendent, Georgina M. Drew, assuming their new responsibilities shortly after Thomas M. Rivers became director of the hospital, gave him invaluable help and maintained the high standards set by Miss Ellicott.

In 1911, when the library of the Institute had accumulated five thousand volumes, the need of a professional librarian became obvious. Simon Flexner offered the post to Lillia M. D. Trask of the New York Public Library — a bold choice, for up to that time Miss Trask had worked almost entirely in children's libraries. Evincing remarkable talent, however, for her new career, she realized that current practices of general libraries were not well suited to a research institution, where books are working tools as much as are scientific instruments, and where the librarian has a special duty to put them to work for the investigators. With abounding energy she devised new methods for this service as well as for the other special requirements of her post, methods which were adopted in similar libraries that sprang up elsewhere. She directed her staff of young women with firm discipline, even at times terrifying some of the more timid scientists with her high standards of bibliographic accuracy and of library deportment.[5] Miss Trask retired in 1938, and was succeeded by Esther Judkins, who had worked with her for a dozen years. Maintaining the same skilled management with a gentler hand, Miss Judkins has effectively directed the growth of the library to fifty thousand volumes, with continuing provision of exceptionally complete bibliographic and book-finding service to the Institute's scientists.

When The Rockefeller Institute took over the *Journal of Experimental Medicine* in 1905, Simon Flexner called upon his secretary, Edith C. Campbell, to assist him with the editorial care of manuscripts and with the details of publication. The preceding year the Institute had begun to assemble scientific reports, made under its auspices or with its cooperation, in a series of bound volumes called *Studies from The Rockefeller Institute for Medical Research*. In 1910 the Institute began a series of larger monographs, published at irregular intervals. Miss Campbell's office, busy with these three undertakings, was at first designated as the Publication Department, and after about 1919 as the Division of Publication. Further responsibilities were soon added. After Christian A. Herter's death in 1910, the *Journal of Biological Chemistry*, which he had founded in 1905, needed institutional sponsorship, and the Institute began in 1914 to publish it with D. D. Van Slyke as editor. By 1925 this journal was able to stand alone, and the Institute relinquished its responsibility. In 1918 Jacques Loeb and W. J. V. Osterhout (then at Harvard University) founded the *Journal of General Physiology*, which the Institute continues to publish. The Division of Publication nearly added another periodical, the *Journal of Clinical Investigation*, begun in 1924 with an editorial board of eight, of whom six were or had been on the staff of the Hospital of The Rockefeller Institute. The Institute had been expected to sponsor this journal, and when the Society for Clinical Investigation took it up instead, the Institute provided a generous subsidy for several years.

Miss Campbell was a vigorous executive, who required her staff to relieve her of all detail work, and equipped them to do so by creating operating rules and procedures for them to follow implicitly. Her department not only handled subscriptions, but also provided the scientists with secretarial services in connection with their papers, even doing proofreading for them. When Miss Campbell retired in 1940, she was succeeded by Florence M. Stewart, who had come from college in 1916 as editorial assistant and proofreader on the *Journal of Experimental Medicine*. At this time, under the direction of Waldo R. Flinn, then assistant business manager of the Institute, there was a general reorganization, under which the department's services became more like those which the editorial office of a publishing house renders to scientific journals; subscriptions were henceforth handled by the business office, and authors were expected to furnish manuscripts ready for press, and were made responsible for their own final proofreading.[6]

Members of the research staff gratefully recognize how indispensable to them have been the services of men and women in all ranks throughout the Institute. One of the foremost among them, because best known to the research staff, was Louis Schmidt, an artist who put his talents at the service of medicine and biology at a time when scientific photography was less adequate than today. He came to the Institute from the University of Pennsylvania in 1910, and headed the Illustrations Department until his death in 1939. An excellent mechanical and freehand draftsman, he drew microscopic specimens particularly well, and taught his staff — notably Miss Ruth Mandelbaum — to make charts and graphs; many Institute workers still rely on Miss Mandelbaum's skill. Louis Schmidt became so good a photographer that the demand on him as a draftsman almost ceased. He became one of the early presidents of the Biological Photographic Association, yet remained a graphic artist, illuminating occasional ceremonial documents for the Institute, and in his spare time making etchings of New York scenes, still cherished by his Institute friends, who recall with amused affection his jovial irascibility, often coupled with a generous act.

The well-loved Frank Capellino, chief telephone operator, rendered services far beyond the usual duties of his post, acting as a sympathetic and effective one-man information service. During the years when the antivivisection movement threatened research, "Frank's" wide acquaintance among New York City politicians enabled him to explain through them to the voting public the vital need for experiments on animals. When he retired, his friends of the Institute tendered him and "Florence" of the dining room, his wife, an immense farewell party.

Other leading members of the supporting staff, past and present, should be mentioned here. From 1909 to 1952 Conrad Hon had charge of the animal house, living there with his family throughout all this time, in order to be available in case of special need. In the early years of the hospital, when pneumonia serums were being made, his charges included a number of horses which had to be bled at predetermined hours, often in the night. Paul Marrongello, his assistant since 1917, succeeded Hon in 1952. William Chadwick was chief engineer from 1908 to 1939, and was succeeded by George Karda, who began his work in the powerhouse as a boy in 1924. William Whitney, head of the carpenter shop from 1913 to 1939, was a kind-hearted martinet and a perfectionist, as his work showed. Joseph Tekverk, Whitney's assistant since 1915, succeeded him; Tekverk's beautifully constructed bookshelves, apparatus cabinets, laboratory tables, and other built-in furniture, constructed to Bernard Lupinek's specifications, have a style of their own. Otto Hopf, master glass blower from 1929 to 1940, and salty character, made the Carrel-Lindbergh pumps. Scores of clerical helpers, too, have contributed their share to the Institute's output of published research, often in complete anonymity. One Member, indeed, who shall be nameless, pleaded for mention in this history of a secretary to whom, he said, the research men in his laboratory owe the correct and clear English of their scientific reports. But a roll of all the alert and faithful people who during fifty years have given their various talents and skills for the benefit of science at The Rockefeller Institute would far exceed the bounds of this chapter.

In 1953, the fiftieth year of operation of the laboratories and the forty-fourth of the hospital, the scientific investigators, including guests and Fellows, numbered about 125. The administrative and supporting staffs, which in 1904 had numbered 7 persons, now included 410 of all ranks and classes in the laboratories, offices, hospital wards and staff residences, record rooms, kitchens, greenhouses, shop, and powerhouse. The money required to maintain this battalion of workers and to purchase supplies for their work came originally entirely from the income of the endowment. During the first two decades, John D. Rockefeller, Sr., gave the Trustees of the Institute something more than $34,000,000 for land, buildings, and endowment; in 1928 he made another gift of $20,-000,000. Adding to these sums certain funds contributed by The Rockefeller Foundation, the Institute's resources then amounted in round numbers to $65,000,000. All building operations after 1918 were paid for out of income. Although there were no further additions to the endowment during the period of this history, conservative management and the rising market value of securities resulted by 1953 in an increase of the dollar value of the endowment to approximately $107,000,000.

CHAPTER TWENTY

World War II
The Institute Completes Its
First Half Century

The Naval Research Unit at the Hospital of The Rockefeller Institute. U.S. Naval Medical Research Unit No. 2 at Guam. Research under OSRD contracts and other civilian war service. Gasser's retirement. The Institute's influence upon research, training of investigators, and the medical progress of the nation.

As THE WORLD events of 1940–1941 ran their tragic course, and it became evident that the United States would sooner or later join the Allies against Hitler's Germany, The Rockefeller Institute began to take thought as to its role in a second World War. T. M. Rivers, Director of the Hospital, recalling that in 1918 the medical service had been seriously upset by dislocation of the staff, began in 1940 to plan to meet the new emergency in an orderly way. He encouraged the young medical men to join the Navy's Medical Reserve Corps, and himself accepted a Commander's commission, with the possibility in mind that the Institute might form a research unit to study epidemic diseases in the naval forces. Acting upon his suggestion that the hospital should care for naval personnel suffering from diseases with which its staff was especially equipped to deal, the Trustees of The Rockefeller Institute made a dollar-a-year contract with the U.S. Naval Hospital in Brooklyn to receive Navy patients at the Institute's hospital. To man this service Rivers organized a group including eleven of the hospital physicians who were naval reservists, with eighteen others chosen both from the Institute's Department of the Laboratories and from outside the Institute. Navy patients began to arrive as early as January 1942, and by March the Naval Reserve officers of the Rockefeller Hospital staff were inducted into active service, continuing their daily work in Medical Corps uniforms instead of in civilian garb.

This group, designated "Naval Research Unit at the Hospital of The Rockefeller Institute," operated throughout the war and until June 30, 1946. Unlike the War Demonstration Hospital of World War I, the unit was not formally commissioned as a separate post, but constituted a branch of the Brooklyn Naval Hospital. Rivers headed the unit until November 1943, when he left for an inspection tour in the South Pacific, preliminary to the formation of another unit, for overseas duty, and was succeeded by Lieutenant Commander Horsfall. The medical men and biochemists of the Institute holding commissions in the Navy Medical Reserve Corps and attached to the home-based unit throughout the war were E. C. Curnen, Vincent P. Dole, Frank L. Horsfall, Jr., Rollin D. Hotchkiss, Maclyn McCarty, Charles Neumann, R. E. Shank, R. F. Watson, and J. E. Ziegler, Jr. Kendall Emerson, Jr., G. S. Mirick, and Lewis Thomas (visiting investigator) worked with the home-based unit for about two years, before going to the Pacific with Rivers's overseas unit in 1944. Walter A. Stewart, after a year and a half, was assigned to psychiatric work in a number of Navy hospitals.[1]

Because of the Navy's concern over epidemics in the Third Naval District (headquarters in New York City) and adjacent areas, the diseases chosen for treatment at the Institute were, at first, atypical pneumonia, under Horsfall's direction, and scarlet fever and other streptococcal infections, under Swift. When, later, the Navy began to send in numerous patients with epidemic hepatitis, Hoagland altered the program of his group to study and care for them. This use of the hospital avoided the diversion and waste of professional skill which so often occurs when emergency medical services are organized *de novo;* it secured for hundreds of seriously ill Navy men of all ranks the best of medical care, and encouraged rather than hindered clinical research under wartime conditions.

Because this research was closely related to the peacetime programs of the investigators who led it, it has practically all been reviewed in preceding chapters. Horsfall's group, including Curnen, Emerson, Mirick, Thomas, and Ziegler, with the cooperation on special techniques of Vincent Dole, studied primary atypical pneumonia. Part of Horsfall's work on interference between viruses was carried on while he was leading the Naval Research Unit. Lewis Thomas and various colleagues studied the viruses of cat and mouse pneumonias. Most of the work of Swift, Lancefield, Watson, Dole, A. T. Wilson, Rothbard, and their associates on streptococci and streptococcal diseases has also been described earlier. Lancefield, as a practical service to the medical profession, had for many years supervised the manufacture of sera for grouping and typing streptococci; demands from the armed forces now made this a very heavy task. In 1943–1945 Wilson directed, at the Naval Medical Center, Bethesda, Maryland, a laboratory for the study and identification of streptococci isolated from patients in Navy hospitals, in close collaboration with Lancefield, through his association with the Institute. The wartime work of Hoagland, Gilder, Shank, and their associates on epidemic hepatitis, recounted in Chapter 18, led to general studies on liver disease, which became a continuing interest of Labby, Henry Kunkel, and Ahrens. Because Maclyn McCarty was one of the Navy contingent, some of the work Avery and he did on the transforming factor of the pneumococcus was credited to the Navy.

In mid-1943 the high command of the Navy Medical Corps, already concerned about the prevalence of scrub typhus, hepatitis, and other infectious diseases in Navy personnel in the Pacific, foresaw that impending campaigns would expose our forces to a great variety of tropical diseases, many of them not well understood, or at least unfamiliar to the Medical Corps. Rivers, promoted to Captain, was therefore sent on an extensive tour of the South Pacific islands, to determine the best location for an advance base as near as possible to the fighting lines, from which research teams could investigate diseases occurring in any part of the area. This was a novel enterprise for the armed forces. Both the Army and the Navy had on occasion sent out commissions to study specific medical problems in the field, but this was the first time that either service had attempted to organize a fully equipped research laboratory in a forward area. On the basis of Rivers's report, Guadalcanal was at first considered as the location of the unit, but the fighting front advanced so rapidly that Guam was finally chosen.

U.S. Naval Medical Research Unit No. 2 was commissioned at the Institute in June 1944, under the command of Captain Rivers. As nucleus of his staff, Rivers had nine experienced investigators connected with The Rockefeller Institute — Binkley, Emerson, Mirick, Schwentker, Shope, and Stoll, with Lewis Thomas, a visiting investigator at the Institute, Horace L. Hodes, a former assistant in Leslie Webster's laboratory, and J. T. Syverton, who came back from Rochester, New York, to join his Rockefeller colleagues. To these he added, from other institutions, a score of specialists in various branches of natural history, qualified to study the insects, snails, other invertebrate animals, and mammals that might transmit infectious diseases or serve as hosts for viruses and parasites. Administrative officers supplied by the Navy brought the total commissioned personnel to forty-four. Navy hospital corpsmen and other selected enlisted men numbered two hundred and fifty.

To house the unit, sixty-two buildings were required, including laboratories which had to have running water, electricity, and sewage systems; some were to be air conditioned and all had to be fully equipped for the study of virology, bacteriology, parasitology, entomology, malacology, aquatic ecology, mammalogy, biochemistry, and statistics. An excellent working library was provided by a grant from the International Health Division of The Rockefeller Foundation. The organization of this large undertaking was a triumph of enterprise and intelligence on the part of the scientific workers in cooperation with experienced supply officers and construction experts of the Navy. Shope was flown to Guam in November 1944, to choose a site for the laboratories and to receive the equipment, which was already at sea. The main body of the unit sailed from a California port December 1, and arrived at Guam January 12, 1945. In less than four months the installation, situated near a large Navy hospital, was completely in operation.

The Iwo Jima campaign was imminent by the time Research Unit No. 2 arrived in Guam, and the fighting front was moving to the westward. The members of the unit occupied themselves chiefly with scientific problems that presented themselves locally. The naturalists surveyed the fauna of the island, making extensive collections of insects, mollusks, and birds, and identifying numerous new species. They took censuses of the rodent populations that might transmit various diseases, and, from general interest rather than wartime need, collected birds for the Smithsonian Institution. The Rockefeller Institute investigators also found much useful work on Guam. Norman Stoll made an extensive study of hookworm in the native population. With a colleague, M. B. Franks, he worked out a method for isolating, from the blood of patients, microfilariae, the parasitic larvae causing tropical elephantiasis, for use as antigen in testing for the disease and preparing a vaccine. Mirick investigated various outbreaks of infectious diseases; Syverton studied a supposedly new disease which the service medical officers called "Okinawa fever," finding it to be paratyphoid fever with some admixture of typhoid. Thomas and Hodes worked with viruses, especially that of the "Japanese B" encephalitis, which broke out on Okinawa. The biochemists, Emerson and Binkley, unraveled the chemical factors in various emergency problems, and later, utilizing knowledge gained from previous research, studied the therapeutic administration of amino acids to severely burned patients. Rivers and his executive officer, Schwentker, were fully occupied with administrative duties.

Richard Shope drew a more exciting assignment. Medical officers of the force that was to attack Okinawa were concerned for the health of their men in a territory supposed to be pest-ridden. To find out whether a scientific survey of potential health hazards for troops ashore could be made under combat conditions, Shope was detailed, with a party of nine other officers and twenty men, to land with the assault party on April 13, 1945. Establishing a laboratory in an abandoned canning factory, they made surveys for malarial mosquitoes, the parasites of schistosomiasis and the snails that harbor them, dysentery bacilli, and other pathogenic organisms. They found that Okinawa was in fact not heavily infested with any of these disease producers, and that the native population was relatively healthy. Shope's contingent were in greater danger from bullets than from disease, for Japanese soldiers were waging guerilla warfare from jungle bases, and the scientists were under fire almost daily. When the occupation forces had the island under control, the research group was ordered back to Guam.

Medical Research Unit No. 2 was decommissioned June 30, 1946, and its personnel returned to the United States beginning early in that year. Before he left active service, Rivers was promoted to the rank of Commodore.[2] Among the excellent enlisted men of the unit, several responded to the stimulus of association with the medical scientists, after returning to civilian life, by studying for careers in medicine or biology. The installation on Guam was temporarily retained by the Navy as a school of tropical medicine, but because of lack of funds and deterioration of the buildings it was closed in 1947. The Naval Medical Research Unit was subsequently recommissioned, under the honored designation "No. 2," and stationed in Formosa, under the command of Captain R. A. Phillips, who had been attached in 1941–1942 to the home-based Institute unit.[3]

Three officers originally of the Rockefeller unit were sent abroad on special assignments in 1942. Lee E. Farr organized and for a year and a half operated laboratory services on the hospital-transport *U.S.S. Tryon*, in the South Pacific. In 1944 at Bethesda, he developed a method of preparing frozen dried hemoglobin for transfusion and, later, worked in medical problems of deep sea diving and submarines. R. A. Phillips was sent to a Navy medical research unit in Cairo, Egypt. Richard E. Shope spent the two years prior to his service on Guam and Okinawa in an enterprise so secret that his colleagues did not know even his whereabouts.

The United States and Canadian governments, fearing that enemy nations might disseminate the highly infectious cattle disease rinderpest among North American herds, tried jointly to produce a vaccine against the virus. Shope, invited by the Secretary of War to direct the research, set up in 1942 a laboratory on Grosse Ile, in the St. Lawrence River below Quebec City, with a staff of three U.S. and two Canadian scientists, including James A. Baker from the Institute's Department of Animal Pathology (now director of the Veterinary Virus Institute at Cornell University). By growing rinderpest virus in hens' eggs, a technique proven useful with other viruses, Shope's group in nineteen months developed an effective vaccine, subsequently used on millions of cattle in Eastern lands where the disease exists. Baker attempted to adapt the virus to rabbits and, by use of a novel technique (alternating passages of the virus through rabbits and calves), finally got it to grow in rabbits alone; however, the virus did not become sufficiently attenuated to afford a vaccine. Incidental to this effort, Baker worked out tests to determine the amount of virus in egg cultures and the degree of immunity it induced in rabbits.

It is a curious fact that the Japanese government, thinking that the Allies might use rinderpest in bacterial warfare, also set up a research group, which succeeded in attenuating the virus in rabbits, thereby producing an effective vaccine. The rinderpest vaccine now in use is a combination of the U.S.–Canadian and the Japanese products. Thus scientific research conceived by two nations at war, in deadly fear of each other, is now joined in peaceful application to human welfare. As a further benefit, Baker's method of adapting the virus of rinderpest to rabbits led directly to the successful production of hog cholera vaccine as now used.

Armin C. Braun, commissioned in the Army Sanitary Corps, had charge of bacteriology, parasitology, and serology in various general hospitals, first at home camps and later in England and France. His collaborators Elrod and Laskaris had similar assignments, Elrod in Europe, Laskaris in the Pacific. Malcolm S. Ferguson, also in the Sanitary Corps, landed on Leyte on the fourth day of the invasion of the Philippines, to study the extent of infestation of fresh water by schistosome larvae, cause of a dangerous infection of the blood and viscera. Later he formed a schistosomiasis research unit on the grounds of the Army's 118th (Johns Hopkins) General Hospital on the island. For a time Frederik B. Bang of the Institute was associated with Ferguson, and the two later wrote a chapter on schistosomiasis for the U.S. Army Medical Department's history of World War II.

Much of the wartime research at the Institute by workers who kept their civilian status was done under contract with the Office of Scientific Research and Development, the great organization built up by Vannevar Bush for promoting and coordinating the work of scientists and engineers in the national emergency. At the head of OSRD's division of medical research was A. Newton Richards of the University of Pennsylvania, one of the original workers in The Rockefeller Institute's first laboratory in 1904.

In 1941 OSRD began an extensive study of chemical warfare agents, especially the war gases. For fundamental research on their physiological action, it enlisted help from four universities and The Rockefeller Institute. Herbert S. Gasser, director of the Institute, was chairman, 1941–1944, of an OSRD subsection on the toxicity of mustard gases, with Stanford Moore of Bergmann's laboratory as "technical aide" or executive officer. Gasser himself conducted at the Institute an extensive study of the detection of mustard gases in the air, using bacteria, protozoa, and other low organisms as test agents. Under five contracts with OSRD, several of the Institute's chemists and pathologists devoted themselves to study of war gas problems.

Northrop and his associates developed an instrument, the Northrop titrimeter, for measuring the concentration of mustard gas, which, after modification at the California Institute of Technology, was widely used in war gas research. Later he devised several other instruments for detection of these gases. Northrop and Kunitz also investigated the enzyme systems involved in the action of the mustard gases upon living tissues. Under another OSRD contract, the whole of Bergmann's group — Fruton, Golumbic, Moore, Stahmann, and Stein — focused their attention on the chemical reactions of mustard gases with organic compounds in the tissues. McMaster and Hogeboom tested on animals several hundred chemical compounds, in a search for substances able to decontaminate skin exposed to mustard gas. Landsteiner, with the collaboration of John G. Kidd, applied his mastery of immunochemistry to the possibility of immunization against war gases; but although they could readily make guinea pigs hypersensitive to mustard gas, they discovered no immunizing agents. Osterhout, using the large-celled aquatic plant *Nitella*, which he understood so well, studied the penetration of the toxic gas into the living cell. MacInnes investigated the "thickening" of H-mustard gas, *i.e.,* increasing the size of drops sprayed from planes to make them more injurious. Using high-speed photography, he followed the distribution of mustard compounds striking clothing. Herriott and Hogeboom supervised groups testing mustard gas in the field, on a large remote reservation in Florida, and in 1944 Herriott led a party for the same purpose to an island off the coast of Panama.[4]

Van Slyke headed his group — Archibald, V. P. Dole, Emerson, Farr, Hamilton, and Phillips — in a study of acute failure of the kidneys following traumatic shock, a subject of great importance in war surgery. This research was not secret and its results were promptly published. Van Slyke's group also devised and published a simple rapid method of determining the blood volume in traumatic shock and after hemorrhage.

Another war problem of major proportions, malarial infection, was the subject of a nation-wide emergency research program in which The Rockefeller Institute took part under four contracts recommended by the OSRD Committee on the Control of Malaria. European organic chemists had created a number of synthetic antimalarial drugs, including atabrin and plasmoquin, improvements upon the familiar quinine. When supplies of atabrin, prepared under the stress of war by American manufacturers, proved in preliminary tests to be toxic in certain dosages, W. A. Jacobs and Lyman C. Craig were asked to examine the material; they prepared a sample of attested purity to serve as a standard. The medical services of the armed forces so greatly feared disastrous effects of malaria in the South Pacific that the invasion of Guadalcanal was postponed until safe supplies of atabrin could be prepared and tested clinically. As other antimalarial drugs were sent to the Institute for chemical study, and Jacobs was forced by illness to withdraw from the work, Craig's laboratory became a center for general studies of the chemical pharmacology of antimalarial compounds. In one of these studies, Craig put his marvelously sensitive countercurrent distribution method to work in separating plasmoquin from a contaminating isomer. The latter was subsequently synthesized by organic chemists at Columbia University, working in association with Craig.

Working under a contract administered by Van Slyke, Archibald, aided by James R. Weisiger, undertook to develop methods for determining the amounts of antimalarial drugs in the circulating blood. Testing a variety of drugs furnished by the OSRD Committee, Archibald, contending with great technical difficulties, worked out useful methods utilizing the principle of fluorimetry. Rudolf W. Glaser made an unsuccessful attempt in Princeton to adapt the parasite to guinea pigs, in a valiant search for an animal host capable of harboring the parasites of human malaria, to be used for testing antimalarial drugs. No better success was obtained elsewhere, and, in the end, the patriotism of numerous American penitentiary inmates, who volunteered for experiments, made it possible to test the drugs on human subjects. The war itself provided a world-wide experiment with some of these antimalarial drugs. William Trager of the Department of Animal Pathology in Princeton, with seven years' experience in the biology of mosquitoes, was commissioned Captain in the Army's Sanitary Corps, for research on malaria. With his colleague Frederik Bang, then of the Army Medical Corps, and two officers from other institutions, he carried on, for a year and a half, studies in New Guinea and Australia. Working in camps where large numbers of men were undergoing rehabilitation following repeated attacks of malaria, they studied the action of atabrin, the antimalarial drug then in most general use, and worked out the optimum program of its dosage and mode of administration for suppressing malarial attacks in infected persons. In later studies, they compared the effectiveness of quinine with the newer drugs administered on various schedules and in various combinations.

Before going to the Pacific, Bang undertook for OSRD a basic investigation of drugs in use or proposed for use in the prophylaxis of gonorrheal infections. No method of making the study on animals was available; although mice can, with some difficulty, be infected with the gonococcus, such infections are not reliable in tests of drug action on the organisms. Utilizing the experience of workers who had grown somewhat similar organisms in chick embryos, Bang achieved the same result with the gonococcus, and used his cultures to test the relative prophylactic value of the silver-protein compounds, argyrol and protargol, and various sulfonamides and arsenicals. Joining in the wartime effort to improve the supply of antibiotic drugs, Herriott, at the Princeton laboratory of physical chemistry, in consultation with the Committee on Medical Research of the OSRD, developed a spectrophotometric method for the rapid and reliable determination of the concentration of penicillin in crude and commercial preparations.

Epidemic influenza is greatly to be dreaded in wartime. In the early 1940's various efforts to achieve a vaccine against some strains of influenza virus had met with highly variable results. Under an OSRD contract recommended by the National Defense Research Committee, Wendell M. Stanley, of the Department of Animal and Plant Pathology, together with C. A. Knight, M. A. Lauffer, and G. L. Miller put aside their chosen research on plant mosaic viruses, and devoted themselves from 1943 to 1946 to an investigation of influenza virus, with a view to the development of useful vaccines. Their findings, published in about twenty papers, cover, first of all, methods of mass production of the virus in chick embryos and quantitative methods of measuring amounts of virus, and for estimating its infectivity. Next, the physical characteristics of the virus were studied, including the size of the particles, their stability in the presence of various chemical agents, and their behavior under centrifugation and electrophoresis. Stanley was able to prescribe technical steps making possible the preparation of vaccines ten times as potent as those commercially available. The comprehensive information about the properties of certain strains of influenza virus assembled by this rapid, systematic group effort has become part of the general knowledge of virologists. In 1945 Stanley and C. E. Duffy, at the invitation of the Army Epidemiological Board's Commission on Neurotropic Virus Diseases, made a similar though less comprehensive study of the biochemical, biophysical, and immunogenic properties of Japanese B encephalitis virus and the vaccines prepared against it.

For the control of bacillary dysentery, a frequent disease in army camps, the OSRD enlisted the aid of Walther F. Goebel. The work done under this contract, with the aid of O. F. Binkley and Ely Perlman, fitted closely into Goebel's lifelong study of immunochemistry, as discussed in Chapter 19. René Dubos prepared the toxin and toxoid of the Shiga dysentery bacillus; when he left for Harvard University in 1942 he took the contract with him, but finished the work after his return to the Institute in 1944.

Carl TenBroeck, John B. Nelson, and Frederik B. Bang of the Department of Animal and Plant Pathology served as members of the Commission on Tropical Diseases of the Army Epidemiological Board. In 1942 they were assigned to study outbreaks of dysentery in army camps of the Southeast Service Command, in order to learn how many men were carrying dysentery bacilli and to identify the types of organisms involved. The following year TenBroeck, Nelson, and Lieutenant Edwin P. Albright of the Army Medical Corps continued these investigations in the Southwest Service Command, with particular attention to the carriage of dysentery bacilli by German and Italian prisoners. In one camp they detected a considerable number of carriers among healthy German troops from Rommel's Afrika Korps. Treatment with sulfadiazine, they found, eliminated the potentially dangerous bacteria.

In 1944 TenBroeck and Nelson went to India for six months on a mission, secret at the time, to study the prevalence of bacillary dysentery among American troops stationed there. With Major G. J. Dammin of the Army Medical Corps, they constituted a Subcommission on Dysentery of the Commission on Tropical Diseases of the Army Epidemiological Board. They set up laboratories for bacteriological diagnosis in army hospitals in Calcutta and at the 20th General Hospital near the Ledo Road in Assam. Here cultures from patients suspected of infection with dysentery organisms, and from hundreds of potential carriers among American and Chinese soldiers, Indian helpers, and Japanese prisoners, were grown on various media for biochemical diagnosis, and subjected to serological classification. Sera for use in identifying the infective organisms, chiefly species of *Shigella,* were prepared in Princeton with the cooperation of Marion Orcutt, and shipped to the laboratories in India in a dried state or diluted with glycerin. Cultures of organisms that proved puzzling were sent to Princeton for more exhaustive study. This mission not only furnished the Army with valuable information as to the types of dysentery and paradysentery infections with which medical officers would have to cope in India, but its success served to demonstrate the feasibility of carrying out bacteriological diagnosis under difficult field conditions.

In 1941 the U.S. Army Medical Corps, facing the possibility of war in many parts of the world, set up the Board for the Investigation and Control of Influenza and Other Epidemic Diseases in the Army, known simply (and mentioned above) as the Army Epidemiological Board, under the chairmanship of Francis G. Blake (formerly of The Rockefeller Institute). The Commission on Neurotropic Virus Diseases, for the study of poliomyelitis, encephalomyelitis, dengue fever, and other virus diseases involving the nervous system, was one of its subdivisions. In order to secure the cooperation of The Rockefeller Institute, a recognized center of research in this field, membership on the Commission was offered to L. T. Webster and P. K. Olitsky. For administrative reasons, these men preferred to act as consultants instead of as members. Later Jordi Casals took part in a similar capacity. During the war years the Institute was the Commission's meeting place not less than twice a year.

In the summer of 1941 an epidemic of Western equine encephalomyelitis occurred in the northern United States and in Canada, becoming in Manitoba a serious military problem. The nature of this disease was first determined by use of a complement-fixation test developed and performed by Casals. Because the clinical use of such tests for virus diseases was in its infancy, the Commission arranged facilities for performing them at four institutions, including The Rockefeller Institute, strategically located throughout the United States. To meet a request from the Army Medical School for a standard technique for neutralization and complement-fixation tests for neurotropic viruses, the Commission formed a committee consisting of Webster, Casals, and A. B. Sabin, of Cincinnati, the two last being Olitsky's former associates at the Institute. Observations made in Olitsky's laboratory and elsewhere contributed to subsequent revisions of the manual of instruction, and Casals prepared standard antigens for performing the tests. One of the most important uses of the complement-fixation tests was for the diagnosis of Japanese B encephalitis on Okinawa Island in 1945.

Meanwhile, early in 1942 the Commission began to concern itself with the general problem of vaccinating human beings against neurotropic virus diseases, assigning individual diseases to the collaborating laboratories. Olitsky worked on Eastern and Western encephalomyelitis; his experiments pointed to the virus strains best adapted to vaccine production. Webster took up Western Nile and Russian tick-borne encephalitis. His death in 1943 left that part of the task unfinished, but Casals and Olitsky afterward resumed it, securing an effective vaccine against the Russian virus. Sabin of Cincinnati chose to prepare a vaccine against Japanese B encephalitis. Later, The Rockefeller Institute contributed to this effort by Stanley's attempts to purify the virus by ultracentrifugation. Practical use of the vaccine is still under investigation. During the entire four years of the war, important basic studies on immunity in neurotropic virus diseases, and methods of measuring it, were made at the Institute by Webster, Olitsky, Casals, R. W. Schlesinger, and Isabel Morgan, whose work contributed materially to experimental knowledge in this field.

The war in the Pacific brought our troops into contact with dengue fever. The Commission therefore asked Albert Sabin, then a colonel in the medical corps, to organize a laboratory for study of that disease, at The Rockefeller Institute's Princeton branch. With the cooperation of the New Jersey State Prison at Trenton, volunteers were secured who were willing to submit themselves to the risk of this extremely painful disease. Sabin, with his chief associate R. W. Schlesinger and others, made a thorough study of the virus, transmitted the disease to human subjects by the bite of infected mosquitoes and by direct instillation into the nasal passages, and adapted the virus to growth in mice, opening the way for production of a vaccine against dengue fever.

Participation by The Rockefeller Institute's investigators in this remarkably effective combined effort of civilian and military medical scientists contributed greatly to its success, which led to the retention of the Commission on Neurotropic Virus Diseases as a permanent unit of the Army medical organization.[5]

THE ROCKEFELLER INSTITUTE, intent on medical and biological service, was barely touched by the great wartime undertaking of the physicists to put atomic energy at the service of mankind for war and, ultimately, for peace. Duncan MacInnes in 1942 received a call to work, in secret under an OSRD contract, on the feasibility of separating uranium isotopes by electrophoresis. Under the prevailing conditions, he and his associate, Lewis G. Longsworth, had difficulty in getting the use of a mass spectrograph; thus handicapped, his work proceeded but slowly. Other methods were developed elsewhere, and his experiments were discontinued.

To Theodore Shedlovsky the Navy Bureau of Aeronautics assigned a peculiar problem, seemingly outside The Rockefeller Institute's scope, and calling for inventiveness as well as command of physical theory. This task was to devise an instrument to determine the temperature of the free air surrounding an airplane in flight. The special difficulty was that a thermometer in a rapid air stream does not indicate the free air temperature, but gives an unduly high reading, varying with the speed, largely because of compression of the air impinging upon it. The reading is slightly raised also by air friction, and this likewise varies with the speed, in about the same manner as the compression effect. The problem could only be solved, therefore, by a heat-measuring system which would remain somehow unaffected by the velocity of the plane.

Shedlovsky achieved this solution by using two thermocouples housed in conical shells of similar dimensions, but reversed in position, one pointing into the air stream, the other away from it. The readings of the two thermocouples of course varied with the speed, but at a systematically different rate of increase, because of the differing impingement of the air stream upon them. When their electrical outputs were fed into a galvanometer with two independent windings, the respective circuits could be adjusted by suitable resistances to give an integrated reading, independent of the velocity factor. Not only did Shedlovsky work out the theoretical design of this simple, sturdy, and entirely novel device, carrying out lengthy wind-tunnel tests with improvised apparatus, but, at the Navy's insistence, he also developed and constructed it for practical trials in the air, without help from outside engineers, a feat made possible by his own training at a school of engineering and by excellent mechanical work in the Institute's shop.

AT THE ROCKEFELLER INSTITUTE the year 1946 was a time of realignment of administrative and research activities, after the digressions and distractions of the war, as the home-based workers turned back to their normal programs, and those who had been away came home again. The transition was easier than it had been in 1918, for, on the whole, the Institute, like the rest of the country, had taken World War II with a wiser kind of patriotic devotion than the First, contributing to the national effort largely by the application of its established lines of research to problems that arose in the emergency. Simon Flexner, whose eightieth birthday had occurred midway in the war years, in 1943, stated to a reporter on that occasion that the practical application of scientific research is often speeded up in time of war, but the important advances are made when quiet, retiring, and studious minds have the opportunity to operate in peace.[6] He had proved this true by making no major changes of direction or policy during the long period of calm between 1918 and his retirement in 1935. Under Herbert S. Gasser's leadership, the years from 1946 to 1953 — when he, in turn, retired — were equally a period of progress along established lines.

Yet although the Institute's investigators were so productive during these years that seven of these chapters have been required merely to outline their accomplishments, the general public scarcely heard of this activity. The New York newspapers, alert for items from The Rockefeller Institute, found little new to report from what one of them called "that cloistered, publicity-shy institution."[7] Simon Flexner's death on May 2, 1946, brought forth a flood of praise for him, and recognition of the Institute's preeminent achievements in the past, to which new emphasis was added by the announcement, in November of that year, of a Nobel award in chemistry to John H. Northrop and Wendell M. Stanley jointly with James B. Sumner of Cornell University. Other newspaper items were mostly nostalgic. On October 2, 1946, the *Herald Tribune* reported, in stricken tones, as if some great man had passed away, the "death" of Carrel's chicken heart culture, discontinued at the Lederle Laboratories when A. H. Ebeling retired from there. In 1947 the impending closure of the Princeton laboratories, though recognized by the newspapers as an effort to consolidate and thereby to strengthen the Institute, could hardly be reported as a forward step. The event considered most newsworthy in 1948 was a tour of the Institute by the ex-

Queen Mother of Rumania. The resignation of John D. Rockefeller, Jr., as president of the Board of Trustees, October 28, 1950, once more pointed to the past, even though the election of his son David to succeed him heralded a new era which the press could not foresee.

In the laboratories, as among the Trustees and the administrative staff, some of the older men were relinquishing their posts and new men were coming to the front. The death of one Member (Hoagland) has been mentioned, and the years 1945 to 1952 inclusive saw the retirement of nine others — Rous, Swift, Jacobs, Louis Kunkel, Van Slyke, MacInnes, Murphy, TenBroeck, and Olitsky — all of whom, with one exception, kept on with their personal researches at the Institute. During the same period thirteen men were appointed to be Members, all after years of productive service in the Institute's laboratories. It is a measure of their repute among fellow scientists that up to the present time of writing (1960) eight of them have been elected to the National Academy of Sciences.

In June 1953 Herbert Gasser ended his eighteen years as director of the Institute. The award of a Nobel Prize, in physiology and medicine, to him jointly with Joseph Erlanger of St. Louis, in 1944, midway in his directorship, indicates the distinction he brought with him to the Institute and maintained throughout his career. The esteem the Institute's workers felt for him as adviser, critic, and fellow investigator has already been set forth. As administrator, he made himself, under the circumstances of the time and of his own temperament, the executive officer of his Trustees and Board of Scientific Directors, rather than the dominant leader Flexner had been; and as such he maintained the research standards of the Institute and held together, through a difficult period, a staff qualified to participate in the transformation to the new and different regime that was to follow his.

A year after Gasser's retirement, his long-time friend Detlev W. Bronk had occasion to pay him tribute when awarding him the Kober medal of the Association of American Physicians. President Bronk spoke first of Gasser's respect for intellectual values and for individual human rights, and then of his devotion to excellence in his own work and in that of the institution over which he had presided. It was no easy task, said the third head of the Institute, to be the successor of Simon Flexner, but Gasser had been fitted for the challenge by more than knowledge and technical skill;

he had the rare quality of understanding those values which best nurture the mind of the scientific investigator.[8]

ON MAY 11, 1906, at the dedication of the first permanent buildings of The Rockefeller Institute, the president of Columbia University predicted that the new institution would exert its influence in three ways: it would add to the sum total of human knowledge in respect to medicine; it would train scientific observers; and it would help spread abroad in the public mind a respect for science and the scientific method.[9]

The judgment of the American public as to how well the Institute, during its first half century, has fulfilled each of these hopes was expressed through responsible newspaper comment in 1953. When the appointment of Detlev W. Bronk as President of the Institute was made known, together with plans for a new administrative structure and the transformation of the Institute into a university faculty of science, the *New York Times* editorially acknowledged both the Institute's contribution to the sum of knowledge and its output of trained observers, by calling it the world's foremost organization for medical research. Its senior scientists, said the *Times,* had always been brilliant leaders in their fields; its junior scientists had received a training that brought out the promise their talents held.[10] Such a pronouncement by the nation's leading newspaper is evidence that The Rockefeller Institute has also helped to create in the public mind a favorable attitude toward scientific research.

This, however, could be only a general estimate. We have no precise scales by which to measure the growth of scientific knowledge, the training of men, and the development of public opinion. A crude measure of the Institute's yield of scientific information can be gained from the library shelves in Founder's Hall, where the *Studies from The Rockefeller Institute,* comprising every research report published by its workers from 1904 to 1953, numbered 147 volumes, averaging about 50 articles to the volume. Many of these articles, of course, are "progress reports" of only ephemeral importance, mere building stones in the edifice of scientific research, but standing out among them are the original accounts of numerous investigations now recognized as landmarks in the history of medical and biological science. Everywhere in the world physicians and scientists are familiar with Flexner's work on cerebrospinal meningitis and poliomyelitis, Noguchi's demonstration of spirochetes in the brains of paretics, the Rous sarcoma, Carrel's tissue culture, Jacques Loeb's application of physical chemistry to living tissues, the cure of African sleeping sickness by Tryparsamide, Landsteiner and Wiener's Rh factor, Stanley's crystalline tobacco mosaic virus, Van Slyke's manometric analysis of blood gases. In time, more recent accomplishments will no doubt be similarly recognized.

Meanwhile, two general histories of medicine, published in the early 1950's, cite between them thirty-one investigations made by thirty-five men and women at The Rockefeller Institute, which the authors thought worthy of a place in the long annals of the medical profession. The *ex cathedra* pronouncements of these historians, which must be relegated to a note,[11] by no means represent the full scope of the Institute's work, for they do not include important contributions in animal and plant pathology and in the more technical areas of biochemistry, pharmacology, and physical chemistry; nor can any such list take account of findings and ideas now inconspicuous among all these records, which later historians may recognize as seminal. Who could have guessed, for example, when Phoebus Levene published in 1910 his identification of ribonucleic acid, that he had provided a key to the mystery of genic inheritance? This example points, moreover, to an element in the total output of a research institution, which can never be measured by listing individual scientists or their separate achievements: the force of continual inquiry, the attack carried on by successive generations of investigators bringing new ways of thinking and new tools of research to the persistent study of nature's problems. Readers of this history have before them the evidence of just such marshaling, through the years, of insight, technical skills, accumulated information, and farseeing imagination which has kept the Institute's investigators continually in the forefront of research in special fields of major importance related to the structure and behavior of protoplasm, the chemistry of the tissues, the biology of bacterial and viral organisms, the mechanisms of infection, malignancy, immunity, and heredity.

Another important contribution of The Rockefeller Institute was the demonstration that a purposeful attack on specific major problems of medicine and biology, as contrasted with the individual investigator's

DAVID ROCKEFELLER

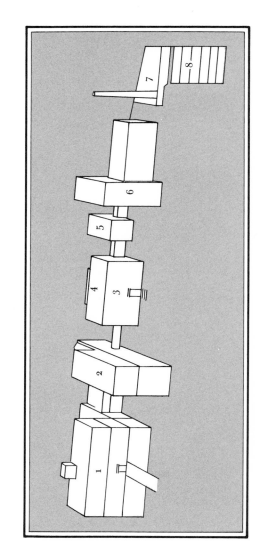

Location of buildings in air view: 1. *Theobald Smith Hall* 2. *Flexner Hall*
3. *Founder's Hall* 4. *Welch Hall (adjoining Founder's Hall)*
5. *Nurses Residence* 6. *Hospital* 7. *Power House* 8. *Greenhouses*

AIR VIEW OF THE ROCKEFELLER INSTITUTE IN 1952

DETLEV W. BRONK

pursuit of questions raised by his private curiosity, can yield valuable results. Although, when the Institute was founded, there were many who doubted the feasibility of its program, its achievement soon stimulated similar work in university and hospital clinics throughout the country. When in 1924 the *Journal of Clinical Research* was founded, four of its editorial board of eight were men whose experience had in significant part been acquired at The Rockefeller Institute.

If the founders of The Rockefeller Institute could now pass judgment on the work of their successors, in the light of their own aims and hopes, they would assuredly be satisfied, but in one respect astonished. They could not have foreseen at the beginning of the century that a corps of investigators chosen primarily to solve problems of infection and epidemic diseases would so soon and so constantly find it necessary to look far behind the immediate problems of human illness into the basic structure and function of the tissues of animals and plants, carrying their search even beyond the microscopic pattern of cell life into the realm of the atom and the electron.

To assess the Institute's contribution to science through the training of investigators is as difficult as to evaluate its acquisition of scientific knowledge. Although the founders chose at first, and despite the doubts of Welch, not to undertake formal instruction leading to advanced degrees, they were aware that research and teaching are inseparable, and that young men fortunate enough to work with such experienced investigators as those of the Institute would be in the highest sense learners. In 1949, Director Gasser, irked by a recent governmental regulation under which the Institute was not classed as an educational institution, eloquently reminded his Trustees that teaching had always figured prominently in the Institute's activities, though it had all been at postgraduate level and its results revealed, not by diplomas, but by the records of men's careers. Thus judged, he said, the extent to which, in proportion to its size, the Institute had enriched the academic world was something of which it might justly be proud.[12]

Some figures Gasser presented in support of this statement have since increased on a rising curve, like money at compound interest. As of 1953, approximately 650 persons had at one time or another been on the research staff in ranks below that of Member. Of these, about 200 have subsequently held full professorships or equivalent positions in research institutes, industry, or public service. (Some, it should be mentioned, are not yet of an age for such appointments.) The figure does not include those who remained at the Institute, reaching, as full Members, rank equivalent to a full professorship. The institutions to which these 200 men went are located in 31 states of the Union and 16 foreign countries on five continents. Men from the Institute are also now high-ranking scientists and physicians with the U.S. Army and Navy, Public Health Service, Department of Agriculture, and the Atomic Energy laboratories at Brookhaven. Adding to this total those of other ranks in the universities and other research institutions (a roster difficult to compile because of constant changes in status and affiliation), The Rockefeller Institute's influence upon the training of scientific leaders looms large indeed.

The Institute cannot, of course, claim all these former workers as alumni in the usual academic sense. All of them held advanced university degrees taken elsewhere, and some of them were at the Institute for only a year or two. Among them, however, is a smaller but more significant (for our purpose of assaying the Institute's educational role) group of men who regard themselves and are cherished by the Institute as alumni in the true sense. Defined somewhat empirically, this group comprises investigators who came to the Institute soon after taking the Ph.D. or the M.D. degree or after an internship, and remained three or more years, entering upon their definitive careers under the leadership of one of the Members. Each of the Members has had younger associates in such a relationship, which is that of teacher and student, even though the teacher conducts no classes and the student already holds a doctor's degree. Avery's brilliant young men, for example, openly proclaimed the relation by calling their chief "The Fess," and, in after years, by rendering allegiance to his memory equaling that of the most academic alumni to a beloved teacher. Similarly, though less colorfully perhaps, the pupil-associates of several other Members — notably, Bergmann, Cole, Flexner, Louis Kunkel, Olitsky, and Van Slyke — have been sufficiently numerous to form little schools of advanced study about their respective chiefs.

It is impossible, of course, to draw up a precise list of "alumni" thus defined, but those who would probably so classify themselves number about 75 of full professorial or equivalent rank. Of these, 25 became

Members of the Institute, and 50 are counted among the 200 mentioned as having gone to other institutions as professors, deans, or directors of advanced research laboratories. Comparison of this extraordinary record with that of other institutions, teaching at a different and more formal level, is pointless; it need only be said that The Rockefeller Institute, making research its primary aim, has nevertheless attracted able young people to its laboratories, and, putting them to work with skilled investigators, has trained them for the nation's scientific *corps d'élite*. Besides the regularly appointed members of the Institute's staff, two or three hundred additional persons have taken part in scientific work in its laboratories, as guest investigators, Fellows of other institutions, transients learning special techniques and in various other capacities. Some of these people came to the Institute for a few weeks only, others for a year or more. They form a group so heterogeneous that they can hardly be listed, or even counted, in any precise way; but, noting among them a score or more of well-known leaders of medical and biological research in this country and abroad, one perceives that the influence of The Rockefeller Institute as a training center has spread more widely than any formal record can indicate.

How far the Institute has also fulfilled the prediction that it would help to create public recognition of scientific values and respect for the scientific method is still more difficult to judge, for it never deliberately aimed at any such general purpose. To be sure, T. Mitchell Prudden, of the founding Board of Directors, hoped and planned for a division of the Institute to be devoted to public health instruction and a museum of hygiene, but neither this idea nor any other that would have diverted the Institute from research was ever seriously considered. Twice in its earliest days, as we have seen, the Institute directly influenced public action, once when the milk investigation of 1901–1902 precipitated reform of the New York City milk supply, and again in 1908–1911 when Welch and Flexner successfully fought legislation adverse to experimentation on animals. Aside from these *ad hoc* efforts, the Institute has affected the public attitude toward science only by making contributions to knowledge, and by its example of successful organization of full-time research.

Its very first program, that of the grants-in-aid from 1901 to 1917, now almost forgotten and never adequately recognized for its pioneering success, was familiar to leaders of the National Research Council, founded in 1916, and must have influenced them and other subsequent organizers of research grant enterprises. Again, the Hospital of The Rockefeller Institute was the first institution where young physicians were given full-time posts for research in clinical medicine. Above all, the scores of men who went from the Institute's laboratories to teaching and research posts in schools of medicine, veterinary medicine, and agriculture carried with them a spirit of scientific investigation that helped to raise standards everywhere in the nation, and to win for research its present high place in the esteem of the American people.

By the middle of the twentieth century, the ideals of research which The Rockefeller Institute and a few of the medical schools had pioneered were well established throughout the United States. The Institute no longer stood almost alone as a fully equipped and expertly manned center of investigation in medicine and related fields of biology. Scores of institutions, in all parts of the country, were rivaling it in one or another of its fields of research, and were competing with it for talented leaders and for the best young recruits. Yet the founders of the Institute would have seen this too as a fulfillment of their hopes, for it meant success in national leadership as well as in research and the training of investigators; in one of his earliest memoranda to John D. Rockefeller, Sr., F. T. Gates insisted that even if the proposed institute should fail to discover anything, the mere fact of its existence would lead to other efforts of the same kind, until research in America should be conducted on so grand a scale that out of the multitude of workers rewards would abundantly flow.[13]

All three men who in 1897 first contemplated the creation of a medical research institute lived to see much of its accomplishment. Gates presided over its Board of Trustees until his death in 1929, in his later years still avowing that "The Rockefeller Institute is the most interesting thing in the world."[14] The elder Rockefeller, living beyond the span of Flexner's directorship, witnessed, when Flexner retired, a world-wide display of respect and regard for the Institute as well as for its first distinguished leader. Rockefeller, Jr., who succeeded Gates as president of the Board of Trustees, served the Institute through nearly all of its first half century. Retiring in 1954, he watched with approval the continuing productivity of the Institute and the beginning of a new era under the chairmanship of his son David. When in 1959 the first student Fellows were graduated, the Trustees took the occasion to express their appreciation of his services by conferring upon him, as the first honorary alumnus of The Rockefeller Institute, the degree of Doctor of Laws.

At mid-century the Trustees found it necessary to review the Institute's pattern of organization, established to meet the needs of earlier decades. The system of distinct laboratories, each devoted to the work of an eminent investigator aided by his personal associates, had sometimes led to cloistral exclusiveness of these groups.[15] Although, in many cases, the system had been freed of its constraints by generous Members determined to encourage independent thinking on the part of their juniors, the structure remained to hamper, in some degree, individual initiative and administrative experimentation. The Institute's cherished protection of its investigators from academic duties and pressures, essential at a time when the colleges and universities did not understand that scientists need to work without distraction, now tended, many of the Trustees thought, to intellectual isolation and inbreeding. The majority of medical schools, meanwhile, had learned not merely to permit, but actually to encourage, research by their teachers, and full-time research posts were therefore no longer incomparably attractive in comparison with professorships. Flexner had felt that a research institute held a great advantage, through its ability to utilize men of foreign birth and natives of exceptional type, not suited to teaching, but even this advantage diminished as the increasingly sophisticated universities provided research professorships for men who could not or would not teach. The once distinctive character of the Institute was disappearing; its laboratories and hospital were, to an increasing extent, being manned by investigators trained in its own environment, and the recruitment of new minds at post-doctoral level only did not sufficiently freshen the atmosphere with youthful enthusiasm. Such were the reflections that guided the Trustees as the time approached when a new head of the Institute must be chosen.

John D. Rockefeller's benefaction had been successful, but in a growing nation, in an advancing culture, success is never final. "Have the past struggles succeeded?" cried Walt Whitman, spokesman of America's progress:

> What has succeeded? yourself? your nation? Nature?
> Now understand me well — it is provided in the essence
> of things that from any fruition of success, no
> matter what, shall come forth something to make a
> greater struggle necessary.

The time had come, in the opinion of the Trustees, for The Rockefeller Institute to put its great resources of intellect, experience in research, equipment, and endowment at the service of the new generation of young men coming from the colleges to begin graduate studies, prepared, as no young men of their age had been prepared fifty or sixty years before, to profit by the leadership of experienced scientists. Realizing that the first requirement for so radical a step was a bold leader, they appointed one of their Board of Scientific Directors, Detlev Wulf Bronk (then president of the Johns Hopkins University), to be president of The Rockefeller Institute, and charged him with the task of transforming it into a university faculty of science. In his Foreword to this book, President Bronk has set forth the aims and hopes of the new era; its progress he will in time narrate. For The Rockefeller Institute, as for every living enterprise of the human intellect, what is past is prologue.

Acknowledgments

✷

Notes on the Text

✷

Appendixes

✷

Major Documentary Sources

✷

Index

Acknowledgments

THOSE WHO HAVE given information and advice useful in the preparation of this book are far too numerous to name individually. Among them are practically all senior members of the scientific and administrative staffs of The Rockefeller Institute, as well as many persons outside its walls. In particular, the author can never sufficiently thank those of the Institute's scientists to whom he submitted passages dealing with their own researches. To condense the efforts and hopes of a scientist's lifetime into a few printed pages is a presumptuous task; to read such an account of one's own work, pieced together by a newcomer to the Institute, must often have been an ordeal; yet the subjects of these brief narratives of research have answered the historian's call for help with uniform courtesy and patience.

To certain collaborators special thanks are due. John B. Blake, now Chief, History of Medicine Division, National Library of Medicine, was at the Institute in 1955–1957 as assistant to the historian, and has since acted as special consultant. He greatly helped to get the work under way by accurately compiling lists of the Institute's workers, running down special sources, and generally contributing his knowledge of American history and experience as a trained historian of medicine and public health. He has also read and most helpfully criticized the manuscript.

Rufus Cole, the late T. M. Rivers, and F. L. Horsfall, Jr., successively directors of the Hospital of The Rockefeller Institute, have read and helped to revise the chapters dealing with that part of the Institute. Carl TenBroeck, Richard E. Shope, and the late Louis Kunkel similarly reviewed the chapters dealing with the Princeton laboratories. Peyton Rous, Member Emeritus of the Institute, has read the manuscript, contributing from his long editorial experience many helpful suggestions. To Miss Esther Judkins, Librarian, and her staff, and to Miss Margaret Wuest of the Business Manager's office, cordial thanks are due for their always helpful response to endless requests for help in searching the archives and pertinent literature. The friendly assistance of many other persons within the Institute and outside it has been acknowledged in the footnotes.

NOTES ON THE TEXT

CHAPTER ONE

The Background and the Need

1   James Bryce, *The American Commonwealth,* London, Macmillan and Company, 1888, Vol. III, p. 431.

2   Samuel E. Morison and Henry S. Commager, *The Growth of the American Republic,* New York, Oxford University Press, 4th ed., revised, 1950, Vol. II, p. 355.

3   Wilson G. Smillie, *Public Health, Its Promise for the Future,* New York, The Macmillan Company, 1955, p. 421.

4   Personal communications from the late George W. Goler and the late Charles W. Dodge.

5   William H. Welch, "Twenty-fifth Anniversary of the Johns Hopkins Hospital, 1889–1914," in *Papers and Addresses of William H. Welch,* Baltimore, Johns Hopkins Press, 1920, Vol. III, p. 21.

6   For a revelation of the inadequacy of American medical education at that time see Abraham Flexner, *Medical Education in the United States and Canada,* New York, Carnegie Foundation for the Advancement of Teaching, 1910.

7   William Osler, "The fixed period," in *Aequanimitas, with Other Addresses,* London, H. K. Lewis and Company, Ltd., 2nd ed., 1925, p. 400.

8   Richard H. Shryock, "Factors influencing medical research in the United States, 1800–1900," *Bulletin of the Society for Medical History,* Vol. 5, pp. 1–18, 1942.

9   Franklin P. Mall, cited by Florence R. Sabin in *Franklin Paine Mall; The Story of a Mind,* Baltimore, Johns Hopkins Press, 1934, pp. 28–29.

10   Lillian E. Prudden, ed., *Biographical Sketches and Letters of T. Mitchell Prudden, M.D.,* New Haven, Yale University Press, 1927, p. 32.

11   Ms. note by Simon Flexner in Welch Papers.

12   Charles A. Beard and Mary R. Beard, *The Rise of American Civilization,* New York, The Macmillan Company, 1927, Vol. II, pp. 175–177.

13   Frederick T. Gates, address at dinner for Simon Flexner, October 16, 1914, files of The Rockefeller Institute.

14   Andrew Carnegie, "The gospel of wealth," in *The Gospel of Wealth and Other Timely Essays,* Garden City, New York, Doubleday, Doran and Company, 1933, p. 5.

15   Carnegie's essay was first printed under the title "Wealth" in the *North American Review,* June 1889, with a supplement in the December 1889 number of the same magazine. William E. Gladstone reprinted it in England with the title "The gospel of wealth." It is most conveniently found in the volume of Carnegie's collected works cited in the previous note.

16   William E. Gladstone, "Mr. Carnegie's 'gospel of wealth,' a review and a recommendation," *Nineteenth Century,* Nov. 1890; reprinted in *Miscellaneous*

(*Notes on Chapter One, continued*)

Writings of Andrew Carnegie, edited by Burton J. Hendrick, Garden City, New York, Doubleday, Doran and Company, 1933, Vol. II, pp. 125–155.

17 Burton J. Hendrick, *Life of Andrew Carnegie,* Garden City, New York, Doubleday, Doran and Company, 1932, Vol. I, p. 349.

18 Franklin McVeagh, quoted in Raphael Pumpelly, *My Reminiscences,* New York, Henry Holt and Company, 1918, Vol. II, p. 659.

19 Allan Nevins, *Study in Power: John D. Rockefeller, Industrialist and Philanthropist,* New York, Charles Scribner's Sons, 1953. Much of the present account is derived from this thoughtful biography.

20 *Ibid.,* p. 166. This book is the best source of information about Gates, of whom there is no biography. Selections from a manuscript autobiography were published in *American Heritage,* Vol. 6, No. 3, pp. 65–86, 1955.

21 John D. Rockefeller, *Random Reminiscences of Men and Events,* New York, Doubleday, Page and Company, 1909 (2nd ed., Garden City, New York, Doubleday, Doran and Company, 1937).

22 In a letter written in 1915 at the request of Starr J. Murphy, printed in full in Appendix I.

23 James G. Mumford, *A Doctor's Table Talk,* Boston, Houghton Mifflin Company, 1912, pp. 254–255. For "Blair" read William Sydney Thayer (1864–1932); for "Superbus," William Osler; for "Liverpool," Baltimore.

24 Elon Obed Huntington, 1869–1926, B.S., Minnesota, 1892; M.D., Columbia, 1896; entered the U.S. Navy Medical Corps in 1898 and served in the Spanish-American War and the Philippine insurrection, retiring in 1910 with the rank of lieutenant commander. (*The Huntington Family in America,* Hartford, Connecticut, 1915; also records of the American Medical Association.)

25 Gates to Starr J. Murphy, Dec. 31, 1915 (Appendix I).

26 A search in the Rockefeller files in 1956 failed to discover the memorandum.

27 Raymond B. Fosdick, *John D. Rockefeller, Jr., a Portrait,* New York, Harper and Brothers, 1956, pp. 111–112.

28 G. H. F. Nuttall to Starr J. Murphy, Jan. 21, 1901, Rockefeller Institute files.

29 Gates to Starr J. Murphy, Dec. 31, 1915 (Appendix I). Unfortunately neither the Harvard archives nor the Rockefeller files have yielded any further documentary evidence of these negotiations.

30 Seth Low to Welch, Aug. 8, 1900, Welch Papers; Welch to Low, Nov. 5, 1900, copy in Rockefeller Institute files. Low to Prudden, in Lillian E. Prudden, ed., *op. cit.* (note 10 above), pp. 280–281.

31 Quoted in New York *Sun,* June 3, 1901.

32 John B. Blake, "Scientific institutions since the Renaissance: Their role in medical research," *Proceedings of the American Philosophical Society,* Vol. 101, pp. 31–62, 1957.

CHAPTER TWO

The Rockefeller Institute
Is Founded

1 L. Emmett Holt, memorandum in Rockefeller Institute files (copy in Welch Papers).

2 John D. Rockefeller, Jr., personal conversation, Nov. 1956. In 1903 Harold F. McCormick established at Chicago the John Rockefeller McCormick Memorial Institute for Infectious Diseases in memory of his eldest son. At that time the story of the boy's death and its effect upon his grandfather got into the New York newspapers (see the *Herald*, Feb. 5, 22, 1903; *Times*, Dec. 10, 1905; *Herald*, May 12, 1906). Most of the articles erroneously implied that this domestic grief was the primary cause of Rockefeller's interest in medical research and consequently of the foundation of The Rockefeller Institute as well as of the McCormick Memorial. These reports were so badly garbled that in one or another of them even the sex of the child and the cause of death were misstated. Finally in 1907 a spokesman for the family set the matter straight (New York *Herald*, Oct. 20) in accord with Rockefeller, Jr.'s recollection as cited in the text. After this the story seems to have been forgotten, both by the public and by those who have written about the history of The Rockefeller Institute.

3 Robert L. Duffus and L. Emmett Holt, Jr., *L. Emmett Holt, Pioneer of a Children's Century*, New York, D. Appleton–Century Company, 1940.

4 Memoirs of Herter are few and inadequate. See *Biochemical Journal*, Vol. 5, xxi–xxxi, 1910–1911; also R. L. Duffus and L. E. Holt, Jr., *op. cit.*, pp. 112–113. Something of Herter's intellectual scope is indicated by his friendships — with Paul Ehrlich and Jacques Loeb, for example, and with the Swiss psychiatrist August Forel, after whom he named one of his sons. Herter loved the fine arts, and his home was full of good talk and music. One of Simon Flexner's friends has spoken of Herter's broadening influence upon Flexner, who for all his achievements was bent only upon science until he and Herter became friends (Peyton Rous, personal communication). Mrs. Herter (Susan Dows), who equaled her husband in mental and social gifts, shared his interest and his devotion to the Institute and friendship with Simon Flexner.

5 Memorandum by Holt, March 9, 1921, Rockefeller Institute files.

6 Christian A. Herter to Welch, March 15, 1901 (copy in Welch Papers, endorsed "Original in file of John D. Rockefeller, Jr.").

7 Donald Fleming, *William H. Welch and the Rise of Modern Medicine*, Boston, Little, Brown and Company, 1954, p. 200. For a full biography see Simon Flexner and James T. Flexner, *William Henry Welch and the Heroic Age of American Medicine*, New York, Viking Press, 1941.

8 C.-E. A. Winslow, *The Life of Herman M. Biggs, M.D., D.Sc., LL.D., Physician and Statesman of the Public Health*, Philadelphia, Lea and Febiger, 1929.

(Notes on Chapter Two, continued)

9 Lillian E. Prudden, ed., *Biographical Sketches and Letters of T. Mitchell Prudden, M.D.*, New Haven, Yale University Press, 1927. Ludvig Hektoen, "Biographical memoir of Theophil Mitchell Prudden, 1849–1924," *Biographical Memoirs of the National Academy of Sciences,* Vol. 12, pp. 73–98, 1928. Alfred E. Cohn, *No Retreat from Reason and Other Essays,* New York, Harcourt, Brace and Company, 1948, p. 252.

10 Among numerous memoirs excellent ones are those of W. Bulloch, *Journal of Pathology and Bacteriology,* Vol. 40, pp. 621–635, 1935; Hans Zinsser, *Biographical Memoirs of the National Academy of Sciences,* Vol. 17, pp. 261–303, 1936; and Paul F. Clark, *Journal of the History of Medicine and Allied Sciences,* Vol. 14, pp. 496–514, 1959.

11 Peyton Rous, "Simon Flexner, 1863–1946," *Obituary Notices of Fellows of the Royal Society,* Vol. 6, pp. 409–445, London, 1949.

12 Herter to Welch, March 15, 1901, Welch Papers.

13 Welch to Herter, March 31, 1901, Welch Papers.

14 Rockefeller, Jr., to Holt, April 29, 1901 (copy in Prudden, ms. History).

15 Gates to Starr J. Murphy, Dec. 31, 1915, Appendix I.

16 Cf. page 26.

17 Herter to Welch, March 15, 1901; Welch to Theobald Smith, May 5, 1901, Welch Papers.

18 John D. Rockefeller, Jr., personal conversation, Nov. 1956.

19 Alfred A. Cohn, *op. cit.* (note 9 above), pp. 229, 230. Dr. Cohn's rhetorical question should have been addressed not to Nicholas Murray Butler but to Seth Low, who was President of Columbia University until just after The Rockefeller Institute was incorporated (1901).

20 Raymond B. Fosdick, *John D. Rockefeller, Jr., A Portrait,* New York, Harper and Brothers, 1956, p. 116.

21 Appendix I.

22 Theobald Smith to Welch, Feb. 11, 1902, Minutes of Board of Directors, March 8, 1902 (copy in Welch Papers).

23 Flexner to Welch, April 8, 1902, entered in Minutes, April 12, 1902 (copy in Welch Papers).

24 Minutes (Exec. Comm.), Jan. 9, 1907; personal communication from Eugene L. Opie.

25 A Report on the Developments of the First Twenty Years of The Rockefeller Institute and an Outlook for Future Growth, presented at the meeting of the Board of Scientific Directors, April 17, 1926, Rockefeller Institute files.

26 "The memoirs of Frederick T. Gates," *American Heritage,* Vol. 6, No. 3, pp. 65–86, 1955.

27 Flexner, memorandum in Welch Papers.

28 Minutes, April 18, 1914. Flexner's memory was at fault when he stated (*William Henry Welch and the Heroic Age of American Medicine,* p. 283) that grants-in-aid were given for the last time in 1903.

29 Richard H. Shryock, *American Medical Research Past and Present,* New York, Commonwealth Fund, 1947. The Rockefeller Institute's only important predecessor as a source of grants for medical research was a National Board of Health set up by Congress in 1879, which spent $30,000 in grants in its three years of operation. The American Medical Association's committee on research did not make its first grant until 1903.

30 See, for example, Sophie D. Aberle and George W. Corner, *Twenty-Five Years of Sex Research,* Philadelphia, W. B. Saunders Company, 1953.

31 Those whose achievements can be recognized from biographical reference works, from their own publications, and from other public records are: Clara Meltzer Auer, V. H. Bassett, W. R. Brinkerhoff, G. A. Charlton, C. W. Duval, H. C. Ernst, W. W. Ford, F. P. Gay, Preston Kyes, W. G. McCallum, E. L. Opie, R. G. Perkins, L. F. Rettger, A. N. Richards, William Salant, Alonzo Taylor, E. E. Tyzzer, Anna W. Williams, Martha Wollstein.

32 Board of Health of the City of New York, Annual Report for 1901, published Jan. 1902.

33 Welch to Rockefeller, Jr., Jan. 13, 1902, Welch Papers.

34 Theobald Smith to Welch, Feb. 11, 1902, Welch Papers.

35 Prudden to Holt, March 6, 1902, Prudden's letter book, at The Rockefeller Institute.

36 Simon Flexner and James T. Flexner, *op. cit.* (note 7 above).

37 This idea of a "Third Division" of the Institute was a pet notion of Prudden. He had suggested such a program to Seth Low as early as 1900. He brought it up in discussion by the Directors several times and in 1914 drew up a fairly definite plan for it; but it never materialized.

38 Holt to Prudden, May 14, 1902, Prudden's letter book, at The Rockefeller Institute.

39 Flexner to Welch, undated draft of letter, spring of 1902, in Flexner Papers.

40 It is confirmed by the following letters, all in the Welch Papers: Flexner to Welch, June 16; Holt to Welch, June 20; Welch to Rockefeller, Jr., June 25, 1902.

41 Prudden to Welch, Jan. 19, 1902, Rockefeller Institute files.

42 Its history is sketched in Appendix II.

43 Lewellys F. Barker to Welch, June 20, 1903, Welch Papers.

CHAPTER THREE

The Laboratories Are Organized

1   Alan M. Chesney, *The Johns Hopkins Hospital and the Johns Hopkins University School of Medicine, a Chronicle,* Baltimore, Johns Hopkins Press, 1958, Vol. II, p. 407 (note).

2   Simon Flexner and James T. Flexner, *William Henry Welch and the Heroic Age of American Medicine,* New York, Viking Press, 1941, p. 285.

3   John B. Blake, "Scientific institutions since the Renaissance; Their role in medical research," *Proceedings of the American Philosophical Society,* Vol. 101, pp. 31–62, 1957.

4   Flexner to Herter, Nov. 21, 1903, Rockefeller Institute files.

5   Prudden, ms. History; Eugene L. Opie, ms. Reminiscences, Rockefeller Institute files.

6   Rockefeller, Jr. to Holt, May 26, 1908, entered in Minutes, May 30, 1908.

7   Minutes, April 11, 1908.

8   Simon Flexner, "Concerning a serum-therapy for experimental infection with *Diplococcus intracellularis,*" *Journal of Experimental Medicine,* Vol. 9, pp. 168–185, 1907.

9   Wade W. Oliver, *The Man Who Lived for Tomorrow, A Biography of William Hallock Park,* New York, E. P. Dutton Company, 1941, pp. 299–304.

10   Simon Flexner and James T. Flexner, *op. cit.* (note 2 above), pp. 242–250; note 6 above.

11   Oswald H. Robertson, "Presentation of the Kober Medal to Peyton Rous," *Transactions of the Association of American Physicians,* Vol. 66, pp. 20–26, 1953.

12   *The Rockefeller Institute for Medical Research; Addresses Delivered at the Opening of the Laboratories in New York City, May 11, 1906,* pamphlet, 1907; also published in *Studies from The Rockefeller Institute,* Vol. 6, pp. 1–44, 1907.

13   As of 1960 these three floors have been altered only by the installation of a few new partitions in the larger rooms and new furniture and lights.

14   Minutes, June 13, 1907; see also Simon Flexner, "The Rockefeller Institute for Medical Research," in *Forschungsinstitut, ihre Geschichte, Organisation und Ziele,* edited by L. Brauer, A. Mendelssohn-Bartholdy, and Adolph Meyer, Hamburg, Paul Hartung Verlag, 1930, Vol. II, p. 464.

15   Minutes, June 9, Oct. 13, 1906; Jan. 12, 1907.

16   Welch to Holt, Nov. 26, 1906, Welch Papers.

17   Donald Fleming, *William H. Welch and the Rise of Modern Medicine,* Boston, Little, Brown and Company, 1954, pp. 155–156.

18   Prudden to Holt, June 3, 1910; Herman M. Biggs to Holt, June 2, 1910, Rockefeller Institute files.

19 Minutes, Oct. 15, 1910.

20 Prudden, ms. History, Rockefeller Institute files.

21 Raymond B. Fosdick, *John D. Rockefeller, Jr., A Portrait*, New York, Harper and Brothers, 1956, p. 115.

22 Minutes (Exec. Comm.), Nov. 14, 1906; Dec. 16, 1908.

23 Minutes, April 13, 1907.

24 Minutes (Exec. Comm.), Nov. 1, Dec. 11, 1906.

25 Osler to Gates, April 26, 1907; Gates to Holt, May 28, 1907; Welch to Gates about Oct. 12, 1907 (copies in Welch Papers); Simon Flexner and James T. Flexner, *op. cit.* (note 2 above), pp. 286–288.

26 Fosdick, Raymond B., *The Story of The Rockefeller Foundation*, New York, Harper and Brothers, 1952.

27 Herter, memorandum of conversation with Charles W. Eliot, Sept. 8, 1907, Rockefeller Institute files.

28 Minutes, June 13, Oct. 12, 1907.

29 Flexner to Susan Dows Herter, Aug. 3, 1913, Rockefeller Institute files.

30 Albert H. Ebeling, personal communication.

31 Robert Soupault, *Alexis Carrel, 1873–1944*, Paris, Librairie Plon, 1952, pp. 27–34.

32 Albert Fischer, "Alexis Carrel as I knew him," *Bibliothek for Laeger*, Copenhagen, Vol. 145, pp. 17–25, 1953.

33 Albert H. Ebeling (personal communication) states from memory of a conversation with Carrel that the popliteal vein was used, not the femoral, as stated by Mosenthal (next note). Circulatory difficulty from a possible subsequent occlusion would be much greater if the femoral vein were used.

34 Herman O. Mosenthal, "Transfusion as a cure for melena neonatorum," *Journal of the American Medical Association*, Vol. 54, p. 1613, May 14, 1910. Transfusion of very young infants is now done more or less readily by injection of blood into a vein through a needle.

35 John D. Rockefeller, *Random Reminiscences of Men and Events*, New York, Doubleday, Page and Company, 1909, pp. 150–152.

36 W. J. V. Osterhout, "Jacques Loeb," *Journal of General Physiology*, Vol. 8, pp. ix–lix, 1928.

37 Jacques Loeb to Herter, Jan. 3, 1902, by courtesy of Robert F. Loeb.

38 Theobald Smith to Flexner, Nov. 23, 1909, Rockefeller Institute files.

39 Loeb to Flexner about Dec. 8, 1909, reproduced in facsimile, without date, *Journal of General Physiology*, Vol. 8, pp. xvii–xix, 1928; the original letter has not been found in The Rockefeller Institute files nor in the Flexner Papers.

40 *New York Times*, March 12; New York *Journal*, April 21, 1911.

(Notes on Chapter Three, continued)

41 This account of Landsteiner's work on poliomyelitis owes much to an unpublished biography of Landsteiner by the late George M. Mackenzie (see Chapter 8, note 16).

42 Lloyd G. Stevenson, "Religious elements in the background of the British antivivisection movement," *Yale Journal of Biology and Medicine,* Vol. 29, pp. 125–157, 1956.

43 New York *Herald,* Oct. 20, 1907.

44 *Collier's Weekly,* April 4, 1908.

45 *Collier's Weekly,* June 3, 1911.

46 *New York Times,* Feb. 15, 1908.

47 *Life,* New York, Aug. 11, 1910.

48 *Collier's Weekly,* March 14, April 25, 1908.

49 Minutes, April 11, Oct. 10, 1908.

50 New York *American,* June 8, 1908.

51 New York *Herald,* Dec. 27, 28, 1909; Jan. 10, 1910.

52 *New York Times,* Jan. 17, Feb. 3, 1910.

CHAPTER FOUR

The Hospital in Its Early Years

1   Flexner to Herter, Jan. 6, 1902, Rockefeller Institute files.

2   Flexner to Welch, April 8, 1902, entered in Minutes, April 12, 1902.

3   Minutes, May 10, 1902.

4   The nature of Herter's illness, if it was ever definitely diagnosed, was not recorded. It seems to have been myasthenia gravis.

5   Herter to Flexner, Dec. 2, 1902, Flexner Papers.

6   Welch to Herter, Sept. 6, 1902, Welch Papers; Flexner to Herter, Sept. 24, 1906, Rockefeller Institute files.

7   See page 65.

8   Rockefeller, Jr., to Holt, Feb. 28, 1907, entered in Minutes, April 13, 1907.

9   Minutes, June 13, 1907.

10 Rockefeller, Jr., to Holt, May 26, 1908, entered in Minutes, May 30, 1908.

11 Flexner to Herter, undated letter, early 1908; Flexner to Herter, Aug. 22, 1908, Rockefeller Institute files.

12 Minutes, Oct. 10, Nov. 28, 1908.

13 For the early history of the full-time plan see Florence R. Sabin, *Franklin Paine Mall; The Story of a Mind,* Baltimore, Johns Hopkins Press, 1934; Donald Fleming, *William H. Welch and the Rise of Modern Medicine,* Boston, Little, Brown and Company, 1954; Simon Flexner and James T. Flexner, *William Henry Welch and the Heroic Age of American Medicine,* New York, Viking Press, 1941.

14 Memorandum to the Board of Directors, Dec. 1908, Rockefeller Institute files.

15 Minutes, Jan. 27, 1909.

16 Rockefeller, Jr., to Board of Directors, Feb. 26, 1909, entered in Minutes (Exec. Comm.), March 4, 1909.

17 Minutes (Building Committee), May 28, 1909; Jan. 8, 1910.

18 Prudden, ms. History, Rockefeller Institute files.

19 The elaborate hydrotherapeutic equipment, which the hospital staff found more or less superfluous, was installed on the advice of Simon Baruch of New York, an enthusiast on hydrotherapy; the diet kitchen represented the ideas of L. Emmett Holt, who as a pediatrician was deeply interested in special diets (personal communication from Rufus Cole). Herter also, if he had lived, would no doubt have called for studies on disorders of metabolism requiring carefully computed diets. Actually, the diet kitchen was not used; special diets were planned and prepared, even after the study of diabetes was undertaken, by the nursing staff under guidance of the house physicians.

20 Similar and stronger fears, thirty years earlier, had dictated the erection at the Johns Hopkins Hospital of a separate ward for infectious diseases which, the designer stated, could be burned down in case it became a source of pollution. Nowadays, at the middle of the twentieth century, many general hospitals put patients with acute infectious diseases in rooms in the same corridors with general medical cases.

21 Jerome D. Greene to Herbert S. Gasser, Feb. 20, 1948, Rockefeller Institute files.

22 *New York Times,* Oct. 18, 1910.

23 New York *Sun,* Oct. 18, 1910.

24 Minutes, Jan. 21, 1911.

25 Information from Dr. Reginald M. Archibald of The Rockefeller Institute Hospital. A few patients dwarfed by other causes (achondroplasia, pituitary deficiency) were also admitted in the first year or two.

26 "Mortality from each cause: United States, 1955–57," in *Vital Statistics — Special Reports. National Summaries,* Vol. 50, No. 1, Jan. 9, 1959, U.S. Public Health Service.

27 Minutes, May 29, Oct. 9, 1909.

28 Rufus Cole to Flexner, Oct. 30, 1911, Rockefeller Institute files.

29 Gates to Flexner, Jan. 4, 1911; Gates to Rockefeller, Sr., June 1, 1916, Rockefeller Institute files.

(*Notes on Chapter Four, continued*)

30   G. Canby Robinson, *Adventures in Medical Education*, Cambridge, Mass., Harvard University Press, 1957, p. 95.

31   Cole to Flexner, Oct. 30, 1911, Flexner Papers.

CHAPTER FIVE

The Rising Tide of Research

1   Peyton Rous, "Acceptance of the Kober Medal for 1953," *Transactions of the Association of American Physicians*, Vol. 66, pp. 27–30, 1953.

2   For a fuller account of the significance of Rous's findings, see Charles Oberling, *The Riddle of Cancer*, translated by W. H. Woglom, New Haven, Yale University Press, 1944, and Isaac Berenblum, *Man Against Cancer, The Story of Cancer Research*, Baltimore, Johns Hopkins Press, 1952.

3   Gustav Eckstein, *Noguchi*, New York, Harper and Brothers, 1931. For a more recent brief account of Noguchi's career, see Paul F. Clark, "Hideyo Noguchi, 1876–1928," *Bulletin of the History of Medicine*, Vol. 33, pp. 1–20, 1959.

4   Peyton Rous, speech at dinner for Simon Flexner given by the staff of The Rockefeller Institute, Oct. 16, 1914, Rockefeller Institute files.

5   Schaudinn, discoverer of the organism, called it *Spirochaeta pallida*, but subsequently biologists divided the spirochetes into two genera, *Spirochaeta* and *Treponema*, classing the germ of syphilis in the latter genus.

6   Clara C. Kast and John A. Kolmer, "Concerning the cultivation of *Spirocheta pallida*," *American Journal of Syphilis*, Vol. 13, pp. 419–453, 1929.

7   Peyton Rous, personal communication.

8   P. A. T. Levene, "The chemical individuality of tissue elements and its biological significance," *Journal of the American Chemical Society*, Vol. 39, pp. 828–836, 1917.

9   Donald D. Van Slyke and Walter A. Jacobs, "Biographical memoir of Phoebus Aaron Theodor Levene, 1869–1940," *Biographical Memoirs of the National Academy of Sciences*, Vol. 23, No. 4, pp. 75–126, 1945.

10   Emil Abderhalden to Flexner, Aug. 13, 1910, Flexner Papers.

11   Alexander Todd, "Synthesis in the study of nucleotides," *Science*, Vol. 127, pp. 789–792, 1958.

12   William H. Howell, "Biographical memoir, Samuel James Meltzer, 1851–1920," *Memoirs of the National Academy of Sciences*, Vol. 21, No. 9, 1926.

13   W. J. V. Osterhout has thoughtfully reviewed Loeb's character and temperament as well as his scientific achievement in his article "Jacques Loeb," *Journal of*

General Physiology, Vol. 8, pp. ix–lix, 1928. For a critical examination of some of his theories, see Henry E. Armstrong, "A chemist's homage to the work of a biologist," *ibid.,* pp. 653–670. See also Leonard Loeb, "Jacques Loeb; Recollections of his career as a scientist," *Rockefeller Institute Quarterly,* Vol. 3, No. 3, pp. 1–4, 6, 1959. The quotation is from Loeb's *Mechanistic Conception of Life,* University of Chicago Press, 1912, p. 31.

14 Simon Flexner, "Alexis Carrel (1873–1944)," in *Year Book of the American Philosophical Society,* Philadelphia, 1944, pp. 344–349.

15 A. Jolly, "A propos des communications de MM. Alexis Carrel et Montrose T. Burrows sur la 'culture des tissus,'" *Comptes rendus de la Société de Biologie de Paris,* Vol. 69, p. 473, 1910.

16 Philadelphia *Public Ledger,* April 24, 1921, reporting an address by Carrel at the American Philosophical Society.

17 A. H. Ebeling, personal communication. See also his article, "Dr. Carrel's immortal chicken heart," *Scientific American,* Vol. 95, and Raymond Parker, *Methods of Tissue Culture,* New York, Hoeber, 2nd ed., 1950, p. 4.

18 R. L. Duffus and L. Emmett Holt, Jr., *L. Emmett Holt, Pioneer of a Children's Century,* D. Appleton–Century Company, New York, 1940, p. 204.

CHAPTER SIX

War and Peace

1 Prudden, ms. History; Henry James to Prudden, March 13, 1913, Rockefeller Institute files.

2 Minutes, Oct. 17, 1914.

3 Minutes, April 12, May 10, 1902.

4 Minutes (Exec. Comm.), April 30, 1914.

5 Simon Flexner and James T. Flexner, *William Henry Welch and the Heroic Age of American Medicine,* New York, Viking Press, 1941, p. 295.

6 Minutes, Jan. 15, 1916.

7 "Letter from Dr. Theobald Smith," *Journal of Bacteriology,* Vol. 27, pp. 19–20, 1934.

8 William H. Howell, "Biographical memoir, Samuel James Meltzer, 1851–1920," *Memoirs of the National Academy of Sciences,* Vol. 21, No. 9, 1926.

9 Jacques Loeb, "Biology and war," *Science,* Vol. 45, pp. 73–77, 1917.

10 Minutes, April 17, 1915.

11 Minutes (Exec. Comm.), March 25, 1915.

12 For the story of the hospital at Compiègne, see Robert Soupault, *Alexis Carrel, 1873–1924,* Paris, Librairie Plon, 1952, pp. 107–142.

(Notes on Chapter Six, continued)

13   *The War Demonstration Hospital,* pamphlet, The Rockefeller Institute for Medical Research, New York, 1917.

14   **Lt. Col. F. W. Weed,** *Medical Department of the U.S. Army in the World War,* Vol. 5, *Military Hospitals in the United States,* Washington, Government Printing Office, 1923, p. 818.

15   A list of all staff members who held commissions is given in *The Rockefeller Institute for Medical Research: History, Organization and Equipment,* New York, The Rockefeller Institute, 1919.

16   Prudden to Henry James, Oct. 28, 1918, in Lillian E. Prudden, ed., *Biographical Sketches and Letters of T. Mitchell Prudden, M.D.,* New Haven, Yale University Press, 1927, pp. 166–169.

17   The flagpole remained until 1957, a conspicuous reminder of World War I. The last relic of the War Demonstration Hospital was a small frame building east of the 64th Street gate, demolished early in 1958. For many years it sheltered the headquarters of the children's gardens operated, with the Institute's permission, by the New York Plant and Flower Guild.

18   Frederick Lamont Gates was the eldest son of Frederick Taylor Gates, President of the Board of Trustees of the Institute.

19   The account of the Institute's war activities up to this point is based on Prudden's ms. History; on a brief report in *The Rockefeller Institute for Medical Research: History, Organization and Equipment,* New York, 1919, pp. 26–30; on an unpublished report to members of the Corporation on the war work of the Institute, Oct. 1919 (Rockefeller Institute files); and on numerous entries in the Minutes, 1914–1919; see also "War work of the Rockefeller Institute for Medical Research, New York," *Military Surgeon,* Vol. 47, pp. 491–512, 1920.

20   Minutes (Exec. Comm.), June 21, 1919.

21   Oswald H. Robertson, "Presentation of the Kober Medal to Peyton Rous," *Transactions of the Association of American Physicians,* Vol. 66, pp. 20–26, 1953.

22   Minutes, Oct. 8, 1919.

23   Minutes, June 5, 1920; personal communication, Edric B. Smith.

24   Pages 10–14.

25   Abraham Flexner, *Medical Education; A Comparative Study,* New York, Macmillan and Company, 1925.

CHAPTER SEVEN

Men and Molecules

1 P. A. T. Levene to Flexner, Feb. 6, 1919, Flexner Papers.

2 Speech at dinner for Simon Flexner, Oct. 16, 1914, Rockefeller Institute files.

3 John H. Northrop, "Jacques Loeb — 1859 to 1924," *Industrial and Engineering Chemistry,* Vol. 16, p. 318, 1924.

4 William J. Robbins, "The influence of Jacques Loeb on the development of plant tissue culture," *Bulletin du Jardin Botanique de l'Etat,* Brussels, Vol. 27, pp. 189–197, 1957.

5 Alexis Carrel to Flexner, Aug. 12, 1935, Flexner Papers.

6 Raymond B. Fosdick, *John D. Rockefeller, Jr., A Portrait,* New York, Harper and Brothers, 1956, p. 122.

7 Peyton Rous, "Simon Flexner, 1863–1946," *Obituary Notices of Fellows of the Royal Society,* Vol. 6, pp. 424–425, London, 1949.

8 A Report on the Developments of the First Twenty Years of The Rockefeller Institute and an Outlook for Future Growth, presented at the meeting of the Board of Scientific Directors, April 17, 1926, Rockefeller Institute files.

9 P. A. T. Levene to Flexner, undated (1909), Flexner Papers.

10 Charles I. Campbell, "Maintenance and construction of our buildings and grounds," *Rockefeller Institute Quarterly,* Vol. 1, No. 4, Dec. 1957.

11 William H. Welch, speech at 20th Anniversary Dinner of the Institute, Rockefeller Institute files.

12 Frederick Lamont Gates to P. K. Olitsky, July 7, 1926, files of Dr. Olitsky.

13 Levene to Flexner, Feb. 6, 1919, Flexner Papers.

14 Peyton Rous, personal communication.

15 Undated card, about Jan. 1917, Flexner Papers (filed under *Davis*). For Osler's use of this pen name, see Harvey Cushing, *The Life of Sir William Osler,* Oxford, Clarendon Press, 1925, Vol. I, pp. 239–241.

16 Hans Zinsser, *As I Remember Him, The Biography of R. S.,* Boston, Little, Brown and Company, 1940, pp. 110–111.

17 Gates to Flexner, Jan. 6, 1908, Flexner Papers.

18 New York *Herald Tribune,* Jan. 17, 1930.

19 The University of Louisville School of Medicine, reorganized after the publication of Abraham Flexner's report, *Medical Education in the United States and Canada* (New York, Carnegie Foundation for the Advancement of Teaching, 1910), has long since taken its place among the fully accredited Class A medical schools.

(Notes on Chapter Seven, continued)

20   (Paul de Kruif) Anonymous article "Medicine," in *Civilization in the United States, An Inquiry by Thirty Americans,* Harold E. Stearns, ed., New York, Harcourt, Brace and Company, pp. 443–456, 1922.

21   Paul de Kruif, personal communication. The discussion of *Arrowsmith* in this book was partly based on an interview with Dr. de Kruif. Since it was set in type, three publications have appeared which cast a somewhat different light on the relation of Sinclair Lewis's characters to actual persons at The Rockefeller Institute: Paul de Kruif, *The Sweeping Wind, A Memoir,* New York, Harcourt, Brace and World, 1962; Mark Schorer, *Sinclair Lewis, An American Life,* New York, McGraw-Hill Book Company, 1961; Charles E. Rosenberg, "Martin Arrowsmith, the scientist as hero," *American Quarterly,* Vol. 15, pp. 448–458, 1963.

22   Erasmus Darwin, *The Loves of the Plants,* Vol. III, p. 238, 1789.

23   Jacques Loeb, *Proteins and the Theory of Colloidal Behavior,* New York, McGraw-Hill Book Company, 1922, p. 285.

24   W. J. V. Osterhout, "Jacques Loeb," *Journal of General Physiology,* Vol. 8, ix–lix, 1928.

25   J. H. Northrop, "The story of the isolation of crystalline pepsin and trypsin," *Scientific Monthly,* Vol. 35, pp. 333–340, 1932.

26   The work up to 1937 is explained with exceptional clarity by MacInnes himself in "The interionic attraction theory of electrolytes," *Science,* Vol. 86, pp. 23–29, 1937.

27   "Leonor Michaelis, January 16, 1875–October 8, 1949, an autobiography. With additions by D. A. MacInnes and S. Granick," *Biographical Memoirs of the National Academy of Sciences,* Vol. 31, pp. 282–321, 1958.

28   Ernest Pollard to P. K. Olitsky, Dec. 16, 1953; Jan. 7, 1954, by courtesy of Dr. Olitsky.

CHAPTER EIGHT

"Pathology Is the Fundamental Branch of Medicine"

1   Flexner to Francis G. Blake, Nov. 15, 1933, by courtesy of John B. Blake.

2   Noguchi to Flexner, Sept. 14, 1913, Flexner Papers.

3   Noguchi to Morinosuke Chiwaki, cited by Gustav Eckstein, *Noguchi,* New York, Harper and Brothers, 1931, p. 214.

4   Noguchi to Flexner, Sept. 18, 1918, Flexner Papers.

5   "Yellow fever about to be conquered," *St. Louis Post-Dispatch,* Dec. 31, 1919.

6   Theobald Smith, remarks at memorial meeting for Hideyo Noguchi, *Bulletin of the New York Academy of Medicine,* Vol. 5, 2nd Series, p. 882, 1929.

7   Letter cited in obituary of Adrian Stokes, *Guy's Hospital Reports,* London, Series 4, Vol. 8, p. 15, 1928.

8   Noguchi to Flexner, Aug. 11, 1924, Flexner Papers.

9   Noguchi to Flexner, May 19, 1927, Flexner Papers.

10   It has been widely rumored and even stated in print that Noguchi committed suicide, some say by gunshot, others say by infecting himself with yellow fever. That the cause of death was indeed yellow fever is confirmed by the autopsy report (Archives of The Rockefeller Foundation; photostatic copy in Historian's file, Rockefeller Institute). The infection must have been accidental; Noguchi would not have thought of killing himself by that means, for he believed he had been rendered immune by an illness, supposed by him to be yellow fever, from which he suffered in January 1928 soon after reaching West Africa.

11   The bust of Noguchi was made by S. Konenkov, then an expatriate Russian, but since honored with the Star of Lenin. A portrait bust of Simon Flexner, in the hall at the Institute named after him, is also by Konenkov.

12   *Science,* Vol. 97, pp. 180–181, Feb. 19, 1943.

13   Peyton Rous, "Karl Landsteiner, 1868–1943," *Obituary Notices of Fellows of the Royal Society,* London, Vol. 5, pp. 295–324, 1947.

14   Personal communication, Merrill W. Chase.

15   For a full discussion of the history of this complex subject, and of the elaborate practical and theoretical developments in recent years, see A. S. Wiener, "History of the rhesus blood types," *Journal of the History of Medicine and Allied Sciences,* Vol. 7, pp. 369–383, 1952.

16   There are excellent accounts of Landsteiner's life and work by Peyton Rous, *op. cit.* (note 13 above), and by Stanhope Bayne-Jones, "Dr. Karl Landsteiner, Nobel Prize Laureate in Medicine, 1930," *Science,* Vol. 73, pp. 599–604, 1931. An unfinished biography by the late George M. Mackenzie, made available by Mrs. Mackenzie, and since deposited (under restrictions) at the American Philosophical Society, Philadelphia, has been of much use in the preparation of this account.

CHAPTER NINE

Cancer, Organ Culture, Cytology

1   Page 109.

2   Sam Granick, unpublished address at memorial meeting for Leonor Michaelis, American Society of European Chemists and Pharmacists, Nov. 3, 1949.

3   Murphy's experiments were supported in part by the proceeds of a bequest from Henry B. Rutherford, a resident of Vermont, who died in New York in 1913, leaving $200,000 to The Rockefeller Institute for investigating the cause and treatment of cancer. Since Murphy's retirement the income has been assigned to Peyton Rous's work (*New York Times*, April 29, 1913; Minutes, *passim*, 1915–1916).

4   Clarence C. Little, "James Bumgardner Murphy, August 4, 1884–August 24, 1950," *Biographical Memoirs of the National Academy of Sciences*, Vol. 34, pp. 183–203, 1960.

5   C. C. Little, "Francisco Duran-Reynals, bacteriologist," *Science*, Vol. 129, pp. 881–882, 1959.

6   Alexis Carrel to Flexner, Feb. 6, 1935, Flexner Papers.

7   Simon Flexner, "The Rockefeller Institute for Medical Research," in *Forschungsinstitut, ihre Geschichte, Organisation und Ziele*, edited by L. Brauer, A. Mendelssohn-Bartholdy, and Adolph Meyer, Hamburg, Paul Hartung Verlag, 1930, Vol. II, p. 24.

8   Robert Soupault, *Alexis Carrel, 1873–1944*, Paris, Librairie Plon, 1952, pp. 169–170.

9   Lars Santesson, "Some physiological characteristics of epithelial tumors of the mouse," *Journal of Experimental Medicine*, Vol. 56, pp. 893–906, 1932.

10   Albert H. Ebeling, personal communication.

11   Edric B. Smith, personal communication.

12   Minutes (Exec. Comm.), April 13, 1928.

13   James T. Flexner, personal communication.

14   Alexis Carrel and Charles A. Lindbergh, *The Culture of Organs*, New York, Paul B. Hoeber, 1938.

15   Pages 136–137.

16   Alexis Carrel, *The Voyage to Lourdes*, translated from the French by Virgilia Peterson, with preface by Charles A. Lindbergh, New York, Harper and Brothers, 1950.

17   New York *Sun*, June 2, 1932.

18   The Rockefeller Institute has a Lindbergh pump, complete with all accessories, as well as a number of the glass parts in various sizes. Another is in the Hall of Fame of the International College of Surgeons in Chicago; a third one is to be exhibited at the United States National Museum, Washington, D.C.

19 For later work on organ culture, see N. T. Werthessen, "Die Technik der Perfusion ganzer Organe zum Studium ihrer Funktionen in vitro," *Zeitschrift für Vitamin-Hormon-Fermentforschung,* Vol. 6, pp. 423–444, 1954; and "A technique of organ culture for protracted metabolism studies," *Endocrinology,* Vol. 44, pp. 109–126, 1949.

20 Charles A. Lindbergh, "An apparatus for the culture of whole organs," *Journal of Experimental Medicine,* Vol. 62, pp. 409–431, 1935.

21 New York *Herald Tribune,* editorial, "Science and death," Dec. 14, 1935.

22 A well-documented account of Carrel's life in France after 1941, and of the circumstances of his death in 1944, is given in Soupault's biography (see note 8 above).

23 "The Rockefeller Institute for Medical Research," *Journal of the American Medical Association,* April 18, 1903, p. 1082.

24 The story of this effort is told fully by Dorothy White Nicholson, whose father, William Charles White, had a prominent part in organizing it, in *Twenty Years of Medical Research,* New York, National Tuberculosis Association, 1943.

25 Georges Canetti, *The Tubercle Bacillus in the Pulmonary Lesion of Man,* New York, Springer Publishing Company, 1955.

26 A statue by Joy Buba of New York, representing Dr. Sabin as she looked when at work at The Rockefeller Institute, was unveiled in Statuary Hall, the Capitol, Washington, D.C., Feb. 25, 1959.

27 Elinor Bluemel, *Florence Sabin, Colorado Woman of the Century,* Boulder, University of Colorado Press, 1959; Vincent T. Andriole, "Florence Rena Sabin — Teacher, scientist, citizen," *Journal of the History of Medicine and Allied Sciences,* Vol. 14, pp. 320–350, 1959.

28 The only record of this transitory conflict is a memorandum in Simon Flexner's handwriting, dated Sept. 5, 1939, in a notebook made available by James T. Flexner. In the same memorandum Flexner says that among William H. Welch's papers which he had recently examined when writing Welch's biography, he found a letter from Holt dated in 1909, suggesting that Welch should give up his Johns Hopkins post and move to New York to give all his time to the development of The Rockefeller Institute. Because Holt introduced this extraordinary proposal by the words "we have had under discussion a plan . . . ," Flexner interpreted it to mean that as late as 1909 some of the Directors, certainly Holt, and possibly Herter and Biggs, were still irked by his assumption of the leading role.

29 Stockard actually held an M.D. degree, taken at Würzburg, long after he entered his professional career in experimental biology and anatomy; he never practiced medicine.

30 James B. Conant, personal communication.

31 What specific interests the unidentified speaker (who may have been Gates himself) had in mind as potentially dangerous in the future was not stated. As this history shows, in the beginning Rockefeller, Jr., and Gates faced and averted the possibility of medical sectarian influence on the Institute, and the Board of Sci-

(*Notes on Chapter Nine, continued*)

entific Directors at various times felt and resisted pressure from within and without its own membership to support inadvisable *ad hoc* research, to form alliances with outside hospitals, to conduct public health education, and to give executive advice on university affairs beyond its scope.

32　Gates to Rockefeller, Jr., Dec. 17, 1926, copy in Corporation files, office of the business manager, Rockefeller Institute.

CHAPTER TEN

The Hospital, 1913–1935

1　René J. Dubos, "Oswald Theodore Avery, 1877–1955," *Biographical Memoirs of Fellows of the Royal Society,* Vol. 2, pp. 35–48, London, 1956.

2　*Ibid.* See also Colin MacLeod, "Oswald Theodore Avery, 1877–1955," *Journal of General Microbiology,* Vol. 17, pp. 539–549, 1957.

3　The string galvanometer of Cohn's original electrocardiographic outfit is preserved at the U.S. National Museum, Washington, D.C.

4　Thomas M. Rivers, personal communication.

5　*New York Times,* Jan. 18, 1930.

6　Frederick M. Allen, Edgar Stillman, and Reginald Fitz, *Total Dietary Regulation in the Treatment of Diabetes,* Monographs of The Rockefeller Institute for Medical Research, No. 11, Oct. 15, 1919.

7　Donald D. Van Slyke, remarks upon receiving the Kober Medal, *Transactions of the Association of American Physicians,* Vol. 57, pp. 41–43, 1942.

8　The background and earlier history of this collaboration is discussed in *Blood, A Study in General Physiology,* by L. J. Henderson, New Haven, Yale University Press, 1928.

9　For an explanation of the Donnan equilibrium, see pages 167–168.

10　John P. Merrill, "General aspects of renal disorders," in *Principles of Internal Medicine,* edited by T. R. Harrison and others, New York, Blakiston, 2nd ed., 1954, p. 1448.

11　Minutes, April 16, 1921.

12　Excerpts from letters, Marcia Davenport to John D. Rockefeller, Jr., and Cornelius P. Rhoads, Oct. 1938, files of the Hospital of The Rockefeller Institute, quoted by permission of Mrs. Davenport.

13　Rufus Cole, "The Hospital of The Rockefeller Institute," in *Forschungsinstitut, ihre Geschichte, Organisation und Ziele,* edited by L. Brauer, A. Mendelssohn-Bartholdy, and Adolph Meyer, Hamburg, Paul Hartung Verlag, Vol. II, 1930.

CHAPTER ELEVEN

Infectious Diseases of Animals
1916–1935

1 Rhoda Erdmann (1871–1935), unhappy in Princeton, returned in 1917 to a former post at Yale, where she had maintained a nominal connection. Having acquired experience with tissue culture methods under Ross G. Harrison, after the war she went back to her native country and became a professor at the University of Berlin and director of the Institut für Experimentelle Zellforschung.

2 Pages 195, 196.

3 The certified milk movement was originated by Dr. Henry Leber Coit of Newark, N.J., in 1892 and the first medical milk commission was set up by the Practitioners' Club of Newark. The first certified milk dairy was that of Stephen Francisco of Caldwell, N.J., who began production May 19, 1893. (Second International Congress of *Gouttes de Lait* [Protection of Infancy], *Compte rendu,* Brussels, 1907, pp. 65–67; M. V. Naylor, "Henry Leber Coit: A biographical sketch," *Bulletin of the History of Medicine,* Vol. 12, pp. 368–370, 1942.) Buffalo had a medical milk commission in 1895, also ahead of New York. (I. M. Snow, "Certified milk in Buffalo," *Archives of Pediatrics,* Vol. 14, pp. 827–832, 1897.) (Information from Dr. John B. Blake.)

4 Robert L. Duffus and L. Emmett Holt, Jr., *L. Emmett Holt, Pioneer of a Children's Century,* New York, D. Appleton–Century Company, 1940, pp. 168–169; also circulars and private communications from the Walker-Gordon Laboratory Company, Mr. A. S. Cook, Vice President.

CHAPTER TWELVE

Parasitology, Genetics,
Plant Pathology, 1916–1935

1 Norman R. Stoll, "Rudolf W. Glaser (1888–1947)," *Journal of Parasitology,* Vol. 34, pp. 165–168, 1948.

2 In later years both D. Wayne Woolley and Howard A. Schneider worked extensively in the vitamin field (as will appear in subsequent chapters).

3 Confidential Reports to the Board of Scientific Directors, April 9, 1927 (Report of the Director of the Department of Animal Pathology, p. 322).

4 Letter quoted by Paul F. Clark, "Theobald Smith, student of disease," *Journal of the History of Medicine and Allied Sciences,* Vol. 14, pp. 490–514, 1959.

5 Simon Flexner and James T. Flexner, *William Henry Welch and the Heroic Age of American Medicine,* New York, Viking Press, 1941, pp. 295–296 and Chapter XIII, note 8.

(Notes on Chapter Twelve, continued)

6   Minutes, Jan. 31, April 12, 1931.

7   William J. Robbins, "The influence of Jacques Loeb on the development of plant tissue culture," *Bulletin du Jardin Botanique de l'Etat*, Brussels, Vol. 27, pp. 189–197, 1957.

8   Wendell M. Stanley, "The isolation and properties of tobacco mosaic and other virus proteins," *Harvey Lectures*, Series 33, pp. 170–204, Baltimore, 1938.

9   See addresses by Ralph W. Shriner and Vincent du Vigneaud on the occasion of the award of the Nicholas Medal of the American Chemical Society for 1946, *Chemical and Engineering News*, Vol. 24, pp. 750–755, 1946.

CHAPTER THIRTEEN

Flexner Retires; A New Director; Neurophysiology, Chemistry, Pharmacology, 1935–1953

1   Minutes, June 1, 1934.

2   Memorandum in Simon Flexner's hand, dated Sept. 5, 1939, in a notebook made available by James T. Flexner.

3   Dates in parentheses indicate terms of service on the Board, whether terminated by resignation, retirement, or death.

4   New York *Herald Tribune*, Oct. 8, 1935. Rumors had reached the newspapers that a well-known pathologist was seriously under consideration for the post. *Yorkville Advance*, New York, May 5, 1935; *Newsweek*, July 20, 1935.

5   Vernon B. Brooks, "Contrast and stability in the nervous system," *Transactions of the New York Academy of Medicine*, Series II, Vol. 21, pp. 387–394, 1959. For a detailed summary, for the general reader, of all the work on the neurophysiology of reflexes, see Charles I. Campbell, "Unravelling the neural patterns of reflex behavior," *Rockefeller Institute Quarterly*, Vol. 3, No. 4, pp. 1–4, 1960.

6   When a physician elicits a knee jerk in his patient, he actually stimulates a whole bundle of these two-neuron arcs; but a laboratory experimenter can initiate and record action currents passing over a single fiber within such a bundle.

7   Memorandum in Simon Flexner's hand, dated June 1938, made available by James T. Flexner.

8   See Chapter 9, note 22.

9   Page 153.

10 Max Bergmann, "Proteins and proteolytic enzymes," *Harvey Lectures*, Series 31, pp. 37–56, Baltimore, 1936.

CHAPTER FOURTEEN

Physical Chemistry,
General Physiology, Nutrition
1935–1953

1 Sam Granick, "The structural and functional relationships between heme and chlorophyll," *Harvey Lectures,* Series 44, pp. 220–245, Springfield, Illinois, 1948–1949.

2 W. J. V. Osterhout, "The mechanism of accumulation in living cells," *Journal of General Physiology,* Vol. 35, pp. 579–594, 1951–1952; "The use of aquatic plants in the study of some fundamental problems," *Annual Review of Plant Physiology,* Vol. 8, pp. 1–9, 1957.

3 For a clear account of Mirsky's work on the chemistry of chromosomes, and its relation to other contemporary research in the field, see his article, "The chemistry of heredity," *Scientific American,* Vol. 188, No. 2, pp. 47–57, Feb. 1953.

4 Peyton Rous, "An inquiry into certain aspects of Eugene L. Opie," *Archives of Pathology,* Vol. 34, No. 1 (Opie Number), pp. 1–6, 1942.

5 Eugene L. Opie, "Osmotic activity in relation to the movement of water under normal and pathological conditions," *Harvey Lectures,* Series 50, pp. 292–315, New York, 1954–1955.

6 Osmotic activity may for the purpose of this brief discussion be defined as the sum of molecular forces holding water on one side or the other of a membrane, such as that of the cell surface, through which, in the absence of such forces, water readily diffuses. In living tissues osmotic pressure depends chiefly upon the concentration of dissolved salts and proteins on the two sides of the membrane respectively — in this case, inside and outside the cell.

7 Conrad A. Elvehjem, R. J. Madden, F. M. Strong, and D. W. Woolley, "Relation of nicotinic acid and nicotinic acid amide to canine black tongue," *Journal of the American Chemical Society,* Vol. 59, p. 1767, 1937.

8 D. Wayne Woolley, *A Study of Antimetabolites,* New York, John Wiley and Sons, 1952.

CHAPTER FIFTEEN

Immunology, Microbiology, Pathology, Cytology, 1935–1953

1   For the sake of complete accuracy, it should be added that to succeed such an experiment requires that the simple substance when injected must be accompanied by a mixture of killed tubercle bacilli (or other mycobacteria) and certain oily substances, the so-called "Freund's adjuvant," which in some mysterious way facilitates the immune reaction.

2   Clarence C. Little, "James Bumgardner Murphy, August 4, 1884–August 24, 1950," *Biographical Memoirs of the National Academy of Sciences,* Vol. 34, pp. 183–203, 1960.

3   Dubos, although he moved his laboratory to the North Building (now Theobald Smith Hall), remained a member of the hospital staff.

CHAPTER SIXTEEN

Princeton: Animal Pathology 1935–1953

1   Frederik B. Bang is a grandson of Bernhard L. F. Bang of Copenhagen (1848–1932), discoverer of the bacterial agent causing contagious abortion of cattle (Bang's disease).

2   For the history of research on bovine mastitis, see Ralph G. Little and Wayne N. Plastridge, eds., *Bovine Mastitis, a Symposium,* New York, McGraw-Hill Book Company, 1946.

3   Glaser's pioneering work on axenic culture is reviewed by Norman R. Stoll, in "Résumé of the studies by R. W. Glaser on germ-free culture," *Lobund Reports,* No. 3, pp. 1–6, Notre Dame University, South Bend, Indiana, 1959.

4   Wade H. Brown, "Constitutional variation and susceptibility to disease," *Harvey Lectures,* Series 24, pp. 106–150, Baltimore, 1930.

5   Minutes, Nov. 27, 1934; April 20, May 6, 1935.

6   John H. Northrop, Moses Kunitz, and Roger M. Herriott, *Crystalline Enzymes,* New York, Columbia University Press, 1948 (2nd ed., 1955).

7   John H. Northrop, "Concerning the nature of bacterial viruses," *Proceedings of the National Academy of Sciences of the U.S.A.,* Vol. 44, pp. 229–235, 1958.

CHAPTER SEVENTEEN

Plant Pathology, 1935–1953

1 Karl Maramorosch, "A versatile virus," *Scientific American,* Vol. 188, No. 6, pp. 78–86, 1953.

2 For the history of plant tissue culture, see Philip R. White, *A Handbook of Plant Tissue Culture,* Lancaster, Pennsylvania, Jacques Cattell Press, 1943.

3 Armin C. Braun, "Plant cancer," *Scientific American,* Vol. 186, No. 6, pp. 66–72, 1952; Charles I. Campbell, "Crown gall and the wider significance of plant pathology," *Rockefeller Institute Quarterly,* Vol. 4, No. 1, pp. 1–5, 1960.

4 Symposium on plant tumors, *Proceedings of the National Academy of Sciences of the U.S.A.,* Vol. 44, pp. 344–349, 1958.

5 Minutes, Board of Trustees, May 2, 1947.

6 Minutes, Board of Scientific Directors, April 19, 1947.

7 The author is indebted to Lindsley F. Kimball of the Board of Trustees and George H. Whipple of the Board of Scientific Directors for information about the considerations involved in the decision to close the Princeton laboratories.

8 Minutes, Board of Scientific Directors, June 7; Trustees, June 11, 1947.

9 J. A. V. Butler, "Rockefeller Institute for Medical Research, Princeton," *Nature,* Vol. 162, pp. 479–480, London, 1948.

CHAPTER EIGHTEEN

The Hospital, 1935–1953

1 For twenty years following his retirement, Rufus Cole devoted himself to historical studies culminating in the publication of a large work illustrating his view of human history as a natural process determined by the total environment: *Human History: The Seventeenth Century and the Stuart Family,* 2 vols., Freeport, Maine, The Bond-Wheelwright Company, 1959.

2 For biographical reference, see Chapter 10, note 1.

3 For a clear account of the discovery and significance of the transforming factor, see Charles I. Campbell, "Bacteriology, genetics, and DNA — a frontier in research," *Rockefeller Institute Quarterly,* Vol. 2, No. 1, pp. 1–5, 1958.

4 In 1960 Horsfall was appointed president and director of the Sloan-Kettering Institute of New York, as successor to Cornelius P. Rhoads.

5 Alfred E. Cohn, *No Retreat from Reason and Other Essays,* Harcourt, Brace and Company, New York, 1948. See also J. Murray Steele, "Alfred Einstein Cohn,

(Notes on Chapter Eighteen, continued)

1879–1957," *Transactions of the American College of Physicians,* Vol. 71, pp. 17–19, 1958.

6   A. L. McCawley to George W. Corner, Dec. 26, 1959; January 4 and 28, 1960, Rockefeller Institute files. The date of Hoagland's birth is given as June 6, 1907, in his application for enrollment in medical school (cited by courtesy of Washington University) and in *American Men of Science,* 7th ed., 1944, but as June 6, 1908 in the adoption papers (transcript kindly furnished by Senator McCawley).

7   The best obituary note on Hoagland is in the Minutes of the Board of Scientific Directors, Jan. 1947 (prepared by Thomas M. Rivers). For published obituaries, see New York *Sun,* Aug. 2; *New York Times,* Aug. 3, 1946.

CHAPTER NINETEEN

The Chemistry of Heredity, Virulence, and Immunity; Antibiotics

1   Florence R. Sabin, "Award of the Trudeau Medal for 1951," *American Review of Tuberculosis,* Vol. 64, pp. 323–325, 1951. For a clear account of the work of Dubos and his group on tuberculosis to 1949, see René J. Dubos, "Tuberculosis," *Scientific American,* Vol. 181, No. 4, pp. 30–40, 1949.

2   Rollin D. Hotchkiss, "The genetic chemistry of the pneumococcal transformations," *Harvey Lectures,* Series 49, p. 124–144, New York, 1955.

3   Charles I. Campbell, "Bacteriology, genetics, and DNA — a frontier in research," *Rockefeller Institute Quarterly,* Vol. 2, No. 1, pp. 1–5, 1958.

4   Charles I. Campbell, "Maintenance and construction of our buildings and grounds," *Rockefeller Institute Quarterly,* Vol. 1, No. 4, pp. 3–4, 7–8, 1957.

5   Esther Judkins, "Lillia M. D. Trask, 1873–1952," *Bulletin of the Medical Library Association,* Vol. 40, pp. 339–340, 1952.

6   Charles I. Campbell, "A half-century of scientific publication at the Institute," *Rockefeller Institute Quarterly,* Vol. 2, No. 3, pp. 1–2, 7–9, 1958.

CHAPTER TWENTY

World War II
The Institute Completes Its
First Half Century

1 Rivers assembled a truly remarkable staff for the two naval units. Almost every young man who was connected with them now stands high in the roll of American physicians and biological scientists. Among the Institute men not named in the text at this point, who were members of the Naval Reserve or volunteered to join the units, Palmer H. Futcher and Henry A. Schroeder were transferred to the Naval Air Force, and Robert H. Green to sea duty and then for more than a year to foreign service with the Office of Strategic Services. Lee E. Farr, Robert A. Phillips, Richard E. Shope, and Armine T. Wilson were detached for special duties mentioned in the text. Joseph E. Smadel, honorably discharged by the Navy for a trivial medical reason, volunteered for the Army Medical Corps, and began a distinguished career in the public service as investigator and administrator in the field of infectious diseases. Charles L. Hoagland was not commissioned, for medical reasons. George P. Berry of the University of Rochester, formerly at the Institute, volunteered for the overseas unit, but was kept on inactive duty for important civilian services, partly in connection with the Manhattan Project. Others, recruited from outside the Institute, and soon transferred to other assignments, were Alvin F. Coburn, Howard A. Howe, Chris P. Katsampes, John A. Lichty, Oliver R. McCoy, J. Mote, J. Sutherland, and C. T. Vicale.

2 Later Rivers was made Rear Admiral, U.S. Naval Reserve.

3 Records of the U.S. Naval Medical Research Unit No. 2, 1944–1947, preserved in the files of the U.S. Navy Medical Corps, Research Division, were made available by the courtesy of Rear Admiral C. B. Galloway. Thomas M. Rivers and other members of the unit have also contributed valuable information by personal communication. A vivid account of the work of the Okinawa party, written by its leader, Richard E. Shope, exists in a manuscript in his possession at The Rockefeller Institute.

4 For a detailed account of The Rockefeller Institute's participation in the national defense work on war gases, see *Science in World War II, Chemistry,* William A. Noyes, Jr., ed., Boston, Little, Brown and Company, 1948.

5 John R. Paul, *History of the Commission on Neurotropic Viruses, 1941–1945,* Army Epidemiological Board of the Preventive Medicine Service, Office of the Surgeon General, U.S. Army, Washington, D.C. (not dated).

6 *New York Times,* March 25, 1943.

7 New York *World Telegram,* April 29, 1946.

8 Detlev W. Bronk, "Presentation of the George M. Kober Medal," *Transactions of the Association of American Physicians,* Vol. 67, 39–43, 1954; reprinted in *Oc-*

(Notes on Chapter Twenty, continued)

casional *Papers by Faculty and Friends of The Rockefeller Institute,* No. 4, New York, Rockefeller Institute Press (not dated).

9   Nicholas Murray Butler, "Scientific research and material progress," *The Rockefeller Institute for Medical Research: Description of the Buildings; Addresses Delivered at the Opening of the Laboratories in New York City, May 11, 1906,* privately printed, 1907.

10   *New York Times* editorial, June 29, 1953.

11   The following list of investigations made at The Rockefeller Institute and deemed historically significant is compiled with as little verbal modification as possible from Arturo Castiglioni, *A History of Medicine,* translated from the Italian and edited by Edward B. Krumhaar, New York, Alfred A. Knopf, 1947; and Ralph H. Major, *A History of Medicine,* 2 vols., Springfield, Illinois, C. C. Thomas, 1954. The choice is strictly that of the above-named authors; their selection does not cover all fields of the Institute's work, and the citations, having been removed from context, are not all adequately indicative of the respective investigations. The list is presented merely to amplify statements made in the text about external estimates of the Institute's work, and should not be quoted as a balanced assessment of its most important researches.

John Auer: recognition of bronchiospasm as cause of death in experimental allergy in the guinea pig. *Oswald T. Avery:* identification of polysaccharide antigens (with *A. Raymond Dochez* and others); recognition of the "transforming principle." *Alexis Carrel:* Carrel-Dakin treatment of infected wounds; development of tissue culture. *René Dubos:* discovery of gramicidin. *Francisco Duran-Reynals:* recognition of the "spreading factor." *Albert H. Ebeling* (with *Anne Carrel*): a successful experimental corneal graft. *Simon Flexner:* serum treatment of epidemic cerebrospinal meningitis; transmission of poliomyelitis to monkeys. *Christian A. Herter:* description of infantilism associated with intestinal disease. *Moses Kunitz:* crystallization of trypsin and chymotrypsin. *Rebecca C. Lancefield:* classification of streptococci. *Karl Landsteiner* and *Alexander S. Wiener:* discovery of the Rh factor. *Phoebus A. T. Levene:* studies on the chemistry of proteins. *Jacques Loeb:* studies on the colloidal behavior of proteins; application of the Donnan equilibrium to living tissues; electrolyte balance in tissue fluids. *Duncan A. MacInnes* and *Lewis G. Longsworth:* advancing the knowledge of proteins through ultracentrifugation and electrophoresis. *Samuel J. Meltzer:* introduction of intratracheal anesthesia. *Leonor Michaelis:* study of reversible oxidation-reduction systems; (with *C. V. Smythe*) measurement of potentials in systems of biological interest. *Hideyo Noguchi:* demonstration of spirochete of syphilis in brains of paretics; proof of the relation of Oroya fever to verruca peruviana and cultivation of the causative organism; luetin test. *John H. Northrop:* crystallization of pepsin. *Peter K. Olitsky:* cultivation of *Bacterium (Dialister) pneumosintes.* *Louise Pearce:* contributions to experimental medicine (should read: discovery of a cure for African sleeping sickness) (with *Wade H. Brown, M. Heidelberger,* and *Walter A. Jacobs*). *Peyton Rous:* production of sarcoma by a virus; storage of blood for transfusion (with *J. R. Turner, Jr.,* and *Oswald H. Robert-*

son). *Florence R. Sabin:* identification of phthioic acid as the stimulus to production of tubercles. *Richard E. Shope:* demonstration that swine influenza is caused by combined action of a virus and a bacillus. *William C. Stadie:* introduction of puncture of human arteries to obtain blood samples. *Wendell M. Stanley:* crystallization of the virus of tobacco mosaic disease. *Homer F. Swift:* hypotheses concerning the cause of rheumatic fever. *Donald D. Van Slyke:* manometric procedures for blood gases; concept of "plasma clearance"; concept of the "alkali reserve" and interpretation of the blood as a physicochemical system (with *A. Baird Hastings, Michael Heidelberger,* and *Franklin C. McLean*); studies on protein metabolism.

In addition, *Frederick M. Allen* and *Rufus Cole* are cited by these historians for general contributions to clinical medicine.

12 Annual Confidential Report to the Members of the Corporation, Oct. 28, 1949.

13 Appendix I.

14 "The memoirs of Frederick T. Gates," *American Heritage,* Vol. 6, No. 3, p. 73, 1955.

15 For a critical view of the organization of The Rockefeller Institute laboratories as seen in 1922 by a visiting worker at the Hospital, see Sir Charles Harington, "The place of the research institute in the advance of medicine," *Lancet,* June 28, 1958, pp. 1345–1351.

APPENDIX I

Recollections of Frederick T. Gates

on the Origin of the Institute

YOU ASKED ME the other day to write you my recollections of the origin of The Rockefeller Institute for Mr. Rockefeller's private files.* You wished me to trace the very idea back to its sources, and accordingly, so far as my recollections will serve, I will give you what may be termed the pre-natal history of the Institute. I have no doubt that the history of the Institute will some time be written, and I am aware that these obscure questions of origin, however unimportant, have a greater interest often than the later and more obvious facts. Moreover, if we who are acquainted with the earlier facts leave no record of them, it will be impossible for our successors to recover them when we have passed away. I therefore leave with you, for the files of Mr. Rockefeller and the Institute, my recollections of the early history of the Institute in this my compliance with your request.

But first of all, the historian of the Institute should be made acquainted with what I may call the atmosphere or spirit of Mr. Rockefeller's private office. During all the twenty-five years in which I have been intimately associated with Mr. Rockefeller, he has been sincerely desirous of employing his great fortune in the service of mankind, at home and abroad, whether that employment be in investments or in bestowal on private or public charity. It has been during all these years my chief end in life, as a member of Mr. Rockefeller's staff, to assist him in this aim, both in the sphere of investment and in the sphere of bestowal. It is not too much to say that every day and hour of my life during these years has had for its underlying motive, watchfulness for such opportunities of public service. With this introductory explanation, to you personally quite unnecessary, but perhaps useful to other eyes, I pass to the narrative. This I will make as full and comprehensive as possible.

* This memorandum to Starr J. Murphy, dated December 31, 1915, has not previously been published in full.

Origins are often very humble. Christianity itself was born in a manger. It is so with the Institute. During the years 1880 to 1888 I was the pastor of the Central Baptist Church of Minneapolis. In my congregation was a young boy named Elon W. [*sic*] Huntington, a member of one of the most useful families in the church, a family which for many reasons was particularly dear to me. Elon himself I baptized as a boy in his teens. In due time, he was graduated from the University of Minnesota. His father, long deceased, had been a physician and Elon chose his father's profession. Not finding in the West the best facilities for the study of medicine, Elon came to New York and became a student in the College of Physicians and Surgeons. This was in the early 90's; probably 1894. I had left my pastorate in Minneapolis in 1888 and at this time was living in Montclair as a member of Mr. Rockefeller's staff, assisting him in his private business investments and in his benefactions in the spirit of my introductory words above. Elon Huntington was a lonely student without a friend and almost without an acquaintance in New York, and he used to come out to visit us in Montclair, often spending the night or the Sunday with us to relieve his loneliness. In this way he spent many hours with me. We used to take long walks together, and the subject of our conversation was quite naturally medicine, the subject in which he was most interested and in which he was then most intelligent. Thus, in simply entertaining Elon I found myself intensely interested in medicine. My interest reached a point in which I determined to know something more definite about medicine, and in the spring of 1897, when Elon, if I recall it, was about to graduate, I told him that I would like to read medicine, and I asked him if he could suggest to me a book which a layman like me might be able to understand and to read with profit. I remember telling him that I did not want any of the ordinary medical books for the family. I wanted to know what the best doctors are reading; I wanted the literature that was being taught currently in the best schools to medical students. Was there any such book preeminently good? He replied that there was one such book; it was Osler's *Principles and Practice of Medicine* and said that this book was being taught to students in the College of Physicians and Surgeons and that it was written in a style so clear that with very slight knowledge of medicine I could read it with understanding and interest. He suggested further that I get a little pocket dictionary of medicine entitled *Twenty Thousand Medical Terms* or something to that effect, and he named the place in New York, a medical book store on Seventeenth Street, if I remember, where I could get Osler's book and the little dictionary that ought to accompany it.

I took my first opportunity to hunt up this book store, and there I bought my precious volume in June 1897. At this time my sole purpose was to become reasonably intelligent, as a layman, on the subject of medicine. Perhaps I ought to delay here long enough to say that this question of medicine had for many years been a subject of more interest to me than it is to laymen in general. My father, before he became a minister, had studied medicine. Then, as a pastor from 1880 to 1888, I had been brought of course into direct and sympathetic relation with hundreds of sick rooms and with both schools of medicine. I had come into confidential relations also with several physicians, and I shall confess that I had come to acquire a profound scepticism about medicine of both schools as it was currently practised. I had read from beginning to end Dr. Hanneman's [*sic*] book known as the New Testament of Homeopathic Medicine. He was the originator of that school and I had come to believe from the reading of that book that Dr. Hanneman, the founder of the Homeopathic School, must have been, to speak charitably, little less than a lunatic, a belief cordially shared by a homeopathic physician friend. I would not be true to my feeling at the time, whether right or wrong, if I used any milder terms. Many years afterwards I wrote a review of Homeopathy in five chapters, which sought to exhibit its errors and impossibilities. But I had hardly more confidence in the allopathic school. My intimate conversations with allopathic physicians, who practised in my church, had led me to see clearly that at least nine tenths of their practice, without guilt on their part, was based substantially on the ignorance and credulity of their patients. I remember very distinctly the impression made on my mind, an impression entirely confirmatory of my previous observation, by the remark to me of one of the most prominent allopathic practitioners in Minneapolis, that at least nine out of every ten calls made by physicians, might, for any possible good they did their patients, precisely as well not be made. I introduce the facts to fully explain my interest in medicine and why and in what spirit I began to read in June 1897, Osler's *Principles and Practice of Medicine*.

The book came into my hands at a time of abundant leisure. I spent a considerable part of the months of July and August following with my family in the Catskill Highlands, at Lake Liberty, in Sullivan County, New York, and I had opportunity to give my undivided attention to Osler's book for a considerable part of every day. My wife's diary of those days shows how my time was divided between kites, water-wheels and frog hunting with my children and reading Osler's *Principles and Practice of Medicine*. I read the whole book without skipping any of it. I speak of this not to commemorate my industry but to celebrate Osler's charm. Osler's *Principles and Practice of Medicine* is one of the very few scientific books that I have ever read possessed of literary charm. There was a fascination about the style itself that led me on and having once started I found a hook in my nose that pulled me from page to page, and chapter to chapter, until the whole of about a thousand closely written pages brought me to the end. But there were other things besides its style that attracted and constantly, in fact, intensified my interest. I had been a sceptic before, not only as to homeopathic medicine but as to allopathic medicine as currently practised. This book not only confirmed my scepticism, but its revelation absolutely astounded and appalled me, sceptic as I was. Let me name some of the things which, commonplace as they are to intelligent physicians, were absolutely appalling to me, a layman, although supposing himself to be a sceptic. I found, for illustration, that the best medical practice did not, and did not pretend to cure more than four or five diseases. That is, medicine had, at that time, specifics for about as many diseases as there are fingers on one hand. It was nature, and not the doctor, and in most instances nature practically unassisted, that performed the cures. I learned that with the exception of two or three, the physician had nothing whatever to prescribe for the infectious diseases, which could effect a cure. Osler's own attitude toward drugs was interesting, and I came at length to approach his curative suggestions with a smile. His chapter on any particular disease would begin with a profound and learned discussion of the definition of the disease, of its extension throughout the world, of the history of discovery about it, of the revelations of innumerable postmortems, of the symptoms, cause and probable results of the disease, and the permanent complications and consequences likely to follow, but when he came to the vital point, namely, the *treatment* of the aforesaid disease, our author, who had up to this time been treading on solid grounds with the confidence and delight of sure knowledge, would almost invariably disclose a mental attitude of doubt and scepticism. He would suggest that such and such had found that this or that treatment was efficacious, but such had not been his own experience; perhaps this or that might be found to be useful in some cases. To the layman student, like me, demanding cures, and specifics, he had no word of comfort whatever. In fact, I saw clearly from the work of this able and honest man, that medicine had, with the few exceptions above mentioned, no cures, and that about all that medicine up to 1897 could do was to nurse the patients and alleviate in some degree the suffering. Beyond this, medicine as a science had not progressed. I found further that a large number of the most common diseases, especially of the young and middle aged, were simply infectious or contagious, were caused by infinitesimal germs that are breathed in with the atmosphere, or are imparted by contact or are taken in with the food or communicated by the incision of insects in the skin, which serves as a protective covering. I learned that of these germs, only a very few had been identified and isolated. I made a list, and it was a very long one at that time, much longer than it is now, of the germs which we might reasonably hope to discover but which as yet had never been, with certainty, identified, and I made a very much longer list of the infectious or contagious diseases for which there had been as yet no specific found.

When I laid down this book, I had begun to realize how woefully neglected in all civilized countries and perhaps most of all in this country, had been the scientific study of medicine. I saw very clearly also why this was true. In the first place, the instruments for investigation, the microscope, the science of chemistry, had not until recently been developed. Pasteur's germ theory of disease was very recent. Moreover, while other departments of science, astronomy, chemistry, physics, etc., had been endowed very generously in colleges and universities throughout the whole civilized world, medicine, owing to the peculiar commercial organization of medical colleges, had rarely, if ever, been any where endowed, and research and instruction alike had been left to shift for itself dependent altogether on such chance as the active practitioner might steal from his practice. It became clear to me that medicine could hardly hope to become a science until medicine should be endowed and qualified men could give themselves to uninterrupted study and investigation, on ample salary, entirely independent of practice. To this end, it seemed to me an Institute of medical research ought to be established in the United States. Here was an opportunity, to me the greatest, which the world could afford, for Mr. Rockefeller to become a pioneer. This idea took possession of me. The more I thought of it, the more enthusiastic I became. I knew nothing of the cost of research; I did not realize its enormous difficulty; the only thing I saw was the overwhelming need and the infinite promise, worldwide, universal, eternal. Filled with these thoughts and enthusiasms, I returned from my vacation on July 24th. The year was, as I have stated, 1897. I brought my Osler into the office at #26 Broadway, and there I dictated to Mr. Jones, my secretary, for Mr. Rockefeller's eye, a memorandum in which I aimed to show to him, the to me amazing discoveries that I had made of the actual condition of medicine in the United States and the world as disclosed by Osler's book. I enumerated the infectious diseases and pointed out how few of the germs had yet been discovered and how great the field of discovery, how few specifics had yet been found and how appalling was the unremedied suffering. I pointed to the Koch Institute in Berlin and at greater length to the Pasteur Institute in Paris. It was either in this connection or a little later, for I kept up my inquiries on the subject, that I pointed out, as I remember the fact, that the results in dollars or francs of Pasteur's discoveries about anthrax and on the diseases of fermentation had saved for the French nation a sum far in excess of the entire cost of the Franco-German War. I remember insisting in this or some subsequent memorandum, that even if the proposed institute should fail to discover anything, the mere fact that he, Mr. Rockefeller, had established such an institute of research, if he were to consent to do so, would result in other institutes of a similar kind, or at least other funds for research being established, until research in this country would be conducted on a great scale and that out of the multitudes of workers, we might be sure in the end of abundant rewards even though those rewards did not come directly from the Institute which he might found.

Mr. Rockefeller was at this time in Cleveland. I myself soon took a very long trip of a month or so to the Pacific Coast on business. I never saw my memorandum again. But that Mr. Rockefeller was impressed by the force of these considerations I have documentary evidence. These studies and memoranda, as I have said, took place in the summer and fall of 1897. In January 1898 an event took place which discloses to us the effect of these considerations on Mr. Rockefeller's mind.

Mr. Rockefeller had begun the work of founding the University of Chicago with a gift in 1889. The University opened its doors in 1892 and for five years had been rapidly expanding. The outlines of the proposed Institute of Research were, of course, only vaguely drawn in our minds at the time of its inception in 1897. We did not know whether the Institute would be practicable or possible. I had indeed received encouragement from such friends as I had addressed on the subject, notably from my physician in Montclair, Dr. J. S. Brown. What counsel, if any, Mr. Rockefeller had taken, I do not know, but it is quite certain that our earliest conceptions associated the proposed medical institution with some great institution of learning and with some great medical school. Mr. Rockefeller was interested in the University of Chicago, as founder, and it was in his mind, as it was in my mind, that the institution of research would be associated, if the idea were ever realized, with that young and flourishing institution.

In 1894 an attempt had been made to associate the Rush Medical College in Chicago with the new University. The matter was discouraged by Mr. Rockefeller in 1894, and the interviews and correspondence on that subject culminating in 1895 led Mr. Rockefeller to suppose that no further attempt would ever be made to associate Rush Medical College with the University of Chicago. To Mr. Rockefeller's very great surprise, and to mine, for I had been privy to all the previous negotiations, we were informed in January 1898 that official action had just been taken, affiliating Rush Medical College with the University of Chicago. The practical effect of this association would be, as we foresaw it, to make Rush Medical College the medical college of the University of Chicago. The history and the ideal of Rush College at that time rendered it an unsuitable basis on which to rear an institute of research. Accordingly, under Mr. Rockefeller's direction, I immediately addressed a letter of earnest dissent to the authorities at Chicago. This letter was dated January 12, 1898. As the letter was important and as our relations with the University of Chicago were extremely intimate, the letter, before being sent, was very carefully considered and was scrutinized in advance of its being sent by Mr. Rockefeller personally. Among other things, the letter contained the following pregnant and significant passage:

> I have no doubt that Mr. Rockefeller would favor an institution that was neither allopath nor homeopath, but simply scientific in its investigations into medical science. That is the ideal. For that the University should wait and reserve the great weight of its influence, authority and prestige, instead of bestowing the same gratuitously on Rush Medical College. Such an institution would have to be endowed and would run on a far higher principle than the principle of Rush College or any other of the ordinary institutions.

In the original letter, and in the letterbook copy from which I take this quotation, these words were made the central point of the entire letter by running along the margin of each side a heavy line. My purpose was to intimate to Dr. Goodspeed, official secretary of the University, to whom the letter was addressed, that this passage contained for him a pregnant meaning. I intended to intimate to him that if he would quietly wait, the founder would probably endow an institute of research in connection with the University of Chicago. Mr. Rockefeller understood the implication of these words of course as well as I did, and he not only permitted, but ordered the letter to be sent with all the implications that it contained. This discloses clearly the fact that at that time the idea of an institution for investigation had already taken root and was germinating in Mr. Rockefeller's mind. This was January 12th, 1898, within six months after my studies in Osler's *Principles and Practice of Medicine*.

Dr. Goodspeed promptly replied, undertaking to justify and excuse, and perhaps to minimize the action of the University. This led to a second letter still more insistent than the first one. This letter was dated January 19th, 1898, just one week later than the first letter. In that letter was a passage still more significant than the one from the first letter which I have quoted above. The passage is as follows:

> The whole effect and tendency of this movement will be to make Rush ultimately the medical department of the University of Chicago, as against that far higher and better conception, which has been one of the dreams of my own mind at least of a medical college in this country, conducted by the University of Chicago, magnificently endowed, devoted *primarily to investigation, making practice itself an incident of investigation* and taking as its students only the choicest spirits quite irrespec-

tive of the question of funds. Against that ideal and possibility, a tremendous if not fatal current has been turned. I believed the ideal to be practicable and I hoped to live to see it realized.

You will observe here that the central thought is an institution for investigation. An institution in which whatever practice of medicine there is, shall be in itself an incident of investigation, that while I said this was a dream of my own I qualified by saying "at least of my own mind," implying that it might also be a dream in another mind, and I not only stated that I believe it to be practical, but I added that I thought it was possible. This letter, with all these implications, passed under the very critical eye of Mr. Rockefeller. He understood the implications perfectly, he knew perfectly well that those who read that letter, although I signed it, would understand and give just the same significance to it as if he signed it himself. I was acting as his secretary, if not his amanuensis in sending it. This statement, therefore, of a week later, reveals still more clearly that the idea of an institution of research had taken such possession of Mr. Rockefeller's mind that he was prepared to endorse the quasi public committal to it which is made in this letter.

But from this time forward Mr. Rockefeller never associated the proposed institute with the University of Chicago. I, for my part, while I still continued to cherish the idea of an institute of research, found it impossible to pursue it in an effective way owing to the multiplicity of other absorbing duties. The matter, however, continued to be referred to and conferred upon for a year or two, particularly with Mr. Rockefeller, Jr., who shared all my interest in it. Any active steps toward founding the institution would involve extensive conference with the leading men of research in this country, a study of the history of similar institutions in Europe and an amount of thought, correspondence and travel, that might well engage a large part of the time of a competent man. I therefore suggested one day to Mr. John D. Rockefeller, Jr., that we employ a man for this exclusive service and suggested a man entirely qualified whom I thought we could command for such a service, my friend and neighbor in Montclair, Mr. Starr J. Murphy.

After my enumeration of Mr. Murphy's rare qualifications, Mr. Rockefeller was so far impressed that he met Mr. Murphy and arrangements were made for his undertaking the work. For several years there was no other thought than that the proposed Institute of Research should be associated in the traditional way with some powerful University. Indeed, negotiations were for a time actively conducted with Harvard, but in the end it was thought best that the Institute be wholly independent, and time has justified the wisdom of this decision.

The story of your conferences and correspondence with the leaders in medical research in the United States, the first cautious tentative experimental gift made under their expert counsel, the gradual confidence of your advisers and the final splendid scheme, awaits your own authoritative and graceful pen.

APPENDIX II

History of the Site of the Institute

THE HISTORY OF the tract of land on which The Rockefeller Institute stands can be followed in Crosswell Tuttle's work, *Abstracts of Farm Titles in the City of New York, 39th–75th Streets, East of the Common Lands,* New York, 1877. The southern part of the tract is part of a sixty-acre farm patented by Governor Sir Edmond Andros in 1676 to Cornelius Mattysen, or Mattisen, with quitrent of one peck of wheat. The original deed, now at the Museum of the City of New York, refers to land lying "Northward of Turtle's Bay, bounded to the southwest by land of Jacob Fabrisius, and to the southeast by the river, being in breadth by the river eighty rods and in length one hundred and twenty rods, being bounded to the northeast by land of John Bassett and to the northwest by the Commons." That part of the tract which lies between York Avenue and the East River from Sixty-fourth to Sixty-sixth Street became known as the Hardenbrook Farm or "Widow Hardenbrook Tract" because it was owned by John Hardenbrook, house carpenter, and by his wife Ann after he died in 1803. Her heirs deeded the farm in 1817 to the Society of the New York Hospital, from which it was purchased the next year by Peter Schermerhorn (1781–1852), whose father Peter (1740–1826) was one of the governors of the hospital. The younger Schermerhorn and his wife had at an earlier date inherited from her father John Jones a parcel of land to the north of the Hardenbrook place, *i.e.,* the southern part of Jones's large "Louvre Farm" which lay between Third Avenue and the river from Sixty-sixth to Seventy-fifth Street. When Peter Schermerhorn added the Hardenbrook land to his wife's inheritance, he renamed the property "Belmont Farm." The Schermerhorns moved at once into the frame farmhouse, one and a half stories high, that stood on the river bluff just north of Sixty-fourth Street, from the mid-eighteenth century until after the Institute's first two buildings were erected. It is tempting to conjecture that this house was built by John Hardenbrook the house carpenter; at any rate Peter Schermerhorn called it "The Hardenbrook House," though after he took up residence there, it was known by his family name.

A lithographic view of the house and its immediate surroundings, prepared by the Major Knapp Engineering and Lithographic Company, 71 Broadway, and published in *D. T. Valentine's Manual,* 1866, sometimes turns up in antique shops. There is a copy at the Museum of the City of New York. The legend, "Residence of the Schermerhorn Family, Foot of 73rd St., East River," should of course read "Foot of 64th Street," as is proved by comparison of the lithograph with extant photographs of the house.

Newspaper articles printed when the place was bought for The Rockefeller Institute (*Evening Telegram,* Feb. 13, 1903; *New York Sun,* Oct. 18, 1903) assert that this house and farm were the summer home of George Clinton, first Governor of the State of New York and afterward Vice-President of the United States. They exaggerate the architectural importance of the house and enlarge the familiar claim that "Washington slept here" to a tale that he made an extended visit to the farm in 1783, adding that on sunny days he and Clinton used to sit and talk under a great tree on the bluff over the river. At least one guidebook accepted this yarn, but there is no evidence at all to support it. New York City was in fact occupied by the British until September 1783 when the definitive peace treaty was signed. It has been impossible to trace the story about Washington and Clinton before 1903.

The last residents of the Hardenbrook house were the family of August Braun, who about the year 1870 took a fifty-year lease on the property from the Schermerhorn estate. Braun conducted a number of recreational activities, the chief of which was a boating and bathing establishment at the foot of Sixty-fourth Street known as Braun's Baths. When The Rockefeller Institute purchased the land from the Schermerhorn estate in 1903, his lease was terminated by agreement. (Information from Dr. Augustus Braun Kinzel, grandson of August Braun.)

The northern part of the present Rockefeller Institute grounds is sometimes said by old New Yorkers to have been part of "Jones's woods." This name properly designated a large area of fields and woodland to the north and west of Seventieth Street and the East River, but was often loosely applied to the whole of the wooded tract, which extended southward beyond Sixty-eighth Street.

APPENDIX III

Roll of the Trustees, Scientific Directors, Scientific Staff, and Senior Administrative Staff of The Rockefeller Institute during the period covered by this history

BOARD OF TRUSTEES

1910–1953

Charles W. Appleton, 1928–1940
Trevor Arnett, 1926–1937
Donald K. David, 1950–
Simon Flexner, 1910–1935
Raymond B. Fosdick, 1921–1936
Herbert S. Gasser, 1935–1953
Frederick T. Gates, 1910–1929
Jerome D. Greene, 1912–1932
Barklie McK. Henry, 1947–
Henry James, 1929–1947
Lindsley F. Kimball, 1947–

George Murnane, 1928–
Starr J. Murphy, 1910–1921
Frederick Osborn, 1938–1946
David Rockefeller, 1940–
John D. Rockefeller, Jr., 1910–
John D. Rockefeller, 3rd, 1932–1950
Charles R. Stockard, 1936–1939
John C. Traphagen, 1936–
William H. Welch, 1910–1933
George H. Whipple, 1939–

DIRECTORS OF THE INSTITUTE

Simon Flexner, 1901–1935   Herbert S. Gasser, 1935–1953

BOARD OF DIRECTORS 1901–1910
BOARD OF SCIENTIFIC DIRECTORS 1910–1953

Hermann M. Biggs, 1901–1923
Francis G. Blake, 1924–1935
Detlev W. Bronk, 1946–1953
Walter B. Cannon, 1936–1945
James B. Conant, 1930–1949
A. Raymond Dochez, 1935–1953
Vincent du Vigneaud, 1949–1953
Herbert S. Gasser, 1935–1953
Ross G. Harrison, 1939–1953
Christian A. Herter, 1901–1910
L. Emmett Holt, 1901–1924

John Howland, 1924–1926
Theodore C. Janeway, 1911–1917
Warfield T. Longcope, 1934–1952
Eugene L. Opie, 1929–1932
W. J. V. Osterhout, 1920–1926
Francis W. Peabody, 1926–1927
T. Mitchell Prudden, 1901–1924
Theobald Smith, 1901–1934
Charles R. Stockard, 1926–1939
William H. Welch, 1901–1933
George H. Whipple, 1936–1953

SCIENTIFIC STAFF 1901–1953

(*Members of The Rockefeller Institute*)

Abernethy, Theodore J., 1933–1936
Adams, Mark H., 1938–1942
Addis, Thomas, 1928–1929
Ahrens, Edward H., Jr., 1946–
Allen, Chester H., 1914–1916
Allen, Frederick M., 1913–1918
Allfrey, Vincent G., 1949–
Alloway, James Lionel, 1930–1932
Alving, Alf S., 1929–1934
Amoss, Harold L., 1912–1922
Anderson, Harold C., 1946–1949
Andrewes, Christopher H., 1923–1925
Andrews, Mary Ruggles
   (Mrs. W. C.), 1916–1918
Anson, Mortimer L., 1927–1942
Anthony, Albert J., 1930–1931
*Archibald, Reginald M., 1940–1946,
   1948–
Armstrong, Alice H., 1927–1929
Auer, John, 1903–1921
Austin, J. Harold, 1919–1921
Austin, Paul R., 1932–1933
Averell, Philip R., 1926–1930
*Avery, Oswald T., 1913–

Babers, Frank H., 1929–1935
Baird, Robert Desmond, 1936–1938
Baker, Edgar Eugene, 1946–1949
Baker, James A., 1940–1947
Baker, Lillian E., 1922–
Bancroft, Frank Watts, 1911–1913
Bang, Frederik B., 1941–1947
Banús, Mario Garcia, 1916–1918
Barber, Marshall Albert, 1919–1920
Barker, Bertha Isabel, 1906–1910
Barker, William Halsey, 1935–1937
Barry, Guy Thomas, 1946–
Bass, Lawrence W., 1925–1929
Battistini, Telémaco S., 1925–1926
Baudisch, Oskar, 1923–1929
Beard, Joseph W., 1932–1937
Bearn, Alexander G., 1951–
Beattie, William Walter, 1925–1926

Beatty, Wallace A., 1905–1907
Beckman, William W., 1940–1942
Beeson, Paul B., 1937–1939
Behrens, Otto K., 1937–1939
Belcher, Donald, 1930–1934, 1941–1945
Benjamin, Bernard, 1929–1932
*Bergmann, Max, 1934–1944
Beringer, Frederick M., 1947–
Berry, George P., 1929–1932
Beutner, Reinhard H., 1911–1914
Bickford, James V., Jr., 1930–1931
Bigelow, Newell M., 1931–1933
Binger, Carl A. L., 1919–1930
Binkley, O. Francis, 1942–1946
Birchard, Frederick J., 1910–1912
Biscoe, Jonathan, 1934–1937
Björkman, Sven Erik, 1947–1948
Black, Lindsay M., 1937–1946
Blake, Francis G., 1916–1917, 1919–1921
Blankenhorn, David Henry, 1952–
Blinks, Lawrence R., 1926–1933
Blondheim, Solomon H., 1949–1951
Böhmig, Richard, 1930–1932
Bomford, Richard R., 1938–1939
Bongiovanni, Alfred M., 1949–1950
Boots, Ralph H., 1920–1923
Boughton, Donald C., 1934–1936
Bourdillon, Jacques, 1936–1939
Boyd, Douglas, 1924–1925
Brakeley, Elizabeth, 1920–1921
Branch, Edmund A. G., 1922–1926
Braun, Armin C., 1938–
Bronfenbrenner, Jacques J., 1910–1928
Broun, Goronwy O., 1920–1922
Brow, George R., 1922–1924
Brown, James Howard, 1917–1923
Brown, Thomas M., 1937–1939
*Brown, Wade Hampton, 1913–1942
Bruce, William Fausset, 1932–1935
Bryant, Gladys, 1923–1925
Buch-Andersen, Erik C., 1928–1929
Bull, Carroll G., 1913–1918
Burch, George E., Jr., 1939–1941

Burgess, Laurie L., 1930–1931
Burrows, Montrose T., 1909–1911
Butler, Allan M., 1926–1928
Butterfield, Elmore E., 1909–1913

Cain, Charles B., 1931–1932
Camber, Bernard, 1949–1951
*Carrel, Alexis, 1906–1944
Casals-Ariet, Jordi, 1936–1952
Casey, Albert E., 1927–1934
Cattell, McKeen, 1915
Chang, Hsiang-Tung, 1947–1948, 1952–
Chase, Merrill W., 1932–
Chesney, Alan M., 1913–1917
Chester, K. Starr, 1933–1937
Chickering, Henry T., 1913–1918
Chinard, Francis P., 1945–1949
Chow, Bacon F., 1934–1935
Christie, Ronald V., 1926–1928
Christman, Clarence C., 1936–1938
Clark, Earl Perry, 1917–1920
Clark, Harry, 1920–1929
Clark, Paul F., 1909–1914
Clarke, Thomas Wood, 1907–1908
Claude, Albert, 1929–1949
Cluff, Leighton E., 1952–
Cochran, George W., 1946–1948
*Cohn, Alfred E., 1911–
*Cole, Rufus, 1909–
Colin, Philip G., 1926–1927
Collins, Arnold M., 1923–1925
Compton, Jack, 1934–1936
Connell, Karl, 1910
Cooper, William Charles, Jr., 1925–1927
Corey, Robert B., 1928–1938
Cortese, Frank, 1930–1933
Cotzias, George C., 1946–1953
Courtney, Angelia M., 1909–1920
Covell, Walter P., 1926–1928
Cowdry, Edmund V., 1921–1928
Cowperthwaite, I. A., 1926–1930
Cox, Herald R., 1932–1936
*Craig, Lyman C., 1933–
Crampton, Charles F., 1953–
Crawford, John H., 1923–1926
Cretcher, Leonard H., 1916–1918

Cullen, Glenn E., 1914–1921
Curnen, Edward C., Jr., 1939–1946

Dahl, Harry W., 1922–1923
Dahl, Lewis K., 1948–1952
Daly, Marie M., 1948–
Dam, Henrik, 1945–1946
Damon, Edwin B., 1925–1930
Davidson, David, 1924–1927
Davies, John A. V., 1926–1927
Davis, John Staige, Jr., 1927–1928
Davis, Leverett, Jr., 1940–1941
Dawson, James R., Jr., 1934–1935
Dawson, Martin H., 1926–1929
Dayhoff, Margaret O.
   (Mrs. Edw. S.), 1948–1951
de Kruif, Paul H., 1920–1922
Derick, Clifford L., 1924–1928
Despopoulos, Agamemnon, 1948–1949
Dexter, Smith O., 1938–1939
Dick, Macdonald, 1930–1932
Di Ferrante, Nicola, 1953–
Dillon, Robert T., 1929–1937
DiSomma, August A., 1936–1939
Doan, Charles A., 1925–1930
Dobriner, Konrad, 1936–1939
Dochez, A. Raymond, 1908–
Dole, Malcolm, 1928–1930
*Dole, Vincent P., Jr., 1941–1946, 1947–
Dorcas, Merrill James, 1925
Dougherty, Katherine M.
   (Mrs. E. H. White), 1919–1922
Dow, Robert S., 1938–1939
Draper, George, 1911–1912
Drury, Douglas R., 1922–1929
Dublin, Thomas D., 1938–1939
*Dubos, René J., 1927–1942, 1944–
Dumbell, Keith R., 1952–1953
Duran-Reynals, Francisco, 1926–1938
Dziewiatkowski, Dominic D., 1948–

Ebeling, Albert H., 1911–1939
Eberson, Frederick, 1917–1918
Ecker, Paul G., 1947–1948
Eder, Howard A., 1946–1950
Edwards, Joshua L., 1953–
Ehrich, Wilhelm E., 1926–1930
Eisenmenger, William J., 1947–

Elderfield, Robert C., 1930–1936
Eldridge, Lewis A., Jr., 1926–1928
Ellis, Sir Arthur W. M., 1911–1914
Elman, Robert, 1923–1925
Elrod, Ralph P., 1941–1947
Emerson, Kendall, Jr., 1939–1946
England, Albert C., 1939–1940
Erdmann, Rhoda, 1916–1918
Erf, Lowell A., 1937–1939
Ewald, Wolfgang F., 1912

Faber, Harold K., 1914–1915
Fales, Helen L., 1911–1922
Farr, Lee E., 1934–1940, 1944–1945
Faulkner, James M., 1926
Febvre, Henri Lucien, 1953–
Felton, Lloyd D., 1920–1922
Ferguson, Malcolm S., 1938–1947
Finkle, Philip, 1925–1926
Fischer, Albert, 1921–1922
Fite, George L., 1932–1934
Fitz, Reginald, 1915–1917
Fitzgerald, Mabel P., 1907–1908
Fleck, Elmer E., 1928–1934
*Flexner, Simon, 1901–1946
Florence, Laura, 1918–1925
Folch-Pi, Jordi, 1935–1944, 1946
Forkner, Claude E., 1927–1929
Forsbeck, Filip C., 1930–1932
Forssman, Claes Olof, 1953–
Foster, Albert D., Jr., 1944–1945
Fox, Maurice S., 1953–
Francis, Thomas, Jr., 1928–1935
Frankel, Florence H., 1916–1917
Fraser, Sir Francis R., 1912–1914
Friedewald, William F., 1938–1942
Fruton, Joseph S., 1934–1945
Furth, Jacob, 1926–1928
Futcher, Palmer H., 1939–1941

*Gasser, Herbert S., 1935–
Gates, Frederick L., 1913–1929
Geiger, John T., 1931–1935
Gelarie, Arnold J., 1913–1914
Genest, Jacques, 1948–1951
Giges, Burton, 1952–1953
Gilchrist, Andrew Rae, 1926–1927

Gilder, Helena
   (Mrs. R. A. Phillips), 1942–1946
Gilding, Henry P., 1928–1929
Gillespie, Louis J., 1911–1913
Ginsberg, Harold S., 1946–1951
Githens, Thomas S., 1910–1919
Glaser, Rudolf W., 1920–1947
*Goebel, Walther F., 1924–
Goldthwaite, Nellie E., 1906–1908
Good, Robert A., 1949–1950
Goodner, Kenneth, 1930–1940
Gould, Robert G., Jr., 1936–1942
Gowen, John W., 1926–1937
Graham, George L., 1933–1947
Granick, Sam, 1938–
Grant, Joseph H. B., 1923–1925
Grave, Thomas B., 1927–1929
Graybill, Harry W., 1916–1924
Green, Robert H., 1941–1947
Greene, Harry S. N., 1931–1941
Gregory, John D., 1947–1949
Greif, Roger L., 1947–1953
Grundfest, Harry, 1935–1945
Gustus, Edwin L., 1926–1930

Haessler, Ferdinand Herbert,
   1919–1920
Hagan, William Arthur, 1921–1922
Haller, Herbert L. J., 1923–1929
Hamilton, Paul B., 1940–1946
Hance, Robert T., 1924–1927
Hanes, Frederic M., 1912–1913
Hanford, John M., 1912
Hannon, Robert R., 1928–1930
Hardy, Paul H., 1947–1948
Harfenist, Elizabeth J.
   (Mrs. Morton), 1949–1953
Harford, Carl G., 1936–1938
Harnes, Alvin R., 1927–1929
Harris, Albert H., 2nd, 1936–1937
Harris, Earl S., Jr., 1925–1929
Harris, Stanton A., 1931–1935
Hastings, Albert Baird, 1921–1926
Hausmann, Werner K., 1949–
Hawkins, James A., 1922–1930
Heggies, Robert M., 1938–1939
Heidelberger, Michael, 1912–1927

Heimrod, George Wm., 1907–1917
Helmer, Oscar M., 1927–1931
Hendricks, Sterling B., 1927–1928
Herriott, Roger M., 1932–1948
*Herter, Christian A., 1908
Hetler, Donald M., 1926–1928
Hill, Edgar S., 1931–1934
Hill, Samuel E., 1929–1938
Hiller, Alma E., 1918–1948
Hirs, Christophe H. W., 1949–
Hirsch, James Gerald, 1950–
Hirst, George K., 1936–1940
Hitchcock, Charles H., 1925–1930
Hitchcock, David I., 1921–1926
*Hoagland, Charles L., 1937–1946
Hodes, Horace L., 1936–1938
Hodge, Benjamin E., 1930–1934
Hoffman, Donald C., 1928–1930
Hoffmann, Alexander, 1926–1928
Hogeboom, George H., 1941–1948
Holden, Raymond F., Jr., 1935–1936
Holman, Delavan V., 1934–1937
Holmes, Francis O., 1932–
*Horsfall, Frank L., Jr., 1934–1937,
    1941–
Horvath, Arthemy, 1927–1930
Hotchkiss, Rollin D., 1935–1937, 1938–
Houghton, Henry S., 1905–1906
Howard, Charles W., 1911–1912
Howe, Paul E., 1917–1924
Hudack, Stephen S., 1930–1934
Huebner, Charles F., 1945–1947
Hughes, Thomas P., 1926–1931
Hummel, Lawrence E., 1935–1937
Hunt, Carlton C., Jr., 1952–
Hurst, Edward W., 1932–1934
Hussey, Raymond G., 1919–1922

Ingebrigtsen, Ragnvald, 1912–1913
Ingvaldsen, Thorsten, 1919–1920
Insull, William, Jr., 1952–
Irons, Vernal C., 1932–1933
Irving, George W., 1939–1942
Irwin, Marian
    (Mrs. W. J. V. Osterhout), 1925–1933

Jacobs, John L., 1931–1936
*Jacobs, Walter A., 1907–

Jacques, Alfred G., 1926–1939
Jaffe, Herbert, 1948–
Jamieson, Ross A., 1914–1916
Jensen, James H., 1931–1935
Jesaitis, Margeris A., 1950–
Jobling, James W., 1906–1909
Johnson, Folke, 1939–1941
Johnston, Christopher, 1928–1930
Jones, Frederick S., 1913–1934
Joseph, Don Rosco, 1907–1912
Joyner, Austin L., 1936–1938
Julianelle, Louis A., 1924–1930

Kamerling, Samuel E., 1932–1934
Kay, Robert L., 1952–
Kelley, William H., 1929–1931
Kendall, Arthur I., 1908
Kidd, John G., 1934–1944
Kilbourne, Edwin D., 1948–1951
King, Lester S., 1937–1940
King, Te Piao, 1953–
Kirk, John Esben, 1931–1934
Kleiner, Israel S., 1910–1919
Kligler, Israel Jacob, 1916–1920
Kline, Benjamin S., 1914–1915
Knight, Claude A., Jr., 1940–1948
Knutti, Ralph E., 1930–1932
Kober, Philip A., 1907–1908
Korb, Charles, 1923–1925
Krampitz, Lester O., 1942–1943
Kreider, Leonard C., 1936–1937
Kreitlow, Kermit W., 1940–1941
Krueger, Albert P., 1929–1931
Kubie, Lawrence S., 1926–1928
Kuhns, William Joseph, 1951–
*Kunitz, Moses, 1913–
*Kunkel, Henry G., 1945–
*Kunkel, Louis O., 1931–
Kuttner, Ann G., 1924–1927

Labby, Daniel H., 1945–1947
Lacaillade, C. W., Jr., 1931–1934
LaForge, Frederick B., 1910–1915
Lamar, Richard V., 1907–1913
Lancefield, Rebecca C., 1922–
*Landsteiner, Karl, 1922–1943
Lange, Fritz, 1928–1929
Lange, Linda B., 1912–1914

Morgan, Hugh J., 1921–1924
Morgan, Isabel M., 1938–1944
Morison, Rufus A., 1916–1917
Morton, John J., Jr., 1914–1917
Muckenfuss, Ralph S., 1925–1929
Mudd, Stuart, 1923–1925
Muller, Henry R., 1928–1929
Murphy, George E., 1946–1953
*Murphy, James B., 1910–1950
Murphy, James Slater, 1951–
Murray, Cecil D., 1923–1924
Murray, Henry A., Jr., 1922–1926
Murray, John Wolcott, 1934–1939

Nakahara, Waro, 1918–1925
Neill, James M., 1921–1924
Nelson, John B., 1925–
Neumann, Charles, 1940–1944
Nicholson, Frederic M., 1921–1924
Niemann, Carl G., 1935–1937
Nigg, Clara, 1929–1937
*Noguchi, Hideyo, 1904–1928
*Northrop, John H., 1915–

Ogilvie, Hanson S., 1912
*Olitsky, Peter K., 1917–
Oliver, Jean, 1916–1917
Olivo, Oliviero Mario, 1928–1929
*Opie, Eugene L., 1904–1910, 1941–
Orcutt, Marion L., 1918–1935
Osborn, Herbert T., 1932–1939
Oster, Gerald, 1945–1948
*Osterhout, W. J. V., 1925–

Page, Irvine H., 1931–1937
Palade, George E., 1946–
Palmer, Walter W., 1915–1917
Parker, Raymond C., 1930–1939
Parker, Robert F., 1933–1936
Parsons, Robert J., 1935–1938
Patterson, A. Lindo, 1929–1931
Peabody, Francis W., 1911–1912
Pearce, John M., 1937–1938
Pearce, Louise, 1913–1950
Pearcy, James F., 1928–1929
Pelletier, S. William, 1951–
Pelluet, Dixie, 1930
Perlman, Ely, 1942–1946

Perlmann, Gertrude E., 1946–
Perlzweig, William A., 1916–1917
Pfaltz, Mimosa H.
   (Mrs. Paul D. Fejos), 1922–1926
Phillips, Robert A., 1940–1946
Pierce, Cynthia H., 1946–
Pittman, Margaret J., 1928–1934
Porter, Keith Roberts, 1939–
Powell, Eugene V., 1920–1921
Price, William Conway, 1932–1945
Price, Winston Harvey, 1946–1951
Pringle, Anna Ludutsky, 1946–1951
Pringle, Ross B., 1947–
Pritchett, Ida W., 1916–1929

Rake, Geoffrey William, 1930–1936
Raymond, Albert L., 1926–1936
Reeves, Richard E., 1937–1938
Reichert, Philip, 1924–1926
Reimann, Hobart A., 1923–1926
Renshaw, Birdsey, 1938–1941
Rhoads, Cornelius P., 1928–1939
Rich, Clayton, Jr., 1951–
Ris, Hans, 1944–1949
*Rivers, Thomas M., 1922–
Robertson, Oswald H., 1915–1920
Robinson, Frank H., 1937–1939
Robinson, George Canby, 1911–1913
Rogers, Edward S., 1932–1934
Rogers, E. Stanfield, 1947–1952
Rolf, Ida Pauline
   (Mrs. W. F. Demmerle), 1918–1927
Rosahn, Paul D., 1930–1935
Rose, William B., 1930–1931
Ross, A. Frank, 1937–1940
Ross, William F., 1934–1936
Rothbard, Sidney, 1941–1948
Rothen, Alexandre, 1927–
Rouiller, Charles August, 1906–1907
*Rous, Peyton, 1909–
Rudzinska, Maria A., 1952–
Rule, Leroy Colter, 1942–1943
Ruth, Edward Samuel, 1910–1911

Sabin, Albert B., 1935–1939
*Sabin, Florence R., 1925–1953
Saddington, Ronald S., 1931–1933

Sager, Ruth
  (Mrs. Seymour Melman), 1949–
Salvesen, Harald A., 1923–1924
Sanderson, Everett S., 1923–1925
Santesson, Lars, 1929–1931
Sarles, Merritt P., 1929–1935
Sato, Yoshio, 1946–1950
Sauvé, Gaston, 1952–
Saxton, John A., Jr., 1936–1938
Saz, Arthur Kenneth, 1947–1948
Scharrer, Ernst, 1938–1940
Scherp, Henry W., 1931–1934
Schlesinger, R. Walter, 1940–1946
Schmidt, Gerhard, 1937–1938
Schneider, Howard A., 1940–
Schorer, Edwin H., 1906–1907
Schormüller, Anton, 1930–1934
Schott, Ralph G., 1931–1932
Schroeder, Henry A., 1937–1946
Schubert, Maxwell P., 1929–1940
Schultz, Mark P., 1929–1935
Schwartz, Irving L., 1950–
Schwentker, Francis F., 1931–1934,
  1943–1944
Scott, Albert B., 1928–1931
Scott, Gordon H., 1927–1928
Scott, T. F. McNair, 1934–1936
Seastone, Charles V., Jr., 1934–1939
Seifried, Oskar, 1929–1932
Sendroy, Julius, Jr., 1920–1937
Senior, James K., 1914–1917
Shaklee, Alfred O., 1908–1910
Shank, Robert E., 1941–1946
Shaw, Elliott N., 1948–
Shedlovsky, Theodore, 1927–
*Shope, Richard E., 1925–1949, 1952–
Silver, Lawrence, 1953–
Simms, Henry S., 1920–1932
Slanetz, Charles A., 1928–1930
Slater, Robert James, 1950–
Smadel, Joseph E., 1934–1946
Smillie, Ernest W., 1916–
Smillie, Wilson G., 1916–1917
Smith, David T., 1923–1925
Smith, Emil L., 1940–1942
Smith, Frederick, 1929–1931
Smith, John Maclean, 1953–

Smith, Margaret H. D., 1946–1948
*Smith, Theobald, 1914–1934
Smith, William E., 1943–1947
Smithburn, Kenneth C., 1930–1938
Smythe, Carl V., 1930–1938
Spencer, Ernest L., 1932–1941
Spring, William C., Jr., 1939–1942
Sprunt, Douglas H., 1930–1932
Stadie, William C., 1918–1921
Stahmann, Mark A., 1942–1945
Stall, Bernard George, III, 1950–1951
*Stanley, Wendell M., 1931–1948
Steele, John Murray, Jr., 1929–1939
Steere, Russell L., 1950–1951
Steiger, Robert E., 1927–1932
*Stein, William H., 1937–
Stern, Herbert, 1949–
Stetson, Chandler A., Jr., 1948–1951
Stevens, Henry, 1926–1929
Stevens, Philip G., 1929–1930
Stewart, Fred W., 1926–1928
Stewart, Harold J., 1922–1932
Stewart, John Morrow, 1952–
Stewart, Walter A., 1942–1944
Stillman, Edgar, 1914–1919
Stillman, Ernest G., 1915–1949
Stoll, Norman R., 1927–
Straub, Elmer L., 1923–1925
Strock, Lester William, 1931–1932
Stumberg, John E., 1931–1933
Sturm, Ernest, 1918–
Suter, Emanuel, 1949–1952
Sweet, Joshua Edwin, 1904–1906
*Swift, Homer F., 1910–1914, 1919–1953
Syverton, Jerome T., 1932–1934

Tallan, Harris H., 1950–
Tamm, Igor, 1949–
Tanzer, Radford C., 1930–1931
Taylor, Fred A., 1917–1923
Taylor, Harriett E.
  (Mrs. Boris Ephrussi), 1945–1947
Taylor, Herbert D., 1915–1918
Taylor, Marian Sibyl
  (Mrs. N. T. Gordon), 1917–1920
*TenBroeck, Carl, 1914–1919,
  1927–1943, 1951–

Terrell, Edward E., 1932–1934
Terry, Benjamin T., 1906–1913
Thaysen, Jørn C. Hess-, 1951–1953
Theiler, Hans, 1925–1926
Therman, Per-Olof, 1940
Thjötta, Theodor, 1920–1921
Thomas, Robert Marrenner, 1930–1935
Thorn, Niels A., 1953–
Thornberry, H. H., 1931–1935
Tibbetts, Helena A. M.
   (Mrs. E. H. Barry), 1920–1923
Tilden, Evelyn B., 1916–1931
Tillett, William S., 1922–1930
Tipson, Robert S., 1930–1939
Toennies, Jan Friedrich, 1936–1939
Trager, William, 1933–
Trask, James D., 1919–1921
Traub, Erich, 1932–1938
Tribble, Charles E., 1932–1933
Tsaltas, Theodore T., 1953–
Turner, Joseph R., Jr., 1914–1915
Tyrrell, David A. J., 1951–
Tytler, William H., 1911–1912

Uhle, Frederick C., 1942–1945
Uhlenhuth, Eduard, 1913–1925
Ullstrup, Arnold J., 1935–1937

Valentine, Francis C. O., 1926
Van Allen, Chester M., 1922–1925
Vanden Schrieck, Henry George,
   1953–
van der Hoeven, B. J. C., 1923–1926
Van der Scheer, James, 1912–1939
*Van Slyke, Donald D., 1907–

Vinograd-Villchur, Mariam, 1912–1916
Volkert, Mogens, 1946–1947

Warburg, Bettina, 1929–1930
Wasteneys, Hardolph, 1910–1916
Watson, Robert F., 1939–1946
*Webster, Leslie T., 1920–1943
Weisiger, James R., 1945–
Weiss, David W., 1952–
Welo, Lars A., 1923–1928
West, Clarence J., 1912–1918
Weyer, Elliott R., 1931–1932
White, Philip R., 1932–1945
Wignall, Ernest W., 1929–1931
Wildman, Ernest A., 1915–1916
Wilson, Armine T., 1940–1942,
   1945–1946
Wilson, George W., 1917–1919
Wilson, Victor Joseph, 1953–
Wiseman, Bruce K., 1929–1930
Witherbee, William D., 1916–1920
Wittenberg, Jonathan B., 1950
Wollstein, Martha, 1907–1921
Wood, Harrison F., 1948–
*Woolley, D. Wayne, 1939–
Worth, Charles Brooke, 1939–1940
Wright, Francis H., 1938–1940
Wyckoff, Ralph W. G. 1926–1938

Yang, Peter S., 1931–1933

Zacharias-Langhans, Gotthard, 1914
Zamecnik, Paul C., 1940–1942
Ziegler, James E., Jr., 1942–1946
Zinder, Norton D., 1952–

SENIOR ADMINISTRATIVE STAFF TO 1953

(WITH HIGHEST POST HELD)

Burrell, Harry De Witt, Bursar	1917
Campbell, Edith Crowninshield, In charge of publications	1906–1940
Campo, Anthony J., Purchasing Agent and Pharmacist	1917–
Carlisle, Julian A., Illustrations	1931–
Christhilf, Katherine M., Housekeeper, Hospital	1910–1925
Dickey, Frank A., Business Manager	1919–1920
Ellicott, Nancy P., Superintendent of the Hospital	1909–1938
Flinn, Waldo R., Assistant Business Manager	1927–
Greene, Jerome D., General Manager	1910–1912
Haulenbeck, Joseph B., Illustrations	1926–1947
Hoffmann, Stella R., Supervisor of Nurses	1919–1953
James, Henry, Manager	1912–1917
Judkins, Esther, Librarian	1925–
Little, Ralph Bulkley, Veterinarian	1914–
Lockie, Alice N., Superintendent of the Hospital	1929–
Lotz, Charles A., Purchasing Agent	1912–1915
Lupinek, Bernard, Superintendent of Maintenance	1911–
Petrzelka, Charles, Bursar	1917–
Robertson, Albert D., Bursar	1917–1946
Schmidt, Louis, Illustrations	1910–1939
Smillie, Ernest William, Superintendent at Princeton	1916–1951
Assistant to Business Manager	1951–
Smith, Edric B., Business Manager	1913–
Spies, Charles B., Purchasing Agent	1915–1938
Stewart, Florence M., In charge of publications	1916–
Trask, Lillia M. D., Librarian	1911–1938

MAJOR DOCUMENTARY SOURCES

Published

Studies from The Rockefeller Institute for Medical Research, 1904–   .
147 volumes (to 1953) containing, in reprinted form, all definitive
scientific papers from the Institute or based on research supported or
sponsored by it. About 500 copies of each volume of this compilation
were issued on subscription or in exchange, and after 1934, 20 to 25
sets on special paper were distributed free to selected libraries in the
United States and abroad.

The *Studies* afford, for those to whom they are accessible, a convenient means of consulting the individual reports, all of which first
appeared in professional journals and most of which can be located
through the *Index Medicus.*

*The Rockefeller Institute for Medical Research: Description of the
Buildings; Addresses Delivered at the Opening of the Laboratories in
New York City, May 11, 1906.* Privately printed, The New Era Print-
ing Company, Lancaster, Pennsylvania, 1907.

(Descriptive Pamphlets) *The Rockefeller Institute for Medical Research: History, Organization and Equipment.* New York, irregu-
larly, annually or biennially, 1911–   .

*Charter, By-laws, and Rules of The Rockefeller Institute for Medical
Research,* New York, published by the Institute, 1939.

Files of The Rockefeller Institute

Minutes: of the Board of Directors, 1901–1910; of the Board of Scientific
Directors, 1911–1953; of the Board of Trustees, 1910–   ; of the
Corporation, 1911–   .

Confidential Reports of the Director of the Laboratories to the Board
of Scientific Directors, 1913–   ; to the Corporation, 1916–   .

Simon Flexner: A Report on the Developments of the First Twenty
Years of The Rockefeller Institute and an Outlook for Future

Growth. Presented at the meeting of the Board of Scientific Directors, April 17, 1926.

Autobiographical statements of certain Members concerning their research programs.

Scrapbooks containing newspaper clippings relative to the Institute and its personnel, 3 volumes, 1901–   .

T. M. Prudden: Unfinished ms. history of The Rockefeller Institute for Medical Research, to about 1922.

Correspondence and other papers of Simon Flexner.

Ms. bibliographies of Members and Associate Members, 1904–   .

At the Johns Hopkins University, Baltimore
Welch Medical Library

Papers of William H. Welch.

Index

THE TEXT OF THIS BOOK IS PRINTED
LETTERPRESS BY CONNECTICUT PRINTERS,
INC. ON SPECIAL WARREN UNIVERSITY
TEXT WOVE, FROM BASKERVILLE AND BULMER
TYPES. THE ILLUSTRATIONS ARE OFFSET
LITHOGRAPHED BY THE MERIDEN GRAVURE
COMPANY, AND THE BINDING IS BY
RUSSELL-RUTTER COMPANY. THE DESIGN
IS BY REYNARD BIEMILLER.